MULTIVARIATE ANALYSIS

Proceedings of an International Symposium held in Dayton, Ohio, June 14–19, 1965

DEDICATED TO THE MEMORY OF
SAMARENDRA NATH ROY
(1906–1964)

MULTIVARIATE ANALYSIS

Proceedings of an International Symposium
held in Dayton, Ohio, June 14–19, 1965

Edited by *PARUCHURI R. KRISHNAIAH*
AEROSPACE RESEARCH LABORATORIES
OFFICE OF AEROSPACE RESEARCH
UNITED STATES AIR FORCE
WRIGHT-PATTERSON AIR FORCE BASE, OHIO

1966

ACADEMIC PRESS New York and London

SPONSORED BY THE OFFICE OF AEROSPACE RESEARCH, UNITED STATES AIR FORCE, WRIGHT-PATTERSON AIR FORCE BASE, OHIO
CONTRACT NUMBER AF33 (615)-3016

ACADEMIC PRESS INC.
111 Fifth Avenue, New York 10003, N. Y.

United Kingdom Edition published by
ACADEMIC PRESS INC. (LONDON) LTD.
Berkeley Square House, London W.1

LIBRARY OF CONGRESS CATALOG CARD NUMBER: 66-26263

PRINTED IN THE UNITED STATES OF AMERICA

List of Contributors

Numbers in parentheses indicate the pages on which the authors' contributions begin.

T. W. Anderson, Department of Mathematical Statistics, Columbia University, New York, New York (5)

V. P. Bhapkar, University of North Carolina, Chapel Hill, North Carolina; University of Poona, Poona, India (29)

Ralph A. Bradley, Department of Statistics, Florida State University, Tallahassee, Florida (507)

Theophilos Cacoullos, Department of Statistics, University of Minnesota, Minneapolis, Minnesota (423)[1]

J. Douglas Carroll, Bell Telephone Laboratories, Murray Hill, New Jersey (561)

E. A. Cornish, Division of Mathematical Statistics, C. S. I. R. O., Adelaide, South Australia (203)

M. H. DeGroot, Carnegie Institute of Technology, Pittsburgh, Pennsylvania (287)

A. P. Dempster, Department of Statistics, Harvard University, Cambridge, Massachusetts (315)

J. J. Fortier, S.M.A., Inc., Montreal, Quebec, Canada (493)

H. Fujisawa, Nagasaki University, Nagasaki, Japan (73)

Seymour Geisser, Department of Mathematical Statistics, State University of New York at Buffalo, Buffalo, New York (149)

[1] Present address: Department of Engineering and Operation Research, New York University, New York, New York

Leon Gleser, Department of Mathematical Statistics, Columbia University, New York, New York (59)[2]

Shanti S. Gupta, Department of Statistics, Purdue University, Lafayette, Indiana (457)

J. Edward Jackson, Eastman Kodak Company, Rochester, New York (507)

Alan T. James, University of Adelaide, Adelaide, South Australia; University of Cambridge, Cambridge, England (209)

Oscar Kempthorne, Statistical Laboratory, Iowa State University of Science and Technology, Ames, Iowa (521)

M. G. Kendall, C-E-I-R Ltd., London, England (165)

J. Kiefer, Department of Mathematics, Cornell University, Ithaca, New York (255)

P. R. Krishnaiah, Aerospace Research Laboratories, United State Air Force, Wright-Patterson Air Force Base, Ohio (477)

A. Kudô, Mathematical Institute, Kyushu University, Kyushu, Japan; Department of Statistics, Iowa State University, Ames, Iowa (73)

Ejnar Lyttkens, University Institute of Statistics, Uppsala, Sweden (335)

P. Masani, Department of Mathematics, Indiana University, Bloomington, Indiana (351)

Kameo Matusita, The Institute of Statistical Mathematics, Tokyo, Japan (187)

V. K. Murthy, Mathematics Research Department, Douglas Aircraft Company, Inc., Santa Monica, California (43)

Ingram Olkin, Department of Statistics, Stanford University, Stanford, California (59)

K. C. Sreedharan Pillai, Department of Statistics, Purdue University, Lafayette, Indiana (237)

Ernest A. Pinson, Office of Aerospace Research, United States Air Force, Arlington, Virginia (1)

Richard F. Potthoff, Department of Statistics, University of North Carolina, Chapel Hill, North Carolina (541)

C. Radhakrishna Rao, Research and Training School, Indian Statistical Institute, Calcutta, India (87)

[2] Present address: Department of Statistics, Johns Hopkins University, Baltimore, Maryland

M. M. Rao, Carnegie Institute of Technology, Pittsburgh, Pennsylvania (287)

M. Haseeb Rizvi, Department of Mathematics, Ohio State University, Columbus, Ohio (477)

M. Rosenblatt, Mathematics Department, University of California, San Diego, La Jolla, California (383)

J. Roy, Research and Training School, Indian Statistical Institute, Calcutta, India (105)

Richard Schwartz, Electronics Laboratory, General Electric Company, Syracuse, New York (275)

Roger N. Shepard, Bell Telephone Laboratories, Murray Hill, New Jersey (561)[3]

Milton Sobel, Department of Statistics, University of Minnesota, Minneapolis, Minnesota (423)

H. Solomon, Department of Statistics, Stanford University, Stanford, California (493)

J. N. Srivastava, Department of Mathematics, University of Nebraska, Lincoln, Nebraska (129)[4]

Herman Wold, University Institute of Statistics, Uppsala, Sweden (391)

[3] Present address: Department of Psychology, Harvard University, Cambridge, Massachusetts

[4] Present address: Department of Mathematics and Statistics, Colorado State University, Fort Collins, Colorado

Preface

The International Symposium on Multivariate Analysis was held at the University of Dayton, Dayton, Ohio on June 14–19, 1965. Brigadier General E. A. Pinson, commander of the Office of Aerospace Research (OAR), was kind enough to make the Opening Remarks. Professor H. Hotelling delivered the Inaugural Address and I am deeply indebted to him for this contribution. Prominent workers in the field presented invited papers in different areas of multivariate analysis. Both methodology and applications were discussed. The areas covered were nonparametric methods, multivariate analysis of variance and related topics, classification, distribution theory, optimum properties of test procedures, estimation and prediction, ranking and selection procedures, and applications. This book consists of the papers presented at this symposium and it will be of interest to mathematical and applied statisticians.

The symposium was sponsored by the Aerospace Research Laboratories (ARL) at Wright-Patterson Air Force Base, Ohio; ARL is a unit of OAR, the research agency of the United States Air Force. While I take complete responsibility for any pitfalls in the organization of the symposium and the editing of this book, I wish to thank several persons for their generous help.

Professors T. W. Anderson, R. E. Bargmann, R. E. Bechhofer, R. C. Bose, H. Chernoff, W. Hoeffding, L. Katz, C. F. Kossack, K. S. Miller, C. R. Rao, P. R. Rider, R. H. Strotz, H. Wold, and Drs. C. W. Dunnett, S. W. Greenhouse, H. L. Harter, M. G. Kendall, A. Madansky, W. F. Mikhail, and H. Smith, Jr., have kindly presided over the different sessions. I am grateful to all persons who have reviewed the papers. The list of people include Professors R. E. Bargmann, B. M. Bennett, V. P. Bhapkar, S. Das Gupta, M. H. DeGroot, S. Geisser, C. G. Khatri, J. Kiefer, A. Kudô, E. Parzen, K. C. S. Pillai, R. F. Potthoff, M. M. Rao, J. Roy, Y. S. Sathe, P. K. Sen, R. N. Shepard, J. N. Srivastava, and Drs. C. W. Dunnett, W. F. Mikhail, and R. Schwartz.

I wish to thank Dr. R. Gnanadesikan and Professor M. M. Rao for their helpful suggestions in the organization of the symposium. Lieutenant Colonel J. V. Armitage, Captain D. R. Barr, S. Back, Mrs. Mary Lum, and Dr. K. C.

Schraut were very helpful in making the local arrangements. I wish to express my appreciation to Colonel R. E. Fontana and to Professor C. R. Rao for their keen interest and encouragement. Thanks are also due the contributors to this book and Academic Press for their excellent cooperation. Part of the editing of the book was done during my stay at the Indian Statistical Institute.

P. R. KRISHNAIAH

Wright-Patterson Air Force Base, Ohio
November 1966

Contents

Power of the Likelihood-Ratio Test Used in Analysis of Dispersion

J. Roy

Some Generalizations of Multivariate Analysis of Variance

J. N. Srivastava

PART III / Classification

Predictive Discrimination

Seymour Geisser

Discrimination and Classification

M. G. Kendall

A Distance and Related Statistics in Multivariate Analysis

Kameo Matusita

PART IV / Distribution Theory

A Multiple Behrens-Fisher Distribution

E. A. Cornish

Inference on Latent Roots by Calculation of Hypergeometric Functions of Matrix Argument

Alan T. James

PART VI / Estimation and Prediction

Multidimensional Information Inequalities and Prediction

M. H. DeGroot and M. M. Rao

Estimation in Multivariate Analysis

A. P. Dempster

On the Fix-Point Property of Wold's Iterative Estimation Method for Principal Components

Ejnar Lyttkens

Recent Trends in Multivariate Prediction Theory

P. Masani

On Some Selection and Ranking Procedures for Multivariate Normal Populations Using Distance Functions

Shanti S. Gupta

Some Procedures for Selection of Multivariate Normal Populations Better than a Control

P. R. Krishnaiah and M. Haseeb Rizvi

PART VIII / Applications

Clustering Procedures

J. J. Fortier and H. Solomon

Sequential Multivariate Procedures for Means with Quality Control Applications

J. Edward Jackson and Ralph A. Bradley

Multivariate Responses in Comparative Experiments

Oscar Kempthorne

Equating of Grades or Scores on the Basis of a Common Battery of Measurements

Richard F. Potthoff

Parametric Representation of Nonlinear Data Structures

Roger N. Shepard and J. Douglas Carroll

Opening Remarks

ERNEST A. PINSON[1]

OFFICE OF AEROSPACE RESEARCH, U.S. AIR FORCE
ARLINGTON, VIRGINIA

It is a great pleasure to be here today to open this symposium on behalf of the Aerospace Research Laboratories. General D. Ostrander[2] regrets that he is not able to be here to welcome you personally, and to meet and talk with you. Both he and I feel that this is a most important and significant occasion.

It is important both because of the eminence of the individuals gathered here, and because of the significance of the subjects to be discussed. We have guests from Australia, Canada, India, Japan, Sweden, and the United Kingdom, as well as the United States.

It is gratifying to note that the very distinguished Professor Harold Hotelling will deliver the Inaugural Address.

Within the Air Force we support research in statistics on a broad front. Internal work is concentrated in our Aerospace Research Laboratories (ARL), here at Wright-Patterson Air Force Base; work in universities and industry is supported by contracts or grants with ARL or with the Air Force Office of Scientific Research.

This symposium is significant, as well as important, because it is indicative of the growing recognition that aerospace research and statistics are intimately related. Furthermore, symposia of this kind present an excellent opportunity to workers in this field to disseminate knowledge accumulated in recent years, to exchange ideas, and to engage in stimulating discussions.

It would be ideal if all statistical problems could be solved by univariate analysis. However, we must take the world as we find it, and we must recognize that the problems it poses usually confront us with a variety of responses, which we wish to characterize by a multivariate distribution. This may sound like a rather obvious generalization, but I make it to emphasize the fact that

[1] Commander of the Office of Aerospace Research since October 15, 1965.
[2] Commander of the Office of Aerospace Research until October 15, 1965.

the Air Force is faced with real and urgent problems that require advanced statistical concepts and techniques for their solution.

I am aware of the very important contributions that have been made in all fields of statistics in the past decade, including your own specialized area, and I am confident that great progress lies ahead.

The methods of multivariate analysis, in large measure, arose out of practical needs. You, as I, recognize the many ways its techniques can help not only the Air Force, but also many other organizations active in the engineering, biological, physical, and social sciences.

It is fitting that the proceedings of this symposium will be dedicated to the memory of the late Professor S. N. Roy, who made significant contributions to this area.

On behalf of OAR, I am appreciative of your interest in attending this symposium and thus furthering our mutual interest in research in multivariate analysis. It is a pleasure to note the great distinction you have achieved in statistics, and especially in multivariate analysis. We can all look forward to a most interesting and very important meeting.

PART I

Nonparametric Methods

Some Nonparametric Multivariate Procedures Based on Statistically Equivalent Blocks[1]

T. W. ANDERSON
DEPARTMENT OF MATHEMATICAL STATISTICS
COLUMBIA UNIVERSITY
NEW YORK, NEW YORK

1. INTRODUCTION

Statistical techniques based on the multivariate normal distribution are highly developed (see Anderson [2], for example). Many of these techniques are applicable to situations where the underlying distribution is not normal, particularly if the number of observations is large, but the performance of a procedure for a nonnormal distribution will differ from that for a normal distribution. There is a need for multivariate methods which can be used regardless of the underlying distribution.

In the univariate case there are available various nonparametric or distribution-free procedures. In this paper we show how to exploit them for multivariate problems. In particular we consider the problem of testing the hypothesis that the distribution from which a sample is drawn is a given one, of testing the hypothesis that the distributions from which two samples are drawn are equal, and of classifying a new observation as coming from one of the two distributions from which two samples have been drawn. These problems are analogues of univariate problems.

The procedures proposed here are based on the properties of *statistically equivalent blocks*, which have been highly developed for use as tolerance limits. We shall review the construction of statistically equivalent blocks and their properties and then show their use in developing nonparametric multivariate methods.

[1] This research was sponsored by the United States Air Force under Contract AF-18(600)941 and Contract AF-41(609)-2653. Reproduction in whole or in part is permitted for any purpose of the United States Government.

2. STATISTICALLY EQUIVALENT BLOCKS

2.1. Random Points on the Unit Interval

Suppose $u_1, \ldots, u_N$ are independently distributed according to the uniform distribution on [0, 1]. Let the ordered values be $u^{(1)} < \cdots < u^{(N)}$, and let the lengths of the intervals in [0, 1] be $v_1 = u^{(1)}$,

$$v_\alpha = u^{(\alpha)} - u^{(\alpha-1)}, \qquad \alpha = 2, \ldots, N, \tag{2.1}$$

and $v_{N+1} = 1 - u^{(N)}$. Then $v_1, \ldots, v_{N+1}$ are barycentric coordinates of a point uniformly distributed in an N-dimensional simplex; that is, $v_\alpha \geq 0$, $\alpha = 1, \ldots, N+1$, and $\sum_{\alpha=1}^{N+1} v_\alpha = 1$. For example, if $N = 2$, the simplex is an equilateral triangle with altitude 1, and v_1, v_2, v_3 are the distances of a point (within the triangle) to the three sides. If $N = 3$, the simplex is a symmetric tetrahedron with altitude 1, and v_1, v_2, v_3, v_4 are the distances of a point to the four faces.

The joint distribution of any subset of $u^{(1)}, \ldots, u^{(N)}$ is a Dirichlet distribution. Let $j_1 < j_2 < \cdots < j_m$ be m of the integers $1, \ldots, N$. The density of $u^{(j_1)}, \ldots, u^{(j_m)}$ for $0 \leq u^{(j_1)} \leq \cdots \leq u^{(j_m)} \leq 1$ is

$$\frac{\Gamma(N+1)}{\Gamma(j_1)\Gamma(j_2 - j_1) \cdots \Gamma(j_m - j_{m-1})\Gamma(N+1-j_m)}$$
$$\times [u^{(j_1)}]^{j_1 - 1}[u^{(j_2)} - u^{(j_1)}]^{j_2 - j_1 - 1} \cdots [u^{(j_m)} - u^{(j_{m-1})}]^{j_m - j_{m-1} - 1}$$
$$\times [1 - u^{(j_m)}]^{N - j_m}. \tag{2.2}$$

The remaining ordered variables form $m + 1$ sets (some possibly vacuous), namely, $u^{(1)}, \ldots, u^{(j_1 - 1)}$; $u^{(j_1+1)}, \ldots, u^{(j_2-1)}$; ... ; $u^{(j_m+1)}, \ldots, u^{(N+1)}$. Given $u^{(j_1)}, \ldots, u^{(j_m)}$, the sets are mutually independent (as verified later). The variables in the ith set are the ordered observations from a set of $j_i - j_{i-1} - 1$ independent observations from the uniform distribution on $[u^{(j_{i-1})}, u^{(j_i)}]$; that is, conditional on $v_1 + \cdots + v_{j_1}$, $v_{j_1+1} + \cdots + v_{j_2}, \ldots, v_{j_{m-1}+1} + \cdots + v_{j_m}$, the $m + 1$ sets are independent and $v_{j_{i-1}+1}/(v_{j_{i-1}+1} + \cdots + v_{j_i}), \ldots, v_{j_i}/(v_{j_{i-1}+1}, \ldots, v_{j_i})$ are uniformly distributed barycentric coordinates.

Conversely, any set of u's or v's satisfying the conditions of the immediately preceding paragraph also satisfy the conditions of the first paragraph.

2.2. Univariate Observations

If $x_1, \ldots, x_N$ are N observations on a scalar random variable x with continuous cumulative distribution function $F(x)$, then $u_1 = F(x_1), \ldots, u_N = F(x_N)$ are independently uniformly distributed on [0, 1], and intervals between ordered u's are distributed as described above. To test the hypothesis that

$F(x) = F_0(x)$, where $F_0(x)$ is specified, one defines $u_\alpha = F_0(x_\alpha)$, $\alpha = 1, \dots, N$, and then tests the hypothesis that $u_1, \dots, u_N$ are uniformly distributed on [0, 1]. Various criteria are available. The distributions of the criteria under the null hypothesis can be derived from the distributions of the u_α's or the v_α's.

2.3. Multivariate Observations

Now let $\mathbf{x}_1, \dots, \mathbf{x}_N$ be N observations on a p-component random vector $\mathbf{x}$ with distribution function $F(\mathbf{x})$. Let $h_1(\mathbf{x}), \dots, h_N(\mathbf{x})$ be N functions of $\mathbf{x}$, not necessarily different, such that the distribution of $h_\alpha(\mathbf{x})$ is a continuous distribution when $\mathbf{x}$ is distributed according to $F(\mathbf{x})$, $\alpha = 1, \dots, N$. [The probability of $h_j(\mathbf{x}_\alpha) = h_j(\mathbf{x}_\beta)$, $\alpha \neq \beta$, is 0.] Let $k_1, k_2, \dots, k_N$ be a permutation of $1, 2, \dots, N$. Use $h_{k_1}(\mathbf{x})$ to order the $\mathbf{x}_\alpha$'s and define $\mathbf{x}^{(k_1)}$ as the k_1th in this ordering; that is, $\mathbf{x}^{(k_1)}$ is the $\mathbf{x}_\alpha$ for which $k_1 - 1$ of $h_{k_1}(\mathbf{x}_\alpha)$ are less than $h_{k_1}(\mathbf{x}^{(k_1)})$ and $N - k_1$ are larger. Then the *cut*

$$h_{k_1}(\mathbf{x}) = h_{k_1}(\mathbf{x}^{(k_1)}) \tag{2.3}$$

defines two *blocks*

$$B_{1\dots k_1} = \{\mathbf{x}\colon\ h_{k_1}(\mathbf{x}) \leq h_{k_1}(\mathbf{x}^{(k_1)})\}, \tag{2.4}$$

$$B_{k_1+1\dots N+1} = \{\mathbf{x}\colon\ h_{k_1}(\mathbf{x}^{(k_1)}) < h_{k_1}(\mathbf{x})\}. \tag{2.5}$$

Let

$$u^{(k_1)} = \int_{B_{1\dots k_1}} dF(\mathbf{x}); \tag{2.6}$$

that is, $u^{(k_1)}$ is the probability [according to $F(\mathbf{x})$] that $h_{k_1}(\mathbf{x}) \leq h_{k_1}(\mathbf{x}^{(k_1)})$, given $\mathbf{x}^{(k_1)}$. The density of $u^{(k_1)}$ $[0 \leq u^{(k_1)} \leq 1]$ is (2.2) for $m = 1$ and $j_1 = k_1$, which is

$$\frac{\Gamma(N+1)}{\Gamma(k_1)\Gamma(N+1-k_1)}\,[u^{(k_1)}]^{k_1-1}[1 - u^{(k_1)}]^{N-k_1}. \tag{2.7}$$

This follows from the preceding discussion by considering the marginal distribution of $h_{k_1}(\mathbf{x})$. Conditional on $\mathbf{x}^{(k_1)}$, the two sets of $k_1 - 1$ and $N - k_1$ $\mathbf{x}_\alpha$'s are independently distributed. The variables in the first set are independently distributed in the region for which $h_{k_1}(\mathbf{x}) \leq h_{k_1}(\mathbf{x}^{(k_1)})$ according to the probability measure defined by $F(\mathbf{x})/u^{(k_1)}$. The variables in the second set are independently distributed in the region for which $h_{k_1}(\mathbf{x}^{(k_1)}) < h_{k_1}(\mathbf{x})$ according to the probability measure defined by $F(\mathbf{x})/(1 - u^{(k_1)})$.

To verify these facts, consider the joint density of $\mathbf{x}_1, \dots, \mathbf{x}_{k_1-1}, \mathbf{x}_{k_1+1}, \dots, \mathbf{x}_N$ conditional on $h_{k_1}(\mathbf{x}_\alpha) \leq c_1$, $\alpha = 1, \dots, k_1 - 1$, and $c_1 < h_{k_1}(\mathbf{x}_\alpha)$, $\alpha = k_1 + 1, \dots, N$, which is

$$\frac{\prod_{\alpha=1}^{k_1-1} f(\mathbf{x}_\alpha)}{[u^{(k_1)}]^{k_1-1}}\,\frac{\prod_{\alpha=k_1+1}^{N} f(\mathbf{x}_\alpha)}{[1 - u^{(k_1)}]^{N-k_1}}, \tag{2.8}$$

where $u^{(k_1)} = \int dF(\mathbf{x})$ for $h_{k_1}(\mathbf{x}) \leq c_1$; for convenience we have assumed $F(\mathbf{x})$ has a density $f(\mathbf{x})$. Since the numbering of the $\mathbf{x}_\alpha$'s is arbitrary, the first factor of (2.8) is the density of the $k_1 - 1$ $\mathbf{x}_\alpha$'s in $B_{1\cdots k_1}$, and the second factor is the density of the $N - k_1$ $\mathbf{x}_\alpha$'s in $B_{k_1+1\cdots N+1}$.

The procedure is continued. Suppose $0 < k_2 < k_1$. Use $h_{k_2}(\mathbf{x})$ to order the $k_1 - 1$ $\mathbf{x}_\alpha$'s in $B_{1\cdots k_1}$, and define $\mathbf{x}^{(k_2)}$ as the k_2th in this ordering; that is, $\mathbf{x}^{(k_2)}$ is the $\mathbf{x}_\alpha$ for which $k_2 - 1$ $\mathbf{x}_\alpha$'s satisfy $h_{k_2}(\mathbf{x}_\alpha) < h_{k_2}(\mathbf{x}^{(k_2)})$ and $h_{k_1}(\mathbf{x}_\alpha) < h_{k_1}(\mathbf{x}^{(k_1)})$ and $k_1 - k_2 - 1$ $\mathbf{x}_\alpha$'s satisfy $h_{k_2}(\mathbf{x}^{(k_2)}) < h_{k_2}(\mathbf{x}_\alpha)$ and $h_{k_1}(\mathbf{x}_\alpha) < h_{k_1}(\mathbf{x}^{(k_1)})$. Let

$$B_{1\cdots k_2} = B_{1\cdots k_1} \cap \{\mathbf{x}\colon h_{k_2}(\mathbf{x}) \leq h_{k_2}(\mathbf{x}^{(k_2)})\}, \tag{2.9}$$

$$B_{k_2+1\cdots k_1} = B_{1\cdots k_1} \cap \{\mathbf{x}\colon h_{k_2}(\mathbf{x}^{(k_2)}) < h_{k_2}(\mathbf{x})\}, \tag{2.10}$$

$$u^{(k_2)} = \int_{B_{1\ldots k_2}} dF(\mathbf{x}); \tag{2.11}$$

that is, $u^{(k_2)}$ is the probability [according to $F(\mathbf{x})$] that $h_{k_2}(\mathbf{x}) \leq h_{k_2}(\mathbf{x}^{(k_2)})$ and $h_{k_1}(\mathbf{x}) \leq h_{k_1}(\mathbf{x}^{(k_1)})$. Then the conditional density of $u^{(k_2)}$ given $u^{(k_1)}$ $[0 \leq u^{(k_2)} \leq u^{(k_1)}]$ is

$$\frac{\Gamma(k_1)}{\Gamma(k_2)\Gamma(k_1 - k_2)} \frac{[u^{(k_2)}]^{k_2-1}[u^{(k_1)} - u^{(k_2)}]^{k_1-k_2-1}}{[u^{(k_1)}]^{k_1-1}}; \tag{2.12}$$

this corresponds to (2.7) for $u^{(k_1)}$, k_1, and N replaced by $u^{(k_2)}/u^{(k_1)}$, k_2, and $k_1 - 1$, respectively. The joint density of $u^{(k_2)}$ and $u^{(k_1)}$ $[0 \leq u^{(k_2)} \leq u^{(k_1)} \leq 1]$ is

$$\frac{\Gamma(N+1)}{\Gamma(k_2)\Gamma(k_1 - k_2)\Gamma(N + 1 - k_1)} [u^{(k_2)}]^{k_2-1}[u^{(k_1)} - u^{(k_2)}]^{k_1-k_2-1}[1 - u^{(k_1)}]^{N-k_1}, \tag{2.13}$$

which is (2.2) for $m = 2$, $j_1 = k_2$, and $j_2 = k_1$. Conditional on $\mathbf{x}^{(k_2)}$ and $\mathbf{x}^{(k_1)}$, the three sets of $k_2 - 1$, $k_1 - k_2 - 1$, and $N - k_1$ $\mathbf{x}_\alpha$'s are independently distributed. The $k_2 - 1$ vectors in the first set are independently distributed in $B_{1\cdots k_2}$ according to the probability measure defined by $F(\mathbf{x})/u^{(k_2)}$. The $k_1 - k_2 - 1$ vectors in the second set are independently distributed in $B_{k_2+1\cdots k_1}$ according to the probability measure $F(\mathbf{x})/[u^{(k_1)} - u^{(k_2)}]$. These facts follow by applying the argument at (2.8) to the $k_1 - 1$ $\mathbf{x}_\alpha$'s in $B_{1\cdots k_1}$.

If $k_1 < k_2$, rank the $N - k_1$ $\mathbf{x}_\alpha$'s in $B_{k_1+1\cdots N+1}$ according to $h_{k_2}(\mathbf{x})$ and let $\mathbf{x}^{(k_2)}$ be the $(k_2 - k_1)$th in the ranking. Then

$$B_{k_1+1\cdots k_2} = B_{k_1+1\cdots N+1} \cap \{\mathbf{x}\colon h_{k_2}(\mathbf{x}) \leq h_{k_2}(\mathbf{x}^{(k_2)})\}, \tag{2.14}$$

$$B_{k_2+1\cdots N+1} = B_{k_1+1\cdots N+1} \cap \{\mathbf{x}\colon h_{k_2}(\mathbf{x}^{(k_2)}) < h_{k_2}(\mathbf{x})\}, \tag{2.15}$$

$$u^{(k_2)} = \int_{B_{1\ldots k_1} \cup B_{k_1+1\ldots k_2}} dF(\mathbf{x}). \tag{2.16}$$

The joint density of $u^{(k_1)}$ and $u^{(k_2)}$ $[0 \leq u^{(k_1)} \leq u^{(k_2)} \leq 1]$ is

$$\frac{\Gamma(N+1)}{\Gamma(k_1)\Gamma(k_2-k_1)\Gamma(N+1-k_2)} \times [u^{(k_1)}]^{k_1-1}[u^{(k_2)}-u^{(k_1)}]^{k_2-k_1-1}[1-u^{(k_2)}]^{N-k_2}. \tag{2.17}$$

At the end of the mth stage there will be $m+1$ blocks: $B_{1\cdots j_1}$, $B_{j_1+1\cdots j_2}$, ..., $B_{j_m+1\cdots N+1}$, where $j_1 < \cdots < j_m$ are $k_1, \ldots, k_m$ arranged in ascending order. Each block will contain a number of $\mathbf{x}_\alpha$'s equal to one less than the number of indices. The $(m+1)$st index k_{m+1} is in one of the $m+1$ sets of subscripts. The function $h_{k_{m+1}}(\mathbf{x})$ is used to rank the $\mathbf{x}_\alpha$'s in the block having k_{m+1} as one of its indices. Then $\mathbf{x}^{(k_{m+1})}$ is the $\mathbf{x}_\alpha$ in this block such that $k_{m+1}-1$ $\mathbf{x}_\alpha$'s are either in lower-ranking blocks (indices less than k_{m+1}) or are ranked lower in this block by $h_{k_{m+1}}(\mathbf{x})$. This block is replaced by its intersection with $\{\mathbf{x} : h_{k_{m+1}}(\mathbf{x}) \leq h_{k_{m+1}}(\mathbf{x}^{(k_{m+1})})\}$ and its intersection with $\{\mathbf{x} : h_{k_{m+1}}(\mathbf{x}^{(k_{m+1})}) < h_{k_{m+1}}(\mathbf{x})\}$. The procedure is continued until after N stages there are $N+1$ blocks, $B_1, \ldots, B_{N+1}$.

Let

$$v_k = \int_{B_k} dF(\mathbf{x}), \qquad k = 1, \ldots, N+1; \tag{2.18}$$

then $v_1, \ldots, v_{N+1}$ are the barycentric coordinates of a point uniformly distributed in the $(N+1)$-dimensional simplex: $v_\alpha \geq 0$, $\alpha = 1, \ldots, N+1$, and $\sum_{\alpha=1}^{N+1} v_\alpha = 1$. From the construction,

$$u^{(j)} = \sum_{k=1}^{j} v_k, \qquad j = 1, \ldots, N, \tag{2.19}$$

and $u^{(1)}, \ldots, u^{(N)}$ are distributed as the ordered values of N observations on a random variable uniformly distributed on $[0, 1]$. To see that these facts follow from the construction of the blocks, we note first that

$$u^{(k_1)} = \int_{B_{1\cdots k_1}} dF(\mathbf{x}) \tag{2.20}$$

has density (2.7), which is (2.2) for $m = 1$ and $j_1 = k_1$, and given $\mathbf{x}^{(k_1)}$, the $k_1 - 1$ $\mathbf{x}_\alpha$'s in $B_{1\cdots k_1}$ and the $N - k_1$ $\mathbf{x}_\alpha$'s in $B_{k_1+1\cdots N+1}$ are independently distributed, the first according to $F(\mathbf{x})/u^{(k_1)}$ in $B_{1\cdots k_1}$ and the second according to $F(\mathbf{x})/(1-u^{(k_1)})$ in $B_{k_1+1\cdots N+1}$. To go on by induction, we assume that at the end of the mth stage $u^{(j_1)}, \ldots, u^{(j_m)}$ have the density (2.2). Here $j_1 < \cdots < j_m$ are the ordered integers $k_1, \ldots, k_m$. Suppose that k_{m+1} falls between j^* and j^{**} (two consecutive indices from $j_1, \ldots, j_m$). Then

$$\frac{u^{(k_{m+1})} - u^{(j^*)}}{u^{(j^{**})} - u^{(j^*)}} = \int_{B_{j^*+1\cdots k_{m+1}}} dF(\mathbf{x}) \Big/ \int_{B_{j^*+1\cdots j^{**}}} dF(\mathbf{x}) \tag{2.21}$$

has the conditional density [given $u^{(j^*)}$ and $u^{(j^{**})}$] for $u^{(j^*)} \leq u^{(k_{m+1})} \leq u^{(j^{**})}$

$$\frac{\Gamma(j^{**} - j^*)}{\Gamma(k_{m+1} - j^*)\Gamma(j^{**} - k_{m+1})} \times \frac{[u^{(k_{m+1})} - u^{(j^*)}]^{k_{m+1} - j^* - 1}[u^{(j^{**})} - u^{(k_{m+1})}]^{j^{**} - k_{m+1} - 1}}{[u^{(j^{**})} - u^{(j^*)}]^{j^{**} - j^* - 1}}. \tag{2.22}$$

The product of (2.22) and (2.2) is (2.2), with m replaced by $m + 1$. This demonstrates the result.

It can be seen from the above procedure that at the $(m + 1)$st stage, the integer k_{m+1} and the function $h_{k_{m+1}}(\mathbf{x})$ may depend on the functions $h_{k_1}(\mathbf{x}), \ldots, h_{k_m}(\mathbf{x})$ and their values $h_{k_1}(\mathbf{x}^{(k_1)}), \ldots, h_{k_m}(\mathbf{x}^{(k_m)})$.

$B_1, \ldots, B_{N+1}$ are called *statistically equivalent blocks*. The procedure has been described by Fraser ([5], Section 4.3) in the above generality and by Wilks ([7], Section 8.7), for $k_1 = 1, \ldots, k_N = N$.

The assumption that $h_j(\mathbf{x})$ have a continuous distribution when $\mathbf{x}$ has the distribution $F(\mathbf{x})$ ensures that the probability of $h_j(\mathbf{x}_\alpha) = h_j(\mathbf{x}_\beta)$, $\alpha \neq \beta$, is 0. Hence the probability is 1 that the procedure leads to a unique ordering or ranking of the N observation vectors $\mathbf{x}_1, \ldots, \mathbf{x}_N$.

2.4. Examples

To illustrate this method, let $N = 8$ and let the vectors be two-dimensional. Let $k_1, \ldots, k_8$ be 3, 6, 1, 2, 4, 5, 7, 8, and let $h_3(\mathbf{x}) = h_6(\mathbf{x}) = x_1$, the first coordinate, and $h_k(\mathbf{x}) = x_2$, the second coordinate, for $k \neq 3, 6$. Then $\mathbf{x}^{(3)}$ is the observation vector with the third smallest value of the first coordinate; that is, two observations have smaller values of the first coordinate and five observations have larger values of the first coordinate. Next, $\mathbf{x}^{(6)}$ is the observation among the latter five which has the third smallest value of the first coordinate; that is two of the five observations have smaller values of the first coordinate and two of the five have larger values. In this case $\mathbf{x}^{(3)}$ and $\mathbf{x}^{(6)}$ correspond to the third and sixth observations ranked according to x_1. Two observations have x_1 coordinates less than $x_1^{(3)}$, two have x_1 coordinates between $x_1^{(3)}$ and $x_1^{(6)}$, and two have x_1 coordinates greater than $x_1^{(6)}$. $\mathbf{x}^{(1)}$ and $\mathbf{x}^{(2)}$ constitute the first set of two; of these $\mathbf{x}^{(1)}$ has the smaller x_2 coordinate. $\mathbf{x}^{(4)}$ and $\mathbf{x}^{(5)}$ constitute the second set of two; of these $\mathbf{x}^{(4)}$ has the smaller x_2 coordinate. $\mathbf{x}^{(7)}$ and $\mathbf{x}^{(8)}$ constitute the third set of two; of these $\mathbf{x}^{(7)}$ has the smaller x_2 coordinate (see Fig. 1).

As an example of blocks in higher dimensions, let $p = 3$, $N = 7$, $(k_1, \ldots, k_7) = (4, 2, 6, 1, 3, 5, 7)$ and $h_4(\mathbf{x}) = x_1$, $h_2(\mathbf{x}) = h_6(\mathbf{x}) = x_2$, and $h_k(\mathbf{x}) = x_3$ for $k = 1, 3, 5, 7$. The first cut is a plane orthogonal to the first coordinate axis. The second and third cuts are planes orthogonal to the second coordinate

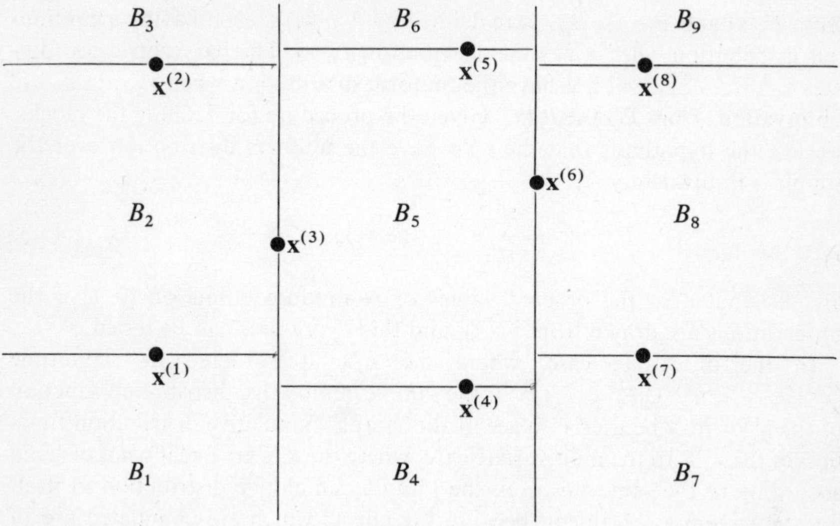

Fig. 1

axis; the blocks B_{12}, B_{34}, B_{56}, and B_{78} have cross sections in the x_1, x_2 plane of quadrants. The remaining cuts are by planes orthogonal to the third coordinate axis. The final blocks $B_1, \ldots, B_8$ are octants.

3. TESTING THE HYPOTHESIS THAT AN UNKNOWN CUMULATIVE DISTRIBUTION IS A SPECIFIED ONE

3.1. The General Procedure

Suppose that N observations $\mathbf{x}_1, \ldots, \mathbf{x}_N$ are taken on a vector random variable $\mathbf{x}$ with cumulative distribution function $F(\mathbf{x})$. Consider testing the null hypothesis that

$$H_0\colon F(\mathbf{x}) = F_0(\mathbf{x}), \quad \text{all } \mathbf{x}, \tag{3.1}$$

where $F_0(\mathbf{x})$ is completely specified. The alternatives are $F(\mathbf{x}) \neq F_0(\mathbf{x})$ on a set of positive probability. One is usually not interested in the cumulative distribution function *per se*, but in the probability measure defined by it.

To test the hypothesis $F(\mathbf{x}) = F_0(\mathbf{x})$, we use the fact that

$$v_j{}^0 = \int_{B_j} dF_0(\mathbf{x}), \qquad j = 1, \ldots, N+1 \tag{3.2}$$

are distributed uniformly over the simplex when $\mathbf{x}_1, \ldots, \mathbf{x}_N$ are observations from $F_0(\mathbf{x})$ and $B_1, \ldots, B_{N+1}$ are defined by N $h_j(\mathbf{x})$'s, each having a continuous distribution when $\mathbf{x}$ has the distribution $F_0(\mathbf{x})$. The barycentric coordinates $v_1{}^0, \ldots, v_{N+1}^0$ will not have the uniform distribution when $\mathbf{x}_1, \ldots, \mathbf{x}_N$ are observations from $F(\mathbf{x}) \neq F_0(\mathbf{x})$. Given the procedure for defining the blocks, we test the hypothesis that the $v_j{}^0$'s have the uniform distribution over the simplex. Equivalently,

$$u_0^{(k)} = \sum_{j=1}^{k} v_j{}^0, \quad k = 1, \ldots, N \tag{3.3}$$

are distributed as the ordered values of N random points on [0, 1] if the observations are drawn from $F_0(\mathbf{x})$, and this hypothesis can be tested.

In the univariate case, where the x_α's are ordered in magnitude $(x^{(1)} < \cdots < x^{(N)})$, $u_0^{(k)} = F_0(x^{(k)})$; the sample cumulative distribution function of the $u^{(k)}$'s may be used in place of the sample cumulative distribution function of the x_α's. In the multivariate case, where the $\mathbf{x}_\alpha$'s are usually not ordered according to the same function, the sample cumulative distribution in itself does not seem as pertinent, because the effects which are cumulated are of different kinds. However, given a procedure for constructing the blocks, one may construct the sample cumulative distribution function of the $u_0^{(k)}$'s and use it in a test procedure, such as Kolmogorov's maximum deviation or the Cramér–von Mises ω^2. Tests of this kind tend to reject the null hypothesis by a large difference between the sample and hypothetical distribution functions in the middle of the range (that is, where the effects have cumulated). Note that here once the blocks have been defined, they can be renumbered; the resulting $v_j{}^0$'s can be cumulated to obtain another analogue of ordered points.

Tests which are based on frequencies and probabilities in small intervals in the scalar case are available and seem more appropriate here. A particular test is to reject the hypothesis $F(\mathbf{x}) = F_0(\mathbf{x})$ if any block probability is extremely large. Under the null hypothesis the probability of the largest $v_j{}^0$ exceeding a number V $[1/(N+1) \leq V \leq 1]$ is (Fisher [4])

$$\Pr\left\{ \max_{j=1,\ldots,N+1} v_j{}^0 > V \right\} = (N+1)(1-V)^N - \binom{N+1}{2}(1-2V)^N + \cdots$$

$$+ (-1)^{k-1}\binom{N+1}{k}(1-kV)^N, \quad \frac{1}{k+1} \leq V \leq \frac{1}{k}, \quad k = 1, \ldots, N. \tag{3.4}$$

If V_ε is the value of V that makes (3.4) equal to ε, a test at significance level ε leads to rejection of the null hypothesis if the largest $v_j{}^0$ exceeds V_ε. The test can be carried out by finding the largest $v_j{}^0$, replacing V on the right side of (3.4) by this value, and rejecting the null hypothesis if the right side is less than ε.

Another test is to reject the hypothesis if any block probability is extremely small. Under the null hypothesis the probability of the smallest $v_j{}^0$ being less than a number $V\,[0 \le V \le 1/(N+1)]$ is $1 - [1 - (N+1)V]^N$, since the distance from the simplex center to the face of the simplex $v_j{}^0 \ge 0$ is $1/(N+1)$ and to the face of the simplex $v_j{}^0 \ge V$ is $[1/(N+1)] - V$, and the probability of $\min v_j{}^0 \ge V$ is proportional to the volume of the smaller simplex. (A test can be based on the fact that the probability that the smallest $v_j{}^0$ is at least $V\,[0 \le V \le 1/(N+1)]$ and the largest $v_j{}^0$ is at least $U\,[1/(k+1) \le U - V \le 1/k,\ k = 1, \dots, N]$ is (3.4), with $1 - jV$ replaced by $1 - (N+1)V - j(U - V)$, $j = 1, \dots, k$.)

3.2. Testing the Hypothesis That a Bivariate Distribution Is a Given Normal Distribution

As an example, let $\mathbf{x}_1, \dots, \mathbf{x}_8$ be eight observations from a bivariate distribution. Consider testing the null hypothesis that the distribution is $N(\mathbf{0}, \mathbf{I})$, the normal distribution with mean vector $\mathbf{0}$ and covariance matrix $\mathbf{I}$. Let the blocks be determined as in Section 2.4. Then

$$\begin{aligned} v_1{}^0 &= \Pr\{x_1 \le x_1^{(3)}, x_2 \le x_2^{(1)} \mid N(\mathbf{0}, \mathbf{I})\} \\ &= \Pr\{x_1 \le x_1^{(3)} \mid N(0,1)\} \Pr\{x_2 \le x_2^{(1)} \mid N(0,1)\} \\ &= \Phi(x_1^{(3)})\Phi(x_2^{(1)}), \end{aligned} \tag{3.5}$$

where

$$\Phi(a) = \int_{-\infty}^{a} \phi(x)\,dx \tag{3.6}$$

and $\phi(x)$ is the density of $N(0, 1)$. Similarly,

$$v_2{}^0 = \Phi(x_1^{(3)})[\Phi(x_2^{(2)}) - \Phi(x_2^{(1)})], \tag{3.7}$$

$$v_3{}^0 = \Phi(x_1^{(3)})[1 - \Phi(x_2^{(2)})], \tag{3.8}$$

$$v_4{}^0 = [\Phi(x_1^{(6)}) - \Phi(x_1^{(3)})]\Phi(x_2^{(4)}), \tag{3.9}$$

$$v_5{}^0 = [\Phi(x_1^{(6)}) - \Phi(x_1^{(3)})][\Phi(x_2^{(5)}) - \Phi(x_2^{(4)})], \tag{3.10}$$

$$v_6{}^0 = [\Phi(x_1^{(6)}) - \Phi(x_1^{(3)})][1 - \Phi(x_2^{(5)})], \tag{3.11}$$

$$v_7{}^0 = [1 - \Phi(x_1^{(6)})]\Phi(x_2^{(7)}), \tag{3.12}$$

$$v_8{}^0 = [1 - \Phi(x_1^{(6)})][\Phi(x_2^{(8)}) - \Phi(x_2^{(7)})], \tag{3.13}$$

$$v_9{}^0 = [1 - \Phi(x_1^{(6)})][1 - \Phi(x_2^{(8)})]. \tag{3.14}$$

The 1% significance point is the solution of

$$9(1 - V)^8 = 0.01, \tag{3.15}$$

which is $V_{0.01} = 0.573$. The hypothesis is rejected if one of $v_1^0, \dots, v_9^0$ is greater than 0.573. This is equivalent to rejecting the hypothesis if $\max v_j^0 > \frac{1}{2}$ and $9(1 - \max v_j^0)^8 < 0.01$.

The use of coordinates as functions to define the blocks has some appeal, because the resulting blocks are somewhat similar to what one would get by use of the cumulative distribution function. Since $N(\mathbf{0}, \mathbf{I})$ is invariant with regard to rotations, one could make any rotation before defining the blocks, or one could choose the angle of rotation at random. The last method would give invariance with regard to rotations. Other methods of using coordinates as cutting functions are given below, Their use permits the calculation of probabilities of v_j^0 by means of tables of the univariate normal distribution.

Other procedures might be devised using the function $\mathbf{x}'\mathbf{x}$ and $\arg \mathbf{x} = \arg(x_1, x_2)$, which is the angle between the positive x_1 axis and the vector (x_1, x_2). These define arcs of circles and segments of radii. For example, if the permutation is again 3, 6, 1, 2, 4, 5, 7, 8, and $h_3(\mathbf{x}) = h_6(\mathbf{x}) = \mathbf{x}'\mathbf{x}$ and $h_k(\mathbf{x}) = \arg \mathbf{x}$, $k \neq 3, 6$, then the observations are ranked according to their distances from the origin, and $\mathbf{x}^{(3)}$ and $\mathbf{x}^{(6)}$ are third and sixth from the origin. Of the two observations within the inner circle, $\mathbf{x}^{(1)}$ is the observation with the smallest angle between the horizontal line to the right of the origin and the radius through the point. There are two observations in the ring between $\mathbf{x}^{(3)}$ and $\mathbf{x}^{(6)}$ and two observations outside the outer circle. Then, for example,

$$u^{(3)} = \Pr\{\chi_2^2 \leq \mathbf{x}^{(3)\prime}\mathbf{x}^{(3)}\}, \tag{3.16}$$

$$u^{(6)} = \Pr\{\chi_2^2 \leq \mathbf{x}^{(6)\prime}\mathbf{x}^{(6)}\}, \tag{3.17}$$

$$u^{(1)}/u^{(3)} = \arg \mathbf{x}^{(1)}/(2\pi), \tag{3.18}$$

$$u^{(2)}/u^{(3)} = (\arg \mathbf{x}^{(2)} - \arg \mathbf{x}^{(1)})/(2\pi), \tag{3.19}$$

where χ_2^2 denotes a random variable having a χ^2 distribution with two degrees of freedom.

As another possible method of constructing blocks, consider an example where $N = 15$ and the permutation is 8, 4, 12, 2, 6, 10, 14, 1, 3, 5, 7, 9, 11, 13, 15, and $h_j(\mathbf{x}) = x_1$ for $j = 8, 2, 6, 10, 14$ and $h_j(\mathbf{x}) = x_2$ for j odd and $j = 4, 12$. Figure 2 shows the pattern. Here $B_1 \cup B_2 \cup B_3 \cup B_4$ forms a quadrant, as do $B_5 \cup B_6 \cup B_7 \cup B_8$, $B_9 \cup B_{10} \cup B_{11} \cup B_{12}$, and $B_{13} \cup B_{14} \cup B_{15} \cup B_{16}$. The idea is that the first cut bisects the plane relative to x_1. Then the second and third cuts bisect the half-planes according to x_2. The next four cuts bisect the respective quadrants according to x_1, and the last eight cuts bisect the eight blocks according to x_2.

If $N + 1$ is a power of 2, say 2^q, the procedure is to define $\mathbf{x}^{(2^{q-1})}$ by x_1, then $\mathbf{x}^{(2^{q-2})}$ and $\mathbf{x}^{(3 \cdot 2^{q-2})}$ by x_2, etc. If $N + 1$ is not a power of 2, we use a sequence of integers and cutting functions that is close to the previous one.

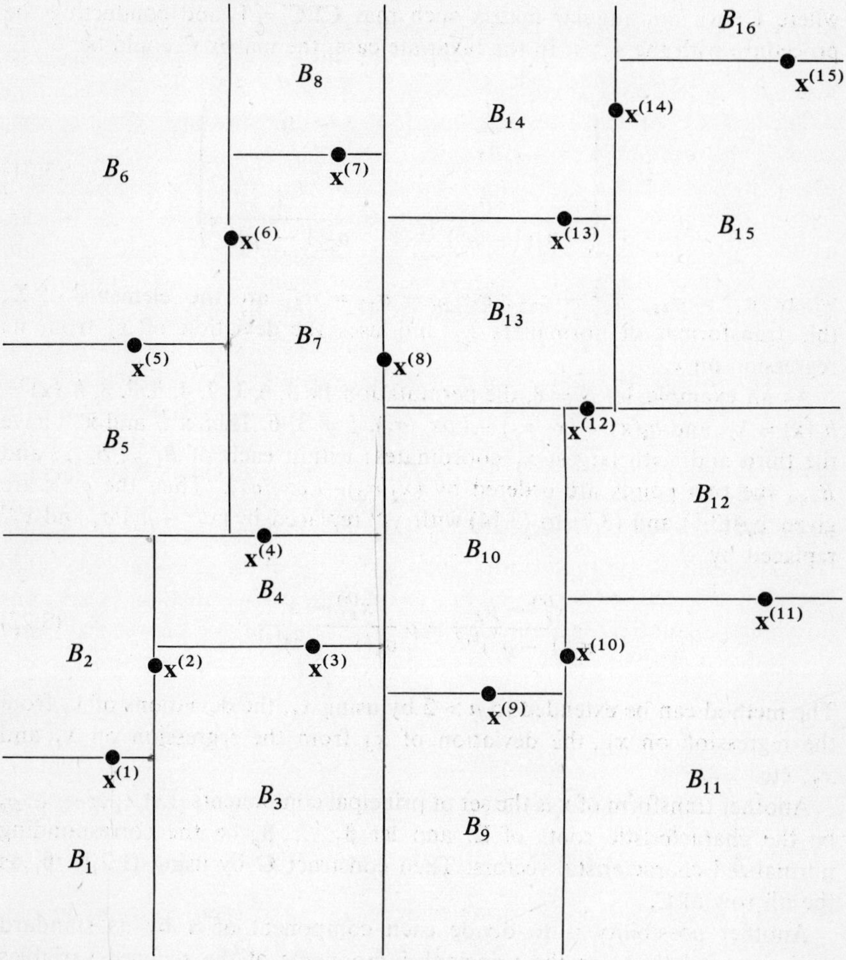

Fig. 2

For instance, let $k_1 = [\frac{1}{2}(N + 1)]$, where $[y]$ denotes the largest integer in y, $k_2 = [(N + 1)/4]$, $k_3 = [3(N + 1)/4]$, $k_4 = [(N + 1)/8]$, ... The procedure is continued until all integers $1, \ldots, N$ are obtained. (Duplicate integers are discarded.)

If the hypothetical distribution is $N(\boldsymbol{\mu}, \boldsymbol{\Sigma})$ for arbitrary mean vector $\boldsymbol{\mu}$ and covariance matrix $\boldsymbol{\Sigma}$, the problem can be transformed to testing the hypothesis of $N(\mathbf{0}, \mathbf{I})$ by transforming $\mathbf{x}_\alpha$ to

$$\mathbf{x}_\alpha{}^* = \mathbf{C}(\mathbf{x}_\alpha - \boldsymbol{\mu}), \tag{3.20}$$

where $\mathbf{C}$ is a nonsingular matrix such that $\mathbf{C\Sigma C}' = \mathbf{I}$, and conducting the procedure with the $\mathbf{x}_\alpha$*'s. In the bivariate case, the matrix $\mathbf{C}$ could be

$$\mathbf{C} = \begin{pmatrix} \dfrac{1}{\sigma_1} & 0 \\ -\dfrac{\rho}{\sigma_1(1-\rho^2)^{1/2}} & \dfrac{1}{\sigma_2(1-{}^2\rho)^{1/2}} \end{pmatrix}, \tag{3.21}$$

where $\sigma_1{}^2 = \sigma_{11}$, $\sigma_2{}^2 = \sigma_{22}$, $\sigma_1\sigma_2\rho = \sigma_{12} = \sigma_{21}$ are the elements of Σ; this transformation normalizes x_1 and uses the deviation of x_2 from its regression on x_1.

As an example, let $N = 8$, the permutation be 3, 6, 1, 2, 4, 5, 7, 8, $h_3(\mathbf{x}) = h_6(\mathbf{x}) = x_1$, and $h_k(\mathbf{x}) = (x_2/\sigma_2) - (\rho x_1/\sigma_1)$, $k \neq 3, 6$. Then $\mathbf{x}^{(3)}$ and $\mathbf{x}^{(6)}$ have the third and sixth largest x_1 coordinates; within each of B_{123}, B_{456}, and B_{789} the two points are ordered by $(x_2/\sigma_2)-(\rho x_1/\sigma_1)$. Then the $v_j{}^0$'s are given by (3.5) and (3.7) to (3.14) with $x_1^{(k)}$ replaced by $(x_1^{(k)} - \mu_1)/\sigma_1$ and $x_2^{(k)}$ replaced by

$$\frac{x_2^{(k)} - \mu_2}{\sigma_2(1-\rho^2)^{1/2}} - \rho\,\frac{x_1^{(k)} - \mu_1}{\sigma_1(1-\rho^2)^{1/2}}. \tag{3.22}$$

The method can be extended to $p > 2$ by using x_1, the deviations of x_2 from the regression on x_1, the deviation of x_3 from the regression on x_1 and x_2, etc.

Another transform of $\mathbf{x}$ is the set of principal components. Let $\lambda_1 \geq \cdots \geq \lambda_p$ be the characteristic roots of Σ, and let $\boldsymbol{\beta}_1, \ldots, \boldsymbol{\beta}_p$ be the corresponding normalized characteristic vectors. Then construct $\mathbf{C}$ by using $[1/\lambda_i]^{1/2}\boldsymbol{\beta}_i$ as the ith row of $\mathbf{C}$.

Another possibility is to divide each component of $\mathbf{x}$ by its standard deviation and then use the principal components of the reduced variables (that is, principal components of the correlation matrix). In the case of $p = 2$ the transformed variates are $(x_1 - \mu_1)/\sigma_1 + (x_2 - \mu_2)/\sigma_2$ and $(x_1 - \mu_1)/\sigma_1 - (x_2 - \mu_2)/\sigma_2$.

3.3. Consistent Procedures

Suppose a procedure for testing $F(\mathbf{x}) = F_0(\mathbf{x})$ at significance level ε is defined for every sample size N ($N = 1, 2, \ldots$). The procedure is *consistent* against an alternative $F_1(\mathbf{x})$ if the probability of rejecting the null hypothesis when the observations are drawn from $F_1(\mathbf{x})$ approaches 1 as N increases indefinitely. We shall show that there exist tests which are consistent against every $F_1(\mathbf{x})$ such that the probability measure defined by $F_1(\mathbf{x})$ differs from the probability measure defined by $F_0(\mathbf{x})$ on a (Borel-measurable) set of positive probability. Since a probability measure uniquely defines a cumulative distribution function and vice versa, the condition on the alternative distributions is that they differ in at least one continuity point.

Consider any test of $F(x) = F_0(x)$ for the univariate case which is consistent against every alternative $F_1(x)$ which is not identical to $F_0(x)$. The Kolmogorov and Cramér–von Mises tests have this property, for example. Let us use such a test procedure with the method of constructing blocks by bisection as indicated in Fig. 2.

A procedure of this kind is consistent. We see that the procedure is consistent against an $F_1(\mathbf{x})$ that differs from $F_0(\mathbf{x})$ with respect to their x_1 medians, for then $u^{([(N+1)/2])}$ would converge in probability to a value different from $\frac{1}{2}$. To prove the result more generally for $p = 2$, divide the plane into blocks (that is, rectangles) by using the distribution of $F_0(\mathbf{x})$. Let $R(0)$ be the left half-plane with probability $\frac{1}{2}$ and $R(1)$ the right half-plane with probability $\frac{1}{2}$. Let $R(0, 0)$ be the lower half of $R(0)$; that is, $R(0, 0)$ is the part of $R(0)$ below a horizontal line, so $R(0, 0)$ has probability $1/4$. $R(0, 1)$ is the other half of $R(0)$. $R(1, 0)$ and $R(1, 1)$ are defined similarly. Cutting these in half by vertical lines defines $R(i, j, k)$, $i, j, k = 0, 1$. The process can be continued. These blocks are the population analogues [according to $F_0(\mathbf{x})$] of the blocks defined by $\mathbf{x}_1, \ldots, \mathbf{x}_N$ for $N = 2^q - 1$. Let $\hat{R}(0) = B_1$ and $\hat{R}(1) = B_2$ for $q = 1$, $\hat{R}(0, 0) = B_1$, $\hat{R}(0, 1) = B_2$, $\hat{R}(1, 0) = B_3$. $\hat{R}(1,1) = B_4$, and $\hat{R}(0) = B_1 \cup B_2$, $\hat{R}(1) = B_3 \cup B_4$ for $q = 2$, etc. Then the index for $\hat{R}(i_1, \ldots, i_q)$ is the binary representation of $j - 1$ for the corresponding B_j. If q is made sufficiently large, the probability is arbitrarily high that $\hat{R}(i_1, \ldots, i_s)$ and the corresponding $R(i_1, \ldots, i_s)$ for fixed s differ by a small amount [that is, probability according to $F_0(\mathbf{x})$].

If for any q and any sequence of 0's and 1's, say $i_1, \ldots, i_q$, $\int dF_1(\mathbf{x})$ over $R(i_1, \ldots, i_q)$ differs from $1/2^q$, then the procedure is consistent against that $F_1(\mathbf{x})$. In any case, if $F_1(\mathbf{x})$ differs from $F_0(\mathbf{x})$, there exists a rectangle, say Q, for which one probability is different from the other. Let $q = 2r$. Then the number of rectangles $R(i_1, \ldots, i_q)$ that straddle a particular side of Q is at most 2^r; hence, the number of rectangles that straddle the sides of Q is at most 2^{r+2}. The probability according to $F_0(\mathbf{x})$ of 2^{r+2} rectangles is $2^{r+2}/2^q = 2^{-(r-2)}$. For r sufficiently large, this is arbitrarily small. Hence Q can be approximated arbitrarily closely by the rectangles in the sense that the probability of Q and the probability of the rectangles $R(i_1, \ldots, i_q)$ contained in Q is arbitrarily small. Since there would be a contradiction if $F_0(\mathbf{x})$ and $F_1(\mathbf{x})$ did not differ on a rectangle $R(i_1, \ldots, i_q)$ for some q, we conclude there is a q and at least one rectangle on which they differ. This fact implies consistency of the procedure.

4. TESTING THE HYPOTHESIS THAT TWO UNKNOWN DISTRIBUTIONS ARE IDENTICAL

4.1. The Problem

Suppose that N observations $\mathbf{x}_1, \ldots, \mathbf{x}_N$ are taken on a vector random variable $\mathbf{x}$ with cumulative distribution function $F(\mathbf{x})$ and M observations $\mathbf{y}_1, \ldots, \mathbf{y}_M$ are taken on a vector random variable $\mathbf{y}$ with cumulative distribution function $G(\mathbf{y})$. Consider testing the hypothesis

$$H_0 : F(\mathbf{x}) = G(\mathbf{x}), \qquad \text{all } \mathbf{x}, \tag{4.1}$$

against the alternatives that $F(\mathbf{x}) \neq G(\mathbf{x})$ on a set of positive probability. We want a test with a significance level ε independent of the common distribution function. We shall propose two classes of tests based on the idea of statistically equivalent blocks as reviewed in Section 2 and used in the previous section.

4.2. Use of Blocks Defined by One Sample

One class of procedures follows from using one sample, say the first, to define $N + 1$ statistically equivalent blocks, $B_1, \ldots, B_{N+1}$. Let m_j be the number of $\mathbf{y}_\beta$'s that fall in B_j, $j = 1, \ldots, N + 1$. Then

$$m_1 + \cdots + m_{N+1} = M, \tag{4.2}$$

and the distribution of $m_1, \ldots, m_{N+1}$ does not depend on $F(\mathbf{x}) = G(\mathbf{x})$ when the hypothesis is true. For the conditional probability of $m_1, \ldots, m_{N+1}$, given $\mathbf{x}^{(1)}, \ldots, \mathbf{x}^{(N)}$, is

$$\frac{M!}{m_1! \cdots m_{N+1}!} v_1^{m_1} \cdots v_{N+1}^{m_{N+1}}, \tag{4.3}$$

where

$$v_j = \int_{B_j} dF(\mathbf{x}) , \qquad j = 1, \ldots, N + 1. \tag{4.4}$$

Multiplication of (4.3) by the density of $v_1, \ldots, v_N$, which is $\Gamma(N + 1)$ over $v_\alpha \geq 0$, $\alpha = 1, \ldots, N$, $\sum_{\alpha=1}^{N} v_\alpha \leq 1$, and 0 otherwise [that is, (2.2) for $j_i = i$, $i = 1, \ldots, N$], gives

$$\frac{\Gamma(M + 1)\Gamma(N + 1)}{\Gamma(m_1 + 1) \cdots \Gamma(m_N + 1)} v_1^{m_1} \cdots v_N^{m_N}(1 - v_1 - \cdots - v_N)^{m_{N+1}}. \tag{4.5}$$

The integral of this over the range of v_α's gives

$$\frac{\Gamma(M + 1)\Gamma(N + 1)}{\Gamma(M + N + 1)} = \frac{M!\,N!}{(M + N)!} = 1 \Big/ \binom{M + N}{N}. \tag{4.6}$$

That (4.6) is the integral can be verified from the fact that the integral of (2.2) is 1. Clearly (4.6) does not depend on $F(\mathbf{x}) = G(\mathbf{x})$. However, if $F(\mathbf{x}) \neq G(\mathbf{x})$, then the density of $v_1, \ldots, v_N$ is not $\Gamma(N+1)$ and the distribution of $m_1, \ldots, m_{N+1}$ is not (4.6). Roughly speaking, when $F(\mathbf{x}) = G(\mathbf{x})$, we expect each v_α to be approximately $M/(N+1)$; when $F(\mathbf{x}) \neq G(\mathbf{x})$, we expect one or more v_α's to be larger and one or more to be smaller.

A test of the hypothesis H_0 is equivalent to a test that $m_1, \ldots, m_{N+1}$ have the distribution (4.6). Any test which is used in the univariate case can be used in the multivariate case. For example, one can use the "empty block" test, as described by Wilks ([7], Section 14.3). The probability under the null hypothesis that exactly s of the m_α's are 0 is

$$\frac{\binom{N+1}{s}\binom{M-1}{N-s}}{\binom{M+N}{N}} \tag{4.7}$$

for $s = N - M + 1, \ldots, N$ if $N \geq M - 1$ and $s = 0, \ldots, N$, otherwise. The probability that the number of empty blocks is at least S is the sum of (4.7) for $s = S, S+1, \ldots, N$. A test procedure at a significance level equal to this probability is to reject the null hypothesis if the number of empty blocks is S or greater.

The procedure for determining blocks $B_1, \ldots, B_{N+1}$ on the basis of the observations $\mathbf{x}_1, \ldots, \mathbf{x}_N$ automatically ranks these observations into $\mathbf{x}^{(1)}, \ldots, \mathbf{x}^{(N)}$, and, as well, the observations $\mathbf{y}_1, \ldots, \mathbf{y}_M$, for the m_j $\mathbf{y}_\alpha$'s which fall into B_j are ranked above $\mathbf{x}^{(j-1)}$ and below $\mathbf{x}^{(j)}$; the assignment of the m_j ranks to the m_j $\mathbf{y}_\alpha$'s in B_j is immaterial. For example, if $N = 2$, $M = 4$, and $m_1 = 2$, $m_2 = 1$, and $m_3 = 1$, then two $\mathbf{y}_\alpha$'s are ranked 1 and 2, $\mathbf{x}^{(1)}$ is 3, another $\mathbf{y}_\alpha$ is 4, $\mathbf{x}^{(2)}$ is 5, and the other $\mathbf{y}_\alpha$ is ranked 6. Diagramatically, the samples are ordered $y\,y\,x\,y\,x\,y$. Since the two samples are, in effect, ranked, any rank test can be used. In some cases a run test may be suitable. Another possibility is to place the α-th observation at $\alpha/(N+M)$ on [0, 1] and use the empirical cumulative distribution functions.

4.3. Use of Blocks Defined by Two Samples

Since the definition of blocks ranks the observations used, one can rank the observations in the two samples by using them to define blocks. Let $\mathbf{x}_1, \ldots, \mathbf{x}_N$, $\mathbf{y}_1, \ldots, \mathbf{y}_M$ be designated $\mathbf{z}_1, \ldots, \mathbf{z}_{N+M}$; let $h_1(\mathbf{z}), \ldots, h_{N+M}(\mathbf{z})$ be $N+M$ functions, and let $k_1, \ldots, k_{N+M}$ be a permutation of $1, \ldots, N+M$. Then use the functions and permutation to define $\mathbf{z}^{(1)}, \ldots, \mathbf{z}^{(N+M)}$. Identification of each $\mathbf{z}^{(\alpha)}$ as an $\mathbf{x}_\beta$ or $\mathbf{y}_\beta$ yields a ranking of these observations. Again, any rank test can be used. (Vincze [6] has suggested the use of $h_1(\mathbf{z}) = \cdots = h_{N+M}(\mathbf{z}) = \sin\theta\, z_1 + \cos\theta\, z_2$, where θ is random.)

It should be noted that if the ranking of the $\mathbf{z}_\alpha$'s is done without the $\mathbf{z}_\alpha$'s being labeled $\mathbf{x}$ or $\mathbf{y}$, it is permissible to look at the plot of points, since under the null hypothesis each possible ranking of the $\mathbf{x}_\alpha$'s and $\mathbf{y}_\alpha$'s is equally likely. (In fact, if the $\mathbf{z}_\alpha$'s are not labeled, any method of ranking is permissible.)

4.4. An Example

Suppose the alternative to $F(\mathbf{x}) = G(\mathbf{x})$ is a shift in location; that is, $G(\mathbf{x}) = F(\mathbf{x} + \boldsymbol{\mu})$ for some vector $\boldsymbol{\mu}$, and suppose we wish to have some power against any such alternative. As an example, take $p = 2$ and $N = 4L$. We use as cutting functions $x_1, x_1, x_2, x_2, x_1, x_1, \ldots, x_2, x_2$ and $1, N, 2, N-1, \ldots, 2L, 2L+1$ as the permutation. Then the blocks are determined by the $\mathbf{x}_\alpha$'s. First $\mathbf{x}^{(1)}$ is the $\mathbf{x}_\alpha$ with the smallest x_1 coordinate and $\mathbf{x}^{(2)}$ is the $\mathbf{x}_\alpha$ with the largest x_1 coordinate:

$$B_1 = \{\mathbf{x}: \quad x_1 \le x_1^{(1)}\}, \tag{4.8}$$

$$B_2 = \{\mathbf{x}: \quad x_1^{(2)} \le x_1\}. \tag{4.9}$$

There are $N-2$ $\mathbf{x}_\alpha$'s with x_1 coordinate between $x_1^{(1)}$ and $x_1^{(2)}$; of these $\mathbf{x}^{(3)}$ has the smallest x_2 coordinate and $\mathbf{x}^{(4)}$ has the largest x_2 coordinate:

$$B_3 = \{\mathbf{x}: \quad x_1^{(1)} \le x_1 \le x_1^{(2)}, x_2 \le x_2^{(3)}\}, \tag{4.10}$$

$$B_4 = \{\mathbf{x}: \quad x_1^{(1)} \le x_1 \le x_1^{(2)}, x_2^{(4)} \le x_2\}. \tag{4.11}$$

The $N-4$ $\mathbf{x}_\alpha$'s within the rectangle with sides $x_1 = x_1^{(1)}$, $x_1 = x_1{}^{(2)}$, $x_2 = x_2{}^{(3)}$, and $x_2 = x_2^{(4)}$ are then ranked with respect to x_1 and x_2 in pairs alternately. The blocks are indicated in Fig. 3 for $N = 8$.

Let the m_1 $\mathbf{y}_\alpha$'s in B_1 be ranked $1, \ldots, m_1$; $\mathbf{x}^{(1)}$ is ranked $m_1 + 1$; the m_2 $\mathbf{y}_\alpha$'s in B_2 are ranked $m_1 + 2, \ldots, m_1 + m_2 + 1$; $\mathbf{x}^{(2)}$ is ranked $m_1 + m_2 + 2$; etc. If the null hypothesis is true, one expects the M $\mathbf{y}_\alpha$'s roughly evenly divided into $m_1, \ldots, m_{N+1}$. If the null hypothesis is not true, the center of the $\mathbf{y}$ distribution is different from that of the $\mathbf{x}$ distribution, and one expects that a relatively large number of $\mathbf{y}_\alpha$'s would fall into the early blocks. That means that some of the m_α's with small indices would be relatively large, or equivalently that the $\mathbf{y}_\alpha$'s tend to be ranked ahead of the $\mathbf{x}_\alpha$'s. These considerations suggest using a univariate rank test that is sensitive to such shifts. One test of this kind is the Wilcoxon-Mann-Whitney test (Wilks [7], Section 14.3). Let the $\mathbf{x}$ ranks be $r_1, \ldots, r_N$ and the $\mathbf{y}$ ranks be $s_1, \ldots, s_M$. Let $T = \sum_{\alpha=1}^{N} r_\alpha$. Then reject the null hypothesis if T is too large.

Other tests of shifting location can be based on other cutting functions. For example, one could use the bisection method or the method of $k-1$ x_1 functions followed by $k(k-1)$ x_2 functions when $N = k^2 - 1$ (as in Section 2.4) and then number the blocks in a spiral fashion from the outside. These

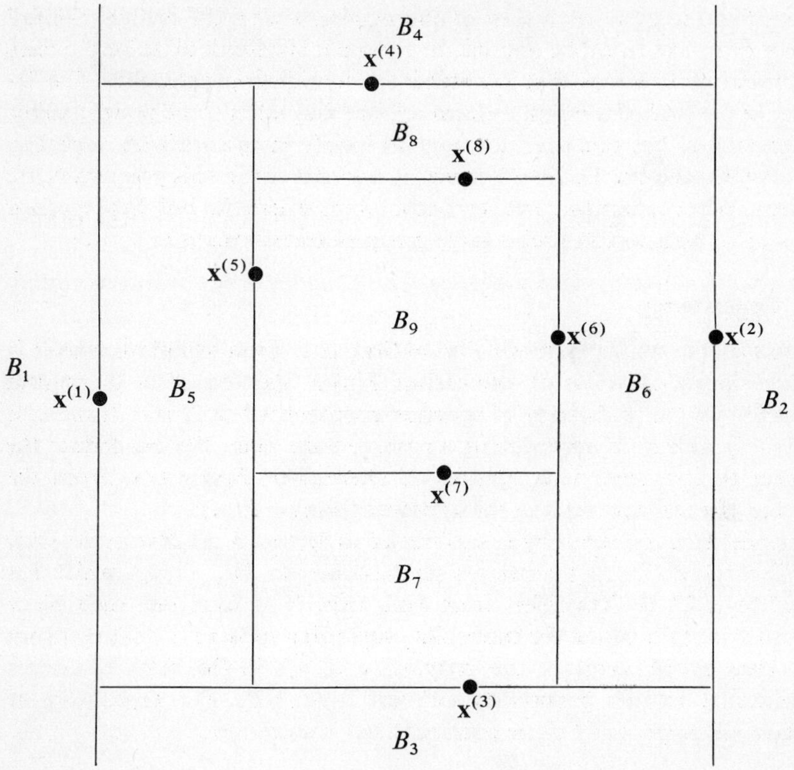

Fig. 3

tests could also be used to test against the alternatives that $G(\mathbf{y})$ has greater spread with the same location parameter.

4.5. Choice of Cutting Functions and Univariate Tests

Choice of cutting functions and a univariate test for constructing a test of the null hypothesis $F(\mathbf{x}) = G(\mathbf{x})$ depends on the alternatives to the null hypothesis. For instance, if the alternative is a shift in location in a given direction, say $G(\mathbf{x}) = F(\mathbf{x} + \boldsymbol{\mu})$, where $\boldsymbol{\mu}$ is given vector, the cutting functions can be taken to emphasize this direction, such as $\boldsymbol{\mu}'\mathbf{x}$. In the example, if the shift can only be in the first coordinate, then we can take $h_j(\mathbf{x}) = x_1$, $j = 1, \ldots, N$; that is, the second coordinate is neglected. The cutting functions suggested in Section 4.4 should give a test sensitive to shifts in location in either the x_1 or x_2 direction.

There are many problems, theoretical and practical, in the choice of cutting functions and tests. Given a class of alternatives, what is the optimal choice? It is not clear how to define optimal. In general it is difficult to define the class of alternatives in a way that is suitable for formulating optimality. For instance, in the case of the shift in location, one may want some power against all alternatives, but one does not want to specify invariance with respect to rotations because the Euclidean metric is not relevant in this nonparametric problem. What conditions are appropriate here where the null hypothesis is invariant with respect to such a large group of transformations?

4.6. Consistency

A test of the null hypothesis $F(\mathbf{x}) = G(\mathbf{x})$ at a given significance level is *consistent* against a class of alternatives $F(\mathbf{x}) \neq G(\mathbf{x})$ (on a set of positive probability) if the probability of rejection approaches 1 as N and M increase indefinitely with N/M approaching a positive finite limit. We can deduce the existence of consistent tests against all alternatives $F(\mathbf{x}) \neq G(\mathbf{x})$ from the existence of consistent tests of the hypothesis $F(\mathbf{x}) = F_0(\mathbf{x})$.

Consider blocks defined by $\mathbf{x}_\alpha$'s as treated in Section 3. As N increases, any sample block $\hat{R}(i_1, \ldots, i_q)$ converges stochastically to $R(i_1, \ldots, i_q)$, which has probability $1/2^q$. If $G(\mathbf{x})$ differs from $F(\mathbf{x})$, there is at least one such block (for suitable q) for which the probability according to $G(\mathbf{x})$ is different from $1/2^q$. Then as M increases, the proportion of $\mathbf{y}_\alpha$'s in the block converges stochastically to this probability different from $1/2^q$. The probability of rejection will approach 1 if the univariate test is consistent.

4.7. Invariance

If the cutting functions are the individual coordinates $x_1, \ldots, x_p$ of $\mathbf{x}$, then the ranking of the $\mathbf{x}_\alpha$'s and the assignment of the $\mathbf{y}_\beta$'s to the blocks is not changed if the coordinates $x_{i\alpha}$ and $y_{i\beta}$ are replaced by $H(x_{i\alpha})$ and $H(y_{i\beta})$, respectively, $\alpha = 1, \ldots, N$, $\beta = 1, \ldots, M$, for any i $(i = 1, \ldots, p)$, where $H(x)$ is a monotonically increasing function, because the rankings in the new coordinate will be the same as in the old coordinate. Thus a test procedure using coordinates as cutting functions is invariant with respect to monotonic transformations of each coordinate.

In the univariate case any continuous cumulative distribution function $F(x)$ can be transformed to the uniform distribution on [0, 1] by a monotonic transformation of the variable x [namely, $F(x)$]. The class of distribution-free tests is identical to the class of tests invariant with respect to monotonic transformations. The information from the samples that is invariant with respect to monotonic transformations consists of the ranks of the observations. Thus distribution-free tests are tests based on ranks.

In the multivariate case, monotonic transformations of the respective coordinates do not carry an arbitrary distribution $F(\mathbf{x})$ to the uniform distribution on the unit cube. If one transforms each coordinate x_i by its marginal cumulative distribution function, say, $F_i(x_i)$, the marginal distributions of the transformed variables are uniform on the unit interval, but the coordinates are not necessarily independent. (Any distribution on the unit cube with uniform marginals and lacking independence furnishes an example.) A procedure may be invariant with respect to monotonic transformations of coordinates, but not distribution-free, because to be distribution-free the probability of rejecting the null hypothesis when $F(\mathbf{x}) = G(\mathbf{x})$ must be the same for all $F(\mathbf{x})$ with uniform marginal distributions on [0, 1].

As an example, consider the procedures that rank the observation vectors on each coordinate; the observation $\mathbf{x}_\alpha$ is replaced by $(r_{1\alpha}, \ldots, r_{p\alpha})$ and the observation $\mathbf{y}_\beta$ is replaced by $(s_{1\beta}, \ldots, s_{p\beta})$, where $r_{i\alpha}$ and $s_{i\beta}$ are the ranks on the ith coordinate. (Chatterjee and Sen [3] have proposed tests based on random permutations of these vectors of ranks.) Tests based on these vectors of ranks are invariant with respect to monotonic transformations of coordinates. Specifically, let $p = 2$, $N = 1$, $M = 1$, and let the rule be to reject H_0 if $r_1 > s_1$, $r_2 > s_2$. If $F(\mathbf{x}) = G(\mathbf{x})$ is the uniform distribution on the unit square, the probability of rejecting the null hypothesis is $\frac{1}{4}$. If $F(\mathbf{x}) = G(\mathbf{x})$ has positive dependence, the probability may be higher; specifically, if $F(\mathbf{x}) = G(\mathbf{x})$ is uniform on the line $x_1 = x_2$, the probability is $\frac{1}{2}$.

Conversely, a distribution-free test does not have to be invariant with respect to monotonic transformations of coordinates. In fact, tests which are based on cutting functions other than coordinates will, in general, not be invariant with respect to monotonic transformations of coordinates.

As noted above, distributions-free tests in the univariate case can be characterized as tests based on ranks. In the multivariate case there is no such characterization.

It should be noted that an implication of the above discussion is that if the cutting functions are coordinates, the test may be used when the data are given in the form of ranks of the coordinates. This means that the method can be used when the scales are not "interval scales" and there is no metric.

5. CLASSIFICATION OF AN OBSERVATION INTO ONE OF TWO POPULATIONS

5.1. The Problem

Suppose $\mathbf{x}_1, \ldots, \mathbf{x}_N$ are N vector observations from a population with distribution function $F(\mathbf{x})$ and $\mathbf{y}_1, \ldots, \mathbf{y}_M$ are M vector observations from a population with distribution function $G(\mathbf{y})$, which is assumed to be different from $F(\mathbf{x})$. Let $\mathbf{z}$ be another observation vector which is drawn from either the first or the second population. We want to classify it as coming from the first or second population. The problem can also be stated as one of testing the null hypothesis that $\mathbf{x}_1, \dots, \mathbf{x}_N$ and $\mathbf{z}$ come from one distribution and $\mathbf{y}_1, \dots, \mathbf{y}_M$ from another against the alternative hypothesis that the $\mathbf{x}_1, \dots, \mathbf{x}_N$ come from one distribution and $\mathbf{z}, \mathbf{y}_1, \dots, \mathbf{y}_M$ from another. (See Chapter 6 of Anderson [2], for example.)

A classification procedure cannot be distribution-free. The problem exists only when $F(\mathbf{x})$ and $G(\mathbf{y})$ are different. The performance of the procedure is measured by the two probabilities of misclassification; that is, the probability of calling $\mathbf{z}$ a $\mathbf{y}$ when $\mathbf{z}$ comes from the population with distribution $F(\mathbf{x})$ and the probability of calling $\mathbf{z}$ an $\mathbf{x}$ when $\mathbf{z}$ comes from the population with distribution $G(\mathbf{y})$. If these probabilities did not depend on $F(\mathbf{x})$ and $G(\mathbf{y})$, they would be constants and hence would hold even if $F(\mathbf{x}) = G(\mathbf{x})$ (by a continuity argument); that is, the probabilities would correspond to a pure randomization procedure.

What is wanted are classification procedures that correspond to the test procedures for the hypothesis $F(\mathbf{x}) = G(\mathbf{x})$. We want procedures which are relatively invariant.

When $F(\mathbf{x})$ and $G(\mathbf{y})$ are known and have densities $f(\mathbf{x})$ and $g(\mathbf{y})$, the $\mathbf{x}$ and $\mathbf{y}$ observations are superfluous, and classification is made on the basis of the likelihood ratio $f(\mathbf{z})/g(\mathbf{z})$. The rule is to classify $\mathbf{z}$ as $\mathbf{x}$ if this ratio is greater than a constant and to classify $\mathbf{z}$ as $\mathbf{y}$ if the ratio is less than the constant. (If the ratio is equal to the constant, the classification is done at random.) When the densities exist but are unknown, the $\mathbf{x}$ and $\mathbf{y}$ observations are used to estimate $f(\mathbf{x})$ and $g(\mathbf{x})$ and their ratio near $\mathbf{x} = \mathbf{z}$. This can be done in the nonparametric case as well as in the parametric case.

Suppose that $\mathbf{x}$, $\mathbf{y}$, and $\mathbf{z}$ are transformed by the same transformation, $\mathbf{w} = h(\mathbf{w}^*)$, where the transformation is one-to-one and differentiable. Then the density of $\mathbf{x}^*$ is $f^*(\mathbf{x}^*) = f[h(\mathbf{x}^*)]J(\mathbf{x}^*)$ and the density of $\mathbf{y}^*$ is $g^*(\mathbf{y}^*) = g[h(\mathbf{y}^*)]J(\mathbf{y}^*)$, where $J(\mathbf{y}^*)$ is the Jacobian of the transformation (that is, the absolute value of the determinant of partial derivatives $\partial w_i/\partial w_j^*$). Then the likelihood ratio at $\mathbf{z}^*$ is

$$\frac{f^*(\mathbf{z}^*)}{g^*(\mathbf{z}^*)} = \frac{f[h(\mathbf{z}^*)]J(\mathbf{z}^*)}{g[h(\mathbf{z}^*)]J(\mathbf{z}^*)} = \frac{f(\mathbf{z})}{g(\mathbf{z})}, \tag{5.1}$$

where $\mathbf{z} = h(\mathbf{z}^*)$. This shows that the likelihood ratio is invariant with respect to one-to-one differentiable transformations.

5.2. The Univariate Case

Let $x_1, \dots, x_N, y_1, \dots, y_M, z$ be $N + M + 1$ scalar values. They can be considered as points on a line. The distribution-free tests of $F(x) = G(x)$ are invariant with respect to monotonically increasing transformations and hence depend only on the ranks of the x_α's and the y_α's. We shall now consider classification procedures which are similarly invariant with respect to monotonically increasing transformations and hence depend only on the ranks, say $r_1, \ldots, r_N, s_1, \ldots, s_M, t$, of the observations $x_1, \ldots, x_N, y_1, \ldots, y_M, z$, respectively.

The general idea of a nonparametric procedure is to classify z as an x if its nearest neighbors are mostly x's and to classify it as a y if its nearest neighbors are mostly y's. For convenience we shall assume $N = M$. The simplest nontrivial procedure is to classify z as an x if the next smaller and the next larger observations are x's, to classify it as a y if the next smaller and the next larger are y's, and to classify it as an x or y with probability $\frac{1}{2}$ if either the next smaller observation is an x and the next larger a y or the next smaller is a y and the next larger is an x. To put it another way, if z falls between two observations of the same kind, classify z accordingly. If z falls between two observations of different kinds, classify it at random; if z is the smallest observation, classify it according to the next largest; if z is the largest observation, classify it as the next smallest.

The performance of this procedure can easily be evaluated in the simplest case where $N = M = 1$ and $F(x)$ and $G(y)$ are normal with a variance of one. If the difference in means is 2, the probability of misclassification by this nonparametric method is 0.333 (not $\frac{1}{3}$) and the probability of misclassification by the usual linear classification statistic is 0.253. (The second procedure is to classify z as an x if z is closer to x than to y.)

The above procedure can be modified to eliminate the randomization. If z falls between an x and a y, go to the next smaller and next larger observations. If these are of the same kind, classify z accordingly; if these are different go on to the next pair of observations. If z falls between an x and a y and there is no smaller observation, classify according to the next larger; if z falls between an x and a y and there is no larger observation, classify according to the next smaller. This procedure can be extended.

There are many nonparametric classification methods that use more information. One method is to count down k observations and count up k observations. If there are more x's than y's among the $2k$ observations, classify z as an x, and if there are more y's, classify as a y. If there are k x's and k y's, increase k to $k + 1$. If there are not k observations smaller and k observations larger than z, use as many as are available.

Another method is to weight the x's and the y's according to their position with respect to z. Let $a_i = 1$ if the pair of observations i away from z are x's, -1 if they are y's, and 0 if one is x and one is y. Let $c_i > 0$, $i = 1, \ldots, k$, and $c_i \geq c_j$ if $i < j$. Then classify z as an x if $\sum_{i=1}^k c_i a_i > 0$ and as a y if $\sum_{i=1}^k c_i a_i < 0$; classify with probability $\frac{1}{2}$ if $\sum_{i=1}^k c_i a_i = 0$.

5.3. The Multivariate Case

The case of the observations being vectors can be treated by ranking the observations according to one of the methods described in Section 4 and then using a univariate method indicated in Section 5.2. For example, rank the $N + M + 1$ vectors by means of the bisection method (that is, $h_{k_1}(\mathbf{x}) = x_1$, $k_1 = [\frac{1}{2}(N + M + 1)]$, $h_{k_2}(\mathbf{x}) = x_2$, $k_2 = [(N + M + 1)/4]$, etc.). Then apply a univariate method to this ranking. Another way is to use the N **x** vectors and the M **y** vectors to construct blocks. Then consider the block that **z** falls in, and classify **z** according to the majority of the observations defining the block (that is, observations on the sides of the cube). An alternative approach is to use the bisection method on the **x**'s and **y**'s and stop after one-fourth of the observations are used. Then each block will contain three observations. Classify **z** according to the majority of the three observations in the block in which it falls (or classify it according to the majority of the observations within or on the faces of the blocks). Still another way is to construct a set of blocks based on $\mathbf{x}_\alpha$'s and a set of blocks based on $\mathbf{y}_\beta$'s. If **z** is in a y block containing no $\mathbf{x}_\alpha$'s but not in an **x** block containing no $\mathbf{y}_\beta$, classify it as a **y**; similarly for **x** and **y** interchanged. If neither of these cases occur, consider the number of $\mathbf{x}_\alpha$'s in the **y** block and the number of $\mathbf{y}_\beta$'s in the **x** block and classify according to the larger number.

Note that if the cutting functions are coordinates, the procedures depend only on the ranks with respect to the p coordinates and hence can be applied to data presented in the form of ranks.

It is also permissible to reorder the blocks. For example, if $N + M + 1 = 15$, and $p = 2$, use the bisection method on all observations and label the blocks $R(0, 0, 0, 0), \ldots, R(1, 1, 1, 1)$. Let the first and third arguments constitute the binary representation of the x_1 coordinate and the second and fourth arguments constitute the x_2 coordinate. Then neighbors can be defined in terms of the two coordinates.

It might be noted that if the N $\mathbf{x}_\alpha$'s and M $\mathbf{y}_\beta$'s are to be ordered, it is permitted to look at them in selecting cutting functions as long as they are not labeled.

5.4. Limiting Probabilities

As $N = M$ increases, the proportion of $\mathbf{x}_\alpha$'s in a given (measurable) set will converge stochastically to the integral $\int dF(\mathbf{x})$ over that set and the proportion of the N **y**'s will converge stochastically to the integral $\int dG(\mathbf{y})$. Suppose $F(\mathbf{x})$ and $G(\mathbf{y})$ have continuous densities. Then if the set decreases in size appropriately as N increases, the ratio of proportion β will converge to the ratio of densities at a point.

Some of the above classification procedures can be made to depend upon

N, so that as N increases the probabilities of misclassification will converge to the probabilities of a procedure based on the knowledge of $f(\mathbf{x})$ and $g(\mathbf{y})$. For instance, in the bisection procedure, using all observations combined with classifying $\mathbf{z}$ according to a majority of its nearest $2k$ neighbors, let $k = k_N$ depend on N so that $k_N \to \infty$ and $k_N/N \to 0$ as $N \to \infty$. For N sufficiently large, each union of k_N blocks (in serial order) will be arbitrarily small in the sense of probabilities according to $F(\mathbf{x})$ and $G(\mathbf{y})$, and the number of observations in each such union will be arbitrarily large. The ratio of the number of $\mathbf{x}$ and $\mathbf{y}$ observations in such a union will tend to $f(\mathbf{z})/g(\mathbf{z})$ for $\mathbf{z}$ in the union. (This argument needs more detail for the sake of rigor.)

Another nonparametric problem is to estimate a density $f(\mathbf{x})$, and somewhat similar methods can be used. However, the density depends on the metric or coordinate system, in that the density is relative to the Lebesgue measure.

Remarks. Some of the ideas were outlined in a contributed paper by the author [1]. Wilks [7] later noted (pp. 444, 451) that blocks could be used to construct tests of $F(\mathbf{x}) = G(\mathbf{x})$, but gave no details.

REFERENCES

1. ANDERSON, T. W. (1955). A method of constructing nonparametric multivariate tests (abstract). *Ann. Math. Statist.* **26** 773.
2. ANDERSON, T. W. (1958). *An Introduction to Multivariate Statistical Analysis.* Wiley, New York.
3. CHATTERJEE, SHOUTIR KISHORE and SEN, PRANAB KUMAR (1964). Non-parametric tests for the bivariate two-sample location problem. *Calcutta Statist. Assoc. Bull.* **13** 18–58.
4. FISHER, R. A. (1929). Tests of significance in harmonic analysis. *Proc. Roy. Soc. London, Ser. A* **125** 54–59.
5. FRASER, D. A. S. (1957). *Nonparametric Methods in Statistics.* Wiley, New York.
6. VINCZE, I. (1961). On two-sample tests based on order statistics. *Proc. Fourth Berkeley Symp. Math. Statist. Prob.* **1** 695–705.
7. WILKS, S. S. (1962). *Mathematical Statistics.* Wiley, New York.

Some Nonparametric Tests for the Multivariate Several Sample Location Problem[1]

V. P. BHAPKAR
UNIVERSITY OF NORTH CAROLINA
CHAPEL HILL, NORTH CAROLINA
UNIVERSITY OF POONA
POONA, INDIA

1. SUMMARY

This paper offers nonparametric tests of the null hypothesis $F_1 = F_2 = \cdots = F_c$ against alternatives of the form $F_i(\mathbf{x}) = F(\mathbf{x} - \boldsymbol{\theta}_i)(i = 1, 2, \ldots, c)$, where the $\boldsymbol{\theta}_i$'s are not all equal and F_i is the unknown continuous cumulative distribution function (c.d.f.) of the p-variate population from which the ith random sample comes. The statistics offered are multivariate analogues of some univariate rank-order test statistics, and all these are shown to be asymptotically distributed as χ^2 with $p(c-1)$ degrees of freedom when the null hypothesis holds.

2. INTRODUCTION AND NOTATION

Quite a few nonparametric tests are available for the several-sample (say c sample) location problem in the univariate case. Among them are the H test of Kruskal and Wallis [12], the M test of Mood [13], and the tests based on c-plets, viz., the V and W tests offered by the author [2] and [3] and the L test offered by Deshpande [5]. Some other tests and references to earlier ones may be found in Dwass [6], Kiefer [10], and Kruskal and Wallis [12].

However, not much work has been done in the corresponding multivariate case. Hodges [8], Vincze [14], and Chatterjee and Sen [4] have developed nonparametric tests for the two-sample problem in the bivariate case. The author [1] had offered a test for the several-sample bivariate problem using a " step-down procedure " in which the regression of one variable on the other

[1] This research was supported by the Mathematics Division of the Air Force Office of Scientific Research Contract AF-AFOSR-760-65.

is assumed to be linear. But there the roles of the two variables do not appear to be symmetrical. The present paper offers symmetric nonparametric tests for the general several-sample multivariate location problem. These will be seen to be multivariate analogues of the univariate V, L, W, and H tests.

Let $\{\mathbf{X}_{ij}, j = 1, 2, \ldots, n_i\}$ be n_i independent observations from a population with continuous nonsingular c.d.f. F_i, $i = 1, 2, \ldots, c$. Let the p components of observation $\mathbf{X}_{ij}$ be denoted by $X_{ij}^{(\alpha)}$, $\alpha = 1, 2, \ldots, p$. $\mathbf{X}'_{ij}$ then denotes the row vector $(X_{ij}^{(1)}, \ldots, X_{ij}^{(p)})$, while $\mathbf{X}_{ij}$ denotes the corresponding column vector. The samples are assumed to be independent. We consider nonparametric tests of the hypothesis

$$H_0: \quad F_1 = F_2 = \cdots = F_c$$

against alternatives of the form $F_i(\mathbf{x}) = F(\mathbf{x} - \boldsymbol{\theta}_i)$ with the vectors $\boldsymbol{\theta}_i$'s not all equal.

Let $v_i^{(\alpha)}$ be the number of c-plets $(\mathbf{X}_{1t_1}, \mathbf{X}_{2t_2}, \ldots, \mathbf{X}_{ct_c})$ that can be formed by choosing one observation from each sample such that $X_{it_i}^{(\alpha)}$ is the smallest among $\{X_{kt_k}^{(\alpha)}, k = 1, 2, \ldots, c\}$. Similarly let $b_i^{(\alpha)}$ be the number of c-plets that can be formed such that $X_{t_i}^{(\alpha)}$ is the largest among $\{X_{kt_k}^{(\alpha)}, k = 1, 2, \ldots, c\}$; denote $b_i^{(\alpha)} - v_i^{(\alpha)}$ by $l_i^{(\alpha)}$. In general, suppose that $n_{ir}^{(\alpha)}$ is the number of c-plets $(\mathbf{X}_{1t_1}, \ldots, \mathbf{X}_{ct_c})$ such that $X_{it_i}^{(\alpha)}$ has rank r among $\{X_{kt_k}^{(\alpha)}, k = 1, 2, \ldots, c\}$, $r = 1, 2, \ldots, c$.

Then we note that $v_i^{(\alpha)} = n_{i1}^{(\alpha)}$ and $b_i^{(\alpha)} = n_{ic}^{(\alpha)}$. Further, let

$$w_i^{(\alpha)} = \sum_{r=1}^{c} (r-1) n_{ir}^{(\alpha)}.$$

Finally, if $R_{ij}^{(\alpha)}$ denotes the rank of $X_{ij}^{(\alpha)}$ among $\{X_{kt}^{(\alpha)}, t = 1, \ldots, n_k$ and $k = 1, \ldots, c\}$, let

$$\bar{R}_i^{(\alpha)} = \sum_{j=1}^{n_i} R_{ij}^{(\alpha)}/n_i.$$

Then the test statistics now being proposed are

$$V = N(2c-1) \sum_{i=1}^{c} p_i (\mathbf{u}_i - \bar{\mathbf{u}})' \mathbf{E}_v^{-1} (\mathbf{u}_i - \bar{\mathbf{u}}), \tag{2.1}$$

where $N = \sum_i n_i$, $p_i = n_i/N$, $u_i^{(\alpha)} = v_i^{(\alpha)}/n_1 n_2 \cdots n_c$, $\mathbf{u}_i' = (u_i^{(1)}, \ldots, u_i^{(p)})$, $\bar{\mathbf{u}} = \sum_i p_i \mathbf{u}_i$ and $\mathbf{E}_v$ is a matrix given by (4.1).

$$B = N(2c-1) \sum_{i=1}^{c} p_i (\mathbf{u}_i - \bar{\mathbf{u}})' \mathbf{E}_B^{-1} (\mathbf{u}_i - \bar{\mathbf{u}}), \tag{2.2}$$

where $u_i^{(\alpha)} = b_i^{(\alpha)}/n_1 n_2 \cdots n_c$ and $\mathbf{E}_B$ is given by (4.2).

$$L = \frac{N(2c-1)(c-1)^2\binom{2c-2}{c-1}}{2c^2\left\{\binom{2c-2}{c-1}-1\right\}} \sum_{i=1}^{c} p_i(\mathbf{u}_i - \bar{\mathbf{u}})\mathbf{E}_L^{-1}(\mathbf{u}_i - \bar{\mathbf{u}}), \tag{2.3}$$

where $u_i^{(\alpha)} = l_i^{(\alpha)}/n_1 n_2 \cdots n_c$ and $\mathbf{E}_L$ is given by (4.3).

$$W = \frac{12N}{c^2} \sum_{i=1}^{c} p_i(\mathbf{u}_i - \bar{\mathbf{u}})'\mathbf{E}_w^{-1}(\mathbf{u}_i - \bar{\mathbf{u}}), \tag{2.4}$$

where $u_i^{(\alpha)} = w_i^{(\alpha)}/n_1 n_2 \cdots n_c$ and $\mathbf{E}_w$ is given by (4.4).

$$H = \frac{12}{N} \sum_{i=1}^{c} p_i\left(\overline{\mathbf{R}}_i - \frac{N+1}{2}\mathbf{j}\right)' \mathbf{E}_w^{-1}\left(\overline{\mathbf{R}}_i - \frac{N+1}{2}\mathbf{j}\right), \tag{2.5}$$

where $\mathbf{j}' = (1)_{1\times c}$.

The V test consists in rejecting H_0 at a significance level α if V exceeds some predetermined number V_α; the same thing holds for the other statistics. In the next section it is shown that, when H_0 is true, each of these statistics is asymptotically distributed as a χ^2 variable with $p(c-1)$ degrees of freedom. Thus large sample approximations for V_α, B_α, L_α, W_α, and H_α are provided by the upper α point of the χ^2 distribution with $p(c-1)$ degrees of freedom. These tests are thus seen to be the multivariate analogues of the corresponding univariate tests.

If $\overline{\mathbf{X}}_i = \sum_j \mathbf{X}_{ij}/n_i$, $\overline{\mathbf{X}} = \sum_{i,j}\mathbf{X}_{ij}/N$, and the populations are p-variate normal with covariance matrix $\mathbf{\Sigma}$, then it is well known that the statistic

$$\sum_i n_i(\overline{\mathbf{X}}_i - \overline{\mathbf{X}})'\mathbf{\Sigma}^{-1}(\overline{\mathbf{X}}_i - \overline{\mathbf{X}}) \tag{2.6}$$

is distributed as χ^2 with $p(c-1)$ degrees of freedom under H_0 and, hence,

$$\sum_i n_i(\overline{\mathbf{X}}_i - \overline{\mathbf{X}})'\mathbf{S}^{-1}(\overline{\mathbf{X}}_i - \overline{\mathbf{X}}) \tag{2.7}$$

is asymptotically distributed as χ^2 with $p(c-1)$ degrees of freedom under H_0, where $\mathbf{S}$ is the covariance matrix obtained from the samples. The statistics being offered now are thus seen to be rank-order analogues of (2.7).

3. THE ASYMPTOTIC DISTRIBUTION OF A TEST CRITERION UNDER H_0

Let

$$U_i^{(\alpha)} = \frac{1}{n_1 n_2 \cdots n_c} \sum_{t_1=1}^{n_1} \cdots \sum_{t_c=1}^{n_c} \Phi_i^{(\alpha)}(\mathbf{X}_{1t_1}, \mathbf{X}_{2t_2}, \ldots, \mathbf{X}_{ct_c}) \tag{3.1}$$

$$(i = 1, 2, \ldots, c;\ \alpha = 1, 2, \ldots, p)$$

and suppose that

$$\Phi_i^{(\alpha)}(\mathbf{X}_1, \mathbf{X}_2, \dots, \mathbf{X}_c) = \Phi_i(X_1^{(\alpha)}, X_2^{(\alpha)}, \dots, X_c^{(\alpha)}), \tag{3.2}$$

and further

$$\Phi_i(x_1, x_2, \dots, x_c) = \Phi(x_i; \{x_j, j \neq i\}), \tag{3.3}$$

which means that Φ is a function of x_i and the set of remaining x_j's and, moreover, is symmetric in x_j's, $j = 1, 2, \dots, c$ except i. We shall also assume that Φ is bounded. Then the following special cases [(3.4), (3.5), (3.6), and (3.7)] will lead to the u's in the statistics [(2.1), (2.2), (2.3), and (2.4), respectively]:

$$\Phi_i(x_1, x_2, \dots, x_c) = \begin{cases} 1 & \text{if } x_i < x_j, j = 1, \dots, c \text{ except } i, \\ 0 & \text{otherwise,} \end{cases} \tag{3.4}$$

$$\Phi_i(x_1, \dots, x_c) = \begin{cases} 1 & \text{if } x_i > x_j, j = 1, \dots, c \text{ except } i, \\ 0 & \text{otherwise} \end{cases} \tag{3.5}$$

$$\Phi_i(x_1, \dots, x_c) = \begin{cases} 1 & \text{if } x_i > x_j, j = 1, \dots, c \text{ except } i, \\ -1 & \text{if } x_i < x_j, j = 1, \dots, c \text{ except } i, \\ 0 & \text{otherwise,} \end{cases} \tag{3.6}$$

$$\Phi_i(x_1, \dots, x_c) = r - 1, \text{ if the rank of } x_i \text{ among } \{x_1, x_2, \dots, x_c\} \text{ is } r, \tag{3.7}$$

so that

$$\Phi_i(x_1, \dots, x_c) = \sum_{j=1}^{c} h(x_i - x_j),$$

where the function h is defined by

$$h(y) = \begin{cases} 1 & \text{if } y > 0, \\ 0 & \text{otherwise.} \end{cases}$$

From (3.1) it is seen that $U_i^{(\alpha)}$ is a generalized U statistic corresponding to $\Phi_i^{(\alpha)}$. For studying the asymptotic distributions we shall write $U_{iN}^{(\alpha)}$ for $U_i^{(\alpha)}$ based on the samples of total size N; also the random variables will be denoted by capital letters and the variables held fixed will be denoted by the corresponding small letters. Let

$$\mathbf{U}_N' = (\mathbf{U}_{1N}', \mathbf{U}_{2N}', \dots, \mathbf{U}_{cN}'), \ \mathbf{U}_{iN}' = (U_{iN}^{(1)}, \dots, U_{iN}^{(p)}), \ \boldsymbol{\eta}' = (\boldsymbol{\eta}_1', \boldsymbol{\eta}_2', \dots, \boldsymbol{\eta}_c'), \tag{3.8}$$

where

$$\boldsymbol{\eta}_i' = (\eta_i^{(1)}, \dots, \eta_i^{(p)}), \ \eta_i^{(\alpha)} = \mathscr{E}[\Phi_i^{(\alpha)}(\mathbf{X}_1, \mathbf{X}_2, \dots, \mathbf{X}_c)]$$

and $\mathbf{X}_i$'s are independent random variables with c.d.f. F_i, $i = 1, 2, \dots, c$, respectively. From the c-sample version (e.g., see [2]) of Hoeffding's theorem

[9] concerning U statistics, it follows that in the limit as $n_i \to \infty$ in such a way that $n_i = Np_i$, the p's being fixed positive numbers such that $\sum_i p_i = 1$, $N^{1/2}[\mathbf{U}_N - \boldsymbol{\eta}]$ is normally distributed with zero mean vector and covariance matrix $\boldsymbol{\Sigma}$, where

$$\boldsymbol{\Sigma} = \begin{bmatrix} \boldsymbol{\Sigma}_{11} & \boldsymbol{\Sigma}_{12} & \cdots & \boldsymbol{\Sigma}_{1c} \\ \boldsymbol{\Sigma}_{21} & \boldsymbol{\Sigma}_{22} & \cdots & \boldsymbol{\Sigma}_{2c} \\ \vdots & & & \\ \boldsymbol{\Sigma}_{c1} & \boldsymbol{\Sigma}_{c2} & \cdots & \boldsymbol{\Sigma}_{cc} \end{bmatrix}, \tag{3.9}$$

$$\boldsymbol{\Sigma}_{ij} = [\sigma_{ij}^{(\alpha,\beta)}] \qquad (\alpha, \beta = 1, 2, \ldots, p),$$

$$\sigma_{ij}^{(\alpha,\beta)} = \sum_{k=1}^{c} \frac{1}{p_k} \zeta_{(k)}^{(\alpha,\beta)}(i, j), \tag{3.10}$$

and

$$\zeta_{(k)}^{(\alpha,\beta)}(i, j) = \mathscr{E}[\Phi_i^{(\alpha)}(\mathbf{X}_1, \ldots, \mathbf{X}_c)\Phi_j^{(\beta)}(\mathbf{Y}_1, \ldots, \mathbf{Y}_c)] - \eta_i^{(\alpha)}\eta_j^{(\beta)}, \tag{3.11}$$

where $\mathbf{X}_i$ and $\mathbf{Y}_i$ are independent random variables with c.d.f. F_i ($i = 1, 2, \ldots, c$), except that $\mathbf{Y}_k = \mathbf{X}_k$.

Now, when H_0 holds, $F_1 = F_2 = \cdots = F_c = F$, say. We shall denote by $F^{(\alpha\ \beta)}$ the marginal c.d.f. of the αth and βth components of $\mathbf{X}$. *Here, and hereafter in this section,* $\mathbf{X}$'s *and* $\mathbf{Y}$'s *are independent random variables each with c.d.f. F.*

Theorem 3.1. *Suppose the functions* $\Phi_i^{(\alpha)}$, $i = 1, 2, \ldots, c$ *and* $\alpha = 1, 2, \ldots, p$ *satisfy the following conditions*:

(a) $\Phi_i^{(\alpha)}(\mathbf{x}_1, \mathbf{x}_2, \ldots, \mathbf{x}_c) = \Phi_i(x_1^{(\alpha)}, x_2^{(\alpha)}, \ldots, x_c^{(\alpha)})$.

(b) $\Phi_i(x_1, x_2, \ldots, x_c) = \Phi(x_i; \{x_j, j \neq i\})$.

(c) *There exists a constant A such that* $|\Phi| < A$.

(d) $\sum_i \Phi_i(x_1, x_2, \ldots, x_c) = cd$, *where d is some constant; it is the only linear constraint on the* Φ_i*'s.*

(e) *The statistic* $\Phi(X_1; \{X_j, j = 2, 3, \ldots, c\})$ *is distribution-free in the class of continuous univariate distributions; i.e., the probability distribution of* $\Phi(X_1; \{X_j, j = 2, \ldots, c\})$, *where the X's are independent random variables each with univariate continuous c.d.f. G, is independent of G.*

(f) *The common distribution of the independent random variables* $\mathbf{X}$*'s is nonsingular.*

Then as $n_i \to \infty$, *in such a way that* $n_i = Np_i$, $i = 1, \ldots, c$, *the p's being fixed positive numbers such that* $\sum_i p_i = 1$, *and, under* H_0, *the asymptotic distribution of the random variable*

$$T_N = \frac{N(c-1)^2}{\mu c^2} \sum_{i=1}^{c} p_i(\mathbf{U}_{iN} - \overline{\mathbf{U}}_N)'\mathscr{P}^{-1}(\mathbf{U}_{iN} - \overline{\mathbf{U}}_N), \tag{3.12}$$

where $\mathbf{U}_{iN}$ *is given by* (3.1) *and* (3.8), $\overline{\mathbf{U}}_N = \Sigma_i p_i \mathbf{U}_{iN}$,

$$\mu = \mathscr{E}[\Phi_1^{(\alpha)}(\mathbf{X}_1, \mathbf{X}_2, \ldots, \mathbf{X}_c)\Phi_1^{(\alpha)}(\mathbf{X}_1, \mathbf{Y}_2, \ldots, \mathbf{Y}_c)] - d^2,$$

and $\mathscr{P} = (\rho_{\alpha\beta})$, $\alpha, \beta, = 1, 2, \ldots, p$ *with*

$$\rho_{\alpha\beta} = \text{corr. coeff. } [\Phi_1^{(\alpha)}(\mathbf{X}_1, \mathbf{X}_2, \ldots, \mathbf{X}_c), \Phi_1^{(\beta)}(\mathbf{X}_1, \mathbf{Y}_2, \ldots, \mathbf{Y}_c)], \quad (3.13)$$

is χ^2 *with degrees of freedom* $p(c-1)$.

Proof. The theorem will follow by the application of the multisample extension of Hoeffding's theorem and noting that under H_0, $F_1 = F_2 = \cdots = F_c = F$, say.

We first see that, in view of conditions (a), (b), and (c), $\mathscr{E}[\Phi_i^{(\alpha)}(\mathbf{X}_1, \ldots, \mathbf{X}_c)]$ is a constant d, independent of any univariate continuous c.d.f. G. Let

$$\psi_i^{(\alpha)}(\mathbf{x}) = \mathscr{E}\Phi_i^{(\alpha)}(\mathbf{X}_1, \ldots, \mathbf{X}_c \mid \mathbf{X}_i = \mathbf{x}) - d. \quad (3.14)$$

Then

$$\psi_i^{(\alpha)}(\mathbf{x}) = \mathscr{E}[\Phi(x^{(\alpha)}, \{X_j^{(\alpha)}\}] - d = \psi^{(\alpha)}(x^{(\alpha)}), \quad (3.15)$$

say, for all i and depends, in general, on $F^{(\alpha)}$, which is the marginal distribution of $X^{(\alpha)}$.

Then from (3.11), under H_0,

$$\zeta_{(i)}^{(\alpha,\alpha)}(i, i) = \mathscr{E}[\psi_i^{(\alpha)}(\mathbf{X})]^2 = \mathscr{E}[\psi^{(\alpha)}(X^{(\alpha)})]^2 = \mu \quad \text{(say)},$$

$$\zeta_{(i)}^{(\alpha,\beta)}(i, i) = \mathscr{E}[\psi^{(\alpha)}(X^{(\alpha)})\psi^{(\beta)}(X^{(\beta)})] = \int \psi^{(\alpha)}(x)\psi^{(\beta)}(y)\, dF^{(\alpha,\beta)}(x, y) = \mu\rho_{\alpha\beta}, \quad (3.16)$$

where $\rho_{\alpha\beta}$ is the correlation coefficient of $\psi^{(\alpha)}(X)$ and $\psi^{(\beta)}(Y)$, where (X, Y) has c.d.f. $F^{(\alpha,\beta)}$ and, in general, will depend on F. We also note that $\rho_{\alpha\beta}$ can be expressed in the form (3.13). Also, if for $i \neq k$,

$$\psi_{i,k}^{(\alpha)}(\mathbf{y}) \equiv \mathscr{E}\Phi_i^{(\alpha)}(\mathbf{X}_1, \ldots, \mathbf{X}_c \mid \mathbf{X}_k = \mathbf{y}) - d, \quad (3.17)$$

then

$$\psi_{i,k}^{(\alpha)}(\mathbf{y}) = \mathscr{E}[\Phi(X_i^{(\alpha)}, \{y^{(\alpha)}, X_j^{(\alpha)}\}] - d = w^{(\alpha)}(y^{(\alpha)}) \quad \text{(say)} \quad (3.18)$$

for all $i \neq k$ and depends, in general, on $F^{(\alpha)}$. Hence

$$\zeta_{(k)}^{(\alpha,\beta)}(i, i) = \mathscr{E}[\psi_{i,k}^{(\alpha)}(\mathbf{Y})\psi_{i,k}^{(\beta)}(\mathbf{Y})] = \mathscr{E}[w^{(\alpha)}(Y^{(\alpha)})w^{(\beta)}(Y^{(\beta)})]. \quad (3.19)$$

But from (a) and (d) we have

$$\mathscr{E}\left[\sum_{i=1}^{c} \Phi_i^{(\alpha)}(\mathbf{x}, \mathbf{X}_2, \ldots, \mathbf{X}_c)\right] = cd;$$

so that

$$\psi^{(\alpha)}(x^{(\alpha)}) = -(c-1)w^{(\alpha)}(x^{(\alpha)}). \tag{3.20}$$

From (3.19), (3.20), and (3.16) it follows that

$$\mu = (c-1)^2 w \quad \text{and} \quad \zeta_{(k)}^{(\alpha,\beta)}(i, i) = w\rho_{\alpha\beta}. \tag{3.21}$$

Similarly, for $i \neq j$,

$$\begin{aligned}\xi_{(j)}^{(\alpha,\alpha)}(i, j) &= \mathscr{E}[\psi_{ij}^{(\alpha)}(\mathbf{X})\psi_j^{(\alpha)}(\mathbf{X})] = \mathscr{E}[w^{(\alpha)}(X^{(\alpha)})\psi^{(\alpha)}(X^{(\alpha)})] \\ &= -(c-1)w \qquad [\text{in view of (3.20)}]\end{aligned} \tag{3.22}$$

and

$$\zeta_{(j)}^{(\alpha,\beta)}(i, j) = \mathscr{E}[\psi_{ij}^{(\alpha)}(\mathbf{X})\psi_j^{(\beta)}(\mathbf{X})] = \mathscr{E}[w^{(\alpha)}(X^{(\alpha)})\psi^{(\beta)}(X^{(\beta)})] = -(c-1)w\rho_{\alpha\beta}.$$

Finally, for $i \neq j \neq k$,

$$\zeta_{(k)}^{(\alpha,\alpha)}(i, j) = \mathscr{E}[\psi_{ik}^{(\alpha)}(\mathbf{X})\psi_{jk}^{(\alpha)}(\mathbf{X})] = \mathscr{E}[w^{(\alpha)}(X^{(\alpha)})]^2 = w, \tag{3.23}$$

and

$$\zeta_{(k)}^{(\alpha,\beta)}(i, j) = \mathscr{E}[\psi_{ik}^{(\alpha)}(\mathbf{X})\psi_{jk}^{(\beta)}(\mathbf{X})] = \mathscr{E}[w^{(\alpha)}(X^{(\alpha)})w^{(\beta)}(X^{(\beta)})] = w\rho_{\alpha\beta}.$$

Thus from (3.10), (3.16), (3.19), (3.21), (3.22), and (3.23), it follows that, under H_0,

$$\sigma_{ii} = \frac{\mu}{p_i} + \sum_{k\neq i}\left(\frac{1}{p_i}\right)w = w\left[q + \frac{c(c-2)}{p_i}\right] \tag{3.24}$$

and

$$\sigma_{ij} = -(c-1)w\left[\frac{1}{p_i} + \frac{1}{p_j}\right] + \sum_{k\neq i,j}\left(\frac{1}{p_k}\right)w = w\left[q - \frac{c}{p_i} - \frac{c}{p_j}\right], \qquad (i \neq j),$$

where $q = \sum_i (1/p_i)$, and $\sigma_{ij}^{(\alpha,\beta)} = \sigma_{ij}\rho_{\alpha\beta}$.

Let $\Sigma^* = (\sigma_{ij})$, $i, j = 1, 2, \dots, c$, where σ's are given by (3.24). Then

$$w^{-1}\mathbf{\Sigma}^* = c^2\mathbf{P}^{-1} - c\mathbf{q}\mathbf{j}' - c\mathbf{j}\mathbf{q}' + q\mathbf{J}, \tag{3.25}$$

where $\mathbf{P}$ = diagonal $(p_i, i = 1, 2, \dots, c)$, $\mathbf{J} = (1)_{c\times c}$,

$$\mathbf{j} = (1)_{c\times 1} \quad \text{and} \quad \mathbf{q}' = (1/p_1, \dots, 1/p_c).$$

Then, from (3.9), under H_0, $\mathbf{\Sigma}_{ij} = \sigma_{ij}\mathscr{P}$ and

$$\mathbf{\Sigma} = \begin{bmatrix}\sigma_{11}\mathscr{P} & \cdots & \sigma_{1c}\mathscr{P} \\ \vdots & & \\ \sigma_{c1}\mathscr{P} & \cdots & \sigma_{cc}\mathscr{P}\end{bmatrix} = \mathscr{P} \otimes \mathbf{\Sigma}^*, \tag{3.26}$$

the Kronecker (or the direct) product of matrices $\mathscr{P}$ and Σ^*. Thus by the extension of Hoeffding's theorem it follows that, under the conditions of Theorem 3.1, $N^{1/2}(\mathbf{U}_N - d\mathbf{j})$ has a limiting normal distribution with zero mean vector and covariance matrix given by (3.26); here again $\mathbf{j}$ stands for a column vector of the appropriate order with unit elements.

Now from (a), (b), and (d), it follows that $\sum_i \mathbf{U}_{iN} = cd\mathbf{j}$ and, moreover, it is the only linear restriction on $\mathbf{U}_{iN}$'s. Hence the distribution of $\mathbf{U}_N$ is singular of rank $p(c-1)$ provided the distribution F of $\mathbf{X}$ is nonsingular in the sense that the unit probability mass is not contained in any lower-dimensional space. The limiting normal distribution of $N^{1/2}(\mathbf{U}_N - d\mathbf{j})$ is then also singular of rank $p(c-1)$ which is, thus, also the rank of Σ given by (3.26). In fact, it can be verified that $\Sigma^*\mathbf{j} = \mathbf{0}$ and that Σ^* is of rank $(c-1)$. It is seen that, as expected, $\mathscr{P}$ is nonsingular; it can be singular if and only if there is some linear constraint on the random variables $w(X^{(\alpha)})$, $\alpha = 1, 2, \ldots, p$ defined in (3.18), which is impossible, since the distribution of $\mathbf{X}$ is assumed to be nonsingular.

If we consider $\mathbf{U}_{0N}' = (\mathbf{U}_{1N}', \ldots, \mathbf{U}_{c-1,N}')$, then $N^{1/2}(\mathbf{U}_{0N} - d\mathbf{j})$ is asymptotically normal with zero mean vector and covariance matrix

$$\Sigma_0 = \mathscr{P} \odot\!\!\!\!\times\; \Sigma_0^*,$$

where

$$\Sigma_0^* = (\sigma_{ij}),\ i, j = 1, 2, \ldots, c-1.$$

Also

$$\Sigma_0^{-1} = \mathscr{P}^{-1} \odot\!\!\!\!\times\; (\Sigma_0^*)^{-1}; \qquad \text{let} \quad (\Sigma_0^*)^{-1} = (\sigma^{ij}).$$

Then

$$\begin{aligned} N(\mathbf{U}_{0N} - d\mathbf{j})'\Sigma_0^{-1}(\mathbf{U}_{0N} - d\mathbf{j}) &= N \sum_{i,j=1}^{c-1}\sum \sigma^{ij}(\mathbf{U}_{iN} - d\mathbf{j})'\mathscr{P}^{-1}(\mathbf{U}_{jN} - d\mathbf{j}) \\ &= N \sum_{i,j=1}^{c-1}\sum \sigma^{ij} \operatorname{tr} \mathscr{P}^{-1}(\mathbf{U}_{jN} - d\mathbf{j})(\mathbf{U}_{iN} - d\mathbf{j})' \\ &= N \operatorname{tr} \mathscr{P}^{-1} \sum_{i,j=1}^{c-1}\sum \sigma^{ij}(\mathbf{U}_{jN} - d\mathbf{j})(\mathbf{U}_{iN} - d\mathbf{j})', \end{aligned}$$

which, after simplification as in [2], can be shown to reduce to

$$\frac{N}{wc^2} \operatorname{tr} \mathscr{P}^{-1}\left[\sum_{i=1}^{c} p_i(\mathbf{U}_{iN} - \overline{\mathbf{U}}_N)(\mathbf{U}_{iN} - \overline{\mathbf{U}}_N)'\right],$$

which is equal to the expression (3.12). The theorem then follows.

Remark. As far as the above theorem is concerned, condition (c) can be replaced by the weaker condition that $\mathscr{E}[\Phi(X_1, X_2, \ldots, X_c]^2$ be finite. The functions Φ defined by (3.4) to (3.7) satisfy the stronger condition (c).

We note that in T_N, given by (3.12), even though μ is independent of F, $\rho_{\alpha\beta}$ does depend, in general, on F, and thus T_N is not a distribution-free statistic. But we can construct unbiased and consistent estimators $e_{\alpha\beta}$ of $\rho_{\alpha\beta}$, i.e., an unbiased and consistent estimator $\mathbf{E} = (e_{\alpha\beta})$ of $\mathscr{P}$ as follows:

Let

$$\mu e_{\alpha\beta(i)} = \frac{1}{n_i(n_i - 1)\cdots(n_i - 2c + 2)} \sum_p \Phi(X_{ij_1}^{(\alpha)}; \{X_{ij_k}^{(\alpha)}, k = 2, 3, \ldots, c\})$$
$$\times \Phi(X_{ij_1}^{(\beta)}; \{X_{ij_k}^{(\beta)}, k = c + 1, \ldots, 2c - 1\}) - d^2$$

where p denotes the summation over all permutations of $(2c - 1)$ integers $(j_1, j_2, \ldots, j_{2c-1})$ that can be chosen out of $(1, 2, \ldots, n_i)$. It can be seen that $e_{\alpha\beta(i)}$ is a U statistic and, hence (see, e.g., [7], p. 142) a minimum-variance unbiased estimator that can be formed from the ith sample of $\rho_{\alpha\beta}$. Moreover, it is well known that $e_{\alpha\beta(i)} \xrightarrow{p} \rho_{\alpha\beta}$ as $n_i \to \infty$. So we can have an unbiased and consistent estimator of $\rho_{\alpha\beta}$ given by $\sum_i e_{\alpha\beta(i)}/c$. We shall prefer another consistent and unbiased estimator,

$$e_{\alpha\beta} = \frac{\sum_{i=1}^{c} n_i(n_i - 1)\cdots(n_i - 2c + 2)e_{\alpha\beta(i)}}{\sum_{i=1}^{c} n_i(n_i - 1)\cdots(n_i - 2c + 2)}. \tag{3.27}$$

If we let

$$T_N^* = \frac{N}{\mu}\frac{(c - 1)^2}{c^2} \sum_{i=1}^{c} p_i(\mathbf{U}_{iN} - \overline{\mathbf{U}}_N)'\mathbf{E}^{-1}(\mathbf{U}_{iN} - \overline{\mathbf{U}}_N), \tag{3.28}$$

it can be easily shown that $T_N - T_N^* \xrightarrow{p} 0$, under the conditions of Theorem 3.1, and hence T_N^* also has a limiting χ^2 distribution with $p(c - 1)$ degrees of freedom. Thus we have.

Theorem 3.2. *Under the conditions of Theorem 3.1, the statistic T_N^* given by (3.28) has a limiting χ^2 distribution, under H_0, with degrees of freedom $p(c - 1)$.*

4. SPECIAL CASES

(a) For Φ given by (3.4), $d = c^{-1}$ and

$$\psi^{(\alpha)}(x) = P[x < X_j^{(\alpha)}, j = 2, 3, \ldots, c] - c^{-1} = [1 - F^{(\alpha)}(x)]^{c-1} - c^{-1},$$

$$\mu = \int_{-\infty}^{\infty} [1 - F^{(\alpha)}(x)]^{2c-2}\, dF^{(\alpha)}(x) - c^{-2} = (c - 1)^2/c^2(2c - 1),$$

$$\mu\rho_{\alpha\beta} = \int_{-\infty}^{\infty}\int_{-\infty}^{\infty} [1 - F^{(\alpha)}(x)]^{c-1}[1 - F^{(\beta)}(y)]^{c-1}\, dF^{(\alpha,\beta)}(x, y) - c^{-2},$$

so that, if $N^* = \sum_{i=1}^{c} n_i(n_i - 1) \cdots (n_i - 2c + 2)$, we have

$$c^{-2} + \mu e_{\alpha\beta} = \frac{1}{N^*} \quad \text{[the number of } (2c-1)\text{-tuples } \mathbf{X}_{ij_1}, \ldots, \mathbf{X}_{ij_{2c-1}} \text{ such that } X_{ij_1}^{(\alpha)} < X_{ij_k}^{(\alpha)},\ k = 2, \ldots, c, \text{ and } X_{ij_1}^{(\beta)} < X_{ij_k}^{(\beta)},\ k = c+1, \ldots, 2c-1], \tag{4.1}$$

and we get the V statistic (2.1) by suppressing N in the subscript of U.

(b) For Φ given by (3.5), $d = c^{-1}$

$$\psi^{(\alpha)}(x) = [F^{(\alpha)}(x)]^{c-1} - c^{-1},$$

$$\mu = (c-1)^2/c^2(2c-1),$$

$$\mu\rho_{\alpha\beta} = \int_{-\infty}^{\infty}\int_{-\infty}^{\infty} [F^{(\alpha)}(x)]^{c-1}[F^{(\beta)}(y)]^{c-1}\, dF^{(\alpha,\beta)}(x, y) - c^{-2},$$

and we have

$$c^{-2} + \mu e_{\alpha\beta} = \frac{1}{N^*} \quad \text{[the number of } (2c-1)\text{-tuples } \mathbf{X}_{ij_1}, \ldots, \mathbf{X}_{ij_{2c-1}} \text{ such that } X_{ij_1}^{(\alpha)} > X_{ij_k}^{(\alpha)},\ k = 2, \ldots, c, \text{ and } X_{ij_1}^{(\beta)} > X_{ij_k}^{(\beta)},\ k = c+1, \ldots, 2c-1], \tag{4.2}$$

and suppressing N we get the B statistic (2.2).

(c) Similarly, for Φ given by (3.6), $d = 0$

$$\psi^{(\alpha)}(x) = P[x > X_j^{(\alpha)}, j = 2, \ldots, c] - P[x < X_j^{(\alpha)}, j = 2, \ldots, c]$$
$$= [F^{(\alpha)}(x)]^{c-1} - [1 - F^{(\alpha)}(x)]^{c-1},$$

$$\mu = \frac{1}{2c-1}\,\frac{2(c-1)!(c-1)!}{(2c-1)!} + \frac{1}{2c-1}$$
$$= \frac{2}{(2c-1)\binom{2c-2}{c-1}}\left[\binom{2c-2}{c-1} - 1\right],$$

$$\mu\rho_{\alpha\beta} = \int_{-\infty}^{\infty}\int_{-\infty}^{\infty} \{[F^{(\alpha)}(x)]^{c-1} - [1 - F^{(\alpha)}(x)]^{c-1}\}\{[F^{(\beta)}(y)]^{c-1} - [1 - F^{(\beta)}(y)]^{c-1}\}\, dF^{(\alpha,\beta)}(x, y),$$

and we have

$$\mu e_{\alpha\beta} = \frac{1}{N^*}[N_1{}^*(\alpha, \beta) + N_2{}^*(\alpha, \beta) - N_3{}^*(\alpha, \beta) - N_4{}^*(\alpha, \beta)], \tag{4.3}$$

where $N_1{}^*(\alpha,\beta)$ and $N_2{}^*(\alpha,\beta)$ are the numbers of $(2c-1)$-tuples mentioned in (4.1) and (4.2), respectively; $N_3{}^*(\alpha,\beta)$ is the number of $(2c-1)$-tuples with $X_{ij_1}^{(\alpha)} > X_{ij_k}^{(\alpha)}$, $k = 2, 3, \ldots, c$ and $X_{ij_1}^{(\beta)} < X_{ij_k}^{(\beta)}$, $k = c+1, \ldots, 2c-1$, and $N_4{}^*(\alpha,\beta)$ is the number like $N_3{}^*(\alpha,\beta)$ obtained from inequalities with signs reversed, and we get the L statistic (2.3).

(d) Finally, for Φ given by (3.7), $d = (c-1)/2$

$$\psi^{(\alpha)}(x) = \sum_{j=2}^{c} P[X_j^{(\alpha)} < x] - (c-1)/2 = (c-1)F^{(\alpha)}(x) - (c-1)/2,$$

$$\mu = (c-1)^2 \int_{-\infty}^{\infty} [F^{(\alpha)}(x)]^2 \, dF^{(\alpha)}(x) - (c-1)^2/4 = (c-1)^2/12,$$

$$\mu\rho_{\alpha\beta} = (c-1)^2 \int_{-\infty}^{\infty}\int_{-\infty}^{\infty} F^{(\alpha)}(x)F^{(\beta)}(y)\, dF^{(\alpha,\beta)}(x,y) - (c-1)^2/4;$$

that is

$$\rho_{\alpha\beta} = 3 \int_{-\infty}^{\infty}\int_{-\infty}^{\infty} [2F^{(\alpha)}(x) - 1][2F^{(\beta)}(y) - 1]\, dF^{(\alpha,\beta)}(x,y),$$

which is the "grade correlation coefficient" ([7], p. 259) between $X^{(\alpha)}$ and $X^{(\beta)}$, and we have

$$3 + e_{\alpha\beta} = 12 \sum_i v_i^{(\alpha,\beta)} \Big/ \sum_i n_i(n_i-1)(n_i-2), \tag{4.4}$$

where $v_i^{(\alpha,\beta)}$ is the number of triplets $\mathbf{X}_{ij_1}, \mathbf{X}_{ij_2}, \mathbf{X}_{ij_3}$ such that $X_{ij_1}^{(\alpha)} > X_{ij_2}^{(\alpha)}$ and $X_{ij_1}^{(\beta)} > X_{ij_3}^{(\beta)}$, and we get the W statistic (2.4). In this case

$$U_i^{(\alpha)} = \frac{1}{n_1 n_2 \cdots n_c} \sum_{j=1}^{c} \frac{n_1 n_2 \cdots n_c}{n_i n_j} \sum_{t_i=1}^{n_i} \sum_{t_j=1}^{n_j} h(x_{it_i}^{(\alpha)} - x_{jt_j}^{(\alpha)}) = \sum_{j=1}^{c} v_{ij}^{(\alpha)}/n_i n_j,$$

where $v_{ij}^{(\alpha)}$ is the number of pairs $(\mathbf{x}_{it_i}, \mathbf{x}_{jt_j})$ such that $x_{it_i}^{(\alpha)} > x_{jt_j}^{(\alpha)}$.

If $n_1 = n_2 = \cdots = n_c = n$, say, then

$$U_i^{(\alpha)} = \frac{1}{n^2}\left[n\bar{R}_i^{(\alpha)} - \frac{n(n+1)}{2}\right] = \frac{c}{N}\left[\bar{R}_i^{(\alpha)} - \frac{n+1}{2}\right]. \tag{4.5}$$

It has been observed [3] that, in the univariate case, even with unequal n_i's, the H statistic [11] is the same as the one obtained from the W statistic by making the transformation (4.5) and, hence, in the multivariate case it is conjectured that the appropriate H statistic will be given from the W statistic by using (4.5), i.e., by (2.5). A rigorous proof for this conjecture can be given by considering the asymptotic normal distribution of $N^{-1/2}[\bar{\mathbf{R}}_N - \mathbf{j}(N+1)/2]$, where $\bar{\mathbf{R}}_N' = (\bar{\mathbf{R}}_{1N}', \ldots, \bar{\mathbf{R}}_{cN}')$, under H_0; the asymptotic normal distribution under H_0 can be obtained either by an appeal to the multivariate extension of the Wald-Wolfowitz theorem (see, e.g., [7], p. 239), or by noting that

$$n_i\bar{R}_i^{(\alpha)} = [n_i(n_i+1)/2] + \sum_j v_{ij}^{(\alpha)} = [n_i(n_i+1)/2] + n_i \sum_j n_j U_{ij}^{(\alpha)},$$

where

$$U_{ij}^{(\alpha)} = \frac{1}{n_i n_j} \sum_{t_i=1}^{n_i} \sum_{t_j=1}^{n_j} h(x_{it_i}^{(\alpha)} - x_{jt_j}^{(\alpha)}),$$

is a two-sample U statistic corresponding to the function $\Phi(x, y) = h(x-y)$, obtained for the sample pair (i, j), and then making an appeal to the joint limiting normal distribution of $N^{1/2}[\mathbf{U}_{ij_N} - \mathbf{j}(1/2)]$'s.

5. REMARKS

It is seen that the U's occurring in these statistics are in the nature of "between-sample" comparisons, while the e's are in the nature of "within-sample" comparisons. The comparisons themselves are with respect to a particular function Φ defined appropriately in each case.

In the univariate case it has been observed [2] that the V statistic is more efficient than the H statistic (or the L and B statistics), in the Pitman sense, for populations bounded below (e.g., exponential distribution $f(y, \alpha) = e^{-(y-\alpha)}$, $y \geq \alpha$). It is expected that the B statistic is similarly more efficient for populations bounded above [e.g., reversed exponential distribution $f(y, \alpha) = e^{(y-\alpha)}$, $y \leq \alpha$]. Both of these are fairly efficient (and the L statistic is much more so) for distributions bounded on both sides [e.g., uniform distribution $f(x, \alpha, \beta) = 1/(\beta - \alpha)$, $\alpha \leq x \leq \beta$]. The W statistic is seen [3] to be as efficient as the H statistic, and these two appear to be more efficient for unbounded distributions.

It is conjectured that the same will be true for the corresponding multivariate analogues. These are also expected to be consistent against the relevant class of alternatives, especially against the class of translation alternatives. Work is in progress on these problems and will be presented in a subsequent communication. Since the distributions are assumed to be continuous, the probability that any two observations are equal is zero. But, in practice, ties do occur. This problem will also be considered in the next communication.

REFERENCES

1. Bhapkar, V. P. (1961). Some nonparametric median procedures. *Ann. Math. Statist.* **32** 846–863.
2. Bhapkar, V. P. (1961). A nonparametric test for the problem of several samples. *Ann. Math. Statist.* **32** 1108–1117.

3. BHAPKAR, V. P. (1964). A nonparametric test for the several sample location problem. Institute of Statistics Mimeo Series No. 411. Univ. North Carolina, Chapel Hill, N.C.
4. CHATTERJEE, S. K. and SEN, P. K. (1964). Nonparametric tests for the bivariate two sample location problem. *Calcutta Statist. Assoc. Bull.* **13** 18–58.
5. DESPHANDE, J. V. (1963). A nonparametric test based on U-statistics for several samples (abstract). *Ann. Math. Statist.* **34** 1624.
6. DWASS, M. (1960). Some k-sample rank-order tests. *Contributions to Probability and Statistics*. Stanford Univ. Press, Stanford, California. 198–202.
7. FRASER, D. A. S. (1957). *Nonparametric Methods in Statistics*. Wiley, New York.
8. HODGES, J. L. Jr. (1955). A bivariate sign test. *Ann. Math. Statist.* **26** 523–527.
9. HOEFFDING, W. (1948). A class of statistics with asymptotic normal distributions. *Ann. Math. Statist.* **19** 293–325.
10. KIEFER, J. (1959). K-sample analogues of the Kolmogorov -Smirnov and Cramér–von Mises tests. *Ann. Math. Statist.* **30** 420–447.
11. KRUSKAL, W. H. (1952). A nonparametric test for the several sample problem. *Ann. Math. Statist.* **23** 525–540.
12. KRUSKAL, W. H. and WALLIS, W. A. (1952). Use of ranks in one-criterion variance analysis. *J. Amer. Statist. Assoc.* **47** 583–621.
13. MOOD, A. M.(1950). *Introduction to the Theory of Statistics*. McGraw-Hill, New York.
14. VINCZE, I. (1961). On two-sample tests based on order statistics. *Proc. Fourth Berkeley Symp. Math. Statist. Prob.* 695–705.

Nonparametric Estimation of Multivariate Densities with Applications[1]

V. K. MURTHY

DOUGLAS AIRCRAFT COMPANY, INC.
SANTA MONICA, CALIFORNIA

SUMMARY

Assuming that the one-dimensional distribution function being sampled has no singular part, the author [4] has previously established the consistency and asymptotic normality of a class of estimators $\{f_n(x)\}$, based on a random sample of observations, for estimating the probability density at all points of continuity of the distribution $F(x)$, where the density $f(x)$ is also continuous. In this paper most of the results for the one-dimensional case are extended to the multivariate case. The multidimensional reliability and then hazard function are defined and confidence estimates are given.

1. SUMMARY OF RESULTS IN THE ONE-DIMENSIONAL CASE

Let $F(x)$ be a probability distribution function. Assuming that the singular part is identically zero, $F(x)$ can be decomposed (see e.g., Cramér [2], pp. 52, 53) into

$$F(x) = F_1(x) + F_2(x), \tag{1.1}$$

where $F_1(x)$ is an everywhere continuous function and $F_2(x)$ is a pure step function with steps of magnitude, say, S_ν, at the points $x = x_\nu$, $\nu = 1, 2, \ldots$, and finally both $F_1(x)$ and $F_2(x)$ are nondecreasing and are uniquely determined. Let $X_1, X_2, \ldots, X_n$ be a random of sample size n from the distribution $F(x)$; i.e., $X_1, X_2, \ldots, X_n$ are independently and identically distributed random variables with the distribution $F(x)$.

[1] This work was supported by the Douglas Independent Research & Development Program.

Let

$$F_n(x) = \frac{1}{n} \quad (\text{number of observations} \leq x \text{ among } X_1, X_2, \ldots, X_n). \quad (1.2)$$

Clearly $F_n(x)$ is a binomially distributed random variable with

$$E[F_n(x)] = F(x)$$

and

$$\text{Var}[F_n(x)] = \frac{1}{n} F(x)[1 - F(x)]. \quad (1.3)$$

A function $K(x)$ is called a one-dimensional window if it satisfies the following conditions:

$$K(x) \geq 0, \qquad K(x) = K(-x),$$
$$\lim_{|x| \to \infty} x\, K(x) = 0, \qquad \int_{-\infty}^{\infty} K(x)\, dx = 1. \quad (1.4)$$

Consider now the class of estimators $f_n(x_0)$ defined by

$$f_n(x_0) = \int_{-\infty}^{\infty} B_n K(B_n(x - x_0))\, dF_n(x) = \frac{B_n}{n} \sum_{j=1}^{n} K(B_n(X_j - x_0)), \quad (1.5)$$

for estimating the density $f(x_0)$ at a point of continuity x_0 of $F(x)$ and the derivative of its absolutely continuous part $f(x)$, where $\{B_n\}$ is a sequence of nonnegative constants such that

$$\lim_{n \to \infty} B_n = \infty. \quad (1.6)$$

The following basic lemma and theorem about $f_n(x_0)$ have been proved by the author [4].

Lemma 1. *Let $K(x)$ be a one-dimensional window satisfying* (1.4). *Let $x_i (i = 0, \pm 1, \pm 2, \cdots)$ be the points of discontinuity of the distribution $F(x)$ and S_i the saltus of $F(x)$ at x_i. Further, let $A_n(x) = B_n K(B_n(x - x_0))$, where B_n satisfies* (1.6) *and x_0 a point of continuity of $F(x)$ and also of $f(x)$, the derivative of the absolutely continuous part of $F(x)$. Then*

$$\lim_{n \to \infty} J(A_n) = \lim_{n \to \infty} \int_{-\infty}^{\infty} A_n(x)\, dF(x) = f(x_0), \quad (1.7)$$

provided the series

$$\sum_i \frac{S_i}{|x_i - x_o'|} < \infty. \quad (1.8)$$

Theorem 1. *Let $K(x)$ and $\{B_n\}$ satisfy* (1.4) *and* (1.6), *respectively. Further, let B_n tend to infinity more slowly than the sample size n in such a way that $B_n/n \to 0$ as $n \to \infty$. Then the estimator $f_n(x_0)$ given by* (1.5) *is consistent and asymptotically normal for estimating $f(x_0)$ at a point of continuity x_0 of the distribution $F(x)$ and also of the density $f(x)$.*

2. MULTIVARIATE CASE

Let

$$\mathbf{X}_{p\times 1} = \begin{pmatrix} X_1 \\ X_2 \\ \vdots \\ X_p \end{pmatrix} \tag{2.1}$$

be a p-dimensional random vector. The corresponding p-variate distribution function $F(\mathbf{x}_{p\times 1}) = F(x_1, x_2, \ldots, x_p)$ is given by

$$\begin{gathered} F(\mathbf{x}) = F(x_1, x_2, \ldots, x_p) = P(X_1 \le x_1, \ldots, X_p \le x_p), \\ 0 \le F(\mathbf{x}) \le 1, \qquad \Delta_n F(\mathbf{x}) \ge 0, \\ F(-\infty, x_2, \ldots, x_p) = \cdots = F(x_1, \ldots, x_{p-1}, -\infty) = 0, \end{gathered} \tag{2.2}$$

where $\Delta_n F$ is the usual nth difference of F,

$$F(+\infty, \ldots, +\infty) = 1,$$

and finally, $F(x_1, \ldots, x_p)$ (see Cramér [2], pp. 80, 81) is nondecreasing and everywhere continuous to the right in each x_ν. The decomposition corresponding to (1.1) is uniquely given in the multivariate case by

$$F(\mathbf{x}) = F_1(\mathbf{x}) + F_2(\mathbf{x}), \tag{2.3}$$

where $F_2(\mathbf{x})$ is a distribution with its whole mass concentrated in discrete mass points, while the first part $F_1(\mathbf{x})$ corresponds to a distribution without discrete mass points. Now, clearly any discrete mass point, $\mathbf{x}_0$, is a point of discontinuity of the distribution $F(x_1, x_2, \ldots, x_p)$. When $p = 1$ the converse is true, namely, that $F(x)$ is continuous at all points x except the one-dimensional discrete mass points. Unfortunately the converse is not true (see Cramér [2], p. 81) when $p > 1$. In fact a multivariate distribution may be such that it has no mass points (single points carrying positive probability mass); however, it may still be discontinuous in certain points (e.g., the whole probability mass is distributed on lines, planes, and hypersurfaces in a certain manner). As in the one-dimensional case, it cannot, therefore be generally assumed that $F_1(\mathbf{x})$ in (2.3) is everywhere continuous.

In what follows it is assumed that we are sampling from a multivariate distribution $F(\mathbf{x})$ having the representation

$$F(\mathbf{x}) = F_1(\mathbf{x}) + F_2(\mathbf{x}), \tag{2.4}$$

where $F_1(\mathbf{x})$ is an absolutely continuous p-variate distribution and $F_2(\mathbf{x})$ is a distribution with its whole mass concentrated in discrete mass points. In most practical cases, the discrete mass points are a set of isolated points; i.e., there exists an ε neighborhood of a discrete mass point which does not contain any other discrete mass points. We therefore, also assume that the set of discontinuities of $F_2(\mathbf{x})$ is a set of isolated points.

A function $K(x_1, x_2, \ldots, x_p)$ of the variables $x_1, x_2, \ldots, x_p$ is called a p-dimensional window if it satisfies the conditions

$$\begin{aligned} &K(x_1, x_2, \ldots, x_p) \geq 0, \\ &K(x_1, x_2, \ldots, x_p) = K(\pm x_1, \pm x_2, \ldots, x_p). \end{aligned} \tag{2.5}$$

For nonnegative $x_{11}, x_{21}, \ldots, x_{p1}$ and $x_{12}, x_{22}, \ldots, x_{p2}$ such that

$$x_{i1} \geq x_{i2} \qquad (i = 1, 2, \ldots, p),$$

$$K(x_{11}, x_{21}, \ldots, x_{p1}) \leq K(x_{12}, x_{22}, \ldots, x_{p2})$$

and

$$\int_{-\infty}^{\infty} \cdots \int_{-\infty}^{\infty} K(x_1, x_2, \ldots, x_n)\, dx_1 \cdots dx_n = 1.$$

We shall now prove:

Lemma 2. *Let $K(x_1, x_2, \ldots, x_p)$ be a p-dimensional window satisfying* (2.5). *Let $F(x_1, x_2, \ldots, x_p)$ be a bounded nonnegative nondecreasing measure function in the variables $x_1, x_2, \ldots, x_p$ satisfying* (2.4). *Let $\{B_{in}\}$, $i = 1, 2, \ldots, p$, be sequences of nonnegative constants depending on the parameter n and tending to infinity as $n \to \infty$. Then*

$$\begin{aligned} \lim_{n\to\infty} I_n = \lim_{n\to\infty} \int_{-\infty}^{\infty} \cdots \int_{-\infty}^{\infty} \prod_{i=1}^{p} B_{in} K(B_{1n}(x_1 - x_1^0), \ldots, B_{pn}(x_p - x_p^0)) \\ \times dF(x_1, x_2, \ldots, x_p) = f(x_1^0, x_2^0, \ldots, x_p^0) \end{aligned} \tag{2.6}$$

at a point of continuity $(x_1^0, x_2^0, \ldots, x_p^0)$ of $F(x_1, x_2, \ldots, x_p)$ and also of $f(x_1, x_2, \ldots, x_p)$ the derivative of the absolutely continuous part of $F(x_1, x_2, \ldots, x_p)$.

Proof. We shall prove the lemma for the case $p = 2$. The extension to the case $p > 2$ is obvious. Since (x_1^0, x_2^0), is a point of continuity of the function $F(x_1, x_2)$ and since $F(x_1, x_2)$, by assumption, has the representation (24).

with at most a countable infinity of isolated points of discontinuity, there exists an (ε, ω) neighborhood of $(x_1{}^0, x_2{}^0)$ in which $F(x_1, x_2)$ is absolutely continuous. Divide the range of integration into nine parts:

$$x_1{}^0 - \varepsilon < x_1 < x_1{}^0 + \varepsilon,\ x_2{}^0 - \omega < x_2 < x_2{}^0 + \omega;$$

$$-\infty < x_1 < x_1{}^0 - \varepsilon,\ -\infty < x_2 < x_2{}^0 - \omega;$$

$$-\infty < x_1 < x_1{}^0 - \varepsilon,\ x_2{}^0 + \omega < x_2 < \infty;$$

$$x_1{}^0 + \varepsilon < x_1 < \infty,\ -\infty < x_2 < x_2\ \ - \omega;$$

$$x_1{}^0 + \varepsilon < x_1 < \infty,\ x_2{}^0 + \omega < x_2 < \infty;$$

$$-\infty < x_1 < x_1{}^0 - \varepsilon,\ x_2{}^0 - \omega < x_2 < x_2{}^0 + \omega;$$

$$x_1{}^0 + \varepsilon < x_1 < \infty,\ x_2{}^0 - \omega < x_2 < x_2{}^0 + \omega;$$

$$x_1{}^0 - \varepsilon < x_1 < x_1{}^0 + \varepsilon,\ -\infty < x_2{}^0 < x_2{}^0 - \omega;$$

and

$$x_1{}^0 - \varepsilon < x_1 < x_1{}^0 + \varepsilon,\ x_2{}^0 + \omega < x_2 < \infty.$$

Let the integrals over these nine parts of the integrand in (2.6) with $p = 2$ be denoted, respectively, by $I_1, I_2, I_3, I_4, I_5, I_6, I_7, I_8$, and I_9. The integral I_1, integrals I_2 to I_5, and integrals I_6 to I_9 will be treated separately.

We shall now establish

$$\lim_{n\to\infty} I_1 = f(x_1{}^0, x_2{}^0). \tag{2.7}$$

We have

$$\begin{aligned} I_1 &= \int_{x_1{}^0-\varepsilon}^{x_1{}^0+\varepsilon}\int_{x_2{}^0-\omega}^{x_2{}^0+\omega} B_{1n}B_{2n}K(B_{1n}(x_1 - x_1{}^0), B_{2n}(x_2 - x_2{}^0))\,dF(x_1, x_2) \\ &= \int_{x_1{}^0-\varepsilon}^{x_1{}^0+\varepsilon}\int_{x_2{}^0-\omega}^{x_2{}^0+\omega} B_{1n}B_{2n}K(B_{1n}(x_1 - x_1{}^0), B_{2n}(x_2 - x_2{}^0))f(x_1, x_2)\,dx_1\,dx_2, \end{aligned} \tag{2.8}$$

since, in view of the assumptions on $F(x_1, x_2)$, it is absolutely continuous in the rectangle $x_1{}^0 - \varepsilon < x_1 < x_1{}^0 + \varepsilon$, $x_2{}^0 - \omega < x_2 < x_2{}^0 + \omega$. Making the transformation $\lambda = B_{1n}(x_1 - x_1{}^0)$, $\mu = B_{2n}(x_2 - x_2{}^0)$, (2.8) becomes

$$I_1 = \int_{-B_{1n}\varepsilon}^{B_{1n}\varepsilon}\int_{-B_{2n}\omega}^{B_{2n}\omega} K(\lambda, \mu) f\left(x_1{}^0 + \frac{\lambda}{B_{1n}}, x_2{}^0 + \frac{\mu}{B_{2n}}\right) d\lambda\,d\mu. \tag{2.9}$$

Taking the limit on both sides of (2.9) as $n \to \infty$, we have, owing to the assumption that $f(x_1, x_2)$ is continuous at $(x_1{}^0, x_2{}^0)$,

$$\lim_{n\to\infty} I_1 = f(x_1{}^0, x_2{}^0)\int_{-\infty}^{\infty}\int_{-\infty}^{\infty} K(x_1, x_2)\,dx_1\,dx_2 = f(x_1{}^0, x_2{}^0). \tag{2.10}$$

Now consider

$$I_2 = \int_{-\infty}^{x_1^0-\varepsilon} \int_{-\infty}^{x_2^0-\omega} B_{1n}B_{2n}K(B_{1n}(x_1 - x_1^0), B_{2n}(x_2 - x_2^0))\, dF(x_1, x_2). \tag{2.11}$$

Since $K(x_1, x_2)$ satisfies (2.5) for $p = 2$, we have

$$I_2 \leq B_{1n}B_{2n}K(B_{1n}\varepsilon, B_{2n}\omega) \int_{-\infty}^{x_1^0-\varepsilon} \int_{-\infty}^{x_2^0-\omega} dF(x_1, x_2) < B_{1n}B_{2n}K(B_{1n}\varepsilon, B_{2n}\omega). \tag{2.12}$$

In a similar manner,

$$I_j < B_{1n}B_{2n}K(B_{1n}\varepsilon, B_{2n}\omega), \qquad j = 3, 4, 5. \tag{2.13}$$

We shall now prove that

$$\lim_{n\to\infty} B_{1n}B_{2n}K(B_{1n}\varepsilon, B_{2n}\omega) = 0. \tag{2.14}$$

We have

$$\int_{B_{1n}\theta}^{2B_{n}\theta} \int_{B_{2n}\phi}^{2B_{2n}\phi} K(x_1, x_2)\, dx_1\, dx_2 \geq B_{ln}B_{2n}\theta\, \phi\, K(2B_{ln}\theta, 2B_{2n}\phi)$$

$$= B_{1n}B_{2n}\frac{\varepsilon\omega}{4} K(B_{1n}\varepsilon, B_{2n}\omega), \tag{2.15}$$

where $\varepsilon = 2\theta$ and $\omega = 2\phi$.

Taking the limit on both sides of (2.15) as $n \to \infty$, we have for given ε and ω, that

$$\lim_{n\to\infty} B_{1n}B_{2n}K(B_{1n}\varepsilon, B_{2n}\omega) = 0. \tag{2.16}$$

Combining (2.12), (2.13), and (2.16) we have proved

$$\lim_{n\to\infty} I_j = 0, \qquad j = 2, 3, 4, 5. \tag{2.17}$$

Now consider

$$I_6 = \int_{-\infty}^{x_1^0-\varepsilon} \int_{x_2^0-\omega}^{x_2^0+\omega} B_{1n}B_{2n}K(B_{1n}(x_1 - x_1^0), B_{2n}(x_2 - x_2^0))\, dF(x_1, x_2)$$

$$< B_{1n}B_{2n} \int_{x_2^0-\omega}^{x_2^0+\omega} K(B_{1n}\varepsilon, B_{2n}(x_2 - x_0))\, dG(x_2), \tag{2.18}$$

where $G(x_2) = F(\infty, x_2)$. Since $G(x_2)$ is absolutely continuous in the ω-neighborhood of x_2^0, (2.18) can be written as

$$I_6 < B_{1n}B_{2n}\int_{x_2^0-\omega}^{x_2^0+\omega} K(B_{1n}\varepsilon, B_{2n}(x_2 - x_2^0))g(x_2)\,dx$$

$$= B_{1n}\int_{-B_{2n}\omega}^{B_{2n}\omega} K(B_{1n}\varepsilon, \lambda)g\left(x_2^0 + \frac{\lambda}{B_{2n}}\right)d\lambda, \tag{2.19}$$

after making the transformation $\lambda = B_{2n}(x_2 - x_2^0)$, where $dG(x_2) = g(x_2)\,dx_2$. Taking the limit as $n \to \infty$ in (2.19) we obtain

$$\lim_{n\to\infty} I_6 < \lim_{n\to\infty} B_{1n}g(x_2^0)\int_{-\infty}^{\infty} K(B_{1n}\varepsilon, \lambda)\,d\lambda = \lim_{n\to\infty} B_{1n}H(B_n\varepsilon)g(x_2^0), \tag{2.20}$$

where

$$H(x_1) = \int_{-\infty}^{\infty} K(x_1, x_2)\,dx_2.$$

Since, in view of the conditions (2.5) imposed on $K(x_1, x_2)$ for $p = 2$, $H(x_1)$ is a monotonic-decreasing function of $x_1 \geq 0$, we have

$$\lim_{n\to\infty} B_{1n}H(B_{1n}\varepsilon) = 0. \tag{2.21}$$

Combining (2.20) and (2.21) we have

$$\lim_{n\to\infty} I_6 = 0. \tag{2.22}$$

In an exactly similar way,

$$\lim_{n\to\infty} I_j = 0, \qquad j = 7, 8, 9. \tag{2.23}$$

Combining (2.10), (2.17), (2.22), and (2.23) we have finally,

$$\lim_{n\to\infty} I_n = f(x_1^0, x_2^0)$$

at a point of continuity (x_1^0, x_2^0) of the distribution $F(x_1, x_2)$ and $f(x_1, x_2)$. The extension to the case $p > 2$ is obvious. We thus have completed the proof of Lemma 2.

If, as assumed in (2.5),

$$\int_{-\infty}^{\infty} \cdots \int_{-\infty}^{\infty} K(x_1, x_2, \ldots, x_p)\,dx_1 \ldots dx_p,$$

is not equal to 1 but is finite, then the limit (2.6) in Lemma 2 is given by

$$\lim_{n\to\infty} I_n = f(x_1^0, x_2^0, \ldots, x_p^0)\int_{-\infty}^{\infty} \cdots \int_{-\infty}^{\infty} K(x_1, x_2, \ldots, x_p)\,dx_1\,dx_2 \cdots dx_p. \tag{2.24}$$

It may be noted that even though the p-dimensional window $K(x_1, x_2, \ldots, x_p)$ does not satisfy the monotonicity condition in (2.5), it can easily be seen that

Lemma 2 still holds as long as $K(x_1, x_2, \dots, x_p)$ is bounded by a function, say, $G(x_1, x_2, \dots, x_p)$, where $G(x_1, x_2, \dots, x_p)$ satisfies the conditions of (2.5). Many weight functions $K(x_1, x_2, \dots, x_p)$ are such that while they do not satisfy the monotonicity condition in (2.5), they are bounded by functions which satisfy the conditions in (2.5).

3. A CLASS OF ESTIMATORS FOR THE MULTIVARIATE DENSITY AT A POINT OF CONTINUITY OF THE DISTRIBUTION $F(x_1, x_2, \dots, x_p)$ AND THE DENSITY $f(x_1, x_2, \dots, x_p)$

Let $F(x_1, x_2, \dots, x_p)$ be the distribution function of a p-dimensional random vector

$$\mathbf{X}_{p\times 1} = \begin{pmatrix} x_1 \\ x_2 \\ \vdots \\ x_p \end{pmatrix}.$$

Let $f(x_1, x_2, \dots, x_p)$ be the density at a point of continuity $(x_1^0, x_2^0, \dots, x_p^0)$ of the distribution $F(x_1, x_2, \dots, x_p)$. Let

$$\begin{pmatrix} x_{1i} \\ x_{2i} \\ \vdots \\ x_{pi} \end{pmatrix}, \qquad i = 1, 2, \dots, n,$$

be a random sample of size n from the distribution $F(x_1, x_2, \dots, x_p)$; i.e.,

$$\mathbf{X}_i = \begin{pmatrix} x_{1i} \\ x_{2i} \\ \vdots \\ x_{pi} \end{pmatrix}, \qquad i = 1, 2, \dots, n,$$

are independently and identically distributed p-dimensional random vectors with the distribution function $F(x_1, x_2, \dots, x_p)$. Let the empirical distribution function $F_n(x_1, x_2, \dots, x_p)$ be defined by

$$F_n(x_1, x_2, \dots, x_p) = \frac{1}{n} \begin{bmatrix} \text{number of observations } X_i, & i = 1, 2, \dots, n \\ \text{such that } X_{ji} < x_j, & j = 1, 2, \dots, p \end{bmatrix}. \tag{3.1}$$

Evidently $F_n(x_1, x_2, \dots, x_p)$ is a binomially distributed random variable with

$$E(F_n(x_1, x_2, \dots, x_p)) = F(x_1, x_2, \dots, x_p)$$

and

$$\operatorname{Var}(F_n(x_1, x_2, \ldots, x_p)) = \frac{1}{n} F(x_1, x_2, \ldots, x_p) R(x_1, x_2, \ldots, x_p),$$

where

$$R(x_1, x_2, \ldots, x_p) = 1 - F(x_1, x_2, \ldots, x_p).$$

Let us propose

$$f_n(x_1{}^0, x_2{}^0, \ldots, x_p{}^0) = \int_{-\infty}^{\infty} \cdots \int_{-\infty}^{\infty} \prod_{i=1}^{p} B_{in} K(B_{1n}(x_1 - x_1{}^0), \ldots, B_{pn}(x_p - x_p{}^0) \times dF_n(x_1, x_2, \ldots, x_n) \tag{3.2}$$

as an estimate of the density $f(x_1, \ldots, x_p)$ at a point of continuity $(x_1{}^0, \ldots, x_p{}^0)$ of $F(x_1, \ldots, x_p)$ and $f(x_1, x_2, \ldots, x_p)$, where $K(x_1, x_2, \ldots, x_p)$ is a p-dimensional window satisfying (2.5) and $\{B_{in}\}$, $i = 1, 2, \ldots, p$, are sequences of nonnegative constants depending on the sample size n and tending to infinity as $n \to \infty$. Equation (3.2) can also be written

$$f_n(x_1{}^0, x_2{}^0, \ldots, x_p{}^0) = \frac{1}{n} \sum_{j=1}^{n} \prod_{i=1}^{p} B_{in} K(B_{1n}(X_{1j} - x_1{}^0), \ldots, B_{pn}(X_{pj} - x_p{}^0)). \tag{3.3}$$

We shall now establish the consistency of the class of estimators given by (3.3) by showing that

$$\lim_{n \to \infty} E(f_n(x_1^0, x_2^0, \ldots, x_p^0)) = f(x_1, x_2, \ldots, x_p), \tag{3.4}$$

and

$$\lim_{n \to \infty} \operatorname{Var}(f_n(x_1{}^0, x_2{}^0, \ldots, x_p{}^0)) = 0 \qquad \text{at a point of continuity}$$

$$(x_1{}^0, \ldots, x_p{}^0) \quad \text{of} \quad F(x_1, \ldots, x_p) \quad \text{and} \quad f(x_1, x_2, \ldots, x_p). \tag{3.5}$$

Taking expectations on both sides of (3.3), we obtain

$$E(f_n(x_1{}^0, x_2{}^0, \ldots, x_p{}^0)) = \int_{-\infty}^{\infty} \cdots \int_{-\infty}^{\infty} \prod_{i=1}^{p} B_{in} K(B_{1n}(x_1 - x_1{}^0, \ldots, \times B_{pn}(x_p - x_p{}^0))\, dF(x_1, x_2, \ldots, x_p). \tag{3.6}$$

Applying Lemma 2 to (3.6) we at once discover that

$$\lim_{n \to \infty} E(f_n(x_1{}^0, \ldots, x_p{}^0)) = f(x_1{}^0, \ldots, x_p{}^0). \tag{3.7}$$

Taking the variance of (3.3) we obtain

$$\operatorname{Var}(f_n(x_1{}^0, \ldots, x_p{}^0)) = \frac{(\prod_{i=1}^{p} B_{in})^2}{n} E[K^2(B_{1n}(x_1 - x_1{}^0), \ldots, B_{pn}(x_p - x_p{}^0))] - E^2[K(B_{1n}(x_1 - x_1{}^0), \ldots, B_{pn}(x_p - x_p{}^0))]. \tag{3.8}$$

In view of (3.6) and (3.7) the limit as $n \to \infty$ of (3.8) is given by

$$\lim_{n\to\infty} \operatorname{Var}(f_n(x_1^0, \ldots, x_p^0))$$
$$= \lim_{n\to\infty} \frac{(\prod_{i=1}^p B_{in})^2}{n} E[K^2(B_{1n}(x_1 - x_1^0), \ldots, B_{pn}(x_p - x_p^0))]$$
$$= \lim_{n\to\infty} \frac{(\prod_{i=1}^p B_{in})^2}{n} \int_{-\infty}^{\infty} \cdots \int_{-\infty}^{\infty} K^2(B_{1n}(x_1 - x_1^0), \ldots, B_{pn}(x_p - x_p^0)) \times dF(x_1, x_2, \ldots, x_p). \tag{3.9}$$

Now applying Lemma 2, as given by (2.24) to (3.9) we discover that

$$\lim_{n\to\infty} \frac{n}{\prod_{i=1}^p B_{in}} \operatorname{Var}(f_n(x_1^0, \ldots, x_p^0)) = f(x_1^0, \ldots, x_p^0) \int_{-\infty}^{\infty} \cdots \int_{-\infty}^{\infty} \times K^2(x_1, \ldots, x_p)\, dx_1 \cdots dx_p \tag{3.10}$$

at every point of continuity $(x_1^0, \ldots, x_p^0)$ of $F(x_1, x_2, \ldots, x_p)$ and $f(x_1, x_2, \ldots, x_p)$ the derivative of the absolutely continuous part of $F(x_1, x_2, \ldots, x_p)$. We shall now finally assume that the $\{B_{in}\}$, $i = 1, 2, \ldots, p$, tend to infinity more slowly than n in such a way that

$$\frac{\prod_{i=1}^p B_{in}}{n} \to 0 \quad \text{as} \quad n \to \infty. \tag{3.11}$$

Taking (3.7), (3.10), and (3.11) together, we have proved the following:

Theorem 2. *Let $K(x_1, x_2, \ldots, x_p)$ satisfy* (2.5). *Let $\{B_{in}\}$, $i = 1, 2, \ldots, p$, be sequences of nonnegative constants tending to infinity as $n \to \infty$ such that*

$$\frac{\prod_{i=1}^p B_{in}}{n} \to 0 \quad \text{as} \quad n \to \infty.$$

Then the estimator

$$f_n(x_1^0, \ldots, x_p^0) = \int_{-\infty}^{\infty} \cdots \int_{-\infty}^{\infty} \prod_{i=1}^{p} B_{in} K(B_{1n}(x_1 - x_1^0), \ldots, B_{pn}(x_p - x_p^0)) \times dF_n(x_1, x_2, \ldots, x_p)$$

is a consistent estimate of $f(x_1^0, \ldots, x_p^0)$ at every continuity point $(x_1^0, \ldots, x_p^0)$ of $F(x_1, x_2, \ldots, x_p)$ and $f(x_1, x_2, \ldots, x_p)$.

4. ASYMPTOTIC NORMALITY OF THE SEQUENCE $\{f_n(x_1, x_2, \ldots, x_p)\}$ AT A POINT OF CONTINUITY OF $F(x_1, x_2, \ldots, x_p)$ AND $f(x_1, x_2, \ldots, x_p)$

The estimator $f_n(x_1^0, x_2^0, \ldots, x_p^0)$ can be written

$$f_n(x_1{}^0, x_2{}^0, \dots, x_p{}^0) = \frac{1}{n} \sum_{j=1}^{n} V_j, \tag{4.1}$$

where

$$V_j = \prod_{i=1}^{p} B_{in} K(B_{1n}(X_{1j} - x_1{}^0), \dots, B_{pn}(X_{pj} - x_p{}^0)), \tag{4.2}$$

and the sequence $\{V_j\}$ are independently, identically, distributed as the random variable

$$V(n) = \prod_{i=1}^{p} B_{in} K(B_{1n}(X_1 - x_1{}^0), \dots, B_{pn}(X_p - x_p{}^0)). \tag{4.3}$$

A sufficient condition for the sequence $\{f_n(x_1{}^0, x_2{}^0, \dots, x_p{}^0)\}$ to be asymptotically normally distributed is (see Murthy [4]) that for some $\sigma > 0$,

$$\frac{E|V(n) - E(V(n))|^{2+\sigma}}{n^{\sigma/2}\,[\mathrm{Var}(V(n))]^{1+\sigma/2}} \to 0 \quad \text{as} \quad n \to \infty. \tag{4.4}$$

Applying Lemma 2 we obtain

$$E|V(n)|^{2+\sigma} \sim \left(\prod_{i=1}^{p} B_{in}\right)^{1+\sigma} f(x_1{}^0, \dots, x_p{}^0) \int_{-\infty}^{\infty} \cdots \int_{-\infty}^{\infty} (K(x_1, \dots, x_p))^{2+\sigma} \times dx_1 \cdots dx_p, \tag{4.5}$$

$$\mathrm{Var}[V(n)] \sim \prod_{i=1}^{p} B_{in} f(x_1{}^0, \dots, x_p{}^0) \int_{-\infty}^{\infty} \cdots \int_{-\infty}^{\infty} K^2(x_1, \dots, x_p)\, dx_1 \cdots dx_p, \tag{4.6}$$

at every point of continuity $(x_1{}^0, \dots, x_p{}^0)$ of $F(x_1, x_2, \dots, x_p)$ and $f(x_1, x_2, \dots, x_p)$. In view of

$$\int_{-\infty}^{\infty} \cdots \int_{-\infty}^{\infty} K(x_1, x_2, \dots, x_p)\, dx_1, \dots, dx_p = 1$$

we have

$$\int_{-\infty}^{\infty} \int_{-\infty}^{\infty} [K(x_1, \dots, x_p)]^{2+\sigma}\, dx_1, \dots, dx_p < \infty \qquad \text{for } \delta \geq 0. \tag{4.7}$$

Taking (4.5), (4.6), and (4.7) and the condition $\prod_{i=1}^{p} B_{in}/n \to 0$ as $n \to \infty$, it is easily verified that condition (4.4) for asymptotic normality is satisfied. Hence:

Theorem 3. *Under the conditions of Theorem 2, the sequence of estimators* $\{f_n(x_1{}^0, \dots, x_p{}^0)\}$ *is asymptotically normal, where* $(x_1{}^0 \cdots x_p{}^0)$ *is a point of continuity of* $F(x_1, x_2, \dots, x_p)$ *and* $f(x_1, x_2, \dots, x_p)$.

5. MULTIDIMENSIONAL WINDOWS

We shall briefly present here a simple method of constructing multidimensional windows. If $K_1(x_1), K_2(x_2), \ldots, K_p(x_p)$ are any p one-dimensional windows each satisfying (2.5) for $p = 1$, then it is easily verified that

$$K(x_1, x_2, \ldots, x_p) = K_1(x_1)K_2(x_2) \cdots K_p(x_p) \tag{5.1}$$

is a p-dimensional window. One-dimensional windows are extensively treated in the literature. Based on his own work and that of several others in the field of spectral estimation, Parzen [6] gave a table of seven well-known one-dimensional windows. Taking into account (5.1), one can construct several combinations of these to provide direct examples of p-dimensional windows.

6. APPLICATIONS TO RELIABILITY AND HAZARD RATE

In analogy with the one-dimensional case, we shall call

$$R(x_1, x_2, \ldots, x_p) = 1 - F(x_1, x_2, \ldots, x_p) \tag{6.1}$$

the reliability function associated with a p-dimensional random vector

$$\mathbf{X}_{p\times 1} = \begin{pmatrix} X_1 \\ X_2 \\ \vdots \\ X_p \end{pmatrix},$$

whose distribution function $F(x_1, x_2, \ldots, x_p)$ has the representation (2.4). At a point of continuity $(x_1, x_2, \ldots, x_p)$ of $F(x_1, x_2, \ldots, x_p)$ and $f(x_1, x_2, \ldots, x_p)$, the hazard function or failure-rate function $Z(x_1, x_2, \ldots, x_p)$ is defined by

$$Z(x_1, x_2, \ldots, x_p) = \frac{f(x_1, x_2, \ldots, x_p)}{1 - F(x_1, x_2, \ldots, x_p)}. \tag{6.2}$$

The case when the random vector $\mathbf{X}_{p\times 1}$ has nonnegative components is important. In this case the components X_i, $i = 1, 2, \ldots, p$, may represent the observed times to failure of the p components of a given system or subsystem. In this case $R(x_1, x_2, \ldots, x_p)$ denotes the simultaneous probability that the p components did not fail by time instants $x_1, x_2, \ldots, x_p$, respectively. Also, $Z(x_1, x_2, \ldots, x_p), dx_1, dx_2, \ldots, dx_p$ denotes the conditional probability that the first, second, ..., to pth component fail between x_1 and $x_1 + dx_1$, x_2 and $x_2 + dx_2$, ..., to x_p and $x_p + dx_p$, respectively, given that the components did not fail by times $x_1, x_2, \ldots, x_p$, respectively. Also if the components of the random vector $\mathbf{X}_{p\times 1}$ denote the ages of the p members of a family of size p, then $Z(x_1, x_2, \dots, x_p)$ denotes what may be called the joint force of mortality.

Let

$$R_n(x_1, x_2, \dots, x_p) = 1 - F_n(x_1, x_2, \dots, x_p), \tag{6.3}$$

$$R_n^*(x_1, x_2, \dots, x_p) = \int_{x_1}^{\infty} \int_{x_2}^{\infty} \cdots \int_{x_p}^{\infty} f_n(y_1, y_2, \dots, y_p)\, dy_1\, dy_2 \cdots dy_p, \tag{6.4}$$

where $F_n(x_1, x_2, \dots, x_p)$ and $f_n(x_1, x_2, \dots, x_p)$ are given by (3.1) and (3.2). Following an argument similar to that given in the one-dimensional case in the author's recent paper [5], it can be easily shown that the estimate $R_n(x_1, x_2, \dots, x_p)$ and the class of estimators $R_n^*(x_1, x_2, \dots, x_p)$ are both consistent estimators of $R(x_1, x_2, \dots, x_p)$ at every point of continuity of the distribution $F(x_1, x_2, \dots, x_p)$. Further, $R_n(x_1, x_2, \dots, x_p)$ and $R_n^*(x_1, x_2, \dots, x_p)$ are asymptotically equivalent in the sense that they have the same order of consistency and the same asymptotic variance

$$\frac{R(x_1, x_2, \dots, x_p)F(x_1, x_2, \dots, x_p)}{n}.$$

Further, they are asymptotically normal. Now let

$$Z_n(x_1, x_2, \dots, x_p) = \frac{f_n(x_1, x_2, \dots, x_p)}{R_n(x_1, x_2, \dots, x_p)}. \tag{6.5}$$

Again following the arguments advanced by the author [5], one obtains in a straightforward manner that

$$\lim_{n\to\infty} P\left(\frac{n^{1/2}}{\prod_{i=1}^{p} B_{in}^{1/2}} \times \frac{Z_n(x_1, x_2, \dots, x_p) - Z(x_1, x_2, \dots, x_p)}{\left\{\dfrac{Z(x_1, \dots, x_p)}{R(x_1, \dots, x_p)} \displaystyle\int_{-\infty}^{\infty} \cdots \int_{-\infty}^{\infty} K^2(x_1, \dots, x_p)\, dx_1 \cdots dx_p\right\}^{1/2}} < x \right) = \frac{1}{(2\pi)^{1/2}} \int_{-\infty}^{x} \exp(-\tfrac{1}{2}y^2)\, dy \tag{6.6}$$

at a point of continuity $(x_1, x_2, \dots, x_p)$ of the distribution $F(x_1, x_2, \dots, x_p)$ and the density $f(x_1, x_2, \dots, x_p)$. The above results on the asymptotic normality of the estimates for the reliability function and the hazard-rate function provide confidence bands on the multidimensional reliability and hazard rate, respectively, for any given level of confidence.

REFERENCES

1. CACOULLOS, T. (1964). Estimation of a multivariate density. Tech. Rept. No. 40. Dept. Statist., University of Minnesota, Minneapolis.
2. CRAMÉR, H. (1946). *Mathematical Methods of Statistics*. Princeton Univ. Press, Princeton, New Jersey.
3. MURTHY, V. K. (1964). Estimation of bivariate probability density (abstract). *Ann. Math. Statist.* **34** 457.
4. MURTHY, V. K. (1965). Estimation of probability density. *Ann. Math. Statist.* **36** 1027–1031.
5. MURTHY, V. K. (1965). Estimation of jumps, reliability and hazard rate. *Ann. Math Statist.* **36** 1032–1040.
6. PARZEN, E. (1961). Mathematical considerations in the estimation of spectra. *Technometrics* **3** 167–190.

PART II

Multivariate Analysis of Variance and Related Topics

A k-Sample Regression Model with Covariance[1]

LEON GLESER[2]
DEPARTMENT OF MATHEMATICAL STATISTICS
COLUMBIA UNIVERSITY
NEW YORK, NEW YORK

INGRAM OLKIN
DEPARTMENT OF STATISTICS
STANFORD UNIVERSITY
STANFORD, CALIFORNIA

1. INTRODUCTION AND SUMMARY

Let $y^{(1)}, \ldots, y^{(k)}$ be k independent random p-dimensional row vectors, each having a multivariate normal distribution with common covariance matrix ψ and mean vector $\mathscr{E}y^{(i)} = \beta^{(i)}X$, where $\beta^{(i)}$ is a q-dimensional row vector and X is a known $q \times p$ matrix of rank $q \le p$, $i = 1, \ldots, k$. We observe N_i independent replications of the vector $y^{(i)}$, $i = 1, \ldots, k$.

The problems of concern in the paper are: (a) to test the hypothesis H: $\beta^{(1)} = \beta^{(2)} = \cdots = \beta^{(k)} \equiv \beta$, and (b) to find maximum-likelihood estimates (MLE) of the $\beta^{(i)}$'s and of ψ, and simultaneous confidence bounds for $\beta^{(1)}, \ldots, \beta^{(k)}$. Associated with each of the above problems is a related distributional problem. These distributional problems are extremely untractable but permit representations in integral form.

A chronology of previous papers is as follows. For the case $k = 1$, the regression model was considered independently by Rao [10] and by Cochran and Bliss [2]. These authors obtained a conditional likelihood-ratio test of H: $\beta = \beta_0$ and the null distribution of that test. Rao [12] obtained conditional and unconditional distributions under general alternatives to H; the

[1] This work was supported in part by National Science Foundation Grants at Columbia University and at Stanford University.

[2] *Present Address:* Department of Statistics, The Johns Hopkins University, Baltimore, Maryland.

unconditional distribution was also derived independently by Narain [7]. More recently, Kabe [5] has given an alternative derivation of the nonnull distribution.

We note that a conditional likelihood-ratio test need not be the same as the unconditional likelihood-ratio test. In some cases the conditional and unconditional likelihood-ratio tests are the same, but a proof of this fact is always necessary. Such a proof can be given for this case. Alternatively, one could begin *ab initio* and directly obtain the unconditional likelihood-ratio test. This was done by Olkin and Shrikhande [8], who, in addition, obtained the null and nonnull distributions of the likelihood-ratio test statistic.

Properties of the likelihood-ratio test of a closely related problem were considered by Giri [3]. His results show that the likelihood-ratio test for his problem is UMP similar invariant. Kiefer and Schwartz [6] prove that the likelihood-ratio test is admissible.

Rao [15] considered the k-sample regression model for $k > 1$ in connection with its application to growth curves. Implicit in his discussion is the conditional likelihood-ratio test for H: $\beta^{(1)} = \beta^{(2)} = \cdots = \beta^{(k)} = \beta$. Both he and Potthoff and Roy [9] have discussed a more general regression model and testing problem than the one we consider in this paper, but none of these authors have explicitly derived the unconditional likelihood-ratio test. (Actually the testing problem that linear combinations of the β's are equal to given constants is equivalent to the Potthoff-Roy model. The interrelation of various such models will be given by the authors in a later paper.) Potthoff and Roy give certain *ad hoc* procedures, whereas Rao has indicated that he uses the conditional likelihood-ratio test. As in the case $k = 1$, we treat our special case of the more general Potthoff-Roy model by deriving the unconditional likelihood-ratio test.

From the point of view of estimation, the papers by Rao [10–12, 14] deal with various conditional and unconditional confidence bounds for both β and linear combinations of β in the case $k = 1$. Gleser and Olkin [4] compare certain confidence procedures, and further obtain the distributions of $\hat{\beta}$ and of $\hat{\psi}$ (the maximum-likelihood estimates of β and ψ, respectively). The present paper extends some of these results to the case $k > 1$.

In Section 2 we reduce the model and problems (a) and (b) to a canonical form. Section 3 contains the likelihood-ratio test for problem (a), the distribution of this test under H, and the asymptotic distribution of this test under the alternatives to H. Finally, Section 4 deals with MLE of the $\beta^{(i)}$'s and ψ, their distributions, and related confidence bounds for $\beta^{(1)}, \ldots, \beta^{(k)}$.

Before beginning our discussion, we call the reader's attention to the following notational conventions: Small Latin letters denote vectors; capital Latin letters denote matrices. Vectors in general are row vectors. To partition a vector we often use a dot notation, i.e., $z = (\dot{z}, \ddot{z})$. The notation $Z\colon\ p \times q$ means that the matrix Z has p rows and q columns; the notation $Z > 0$ means that the matrix Z is positive-definite. For a random vector z, $\mathscr{L}(z) = \mathscr{N}(\mu, \Sigma)$ means that z has a multivariate normal distribution with mean vector μ and covariance matrix Σ. For a random $p \times p$ matrix Z, $\mathscr{L}(Z) = \mathscr{W}(\Sigma; p, n)$ means that Z has a Wishart distribution, i.e.,

$$p(Z) = c(p, n)|Z|^{(n-p-1)/2}|\Sigma|^{-n/2} \exp(-\tfrac{1}{2} \operatorname{tr} \Sigma^{-1}Z), \qquad Z > 0, \Sigma > 0,$$

where

$$[c(p, n)]^{-1} = 2^{pn/2}\pi^{p(p-1)/4} \prod_{i=1}^{p} \Gamma\left(\frac{n-i+1}{2}\right).$$

By $\mathscr{L}(z) = \beta(a, b)$ we mean that the random variable z has a beta distribution with parameters a and b.

2. A CANONICAL FORM

We are given N_j independent observations on $y^{(j)}$, say $y_1^{(j)}, y_2^{(j)}, \ldots, y_{N_j}^{(j)}$, where $\mathscr{L}(y_i^{(j)}) = \mathscr{N}(\beta^{(j)}X, \psi)$, $i = 1, \ldots, N_j$, $j = 1, \ldots, k$. We need only consider the sufficient statistic $(\bar{y}^{(1)}, \bar{y}^{(2)}, \ldots, \bar{y}^{(k)}, S)$, where

$$\bar{y}^{(j)} = \frac{1}{N_j} \sum_{i=1}^{N_j} y_i^{(j)}, \qquad i = 1, \ldots, k,$$

and

$$S = \sum_{j=1}^{k} \sum_{\alpha=1}^{N_j} (y_\alpha^{(j)} - \bar{y}^{(j)})'(y_\alpha^{(j)} - \bar{y}^{(j)}).$$

The $\bar{y}^{(j)}$ and S are mutually independent with $\mathscr{L}(\bar{y}^{(j)}) = \mathscr{N}(\beta^{(j)}X, \psi/N_j)$, $\mathscr{L}(S) = \mathscr{W}(\psi; p, n)$, $j = 1, \ldots, k$, where $n = \sum_{j=1}^{k} N_j - k$ and $n \geq p$.

Since X is assumed to be of full rank q, there exists a $p \times p$ orthogonal matrix Γ and a $q \times q$ nonsingular, lower-triangular matrix T such that

$$X = T(I_q, 0)\Gamma.$$

Make the transformations $z^{(j)} = \bar{y}^{(j)}\Gamma'$, $j = 1, \ldots, k$, $V = \Gamma S \Gamma'$. Then the $z^{(j)}$ and V are mutually independent,

$$\mathscr{L}(z^{(j)}) = \mathscr{N}(\theta^{(j)}, \Sigma/N_j), \qquad \mathscr{L}(V) = \mathscr{W}(\Sigma; p, n), \tag{2.1}$$

where

$$\Sigma = \Gamma\psi\Gamma', \qquad \theta^{(j)} = (\dot{\theta}^{(j)}, 0) \equiv (\beta^{(j)}T, 0),$$

and each $\dot{\theta}^{(j)}$: $1 \times q$, $j = 1, \ldots, k$.

Since Γ is a known orthogonal matrix independent of the parameters, $(z^{(1)}, \ldots, z^{(k)}, V)$ is a sufficient statistic for problems (a) and (b). Further, since Γ and T are nonsingular and known, questions of estimation of $(\beta^{(1)}, \ldots, \beta^{(k)}, \psi)$ reduce to questions of estimation of $(\dot{\theta}^{(1)}, \ldots, \dot{\theta}^{(k)}, \Sigma)$. Finally, testing

H: $\beta^{(1)} = \beta^{(2)} = \cdots = \beta^{(k)} \equiv \beta$ is equivalent to testing H*: $\dot{\theta}^{(1)} = \dot{\theta}^{(2)} = \cdots = \dot{\theta}^{(k)} \equiv \theta$. We have thus reduced the model and problems (a) and (b) to a canonical form.

For notational convenience, let

$$Z = (\dot{Z}, \ddot{Z}) \equiv \begin{pmatrix} z^{(1)} \\ \vdots \\ z^{(k)} \end{pmatrix}, \qquad \Theta = (\dot{\Theta}, 0) \equiv \begin{pmatrix} \theta^{(1)} \\ \vdots \\ \theta^{(k)} \end{pmatrix},$$

where Z and Θ are $k \times p$, $\dot{Z}$ and $\dot{\Theta}$ are $k \times q$. Similarly, let

$$\boldsymbol{\beta} = \begin{pmatrix} \beta^{(1)} \\ \vdots \\ \beta^{(k)} \end{pmatrix}: \ k \times q, \qquad \overline{Y} = \begin{pmatrix} \bar{y}^{(1)} \\ \vdots \\ \bar{y}^{(k)} \end{pmatrix}: \ k \times p.$$

Then the sufficient statistic for $(\boldsymbol{\beta}, \psi)$ is $(\overline{Y}, S)$; the sufficient statistic for $(\dot{\Theta}, \Sigma)$ is (Z, V).

We might now ask for a group of transformations which leave the canonical model invariant. As in the case $k = 1$, one such group is the group $\mathscr{A}$ of nonsingular $p \times p$ matrices A of the form

$$A = \begin{pmatrix} A_{11} & 0 \\ A_{21} & A_{22} \end{pmatrix}, \qquad A_{11}: \ q \times q,$$

with the transformation taking Z into ZA, V into $A'VA$.

To find the maximal invariant, consider any invariant function f (i.e., any f such that $f(Z, V) = f(ZA, A'VA)$, all $A \in \mathscr{A}$). Choose $A \in \mathscr{A}$ such that $A = T\Gamma$, where $T'VT = I$,

$$V = \begin{pmatrix} V_{11} & V_{12} \\ V_{21} & V_{22} \end{pmatrix}, \qquad T = (T_{(1)}, T_{(2)}) = \begin{pmatrix} T_{11} & 0 \\ T_{21} & T_{22} \end{pmatrix}, \qquad \Gamma = \begin{pmatrix} \Gamma_1 & 0 \\ 0 & \Gamma_2 \end{pmatrix},$$

V_{11}, T_{11}, Γ_1: $q \times q$, and Γ is orthogonal. This choice defines T but leaves Γ free. Now choose Γ such that

$$ZA = (ZT_{(1)}\Gamma_1, \ddot{Z}T_{(2)}\Gamma_2) = (\delta_1, 0, \ldots, 0, \delta_2, 0, \ldots, 0),$$

where

$$\delta_1^2 = ZT_{(1)}T_{(1)}'Z' = ZV^{-1}Z' - \ddot{Z}V_{22}^{-1}\ddot{Z}', \delta_2^2 = \ddot{Z}T_{22}T_{22}'\ddot{Z}' = \ddot{Z}V_{22}^{-1}\ddot{Z}'.$$

Consequently, f is a function only of the ordered pair

$$U = (U_1, U_2) = (ZV^{-1}Z', \ddot{Z}V_{22}^{-1}\ddot{Z}'). \tag{2.2}$$

Since U is invariant under the group $\mathscr{A}$, we conclude that U is the maximal invariant in the sample space under the group $\mathscr{A}$.

A similar proof shows that the maximal invariant in the parameter space under $\mathscr{A}$ is $\Phi \equiv \dot{\Theta}\Lambda_{11}\dot{\Theta}'$, where

$$\Lambda \equiv \Sigma^{-1} = \begin{pmatrix} \Lambda_{11} & \Lambda_{12} \\ \Lambda_{21} & \Lambda_{22} \end{pmatrix}, \qquad \Lambda_{11}: \ q \times q.$$

In terms of the original (noncanonical) model,

$$U = (\bar{Y}S^{-1}\bar{Y}',\ \bar{Y}X_0'(X_0SX_0')^{-1}X_0\bar{Y}'), \qquad \Phi = \boldsymbol{\beta}X\psi^{-1}X'\boldsymbol{\beta}', \tag{2.3}$$

where X_0 is any $p-q \times p$ matrix whose rows are orthogonal to the q-dimensional subspace spanned by the rows of X.

The testing problem (a) is also invariant under the transformation group $\mathscr{A} \times \mathscr{F}$, where $\mathscr{A} \times \mathscr{F} = \{(A, f)\colon\ A \in \mathscr{A}, f\colon\ 1 \times q\}$ and where the transformation takes Z into $ZA + e_k'(f, 0)$, V into $A'VA$, $e_k = (1, 1, \dots, 1)\colon\ 1 \times k$. A modification of the previous proof shows that the maximal invariant in the sample space under $\mathscr{A} \times \mathscr{F}$ is the ordered pair $[(Z - e_k'(\dot{\bar{z}}, 0))V^{-1}(Z - e_k'(\dot{\bar{z}}, 0))', \ddot{Z}V_{22}^{-1}\ddot{Z}']$, where $\bar{z} = (\dot{\bar{z}}, \ddot{\bar{z}}) = k^{-1}e_kZ$. The maximal invariant in the parameter space under $\mathscr{A} \times \mathscr{F}$ is $(I - k^{-1}e_k'e_k)\Phi(I - k^{-1}e_k'e_k)$.

3. THE LIKELIHOOD-RATIO TEST FOR TESTING THE EQUALITY OF THE $\beta^{(i)}$

We now find the likelihood-ratio test for the hypothesis H*: $\dot{\theta}^{(1)} = \dot{\theta}^{(2)} = \cdots = \dot{\theta}^{(k)} \equiv \dot{\theta}$ versus general alternatives H_A in terms of the canonical variables (Z, V). From this result the likelihood-ratio test for H: $\beta^{(1)} = \beta^{(2)} = \cdots = \beta^{(k)} \equiv \beta$ in terms of the original variables $(\bar{Y}, S)$ can easily be found.

From (2.1) the joint distribution of (Z, V) is

$$p(Z, V) \propto |\Lambda|^{(n+k)/2}|V|^{(n-p-1)/2}\exp\{-\tfrac{1}{2}\operatorname{tr}\Lambda[V + (Z - \Theta)'D_N(Z - \Theta)]\}, \tag{3.1}$$

where $\Lambda = \Sigma^{-1}$ and $D_N = \operatorname{diag}(N_1, \dots, N_k)$. To find the MLE of $(\dot{\Theta}, \Sigma)$ we maximize $p(Z, V)$ first with respect to Σ and then with respect to $\dot{\Theta}$.

From (3.1) it is immediate that $p(Z, V)$ is maximized at

$$\hat{\Sigma}(\dot{\Theta}) = \frac{V + (Z - \Theta)'D_N(Z - \Theta)}{n + k}, \tag{3.2}$$

so that the MLE of $\dot{\Theta}$ is obtained by minimizing

$$\begin{aligned}|\hat{\Sigma}(\dot{\Theta})| &= \frac{|V + (Z - \Theta)'D_N(Z - \Theta)|}{(n + k)^p} \\ &= \frac{|V|}{(n + k)^p}\,|I + D_N^{1/2}(Z - \Theta)V^{-1}(Z - \Theta)'D_N^{1/2}|.\end{aligned} \tag{3.3}$$

Note that

$$\begin{aligned}&(Z - \Theta)V^{-1}(Z - \Theta)' \\ &\quad = (\dot{Z} - \ddot{Z}V_{22}^{-1}V_{21} - \dot{\Theta})(V^{-1})_{11}(\dot{Z} - \ddot{Z}V_{22}^{-1}V_{21} - \dot{\Theta})' + \ddot{Z}V_{22}^{-1}\ddot{Z}.\end{aligned} \tag{3.4}$$

Using this expansion we see that (3.3) is minimized by

$$\hat{\Theta} = \dot{Z} - \ddot{Z} V_{22}^{-1} V_{21}. \tag{3.5}$$

Substituting in (3.2) yields

$$\hat{\Sigma} = \frac{1}{n+k} [V + (\ddot{Z} V_{22}^{-1} V_{21}, \dot{Z})' D_N (\ddot{Z} V_{22}^{-1} V_{21}, \dot{Z})]. \tag{3.6}$$

We remark that

$$|\hat{\Sigma}| = \frac{|V|}{(n+k)^p} |I + D_N^{1/2} \ddot{Z} V_{22}^{-1} \ddot{Z}' D_N^{1/2}|.$$

For the hypothesis H*, the sufficient statistic becomes $(\bar{z}, W)$, where $\bar{z} = (n+k)^{-1} e_k D_N Z$ and

$$W = V + Z' D_N^{1/2} C_k D_N^{1/2} Z, \qquad C_k = I - (n+k)^{-1} D_N^{1/2} e_k' e_k D_N^{1/2}. \tag{3.7}$$

Here $\bar{z}$ and W are independent, $\mathscr{L}(\bar{z}) = \mathscr{N}((\dot{\theta}, 0), \Sigma/(n+k))$, and $\mathscr{L}(W) = \mathscr{W}(\Sigma; p, n+k-1)$. Thus the form of this model is similar to that treated in this section with $\bar{z}$ in place of Z, W in place of V, $(n+k)$ in place of D_N, and 1 in place of k. It follows that

$$\hat{\Theta} = \dot{\bar{z}} - \ddot{\bar{z}} W_{22}^{-1} W_{21},$$

$$\hat{\Sigma}_{\mathrm{H}^*} = \frac{1}{n+k} \{W + (n+k)(\ddot{\bar{z}} W_{22}^{-1} W_{21}, \ddot{\bar{z}})'(\ddot{\bar{z}} W_{22}^{-1} W_{21}, \ddot{\bar{z}}),$$

so that

$$|\hat{\Sigma}_{\mathrm{H}^*}| = \frac{|W|}{(n+k)^p} |I + (n+k) \ddot{\bar{z}} W_{22}^{-1} \ddot{\bar{z}}'|.$$

We conclude that the likelihood-ratio statistic λ_{H^*} for testing H* versus general alternatives is determined by

$$\begin{aligned} \lambda_{\mathrm{H}^*}^{2/(n+k)} &= \frac{|\hat{\Sigma}|}{|\hat{\Sigma}_{\mathrm{H}^*}|} \\ &= \frac{|I + C_k D_N^{1/2} \ddot{Z} V_{22}^{-1} \ddot{Z}' D_N^{1/2} C_k|}{|I + C_k D_N^{1/2} Z V^{-1} Z' D_N^{1/2} C_k|} = \frac{|V| \; |V_{22} + \ddot{Z}' D_N^{1/2} C_k^{\,2} D_N^{1/2} \ddot{Z}|}{|V_{22}| \; |V + Z' D_N^{1/2} C_k^{\,2} D_N^{1/2} Z|}, \end{aligned} \tag{3.8}$$

where we recall from (3.7) that $C_k = (I - (n+k)^{-1} D_N^{1/2} e_k' e_k D_N^{1/2})$.

In terms of the original observations, the likelihood-ratio statistic λ_{H} for H: $\beta^{(1)} = \beta^{(2)} = \cdots = \beta^{(k)} \equiv \beta$ is determined by

$$\lambda_{\mathrm{H}}^{2/(n+k)} = \lambda_{\mathrm{H}^*}^{2/(n+k)} = \frac{|I + C_k D_N^{1/2} U_2 D_N^{1/2} C_k|}{|I + C_k D_N^{1/2} U_1 D_N^{1/2} C_k|}, \tag{3.9}$$

where $U = (U_1, U_2)$ is given by (2.3).

3.1. The Distribution of the Likelihood-Ratio Statistic in the Central Case

Since $\lambda_{H*} = \lambda_H$ and since the hypotheses H and H* are equivalent, we need only consider the distribution of $\lambda_{\mathrm{H}*}$ when H* is true. Further, from (3.8) and from (2.2) we see that $\lambda_{\mathrm{H}*}$ is a function of the maximal invariant in the sample space under $\mathscr{A}$ and is thus invariant under $\mathscr{A}$. There exists $A_0 \in \mathscr{A}$, A_0: $p \times p$ lower-triangular, such that $A_0'\Sigma A_0 = I$, and thus it follows that we can assume $\Sigma = I$ in deriving the distribution of $\lambda_{\mathrm{H}*}$. Finally, when H* holds, we may assume that $\theta = 0$, for $\lambda_{\mathrm{H}*}$ is also a function of the maximal invariant in the sample space under the group $\mathscr{A} \times \mathscr{F}$.

From (3.8) and our assumptions above we have that

$$\lambda_{\mathrm{H}*} = \frac{|V|}{|V_{22}|}\frac{|V_{22} + \ddot{Z}'D_N^{1/2}C_k{}^2D_N^{1/2}\ddot{Z}|}{|V + Z'D_N^{1/2}C_k{}^2D_N^{1/2}Z|},$$

where Z and Y are independently distributed,

$$p(Z, V) \propto |V|^{(n-p+1)/2} \exp -\tfrac{1}{2}\{\operatorname{tr} V + \operatorname{tr} D_N ZZ'\}. \tag{3.10}$$

Now $C_k{}^2 = C_k$ (i.e., C_k is idempotent), C_k is of rank $k-1$, and thus there exists a $k \times k$ orthogonal matrix Δ such that $\Delta C_k \Delta' = (0, I_{k-1})'\ (0, I_{k-1})$. Letting

$$F = (0, I_{k-1})\Delta D_N^{1/2} Z \equiv (\dot{F}, \ddot{F}),$$

where $\dot{F}$: $k-1 \times q$, F: $k-1 \times p$, we therefore have

$$t \equiv \lambda_{\mathrm{H}*}^{2/(n+k)} = \frac{|V|}{|V_{22}|}\frac{|V_{22} + \ddot{F}'\ddot{F}|}{|V + F'F|} = \frac{|I + \ddot{F}V_{22}^{-1}\ddot{F}'|}{|I + FV^{-1}F'|}.$$

We can rewrite t as

$$t = \frac{|I + \ddot{F}V_{22}^{-1}\ddot{F}'|}{|I + \ddot{F}V_{22}^{-1}\ddot{F}' + (\dot{F} - \ddot{F}V_{22}^{-1}V_{21})(V^{-1})_{11}(\dot{F} - \ddot{F}V_{22}^{-1}V_{21})'|}. \tag{3.11}$$

Make the transformations

$$L = V_{22}^{-1/2}V_{21}, \qquad M = V_{11} - L'L, \qquad V_{22} = V_{22},$$
$$Q = \ddot{F}V_{22}^{-1/2}, \qquad R = \dot{F} - \ddot{F}V_{22}^{-1}V_{21} = \dot{F} - QL,$$

so that

$$t = \frac{|I + QQ'|}{|I + QQ' + RM^{-1}R'|}.$$

From (3.10) we obtain

$$p(R, Q, M, L, V_{22}) \propto |V_{22}|^{(n-(p-q)+k-2)/2}|M|^{(n-p-1)/2}$$
$$\times \exp -\tfrac{1}{2}[\operatorname{tr}(R + QL)(R + QL)' + \operatorname{tr} QV_{22}Q' + \operatorname{tr} M + \operatorname{tr} LL' + \operatorname{tr} V_{22}],$$

for $V_{22} > 0$, $M > 0$, and R, L, and Q unrestricted. Integrating over $V_{22} > 0$, we have

$$p(R, Q, M, L) \propto \frac{|M|^{(n-p-1)/2} \exp -\frac{1}{2}[\operatorname{tr}(R+QL)(R+QL)' + \operatorname{tr} LL' + \operatorname{tr} M]}{|I+QQ'|^{(n+k-1)/2}}.$$

The exponent may be written

$$\operatorname{tr}[L' + R'Q(I+Q'Q)^{-1}](I+Q'Q)[L + (I+Q'Q)^{-1}Q'R] + \operatorname{tr} M + \operatorname{tr} R'R - \operatorname{tr} R'Q(I+Q'Q)^{-1}Q'R,$$

and hence, for R and Q fixed, the matrix L is normally distributed. We thus may integrate over L, yielding

$$p(R, Q, M) \propto \frac{|M|^{(n-p-1)/2}}{|I+QQ'|^{(n+k+q-1)/2}} \times \exp -\frac{1}{2}\{\operatorname{tr} M + \operatorname{tr} R'[I - Q(I+Q'Q)^{-1}Q']R\}.$$

Note that $(I+QQ')^{-1} = I - Q(I+Q'Q)^{-1}Q'$, and

$$t^{-1} = |I + (I+QQ')^{-1/2}RM^{-1}R'(I+QQ')^{-1/2}|.$$

Thus, by letting $B = (I+QQ')^{-1/2}RM^{-1/2}$, we find that $t^{-1} = |I+BB'|$ and

$$p(B, Q, M) \propto \frac{|M|^{(n-p+k)/2-1}}{|I+QQ'|^{(n+k-1)/2}} \exp -\frac{1}{2} \operatorname{tr} M(I+B'B).$$

A final integration over M and Q yields

$$p(B) \propto |I+BB'|^{-(n+k+q-p-1)/2},$$

for B unrestricted. Since B is a $k-1 \times q$ matrix, we must consider the two cases $k \geq q+1$ and $k < q+1$.

If $k \geq q+1$, then from Hsu's theorem [1, p. 319], the distribution of $G = B'B$ is

$$p(G) \propto \frac{|G|^{(k-q-2)/2}}{|I+G|^{(n+k+q-p-1)/2}}, \qquad G > 0.$$

If $k < q+1$, then the distribution of $G = BB'$ is

$$p(G) \propto \frac{|G|^{(q-k)/2}}{|I+G|^{(n+k+q-p-1)/2}}, \qquad G > 0.$$

In either case we ask for the distribution of $t = |I+G|^{-1}$. Comparing moments, we see that $\mathscr{L}(t) = \mathscr{L}(\prod_{i=1}^{a_1} t_i)$, where the t_i are mutually independent with $\mathscr{L}(t_i) = \beta(\frac{1}{2}(n+a_1-p-i+1), \frac{1}{2}a_2)$, $a_1 = \min(q, k-1)$, $a_2 =$

max $(q, k-1)$. The method of Box (viz. Anderson [1, pp. 203–209]) gives an excellent approximation to the distribution of t for $(n+k)$ large, namely,

$$P\left\{-m \log t \leq x\right\} = \left[\left(1-\frac{v_1}{m^2}\right)^2 + \frac{v_1}{m^2} - \frac{v_2}{m^4}\right] P\{\chi^2_{q(k-1)} \leq x\}$$
$$+ \frac{v_1}{m^2}\left(1-\frac{v_1}{m^2}\right) P\{\chi^2_{q(k-1)+4} \leq x\}$$
$$+ \frac{v_2}{m^4} P\{\chi^2_{q(k-1)+8} \leq x\} + O((n+k)^{-6}),$$

where

$$m = n - p - 1 + \frac{q+k}{2}, \qquad v_1 = \frac{q(k-1)[q^2+(k-1)^2-5]}{48},$$

and

$$v_2 = \tfrac{1}{2}{v_1}^2 + \frac{q(k-1)}{1920}$$
$$\times [3q^4 + 3(k-1)^4 + 10q^2(k-1)^2 - 50q^2 - 50(k-1)^2 + 159].$$

3.2. The Limiting Nonnull Distribution of the Likelihood-Ratio Statistic

Let us assume that as $n \to \infty$, $(n+k)^{-1}D_N$ converges to diag$(\lambda_1, \lambda_2, \ldots, \lambda_k)$ $\equiv D_\lambda$. (Recall that $\Sigma N_i = n + k$, so that $\Sigma\lambda_i = 1$.) Then from (3.7), lim C_k $= I - D_\lambda^{1/2}e_k{}'e_k D_\lambda^{1/2} \equiv C_\lambda$. Further, $\text{plim}_{n\to\infty}\,[V/(n+k)] = \Sigma$ and $\text{plim}_{n\to\infty}\, Z$ $= \Theta = (\dot{\Theta}, 0)$.

Letting $B = I + C_k D_N^{1/2}\ddot{Z}V_{22}^{-1}\ddot{Z}'D_N^{1/2}C_k$, we can write $t = \lambda_{H^*}^{2/(n+k)}$ as

$$t = |I + B^{-1/2}C_k D_N^{1/2}(\dot{Z} - \ddot{Z}V_{22}^{-1}V_{21})(V^{-1})_{11}(\dot{Z} - \ddot{Z}V_{22}^{-1}V_{21})'D_N^{1/2}C_k B^{-1/2}|.$$

Since $\text{plim}_{n\to\infty} B = I$ and from the above, the limiting distribution of t is the same as that of

$$r = |I + C_\lambda GG'C_\lambda|,$$

where $G = (n+k)^{-1/2}D_N^{1/2}(\dot{Z} - \ddot{Z}\Sigma_{22}^{-1}\Sigma_{21})\Lambda_{11}^{1/2}$. By inspection, each row of G has covariance matrix $(n+k)^{-1}I$, each row of G obeys the multivariate normal distribution, the rows of G are mutually independent, and $\mathscr{E}G$ $= (n+k)^{-1/2}D_N^{1/2}\dot{\Theta}\Lambda_{11}^{1/2}$. Since $(n+k)^{-1/2}D_N^{1/2}$ converges to $D_\lambda^{1/2}$ as $n \to \infty$, we can assume that

$$\mathscr{E}G = D_\lambda^{1/2}\dot{\Theta}\Lambda_{11}^{1/2}.$$

Instead of the limiting distribution of r, we consider the limiting distribution of $\log r = \log|I + C_\lambda GG'C_\lambda|$, and show that

$$\lim_{n\to\infty} \mathscr{L}(\log|I + C_\lambda GG'C_\lambda| - \log|I + C_\lambda \Omega C_\lambda)|) = \mathscr{N}(0, \delta), \quad (3.12)$$

where

$$\Omega = (\mathscr{E}G)(\mathscr{E}G)' = D_\lambda^{1/2}\dot{\Theta}\Lambda_{11}\dot{\Theta}'D_\lambda^{1/2},$$

and

$$\delta = 4\,\mathrm{tr}[(I + C_\lambda\Omega C_\lambda)^{-2}C_\lambda\Omega C_\lambda].$$

From this it follows that

$$\lim_{n\to\infty} \mathscr{L}(\log t - \log|I + C_\lambda\Omega C_\lambda|) = \mathscr{N}(0, \delta), \quad (3.13)$$

since $\log t$ and $\log r$ have the same limiting distribution.

We prove (3.12) by expanding $\log r = \log|I + C_\lambda GG'C_\lambda|$ in a Taylor series in G about the mean of G:

$$(n + k)^{1/2}(\log r - \log|I + C_\lambda\Omega C_\lambda|)$$
$$= (n + k)^{1/2}\left[\sum_{i=1}^{k-1}\sum_{j=1}^{q}\left(\frac{\partial \log r}{\partial g_{ij}}\right)\bigg|_{g_{ij}=\mathscr{E}g_{ij}}(g_{ij} - \mathscr{E}g_{ij})\right] + o_p(1),$$

where $G = (g_{ij})$, $i = 1, \ldots, k-1$, $j = 1, \ldots, q$. But we know that

$$\mathscr{L}((n + k)^{1/2}(g_{ij} - \mathscr{E}g_{ij})) = \mathscr{N}(0, 1)$$

and that the g_{ij} are independently distributed. Thus

$$\mathscr{L}((n + k)^{1/2}(\log r - \log|I + C_\lambda\Omega C_\lambda|)) = \mathscr{N}\left(0, \sum_{i=1}^{k-1}\sum_{j=1}^{q}\left(\frac{\partial \log r}{\partial g_{ij}}\right)^2\bigg|_{g_{ij}=\mathscr{E}g_{ij}}\right). \quad (3.14)$$

Lemma. *If* $L = (l_{ij})$: $a \times b$ *and* C: $c \times a$,

$$\sum_{i=1}^{a}\sum_{j=1}^{b}\left(\frac{\partial \log|I + CLL'C'|}{\partial l_{ij}}\right)^2 = 4\,\mathrm{tr}\,LL'(C'W^{-1}C)^2,$$

where $W = I + CLL'C' = (w_{ij})$.

Proof. First let $f_{ij} = \partial(\log|I + CLL'C'|)/\partial l_{ij}$ and let $F = (f_{ij})$. Note that $\sum_{i=1}^{a}\sum_{j=1}^{b} f_{ij}^2 = \mathrm{tr}\,FF'$ and, by the chain rule, that

$$\frac{\partial \log|I + CLL'C'|}{\partial l_{ij}} = \sum_{\alpha,\beta}\frac{\partial \log|W|}{\partial w_{\alpha\beta}}\frac{\partial w_{\alpha\beta}}{\partial l_{ij}} = \mathrm{tr}\left(\frac{\partial \log|W|}{\partial w_{\alpha\beta}}\right)\left(\frac{\partial w_{\alpha\beta}}{\partial l_{ij}}\right),$$

where $(\partial \log|W|/\partial w_{\alpha\beta})$ is the $c \times c$ matrix of partial derivatives of $\log|W|$ with respect to the $w_{\alpha\beta}$, and where for each l_{ij}, $(\partial w_{\alpha\beta}/\partial l_{ij})$ is the $c \times c$ matrix of partial derivatives of $w_{\alpha\beta}$ with respect to l_{ij}. But $\partial \log |W|/\partial w_{\alpha\beta} = w^{\alpha\beta}$, where $W^{-1} = (w^{\alpha\beta})$, and $\partial w_{\alpha\beta}/\partial l_{ij}$ is obtained from the equation

$$dW = C[(dL)L' + L(dL)']C',$$

namely,

$$\left(\frac{\partial w_{\alpha\beta}}{\partial l_{ij}}\right) = C\left[\Phi_{ij} L' + L\Phi_{ji}\right]C',$$

where Φ_{ij} is the $a \times b$ matrix having a 1 in the (i, j)th place and zeros elsewhere. Thus

$$f_{ij} = \operatorname{tr}\left(\frac{\partial \log |W|}{\partial w_{\alpha\beta}}\right)\left(\frac{\partial w_{\alpha\beta}}{\partial l_{ij}}\right) = \operatorname{tr} W^{-1}C\left(\Phi_{ij}\, L' + L\, \Phi_{ji}\right)C'$$

$$= 2 \operatorname{tr} L'C'W^{-1}C\, \Phi_{ij} = 2(L'C'W^{-1}C)_{ij}.$$

Finally,

$$\operatorname{tr} FF' = 4 \operatorname{tr} L'C'W^{-1}CC'W^{-1}CL = 4 \operatorname{tr} LL'(C'W^{-1}C)^2.$$

The result (3.12) is now obtained as a direct consequence of the lemma and the fact that $C_\lambda{}^2 = C_\lambda$.

4. THE DISTRIBUTION OF THE MAXIMUM-LIKELIHOOD ESTIMATORS

From (3.5) and (3.6) the MLE of $\dot{\Theta}$ and Σ are

$$\hat{\Theta} = \dot{Z} - \ddot{Z}V_{22}^{-1}V_{21}, \qquad \hat{\Sigma} = \frac{1}{n+k}[V + (\ddot{Z}V_{22}^{-1}V_{21}, \ddot{Z})'D_N(\ddot{Z}V_{22}^{-1}V_{21}, \ddot{Z})],$$

which in terms of the original model becomes

$$\hat{\boldsymbol{\beta}} = \bar{Y}S^{-1}X'(XS^{-1}X')^{-1}, \qquad \hat{\psi} = \frac{1}{n+k}[S + (\bar{Y} - \hat{\boldsymbol{\beta}}X)'(\bar{Y} - \hat{\boldsymbol{\beta}}X)]. \quad (4.1)$$

4.1. The Distribution of $\hat{\dot{\Theta}}$

To find the distribution of $\hat{\Theta}$ we make use of invariance. Let $A_0 \in \mathscr{A}$ be the $p \times p$ lower-triangular matrix such that $A_0'\Sigma A_0 = I$. Partition A_0 as

$$A_0 = \begin{pmatrix} A_0^{(1)} & 0 \\ A_0^{(2)} & A_0^{(3)} \end{pmatrix}, \qquad A_0^{(1)}\colon\; q \times q,$$

and let $F = (\dot{F}, \ddot{F}) = D_N^{1/2}(\dot{Z} - \dot{\Theta}, \ddot{Z})A_0$, $W = A_0'VA_0$. Then F and W are independent, $\mathscr{L}(W) = \mathscr{W}(I; p, n)$, the rows of F are mutually independent, with each row having the distribution $\mathcal{N}(0, 1)$, and

$$D_N^{1/2}(\hat{\Theta} - \dot{\Theta})A_0^{(1)} = \dot{F} - \ddot{F}W_{22}^{-1}W_{21}. \tag{4.2}$$

Letting $\tilde{\Theta} = D_N^{1/2}(\hat{\Theta} - \dot{\Theta})A_0^{(1)}$, we have

$$\mathcal{L}(\tilde{\Theta} \mid W) = \mathcal{N}(0, I + W_{12}W_{22}^{-2}W_{21}).$$

Now let $L = W_{12}W_{22}^{-1}$: $q \times p - q$. From the distribution of W we find by standard techniques that

$$P(L) \propto |I + LL'|^{-(n+q)/2}.$$

Thus

$$p(\tilde{\Theta}, L) \propto \frac{\exp -\frac{1}{2}(\operatorname{tr} \tilde{\Theta}(I + LL')^{-1}\tilde{\Theta}')}{|I + LL'|^{(n+q)/2}},$$

and

$$p(\tilde{\Theta}) \propto \int_{L \text{ unrestricted}} \frac{\exp -\frac{1}{2} \operatorname{tr}[\tilde{\Theta}'\tilde{\Theta}(I + LL')^{-1}]}{|I + LL'|^{(n+q)/2}} \, dL. \tag{4.3}$$

If $q \le p - q$, then by Hsu's theorem this can be further reduced to

$$p(\tilde{\Theta}) \propto \int_{0<H<I} |H|^{(n-p+q-1)/2}|I - H|^{(p-2q-1)/2} \exp -\tfrac{1}{2} \operatorname{tr}(\tilde{\Theta}'\tilde{\Theta}H) \, dH, \tag{4.4}$$

where $H = (I+LL')^{-1}$. For $k = 1$, (4.3) and (4.4) simplify to

$$p(\tilde{\Theta}) = C_1 \int_0^1 r^{(n+q-p-1)/2}(1 - r)^{(p-q-2)/2} \exp -\tfrac{1}{2}r \operatorname{tr} \tilde{\Theta}\tilde{\Theta}' \, dr,$$

where $C_1^{-1} = (2\pi)^{q/2}\beta(\frac{1}{2}(n - p + 1), \frac{1}{2}(p - q))$. Alternatively, this can be written as a confluent hypergeometric function:

$$p(\tilde{\Theta}) = C_1\beta\left(\frac{n + q - p + 1}{2}, \frac{p - q}{2}\right){}_1F_1\left(\frac{n + q - p + 1}{2}, \frac{n + 1}{2}; -\tfrac{1}{2} \operatorname{tr} \tilde{\Theta}\tilde{\Theta}'\right).$$

We note that the distribution of $\tilde{\Theta}$ depends only on the sum of the roots of $\tilde{\Theta}\tilde{\Theta}'$. The distribution of $Q = \mathrm{D}_N^{1/2}(\hat{\boldsymbol{\beta}} - \boldsymbol{\beta})(X\psi X')^{-1/2}$ is (for any $k \ge 1$),

$$p(Q) \propto \int_{L \text{ unrestricted}} \frac{\exp -\frac{1}{2} \operatorname{tr}[Q'Q(I + LL')^{-1}]}{|I + LL'|^{(n+q)/2}} \, dL. \tag{4.5}$$

4.2. The Distribution of $\hat{\Sigma}$

In terms of the random variables $\ddot{F} = D_N^{1/2}\ddot{Z}A_0$ and $W = A_0'VA_0$ we have that

$$(n + k)\hat{\Sigma} = \Sigma^{1/2}[W + (\ddot{F}W_{22}^{-1}W_{21}, \ddot{F})'(\ddot{F}W_{22}^{-1}W_{21}, \ddot{F})]\Sigma^{1/2},$$

where the rows of $\ddot{F}$: $k \times p - q$ are independent with the common distribution $\mathcal{N}(0, I_{p-q})$ and independent of W, $\mathcal{L}(W) = \mathcal{W}(I;\ p, n)$. By an argument similar to that of [4, Section 5], we obtain

$$p(\hat{\Sigma}) = [c(p, n)|\Lambda|^{n/2}|\hat{\Sigma}|^{(n-p-1)/2} \exp -\tfrac{1}{2} \operatorname{tr} \Lambda\hat{\Sigma}]$$

$$\cdot \frac{|\hat{\Sigma}_{22}|^{k/2}}{|\Sigma_{22}|^{k/2}(2\pi)^{(p-q)k/2}} \int_{0 \le Y'Y \le I} |I - Y'Y|^{(n+2q-p-1)/2} \exp \tfrac{1}{2}(\operatorname{tr} D_\nu Y'Y)\, dY, \tag{4.6}$$

where $\hat{\Sigma} > 0$, Y: $k \times p - q$, $D_\nu = \operatorname{diag}(\nu_1, \ldots, \nu_{p-q})$, and the ν's are the characteristic roots of $\mathcal{R}(\Sigma^{-1/2}\hat{\Sigma}\Sigma^{-1/2})$, where for a positive-definite matrix H: $p \times p$ with

$$H = \begin{pmatrix} H_{11} & H_{12} \\ H_{21} & H_{22} \end{pmatrix}, \qquad H_{11}\colon\ q \times q,$$

we have $\mathcal{R}(H) = H_{22}^{-1/2} H_{21} H_{12} H_{22}^{-1/2}$.

The distribution of $\hat{\psi}$ has the form (4.6) with $\hat{\Sigma}$ replaced by $\hat{\psi}$ and Σ replaced by ψ.

4.3. Confidence Bounds for $\dot{\Theta}$

Recall that

$$\dot{\Theta} = \begin{pmatrix} \dot{\theta}^{(1)} \\ \dot{\theta}^{(2)} \\ \vdots \\ \dot{\theta}^{(k)} \end{pmatrix}.$$

Let $\hat{\Theta}$ be partitioned similarly. Then from [14] the statistics

$$\frac{n-p+1}{q} N_i \frac{(\hat{\theta}^{(i)} - \dot{\theta}^{(i)})(V^{-1})_{11}(\hat{\theta}^{(i)} - \dot{\theta}^{(i)})'}{1 + \ddot{Z}^{(i)} V_{22}^{-1} \ddot{Z}^{(i)\prime}}$$

each have Snedecor's F distribution with q and $n - p + 1$ degrees of freedom. If we wish a $1 - \alpha$ confidence region for $\dot{\Theta}$, we may use the Bonferroni inequality to obtain the region

$$\left\{\dot{\Theta}\colon \quad \max_{i=1,\ldots,k} \frac{n-p+1}{q} N_i \frac{(\hat{\theta}^{(i)} - \dot{\theta}^{(i)})(V^{-1})_{11}(\hat{\theta}^{(i)} - \dot{\theta}^{(i)})'}{1 + \ddot{Z}^{(i)} V_{22}^{-1} \ddot{Z}^{(i)\prime}} \le F_{q,n-p+1}^{(k-\alpha)/k}\right\},$$

where $F_{q,n-p+1}^{\nu}$ is the number such that if $\mathcal{L}(x) = F_{q,n-p+1}$ (i.e., Snedecor's F), then $P\{x \le F_{q,n-p+1}^{\nu}\} = \nu$. This region actually has confidence greater than $1 - \alpha$ and is thus conservative.

In terms of the $\beta^{(i)}$ the confidence region is

$$\left\{\boldsymbol{\beta}: \max_{i=1,\ldots,k} \frac{n-p+1}{2} N_i \frac{(\hat{\beta}^{(i)}-\beta)(XS^{-1}X')(\hat{\beta}^{(i)}-\beta^{(i)})'}{1+N_i(\bar{y}^{(i)}-\hat{\beta}^{(i)}X)S^{-1}(\bar{y}^{(i)}-\hat{\beta}^{(i)}X)'} \le F_{q,n-p+1}^{(k-\alpha)/k}\right\}.$$

This confidence region is *ad hoc* and is devised chiefly to avoid difficult distribution problems that result from working directly with the distribution of $\hat{\boldsymbol{\beta}}$.

REFERENCES

1. ANDERSON, T. W. (1958). *Introduction to Multivariate Statistical Analysis.* Wiley, New York.
2. COCHRAN, W. G. and BLISS, C. I. (1948). Discriminant functions with covariance. *Ann. Math. Statist.* **19** 151–176.
3. GIRI, N. C. (1964). On the likelihood ratio test of a normal multivariate testing problem. *Ann. Math. Statist.* **35** 181–189.
4. GLESER, L. J. and OLKIN, I. (1964). Estimation for a regression model with covariance. Tech. Rep. 15 (NSF Grant GP-214), Stanford Univ., Stanford, California.
5. KABE, D. G. (1965). On the non-central distribution of Rao's U statistic. *Ann. Inst. Statist. Math.* **17** 75–80.
6. KIEFER, J. and SCHWARTZ, R. (1965). Admissible Bayes character of T^2-, R^2-, and other fully invariant tests for classical multivariate normal problems. *Ann. Math. Statist.* **36** 747–770.
7. NARAIN, R. D. (1950). Some results on discriminant functions. *J. Indian Soc. Agric. Statist.* **II** 49–59.
8. OLKIN, I. and SHRIKHANDE, S. S. (1954). On a modified T^2 problem. *Ann. Math. Statist.* **25** 808.
9. POTTHOFF, R. F. and ROY, S. N. (1964). A generalized multivariate analysis of variance model useful especially for growth curve problems. *Biometrika* **51** 313–327.
10. RAO, C. R.(1946). Tests with discriminant functions in multivariate analysis. *Sankhyā* **7** 407–414.
11. RAO, C. R. (1949). On some problems arising out of discrimination with multiple characters. *Sankhyā* **9** 343–366.
12. RAO, C. R. (1950). A note on the distribution of $D_{p+q}^2 - D_q^2$ and some computational aspects of D^2 statistic and discriminant function. *Sankhyā* **10** 257–268.
13. RAO, C. R. (1958). Some statistical methods for the comparison of growth curves. *Biometrics* **14** 1–17.
14. RAO, C. R. (1959). Some problems involving linear hypotheses in multivariate analysis. *Biometrika* **46** 49–58.
15. RAO, C. R. (1961). Some observations on multivariate statistical methods in anthropological research. *Bull. Inst. Statist. Math.* **38** 99–111.

Some Multivariate Tests with Restricted Alternative Hypotheses[1,2]

A. KUDÔ

MATHEMATICAL INSTITUTE
KYUSHU UNIVERSITY
KYUSHU, JAPAN

DEPARTMENT OF STATISTICS
IOWA STATE UNIVERSITY
AMES, IOWA

H. FUJISAWA

NAGASAKI UNIVERSITY
NAGASAKI, JAPAN

1. A BIVARIATE ANALOGUE OF A TWO-SIDED TEST

In a previous paper the authors [7] derived a bivariate normal test with a two-sided alternative by the likelihood ratio method, and furnished a table of the percentage points appropriate to the test. In this paper we are concerned with the power function of this test. For the sake of convenience, we shall state the problem and the results.

Suppose (X, Y) has a bivariate normal distribution with known variance matrix, which we assume without loss of generality, to have unit variance, correlation ρ, and unknown means θ_1 and θ_2. We consider the problem of testing the hypothesis $\mathrm{H}_0: \theta_1 = \theta_2 = 0$ against the alternative that the means are either in the 1st or 3rd quadrant, namely, $\mathrm{H}_1: (\theta_1 \geq 0$ and $\theta_2 \geq 0)$ or $(\theta_1 \leq 0$ and $\theta_2 \leq 0)$, where at least one of the inequalities are strict in both cases.

Let (x_1, y_1) $(x_2, y_2), \ldots, (x_n, y_n)$ be a random sample and let $(\bar{x}, \bar{y})$ be the

[1] This work was supported in part by the National Science Foundation, Grant GP-3918.

[2] *Note added in proof.* Recently a paper by Nüesch [8] was published. His results include the case of the unknown variance matrix which was not treated by Kudô [6].

sample mean vector. The maximum likelihood estimate (MLE) of the population mean vector was found to be as follows:

$$\begin{aligned}
&\hat{\theta}_1 = \bar{x},\ \hat{\theta}_2 = \bar{y} && \text{if } \bar{x} \text{ and } \bar{y} \text{ are of same sign,}\\
&\hat{\theta}_1 = \bar{x} - \rho\bar{y},\ \hat{\theta}_2 = 0 && \text{if } \bar{x} \text{ and } \bar{y} \text{ are of different sign}\\
& && \quad \text{and } |\bar{x}| > |\bar{y}|, \qquad (1)\\
&\hat{\theta}_1 = 0,\ \hat{\theta}_2 = \bar{y} - \rho\bar{x} && \text{if } \bar{x} \text{ and } \bar{y} \text{ are of different sign}\\
& && \quad \text{and } |\bar{x}| < |\bar{y}|.
\end{aligned}$$

Let us first define

$$\begin{aligned}
z_1 &= (\bar{x} - \rho\bar{y})/(1 - \rho^2)^{1/2},\\
z_2 &= (\bar{y} - \rho\bar{x})/(1 - \rho^2)^{1/2}
\end{aligned} \qquad (2)$$

and

$$\bar{\chi}^2 = (\bar{x}^2 - 2\rho\bar{x}\bar{y} + \bar{y}^2)/(1 - \rho^2) = z_1{}^2 + \bar{y}^2 = \bar{x}^2 + z_2{}^2, \qquad (3)$$

which give the rejection region

$$\begin{array}{rlll}
\text{(I)} & n\bar{\chi}^2 \geq \bar{\chi}_0{}^2 & \text{if} & \bar{x} > 0,\ \bar{y} > 0,\\
\text{(II,1)} & n^{1/2}z_1 \leq -\bar{\chi}_0 & \text{if} & \bar{x} < 0,\ \bar{y} > 0,\ |\bar{x}| > |\bar{y}|,\\
\text{(II,2)} & n^{1/2}z_2 \geq \bar{\chi}_0 & \text{if} & \bar{x} < 0,\ \bar{y} > 0,\ |\bar{x}| < |\bar{y}|,\\
\text{(III)} & n\bar{\chi}^2 \geq \bar{\chi}_0{}^2 & \text{if} & \bar{x} < 0,\ \bar{y} < 0,\\
\text{(IV,1)} & n^{1/2}z_2 \leq -\bar{\chi}_0 & \text{if} & \bar{x} > 0,\ \bar{y} < 0,\ |\bar{x}| < |\bar{y}|,\\
\text{(IV,2)} & n^{1/2}z_1 \geq \bar{\chi}_0 & \text{if} & \bar{x} > 0,\ \bar{y} < 0,\ |\bar{x}| > |\bar{y}|,
\end{array}$$

where $\bar{\chi}_0$ is a constant depending on ρ and the significance level α.

It is interesting to observe the shape of the rejection region. It is symmetric around the origin. In the first and third quadrant, the shape of the boundary is the same as that of the concentration ellipsoid of the population variance-covariance matrix, and in the second and the fourth quadrant, the boundary is formed by two straight lines, which are the tangents of the concentration ellipsoid at the x and the y axis.

The constant $\bar{\chi}_0{}^2$ is determined, keeping the property of symmetry in mind, by the relation

$$\begin{aligned}
\alpha &= 2\{\Pr(n\bar{\chi}^2 \geq \bar{\chi}_0{}^2, \bar{x} \geq 0, \bar{y} \geq 0) + \Pr(\bar{x} \leq 0, n^{1/2}z_2 \geq \bar{\chi}_0)\\
&\quad + \Pr(\bar{y} \geq 0, -n^{1/2}z_1 \geq \bar{\chi}_0) - \Pr(-n^{1/2}z_1 \geq \bar{\chi}_0, n^{1/2}z_2 > \bar{\chi}_0)\}\\
&= 2\Big\{\exp(-\bar{\chi}_0{}^2/2)\frac{1}{2\pi}\cos^{-1}(-\rho) + \int_{\bar{\chi}_0}^{\infty}\frac{1}{(2\pi)^{1/2}}\exp(-x^2/2)\,dx\\
&\quad - \int_{\bar{\chi}_0}^{\infty}\int_{\bar{\chi}_0}^{\infty}\frac{1}{2\pi(1 - \rho^2)^{1/2}}\exp[-(x^2 - 2\rho xy + y^2)/2(1 - \rho^2)]\,dx\,dy\Big\}. \qquad (4)
\end{aligned}$$

The first term represents the probability of rejecting the null hypothesis when $(\bar{x}, \bar{y})$ is either in the first or the third quadrant, and the sum of the second and the third terms represents the probability of rejecting the null hypothesis when $(\bar{x}, \bar{y})$ falls in either the second or the fourth quadrant.

A table of $\bar{\chi}_0$ can be easily computed, and in the previous paper [7] we presented the values of $\bar{\chi}_0$ for $\alpha = .05$ and $.01$ for $\rho = -.95(.05).95$ through two decimal places.

2. THE POWER FUNCTION

In case the alternative hypothesis is not restricted, namely $H_1: \theta_1 \neq 0$, $\theta_2 \neq 0$, the ordinary test of significance based on a χ^2 distribution would be the most appropriate one. One of the most interesting properties of this test is that its power function depends only on the Mahalanobis distance of the population mean vector from the origin, in our particular case,

$$\Delta^2 = (\theta_1, \theta_2)\begin{pmatrix} 1 & \rho \\ \rho & 1 \end{pmatrix}^{-1}\begin{pmatrix} \theta_1 \\ \theta_2 \end{pmatrix} = (\theta_1{}^2 - 2\rho\theta_1\theta_2 + \theta_2{}^2)/(1-\rho^2) \tag{5}$$

(cf. [1], pp. 54–59). It seems appropriate, therefore, to determine the behavior of the power function on the concentration ellipsoid. To do this let us make the following transformation:

$$\xi = \frac{1}{(1-\rho^2)^{1/2}}(x - \rho y), \qquad \eta = y \tag{6}$$

or

$$y = \eta \qquad x = (1-\rho^2)^{1/2}\xi + \rho\eta. \tag{7}$$

(ξ, η) is distributed as a bivariate normal with mean

$$\left(\frac{\theta_1}{(1-\rho^2)^{1/2}} - \frac{\rho\theta_2}{(1-\rho^2)^{1/2}}, \theta_2\right) = (\mu_1, \mu_2),$$

and common variance 1 and covariance 0. The null and the alternative hypotheses are transformed as $H_0': \mu_1 = \mu_2 = 0$, and

$$H_1': (1-\rho^2)^{1/2}\mu_1 + \rho\mu_2 \geq 0, \mu_2 \geq 0 \quad \text{or} \quad (1-\rho^2)^{1/2}\mu_1 + \rho\mu_2 \leq 0, \mu_2 \leq 0,$$

where at least one of the inequalities is strict in both cases.

We also note the relation

$$\bar{\chi}^2 = \xi^2 + \eta^2, \qquad \Delta^2 = \mu_1{}^2 + \mu_2{}^2 = (\theta_1, \theta_2)\begin{pmatrix} 1 & \rho \\ \rho & 1 \end{pmatrix}^{-1}\begin{pmatrix} \theta_1 \\ \theta_2 \end{pmatrix}. \tag{8}$$

The rejection region, after simple analysis, proves to be

$$\begin{aligned}
&\text{(I)} \quad n\bar{\chi}^2 \geq \bar{\chi}_0{}^2 && \text{if } \bar{\eta} \geq 0,\ (1-\rho^2)^{1/2}\bar{\xi} + \rho\bar{\eta} \geq 0,\\
&\text{(II)} \quad \left.\begin{array}{l} n^{1/2}\bar{\xi} \leq -\bar{\chi}_0 \\ \text{or} \\ n^{1/2}((1-\rho^2)^{1/2}\eta - \rho\bar{\xi}) \geq \bar{\chi}_0 \end{array}\right\} && \text{if } \bar{\eta} \geq 0,\ (1-\rho^2)^{1/2}\bar{\xi} + \rho\bar{\eta} \leq 0,\\
&\text{(III)} \quad n\bar{\chi}^2 \geq \bar{\chi}_0{}^2 && \text{if } \bar{\eta} \leq 0,\ (1-\rho^2)^{1/2}\bar{\xi} + \rho\bar{\eta} \leq 0,\\
&\text{(IV)} \quad \left.\begin{array}{l} n^{1/2}\bar{\xi} \geq \bar{\chi}_0 \\ \text{or} \\ n^{1/2}((1-\bar{\chi}\rho^2)^{1/2}\bar{\eta} - \rho\bar{\xi}) \leq -\bar{\chi}_0 \end{array}\right\} && \text{if } \bar{\eta} \leq 0,\ (1-\rho^2)^{1/2}\bar{\xi} + \rho\bar{\eta} \geq 0.
\end{aligned} \tag{9}$$

We now make an angular transformation,

$$\begin{aligned}
\eta &= r\sin\beta, \qquad \mu_2 = \Delta\sin\phi, \qquad 0 \leq r, \Delta < \infty,\\
\xi &= r\cos\beta, \qquad \mu_1 = \Delta\cos\phi, \qquad 0 \leq \beta, \phi < 2\pi
\end{aligned} \tag{10}$$

which reduces the alternative hypothesis to the much simpler form

$$H_1'': 0 \leq \phi \leq \alpha \qquad \text{or} \qquad \pi \leq \phi \leq \pi + \alpha$$

where $\alpha = \cos^{-1}(-\rho)$.

It is now a straightforward matter to work out the power function. The probability P of rejecting the null hypothesis, when the population mean is (μ_1, μ_2), is found to be

$$P = P_1 + P_2 - P_3, \tag{11}$$

where

$$P_1 = \frac{1}{2\pi}\exp(-\Delta^2/2)\int_{\bar{\chi}_0}^{\infty} x\exp(-x^2/2) \int_{-\phi}^{\alpha-\phi} (e^{x\Delta\cos\beta} + e^{-x\Delta\cos\beta})\, d\beta\, dx, \tag{12}$$

$$\begin{aligned}
P_2 = {} & \Phi(\bar{\chi}_0 - \Delta\cos\phi)\Phi(\Delta\sin\phi)\\
& + \Phi(\bar{\chi}_0 + \Delta\cos\phi)\Phi(-\Delta\sin\phi)\\
& + \Phi(\bar{\chi}_0 + \Delta\cos(\alpha-\phi))\Phi(-\Delta\sin(\alpha-\phi))\\
& + \Phi(\bar{\chi}_0 - \Delta\cos(\alpha-\phi))\Phi(\Delta\sin(\alpha-\phi)),
\end{aligned} \tag{13}$$

$$P_3 = \int_{\bar{\chi}_0 + \Delta \cos(\alpha - \phi)}^{\infty} \int_{\bar{\chi}_0 - \Delta \cos \phi}^{\infty} f(x_1, x_2; \rho)\, dx_1\, dx_2$$

$$+ \int_{\bar{\chi}_0 - \Delta \cos(\alpha - \phi)}^{\infty} \int_{\bar{\chi}_0 + \Delta \cos \phi}^{\infty} f(x_1, x_2; \rho)\, dx_1\, dx_2, \tag{14}$$

$$\Phi(y) = \int_y^{\infty} \frac{1}{(2\pi)^{1/2}} \exp(-x^2/2)\, dx, \tag{15}$$

and

$$f(x_1, x_2; \rho) = \frac{1}{2\pi(1-\rho^2)^{1/2}} \exp\left[-\frac{1}{2(1-\rho^2)}(x_1{}^2 - 2\rho x_1 x_2 + x_2{}^2)\right], \tag{16}$$

and among the parameters we have the relation

$$\Delta \cos \phi = (\theta_1 - \rho\theta_2)/(1-\rho^2)^{1/2}, \qquad \Delta \sin \phi = \theta_2 . \tag{17}$$

If we make the transformation

$$\begin{aligned} \eta &= r \sin(\beta + \alpha/2), \qquad & \mu_2 &= \Delta \sin(\psi + \alpha/2), \\ \xi &= r \cos(\beta + \alpha/2), \qquad & \mu_1 &= \Delta \cos(\psi + \alpha/2), \end{aligned} \tag{18}$$

instead of that given in (10), the alternative hypothesis will be slightly different, and (12), (13), and (14) will also be slightly changed. By a simple calculation we can easily see that the maximum of the power for fixed Δ is attained at $\psi = 0$ and the minimum at $\psi = \pm\alpha/2$. The power function can be easily seen to have a symmetric property, namely, for fixed Δ, the powers at the four points ψ, $-\psi$, $\pi + \psi$, and $\pi - \psi$ are the same.

These properties can be used in the original problem as follows: On a concentration ellipsoid given in (5), the maximum power is attained at the two points $\theta_1 = \theta_2 = \pm\Delta[(1+\rho)/2]^{1/2}$, and the minimum is attained at the four points $(\theta_1 = 0,\ \theta_2 = \pm\Delta(1-\rho^2)^{1/2})$ and $(\theta_1 = \pm\Delta(1-\rho^2)^{1/2},\ \theta_2 = 0)$. The symmetric property implies that the power at (θ_1, θ_2), (θ_2, θ_1), $(-\theta_1, -\theta_2)$, and $(-\theta_2, -\theta_1)$ is the same in the original problem. Because of the symmetry, we are obliged to investigate the behavior of the power function in the area of, so to speak, the first "octant."

As for the numerical work, the values of P_1 were evaluated by expanding the inner integral as a power series in x, the P_2 values were obtained from a table of the normal probability integral, and the P_3 values were computed by the ordinary formula of expansion, (cf. Cramér [4], p. 290), utilizing the recurrence relations of the Hermite polynomials.

3. NUMERICAL RESULTS AND DISCUSSIONS

We have so far tabulated the maxmium and the minimum power for $\rho = -.95(.05)\,.95$, $\Delta^2 = 1$ and 2, and their ratios to the power of the ordinary test based on χ^2 distributions. The results are given in Table I. A quick glance at the table reveals that a gain in power is guaranteed when the correlation is negative.

As was mentioned by Kudô and Fujisawa [7], this test furnishes an exact two-sided test of homogeneity of three means with ordered alternatives (cf. [2], and [3]). Suppose we have samples from three normal distributions with different means μ_1, μ_2, μ_3 and known common variance, and suppose we want to test the hypothesis H_0: $\mu_1 = \mu_2 = \mu_3$. Sometimes the practical situation requires us to test the hypothesis against the restricted alternative hypothesis, such as

$$H_1: (\mu_1 \geq \mu_2 \geq \mu_3 \text{ or } \mu_1 \leq \mu_2 \leq \mu_3)$$

or

$$H_2: (\mu_1 \geq \mu_2, \mu_1 \geq \mu_3 \text{ or } \mu_1 \leq \mu_2, \mu_1 \leq \mu_3)$$

where at least one of the inequalities is strict in all the cases. In case of H_1, the two differences in sample means $y_1 = \bar{x}_1 - \bar{x}_2$, $y_2 = \bar{x}_2 - \bar{x}_3$ will have a bivariate normal distribution with known variance-covariance matrix and the means are both zero under the null hypothesis, and either both are positive or negative under the alternative. Therefore we can legitimately apply the test discussed in this paper. We can work on $y_1 = \bar{x}_1 - \bar{x}_2$ and $y_2 = \bar{x}_1 - \bar{x}_3$ in case the alternative hypothesis is H_2. The correlation between y_1, y_2 is negative in case of H_1 and positive in case of H_2. In view of the numerical results in Table I, our present test has an advantage over the conventional method of analysis of variance in case of H_1, whereas it may be somewhat less powerful, although not markedly so, in case of H_2.

If the common variance is unknown, we can apply the test discussed in the previous paper, where we assumed that the correlation coefficient was known, that the common variance was unknown, but that there was an estimate of the common variance distributed in a χ^2 distribution with r degrees of freedom and statistically independent of the sample mean vector. The test requires tables of the F distribution with $(1 \cdot r)$ and $(2 \cdot r)$ degrees of freedom and of the bivariate analogue of Student's t distribution [5]. If the power function of this test behaves in a manner similar to that of our present test, the recommendations about the test of homogeneity of the means against an alternative H_1 or H_2 would be the same.

It would be interesting to compare the work of Bartholomew concerning, so to speak, the one-sided version of H_1 and H_2, namely, H_1': $\mu_1 \geq \mu_2 \geq \mu_3$ and H_2': $\mu_1 \geq \mu_2$, $\mu_1 \geq \mu_3$. He considered the power-function case when the sizes of three samples are the same, hence the correlation between y_1 and y_2 is $\pm\frac{1}{2}$. His findings indicate considerable advantage in the power of the tests he devised over the usual test based on the χ^2 distribution, even when the correlation is $+\frac{1}{2}$. It would be desirable to have the power computed in a

TABLE I

The Maximum and Minimum Powers of the Likelihood Ratio Test and Their Ratio to Those of an Ordinary Test Based on χ^2 Distribution

	$n\Delta^2 = 1$				$n\Delta^2 = 2$			
	Power		Ratio		Power		Ratio	
ρ	Max	Min	Max	Min	Max	Min	Max	Min
−.95	.16888	.16626	1.273	1.253	.51227	.50475	1.233	1.215
−.90	.16768	.16284	1.264	1.227	.40860	.49540	1.224	1.192
−.85	.16648	.15971	1.254	1.203	.50494	.48717	1.215	1.173
−.80	.16526	.15680	1.245	1.182	.50134	.47978	1.207	1.155
−.75	.16403	.15409	1.236	1.161	.49780	.47304	1.198	1.139
−.70	.16285	.15159	1.127	1.142	.49435	.46690	1.190	1.124
−.65	.16167	.14926	1.218	1.125	.49097	.46123	1.182	1.110
−.60	.16049	.14709	1.209	1.108	.48766	.45597	1.174	1.098
−.55	.15927	.14502	1.200	1.093	.48429	.45100	1.166	1.086
−.50	.15815	.14317	1.192	1.079	.48114	.44647	1.158	1.078
−.45	.15699	.14142	1.183	1.066	.47795	.44218	1.150	1.064
−.40	.15583	.13979	1.174	1.053	.47481	.43815	1.143	1.055
−.35	.15469	.13830	1.166	1.042	.47184	.43440	1.136	1.046
−.30	.15356	.13694	1.157	1.032	.46872	.43091	1.128	1.037
−.25	.15244	.13569	1.149	1.022	.46573	.42766	1.121	1.029
−.20	.15133	.13457	1.140	1.014	.46280	.42465	1.114	1.022
−.15	.15023	.13355	1.132	1.006	.45991	.42186	1.107	1.015
−.10	.14913	.13264	1.124	.999	.45705	.41929	1.100	1.009
−.05	.14808	.13186	1.116	.994	.45429	.41699	1.094	1.004
.00	.14704	.13119	1.108	.989	.45160	.41493	1.087	.999
.05	.14600	.13061	1.100	.984	.44894	.41307	1.081	.994
.10	.14499	.13013	1.093	.981	.44634	.41145	1.074	.990
.15	.14399	.12974	1.085	.978	.44379	.41004	1.068	.987
.20	.14303	.12945	1.078	.975	.44133	.40888	1.062	.984
.25	.14210	.12926	1.071	.974	.43896	.40736	1.057	.981
.30	.14119	.12914	1.064	.973	.43665	.40724	1.051	.980
.35	.14031	.12909	1.057	.973	.43443	.40675	1.046	.979
.40	.13945	.12916	1.051	.973	.43227	.40650	1.041	.978
.45	.13864	.12927	1.045	.974	.43022	.40645	1.036	.978
.50	.13785	.12944	1.039	.975	.42823	.40659	1.031	.979
.55	.13710	.12969	1.033	.977	.42635	.40697	1.026	.980
.60	.13639	.12998	1.028	.979	.42457	.40753	1.022	.981
.65	.13572	.13031	1.023	.982	.42291	.40828	1.018	.983
.70	.13512	.13070	1.018	.985	.42140	.40917	1.014	.985
.75	.13454	.13110	1.014	.988	.41995	.41022	1.011	.987
.80	.13402	.13152	1.010	.991	.41867	.41138	1.008	.990
.85	.13356	.13194	1.006	.994	.41753	.41257	1.005	.993
.90	.13318	.13234	1.004	.997	.41658	.41381	1.003	.996
.90	.13318	.13234	1.004	.997	.41658	.41381	1.003	.996
.95	.13282	.13273	1.001	1.000	.41572	.41498	1.001	.999

wider range of ρ before we make any definite statement about the difference between one-sided and two-sided situations.

4. AN ALTERNATIVE TEST

When a statistician is to test a hypothesis with multivariate data, he is usually interested not only in the over-all configuration of the components but also in each one of the components separately. As it may be easier for the interpretation of the outcome of the test, we are tempted to use a series of univariate tests simultaneously. This is not legitimate, of course, since there is a disturbance in the significance level. The question now arises as to what happens when we keep the significance level exact. To answer this question we shall here examine an alternative test, which is based on $n^{1/2}\max(|\bar{x}|,|\bar{y}|)$, under the same situation—that we have a bivariate normal population with variance 1 and known correlation coefficient and we want to test the same null hypothesis, that means are both zero against the same alternative hypothesis, that the mean vector is either in the 1st or 3rd quadrant, and that we have a sample of size n. The percentage point of this statistic $n^{1/2}\max(|\bar{x}|,|\bar{y}|)$ depends on the correlation coefficient, but it is clear it depends only on the absolute value of the correlation coefficient. The percentage points are tabulated in Table II.

TABLE II

The Upper Percentage Points of $n^{1/2}\max(|\bar{x}|, |\bar{y}|)$

$\pm\rho$	$P = .05$	$P = .01$
.00	2.2366	2.8066
.05	2.2364	2.8065
.10	2.2357	2.8063
.15	2.2347	2.8058
.20	2.2340	2.8052
.25	2.2311	2.8044
.30	2.2294	2.8033
.35	2.2256	2.8018
.40	2.2227	2.8000
.45	2.2176	2.7976
.50	2.2130	2.7946
.55	2.2061	2.7909
.60	2.1996	2.7863
.65	2.1902	2.7805
.70	2.1807	2.7733
.75	2.1678	2.7642
.80	2.1532	2.7525
.85	2.1337	2.7371
.90	2.1091	2.7157
.95	2.0713	2.6824

The power function of this test procedure has been computed at the same parameter points as those computed in the case of the likelihood ratio test, and are tabulated in Table III. It is interesting to note from this table that the power function at $\theta_1 = \theta_2$ is an increasing function of ρ, whereas it is a decreasing function in case of the likelihood test. When $\Delta^2 = 1$, it is more powerful than the likelihood ratio test in the range $\rho \geq .30$. It appears, however, that the power does not seem to increase favorably with Δ^2, and it is, in fact, considerably less than that of the ordinary test based on the χ^2 distribution, when either $\theta_1 = 0$ or $\theta_2 = 0$.

5. THE SCOPE OF GENERALIZATIONS

In a previous paper of one of the authors [6], the following problem was considered. Given a multivariate normal population with known variance matrix, what test is appropriate to determine whether the means are slipped to the right? We are concerned with a multivariate normal population with the mean vector

$$\boldsymbol{\theta}:\boldsymbol{\theta}' = (\theta_1, \theta_2, \dots, \theta_k)$$

and a known variance matrix, Λ, which is assumed to be nonsingular. Our problem is to test the hypothesis $H_0:\theta_i = 0$ $(i = 1, 2, \dots, k)$ against the alternative hypothesis $H_1:\theta_i \geq 0$ $(i = 1, 2, \dots, k)$, where the inequality is strict for at least one value of i, on the basis of the sample $\mathbf{X}^{(1)}, \mathbf{X}^{(2)}, \dots, \mathbf{X}^{(n)}$. The statistic appropriate to this test was derived by the likelihood ratio criterion, which is

$$\bar{\chi}^2 = n\{\overline{\mathbf{X}}'\Lambda^{-1}\overline{\mathbf{X}} - \min_{\theta_i \geq 0} (\overline{\mathbf{X}} - \boldsymbol{\theta}')\Lambda^{-1}(\overline{\mathbf{X}} - \boldsymbol{\theta})\} \qquad (i = 1, \dots, k). \tag{19}$$

By the transformation, $\mathbf{Y} = A\overline{\mathbf{X}}$, where A is a nonsingular matrix such that

$$A\Lambda A' = I, \tag{20}$$

and I is the unit matrix, we can make the variable Y uncorrelated, which gives

$$\bar{\chi}^2 = n\{\mathbf{Y}'\mathbf{Y} - \min_{L_i \geq 0} (\mathbf{Y} - \mathbf{m})'(\mathbf{Y} - \mathbf{m})\} \qquad (i = 1, \dots, k), \tag{21}$$

where $\mathbf{m} = A\mathbf{L} = AE(\mathbf{X})$, $\mathbf{L} = A^{-1}\mathbf{m}$. Therefore, by writing $A^{-1} = (a_{ij})$, $\bar{\chi}^2$ can be interpreted as being proportional to the difference between the square of the length of $\overline{\mathbf{Y}}$ and the square of the distance from $\overline{\mathbf{Y}}$ to the convex polyhedral defined by the inequality

$$L_i = \sum_{j=1}^{k} a^{ij} m_j \geq 0 \qquad (i = 1, \dots, k). \tag{22}$$

TABLE III

The Powers of an Alternative Test and Their Ratio to Those of the Ordinary Test Based on χ^2 Distribution

	$n\Delta^2 = 1$						$n\Delta^2 = 2$					
	Power			Ratio			Power			Ratio		
$\|\rho\|$	Max[a] $\rho > 0$	Max $\rho < 0$	Min	Max $\rho > 0$	Max $\rho < 0$	Min	Max $\rho > 0$	Max $\rho < 0$	Min	Max $\rho > 0$	Max $\rho < 0$	Min
0	.12521	.12521	.13129	.944	.944	.990	.20564	.20564	.22569	.495	.495	.543
.05	.12838	.12062	.13107	.967	.909	.988	.21202	.19588	.22521	.511	.472	.542
.10	.13148	.11614	.13043	.991	.875	.983	.21822	.18636	.22383	.525	.449	.539
.15	.13448	.11173	.12934	1.013	.842	.974	.22418	.17704	.22151	.539	.424	.533
.20	.13719	.10732	.12766	1.034	.808	.962	.22965	.16771	.21802	.553	.404	.525
.25	.14022	.10319	.12594	1.057	.777	.949	.23547	.15906	.21416	.567	.383	.515
.30	.14272	.09887	.12342	1.076	.745	.930	.24047	.15051	.20885	.579	.361	.503
.35	.14552	.09495	.12087	1.096	.716	.911	.24581	.14186	.20316	.592	.342	.489
.40	.14784	.09082	.11761	1.114	.684	.886	.25041	.13339	.19614	.603	.321	.472
.45	.15041	.08705	.11429	1.134	.656	.861	.25528	.12547	.18871	.615	.302	.454
.50	.15253	.08311	.11031	1.150	.626	.831	.25946	.11744	.18006	.625	.283	.434
.55	.15493	.07952	.10631	1.167	.599	.801	.26395	.10994	.17105	.635	.265	.412
.60	.15682	.07576	.10166	1.182	.571	.766	.26768	.10230	.16085	.644	.246	.387
.65	.15900	.07232	.09700	1.198	.545	.731	.27175	.09518	.15035	.654	.229	.362
.70	.16070	.06875	.09176	1.211	.518	.692	.27510	.08798	.13879	.662	.212	.334
.75	.16262	.06546	.08644	1.226	.493	.651	.27870	.08120	.12689	.671	.195	.306
.80	.16419	.06212	.08065	1.237	.468	.608	.28177	.07449	.11416	.678	.179	.275
.85	.16588	.05898	.07465	1.249	.444	.562	.28494	.06808	.10096	.686	.164	.243
.90	.16721	.05580	.06809	1.261	.421	.513	.28759	.06175	.08688	.692	.149	.209
.95	.16872	.05287	.06102	1.272	.399	.460	.29043	.05579	.07191	.699	.134	.173

[a] The words max and min are used conventionally for the sake of comparison with Table I.

If $\overline{\mathbf{Y}}$ is outside the convex polyhedral cone, the distance to the cone is attained by a point $\hat{\mathbf{Y}}_1$ on the boundary, which is nothing but the maximum-likelihood estimate of **m**. Therefore, if $\overline{\mathbf{Y}}$ is outside, *or*, equivalently, not all the components of $\bar{\chi}$ are positive, the maximum likelihood estimate of θ has at least one component which is zero.

The probability distribution of $\bar{\chi}^2$ was found to be

$$P_r(\bar{\chi}^2 \geq \bar{\chi}_0{}^2) = \sum_{\phi \leq M \leq K} P_r(\chi^2_{n(M)} \geq \bar{\chi}_0) P\{(\Lambda_{M'})^{-1}\} P\{\Lambda_{M:M'}\}, \tag{23}$$

where the summation runs over all the subsets M of $K = \{1, 2, \ldots, k\}$, $n(M)$ is the number of elements in M, M' is the compliment of M, Λ_M is the variance matrix of x_i, $i \in M$, $\Lambda_{M:M'}$ is the same under the condition $x_j = 0$, $j \notin M$, and $P\{\Sigma\}$ is the probability that the variable distributed in a multivariate normal with mean zero and variance covariance matrix Σ are all positive $\chi^2_{n(M)}$ has the χ^2-distribution with $n(M)$ degrees of freedom, where $\chi^2_{n(\phi)}$ is understood to be constantly zero, $P\{\Lambda_{\phi:K}\} = 1$, and $P\{(\Lambda_{K'})^{-1}\} = P\{(\Lambda_\phi)^{-1} = 1$.

Now $P_r\ \{(\Lambda_{M'})^{-1}\} P_r\{\Lambda_{M:M'}\}$ represents the probability that the maximum likelihood estimate $\hat{\boldsymbol{\theta}}$ of $\boldsymbol{\theta}$ satisfies $\theta_i > 0$ for $i \in M$ and $\theta_i = 0$ for $i \notin M$, or equivalently the maximum-likelihood estimate $\hat{\mathbf{m}}$ of **m** is on the boundary where $L_i = 0$, $i \notin M$, and $L_i > 0$, $i \in M$. We shall denote this condition as C_M. Further $\Lambda_{M:M}{}'$ is the variance-covariance matrix of the distribution of the projection of **Y** on the surface defined by $L_i = 0$, $i \in M$, and $P\{\Lambda_{M:M'}\}$ represents the probability that the projection satisfies $L_i > 0$, $i \in M$.

The proof of the above interpretation of these probabilities can be found in the proof of Theorem 3.1 of [6], but this interpretation is not clearly stated and perhaps this would help the reader of the paper to understand the arguments there.

Kudô is now working on the problem of a multivariate analogue of a two-sided test, which means we have an alternative hypothesis of the form $H_1: (\theta_i \geq 0, i = 1, \ldots, k)$ or $(\theta_i \leq 0, i = 1, \ldots, k)$, where the inequality is strict for at least one value of i in either case.

The test statistic derived by the likelihood ratio method is in this case

$$\bar{\bar{\chi}}^2 = n\{\overline{\mathbf{X}}'\Lambda^{-1}\overline{\mathbf{X}} - \min_{\substack{\theta_i \geq 0,\, i=1,\cdots,k \\ \text{or } \theta_i \leq 0,\, i=1,\cdots,k}} (\overline{\mathbf{X}} - \theta)'\Lambda^{-1}(\bar{x} - \theta)\}, \tag{24}$$

or in terms of **Y**,

$$\bar{\bar{\chi}}^2 = n\{\mathbf{Y}'\mathbf{Y} - \min_{\substack{L_i \geq 0,\, i=1,\cdots,k \\ \text{or } L_i \leq 0,\, i=1,\cdots,k}} (\mathbf{Y} - \mathbf{m})'(\mathbf{Y} - \mathbf{m})\}. \tag{25}$$

This statistic is nothing but the maximum of the statistic $\bar{\chi}^2(+)$ for the test with $H_1(+)\colon \theta_i \geq 0$ $(i = 1, \ldots, k)$ and $\bar{\chi}^2(-)$ for the test with $H_1(-)\colon \theta_i \leq 0$ $(i = 1, \ldots, k)$. We have two convex polyhedral cones defined by

$$L_i = \sum_{j=1}^{k} a^{ij} m_j \geq 0 \qquad (i = 1, \ldots, k), \tag{26}$$

and

$$L_i = \sum_{j=1}^{k} a^{ij} m_j \leq 0 \qquad (i = 1, \ldots, k), \tag{27}$$

and similarly we have the conditions on the maximum-likelihood estimates corresponding to $H_1(+)$ and $H_1(-)$, which are denoted by $C_M(+)$ and $C_M(-)$.

Because of the symmetry of the convex polyhedral cones defined by (26) and (27), the distributions of $\bar{\chi}^2(+)$ and $\bar{\chi}^2(-)$ are the same. Therefore, the distribution of $\bar{\bar{\chi}}^2$ can be written

$$\begin{aligned} P_r(\bar{\bar{\chi}}^2 \geq \bar{\bar{\chi}}^2) &= 2P_r(\bar{\chi}^2 \geq \bar{\chi}_0{}^2) - P_r(\bar{\chi}^2(+) \geq \bar{\bar{\chi}}_0{}^2, \bar{\chi}^2(-) \geq \bar{\bar{\chi}}_0{}^2) \\ &= 2 \sum_{\phi \leq M \leq K} P_r(\chi^2_{n(M)} \geq \bar{\bar{\chi}}_0{}^2) P_r(\Lambda_M^{-1}) P_r(\Lambda_{M:M'}) \\ &\quad - \sum_{\phi \leq M_1 \leq K} \sum_{\phi \leq M_2 \leq K} P_r(\bar{\chi}^2(+) \geq \bar{\bar{\chi}}_0{}^2, \bar{\bar{\chi}}^2(-) \geq \bar{\bar{\chi}}_0{}^2, \\ &\quad \times C_{M_1}(+), C_{M_2}(-)). \end{aligned} \tag{28}$$

The first summation is self-explanatory and in the second sum the summation runs over all subsets M_1 and M_2 of K where each term is the probability that both $\bar{\chi}^2(+)$ and $\bar{\chi}^2(-)$ exceed $\bar{\bar{\chi}}_0{}^2$ and the conditions $C_{M_1}(+)$ and $C_{M_2}(-)$ are satisfied.

As for the first sum, each term can be evaluated as in the previous paper, and each term in the second sum can be evaluated by utilizing Theorem 3.1 of [6]. A detailed treatment of the evaluation of the second sum, and some numerical tables, will be published elsewhere.

Acknowledgments

Table I was prepared at Kyushu University, and Tables II and III at Iowa State University. The authors are grateful to Miss S. Mori and Mrs. G. Snowdon for preparing programs, and Mr. I. Wey for help in computation. Finally, the authors would like to express their gratitude to Mr. I. Hall for his help in improving the exposition.

REFERENCES

1. Anderson, T. W. (1958). *An Introduction to Multivariate Statistical Analysis*. Wiley, New York.

2. Bartholomew, D. J. (1961). A test of homogeneity of means under restricted alternatives. *J. Roy. Statist. Soc. Ser. B* 239–281.
3. Bartholomew, D. J. (1961). Ordered tests in the analysis of variance. *Biometrika* **48** 325–332.
4. Cramér, H. (1946). *Mathematical Methods of Statistics*. Princeton Univ. Press, Princeton, New Jersey.
5. Dunnett, C. W. and Sobel, M. (1954). A bivariate generalization of Student's *t*-distribution with tables for certain cases. *Biometrika* **41** 153-169.
6. Kudô, A. (1963). A multivariate analogue of the one-sided tests. *Biometrika* **50** ~~55–70~~. 403–418
7. Kudô, A. and Fujisawa, H. (1964). A bivariate normal test with two-sided alternative. *Mem. Faculty of Science, Kyushu Univ. Ser. A* **18** No. 1.
8. Nüesch, P. E. (1966). On the problem of testing location in multivariate populations for restricted alternatives. *Ann. Math. Statist.* **37** 113–119.

Covariance Adjustment and Related Problems in Multivariate Analysis

C. RADHAKRISHNA RAO
RESEARCH AND TRAINING SCHOOL
INDIAN STATISTICAL INSTITUTE
CALCUTTA, INDIA

1. SUMMARY

In this paper are considered a number of problems arising out of discrimination between two populations when it is known that they do not differ with respect to a given subset of characters. Such characters may be called, for convenience, *concomitant variables* (although ancillary variables would be a better term) to distinguish them from other (main) variables in which the populations may differ. The concomitant variables, although they by themselves do not discriminate between the populations, may provide additional discrimination in the presence of other variables in which the populations differ. This happens when the concomitants are correlated with the main variables. However, in practice, when the correlations are unknown and have to be estimated from data (for utilizing the concomitants through the technique of covariance adjustment), there may, indeed, be loss of information, unless the correlations are high. Therefore, some caution is needed in the choice and use of concomitant variables.

The methods are extended to the general case of analysis of dispersion under the Gauss-Markoff setup for multiple variables, given that certain linear functions of parameters occurring in the expectations of some functions of the variables have known values. Such functions of the variables are chosen as concomitants and the conditional expectations of the others given the concomitants is considered, which is also of the Gauss-Markoff type. The multivariate least-squares theory applied to the conditional expectations provides a generalization of analysis of covariance which is well known in the context of univariate analysis of variance (A.V.). Such an analysis may be called analysis of dispersion (A.D.) with covariance adjustment.

It is shown that a model for multiple variables recently considered by Potthoff and Roy [3] can be reduced to a Gauss-Markoff model of the conditional type. Thus an appropriate analysis of their model is provided which is different from the one proposed by them.

2. DISCRIMINATION BETWEEN TWO POPULATIONS

Consider a $(p + q)$-dimensional random variable $(\mathbf{Y}, \mathbf{Z})$, where $\mathbf{Y}$ is p-dimensional and $\mathbf{Z}$ is q-dimensional. We shall refer to $\mathbf{Y}$ as the main variable and $\mathbf{Z}$ as the concomitant variable. Let E_1 and E_2 denote expectations with respect to two $p + q$ variate normal distributions with the same dispersion matrix and possibly different mean vectors. Some hypotheses of interest are as follows:

$$\mathrm{H}_{01}: \quad E_1(\mathbf{Y}) = E_2(\mathbf{Y}), \quad E_1(\mathbf{Z}) = E_2(\mathbf{Z}).$$

$$\mathrm{H}_{02}: \quad E_1(\mathbf{Y} \mid \mathbf{Z}) = E_2(\mathbf{Y} \mid \mathbf{Z}), \quad \text{whether } E_1(\mathbf{Z}) = E_2(\mathbf{Z}) \text{ or not.}$$

$$\mathrm{H}_{03}: \quad E_1(\mathbf{Y}) = E_2(\mathbf{Y}) \quad \text{given } E_1(\mathbf{Z}) = E_2(\mathbf{Z}).$$

$$\mathrm{H}_{04}: \quad E_1(\mathbf{Y}) = E_2(\mathbf{Y}).$$

The interpretations of these hypotheses and their tests based on independent samples of sizes n_1 and n_2 from the two distributions, although well known, need some re-examination in the light of numerous applications made during recent years.

The hypotheses H_{01} and H_{04} can be tested by using Hotelling's T^2 or Mahalanobis's D^2. The test for H_{02} for a general p was first given by the author [4]; the special case for $p = 1$ was well known in the context of analysis of variance (of a single variable) with covariance adjustment (for a number of concomitants). A test for H_{03}, different from that of H_{02}, was developed in [5]. Let D_{p+q}, D_p^2, and D_q^2 be the estimated Mahalanobis' distances based on all the $p + q$ variables $(\mathbf{Y}, \mathbf{Z})$, the main variable $(\mathbf{Y})$, and the concomitant $(\mathbf{Z})$, respectively. Further let $c = n_1 n_2/(n_1 + n_2)$ and $N = n_1 + n_2$. Then the suggested test criteria for the hypotheses H_{01} to H_{04} are as follows:

Hypothesis	*Test criterion*	*Null distribution*
H_{01}	$\mathrm{T}_1 = \dfrac{c(N-p-q-1)}{(p+q)(N-2)} D^2_{p+q}$	$F(p+q, N-p-q-1)$
H_{02}	$\mathrm{T}_2 = \dfrac{N-p-q-1}{p} \dfrac{c(D^2_{p+q} - D_q^2)}{N-2+cD_q^2}$	$F(p, N-p-q-1)$
H_{03}	$\mathrm{T}_3 = \dfrac{c}{N-2}(D^2_{p+q} - D_q^2)$	Given in (2.1)
H_{04}	$\mathrm{T}_4 = \dfrac{c(N-p-1)}{p(N-2)} D_p^{\,2}$	$F(p, N-p-1)$

In the case of T_3 it is convenient to use the related statistic $W = T_3/(1 + T_3)$, with large values of W indicating significance, which has the density

$$P(W) = \left[\Gamma\left(\frac{N+p-q-1}{2}\right)\Gamma\left(\frac{N-1}{2}\right)\Big/\Gamma\left(\frac{N-p-q-1}{2}\right)\Gamma\left(\frac{p}{2}\right)\Gamma\left(\frac{N+q-1}{2}\right)\right]$$
$$\times W^{(p/2)-1}(1-W)^{[(N-p-q-1)/2]-1}$$
$$\times {}_2F_1\left(\frac{q}{2}, \frac{N-q-1}{2}; \frac{N+p-1}{2}, W\right), \tag{2.1}$$

where ${}_2F_1$ is the hypergeometric function of the second kind.

Let Δ_{p+q}^2, $\Delta_p{}^2$, and $\Delta_q{}^2$ be the true Mahalanobis' distances based on the variables (**Y**, **Z**), **Y**, and **Z** only. Then the hypotheses H_{01} to H_{04} can be stated in alternative forms:

H_{01}: $\Delta_{p+q}^2 = 0$

H_{02}: $\Delta_{p+q}^2 - \Delta_q{}^2 = 0$ whether $\Delta_q{}^2$ is zero or not

H_{03}: $\Delta_{p+q}^2 = 0$ given $\Delta_q{}^2 = 0$, equivalent to $\Delta_p{}^2 = 0$ given $\Delta_q{}^2 = 0$

H_{04}: $\Delta_p{}^2 = 0$

It is, however, customary to use the same criterion T_2 for both the hypotheses H_{02} and H_{03}, as H_{03} implies H_{02} under the condition $E_1(\mathbf{Z}) = E_2(\mathbf{Z})$. See, for instance, the papers by Cochran and Bliss [2] and Cochran [1]. The author has shown elsewhere [5] that there is a slight advantage in using T_3 for testing H_{03}. Such a conclusion was reached by computing the variances of estimates of Δ_{p+q}^2 based on the statistics T_2 and T_3, when $\Delta_q{}^2$ is given to be zero, and observing that the variance is smaller for the latter. The percentage points of the distribution (2.1) are, however, not available, but it is hoped to provide the necessary tables in the near future. A good approximation is provided by the use of

$$F = \frac{N-q-1}{N-1}\,\frac{N-p-q-1}{p}\,T_3 \tag{2.2}$$

as a variance ratio on p and $N-p-q-1$ d.f. The nonnull distribution of W is also derived in [5] in a form suitable for the computation of the power function of W. A tabulation of the power function of W may be needed to examine more fully the relative performances of the tests T_2 and T_3.

When $E_1(\mathbf{Z}) = E_2(\mathbf{Z})$, that is, $\Delta_q{}^2 = 0$, the hypotheses H_{01} to H_{04} are equivalent and, therefore, T_1 and T_4 may also be considered as alternatives to T_2 or T_3. It is expected that T_1 would be inefficient compared to T_2 (or T_3), since the degrees of freedom of the numerator for the corresponding variance ratio test is not based on the effective number p but on the larger number $p+q$. A rough computation of the loss of efficiency in using T_1 instead of T_2 has been made recently by Cochran [1].

But a real competitor to T_2 (or T_3) may be T_4, the test based on $D_p^{\,2}$ ignoring the observations on the q characters. It is clear that when the two sets of variables **Y** and **Z** are uncorrelated, the observations on **Z** do not provide any information on the distribution of **Y**, and consequently the test T_4 should be better than T_2 (or T_3). If the correlations are small, T_4 will still be better, unless the sample sizes n_1 and n_2 are large. In practice we usually have a situation where a test of the type T_2 (or T_3) using a subset of the available concomitants would be more efficient. An examination of the estimated correlations between the sets of variables **Y** and **Z** may enable us to choose such a subset $\mathbf{Z}_1$ (of **Z**). The set $\mathbf{Z}_1$ may be empty, in which case T_4 is the appropriate test.

3. DISCRIMINANT FUNCTIONS

A closely related problem is the estimation of the discriminant function in the following situations

(a) $E_1(\mathbf{Y}) \neq E_2(\mathbf{Y}), \quad E_1(\mathbf{Z}) \neq E_2(\mathbf{Z})$.
(b) $E_1(\mathbf{Y} \mid \mathbf{Z}) \neq E_2(\mathbf{Y} \mid \mathbf{Z})$, using conditional distributions only.
(c) $E_1(\mathbf{Y}) \neq E_2(\mathbf{Y})$ given that $E_1(\mathbf{Z}) = E_2(\mathbf{Z})$.

Let $\boldsymbol{\delta}_\mathbf{Y} = E_1(\mathbf{Y}) - E_2(\mathbf{Y})$, $\boldsymbol{\delta}_\mathbf{Z} = E_1(\mathbf{Z}) - E_2(\mathbf{Z})$, and let the dispersion matrix of (**Y**, **Z**) be

$$\Sigma = \begin{pmatrix} D(\mathbf{Y}) & C(\mathbf{Y}, \mathbf{Z}) \\ C(\mathbf{Y}, \mathbf{Z}) & D(\mathbf{Z}) \end{pmatrix} = \begin{pmatrix} \Sigma_{\mathbf{YY}} & \Sigma_{\mathbf{YZ}} \\ \Sigma_{\mathbf{ZY}} & \Sigma_{\mathbf{ZZ}} \end{pmatrix}.$$

The discriminant function in terms of population parameters in the case of (a) is

$$(\boldsymbol{\delta}_\mathbf{Y}' \vdots \boldsymbol{\delta}_\mathbf{Z}')\Sigma^{-1}\begin{pmatrix} \mathbf{Y} \\ \mathbf{Z} \end{pmatrix} = (\boldsymbol{\delta}_\mathbf{Y}'\Sigma'' + \boldsymbol{\delta}_\mathbf{Z}'\Sigma^{21})\mathbf{Y} + (\boldsymbol{\delta}_\mathbf{Y}'\Sigma^{12} + \boldsymbol{\delta}_\mathbf{Z}'\Sigma^{22})\mathbf{Z}$$

and in the case of (c),

$$(\boldsymbol{\delta}_\mathbf{Y}' \vdots \mathbf{0})\Sigma^{-1}\begin{pmatrix} \mathbf{Y} \\ \mathbf{Z} \end{pmatrix} = \boldsymbol{\delta}_\mathbf{Y}'\Sigma^{11}\mathbf{Y} + \boldsymbol{\delta}_\mathbf{Y}'\Sigma^{12}\mathbf{Z}, \tag{3.2}$$

where

$$\Sigma^{-1} = \begin{pmatrix} \Sigma^{11} & \Sigma^{12} \\ \Sigma^{21} & \Sigma^{22} \end{pmatrix}.$$

The discriminant functions (3.1) and (3.2) can be estimated by substituting for $\boldsymbol{\delta}_Y$, $\boldsymbol{\delta}_Z$, and Σ^{-1} their estimates from the sample. The discriminant function in the case (b) obtained from the likelihood ratio of the conditional distributions of **Y** given **Z** is

$$L(\mathbf{Y} \mid \mathbf{Z}) = (\boldsymbol{\delta}_Y' \,\vdots\, \boldsymbol{\delta}_Z')\Sigma^{-1}\begin{pmatrix}\mathbf{Y}\\ \mathbf{Z}\end{pmatrix} - \boldsymbol{\delta}_Z'\Sigma_{22}^{-1}\mathbf{Z}, \tag{3.3}$$

which is the difference between the discriminant functions based on (**Y**, **Z**) and **Z**. For estimating the function (3.3), we substitute for $\boldsymbol{\delta}_Y$, $\boldsymbol{\delta}_Z$, Σ^{-1}, and Σ_{22}^{-1} their estimates.

The status of the discriminant function (3.3) must be clearly understood. If $L(\mathbf{Y}, \mathbf{Z})$ is the discriminant function based on (**Y**, **Z**) and $L(\mathbf{Z})$ that based on **Z** alone, then we have the decomposition of $L(\mathbf{Y}, \mathbf{Z})$,

$$L(\mathbf{Y}, \mathbf{Z}) = L(\mathbf{Z}) + L(\mathbf{Y} \mid \mathbf{Z}), \tag{3.4}$$

into two independent components. In using $L(\mathbf{Y} \mid \mathbf{Z})$ we are considering only the information provided by **Y** independent of **Z**. There may be practical situations where it may be necessary to do so.

Cochran and Bliss [2] and Cochran [1] recommend the use of an estimate of $L(\mathbf{Y} \mid \mathbf{Z})$ substituting $\mathbf{d}_Z$ (the observed differences) for $\boldsymbol{\delta}_Z$ even in the case of (c), which specifies that the true values of $\boldsymbol{\delta}_Z$ is zero. A more appropriate discriminant function for the case (c) is the expression (3.2).

4. THE EFFECT OF INCREASING THE NUMBER OF CHARACTERS

Suppose there are two experimental conditions (treatments), and on each individual subjected to a treatment multiple measurements have been obtained. The differences between treatments in such a situation can be tested by using Hotelling's T^2 or Mahalanobis's D^2, taking into consideration a certain number of measurements (variables). But it is not uncommon in practice to find significant differences at a given level by applying Student's t test on each individual measurement, whereas the T^2 or D^2 test utilizing all the measurements simultaneously fails to indicate significance at the same level. An example from an anthropometric investigation is given in Table I. The F statistic (square of t) for each character is significant at the 5% level. The T_4 statistic for testing the joint hypothesis (H_{04}) that the population means of femur and humerus are the same for both the communities is 2.685, which as a variance ratio on 2 and 44 d.f. is not significant at the 5% level. Here is a dangerous situation where the inclusion of an extra character decreases the discriminatory power of the test.

To study the effect of increase in the number of characters on tests of

TABLE I

Tests of Differences between Communities by Individual Characters

	Sample size	Mean length of Femur	Mean length of Humerus
Community 1	27	460.4	335.1
Community 2	20	444.3	323.2
F statistic for each character		5.301 (1, 45 d.f.)	4.901 (1, 45 d.f)

significance we have to compute the power function of the test T_4 for different value of p. For given sample sizes n_1 and n_2, the power depends only on p, the number of characters, and Δ_p^2, the true distance between populations. Figures 1, 2, and 3 give the power functions for values of $p = 2(1)9$ when the sample sizes are equal and the common sample size $N = 10$, 20, and 30, respectively. It is seen from these charts that for a given sample size, the power can decrease with increase in the number of characters from q to $p + q$ unless the increase in the true Mahalanobis distance $\Delta_{p+q}^2 - \Delta_q^2$ is of a certain order of magnitude. The difference in Mahalanobis distances necessary to maintain the same power decreases, however, as the sample size increases for any given p and q and also as q increases for given p and sample size.

For instance, in the numerical example, the D^2 for femur alone is $D_1^2 = 0.4614$ and that due to femur and humerus is $D_2^2 = 0.4777$, so that the increase in D^2 due to the inclusion of humerus is 0.0163, indicating that the increase in the population Δ^2 is small. Such a small increase is not of value in samples of sizes 20 and 27 from the two populations. Perhaps with 10 more observations on the total and equal distribution of sample sizes, the inclusion of humerus would have increased the power of discrimination.

5. ANALYSIS OF DISPERSION WITH COVARIANCE ADJUSTMENT

The Gauss-Markoff model in the multivariate case can be written

$$E(\mathbf{X}) = \mathbf{A}\mathbf{T}_0, \tag{5.1}$$

where $\mathbf{X}$ is an $n \times p$ matrix of observations, $\mathbf{A}$ is an $n \times m$ matrix of known coefficients, and $\mathbf{T}_0$ is an $m \times p$ matrix of unknown parameters. The rows of $\mathbf{X}$ are independently distributed, while the components of any row have a p-variate distribution with a dispersion matrix $\mathbf{\Sigma}$. Let $\mathbf{C}$ be an $n \times q$ matrix

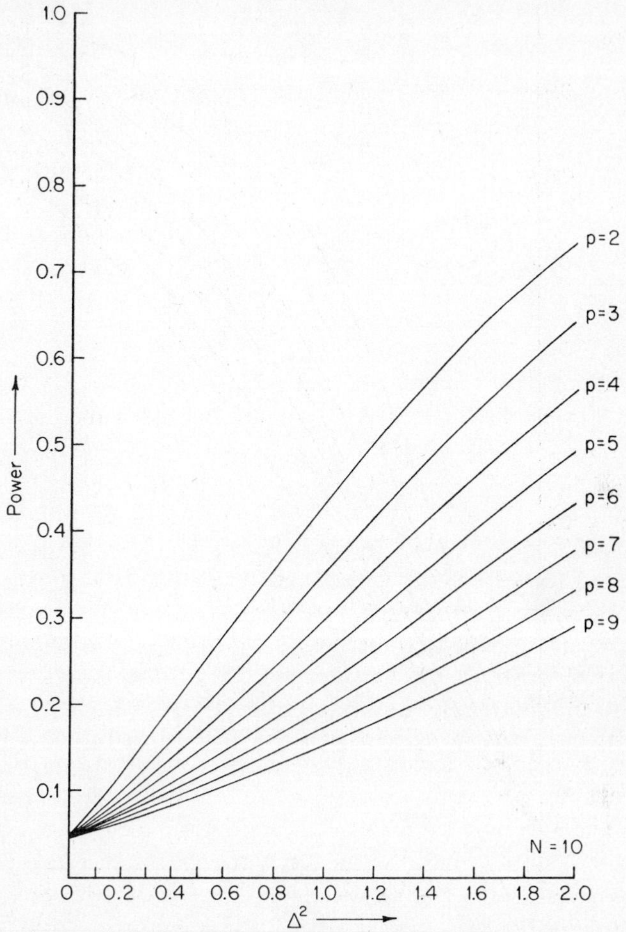

Fig. 1. Power function of the D^2 statistic with $N = 10$.

of concomitant observations, and assume that the conditional expectation of **X** given **C** is

$$E(\mathbf{X} \mid \mathbf{C}) = \mathbf{AT} + \mathbf{CB}, \tag{5.2}$$

where **B** is a $q \times p$ matrix of unknown regression coefficients. The conditional model (5.2) is again of the Gauss-Markoff type, involving the unknown parameters (**T**, **B**), the known coefficients (**A**, **C**), and the observations **X**, and therefore no new problem arises if conditional inference is needed.

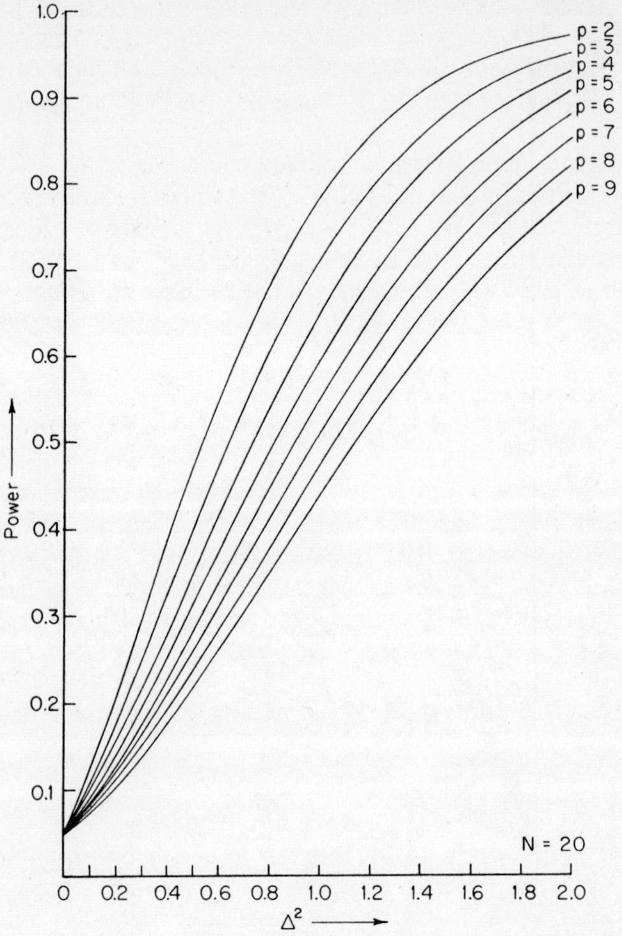

Fig. 2. Power function of the D^2 statistic with $N = 20$.

The parameters **T** and $\mathbf{T}_0$ may not, however, be the same. In the context of multivariate normal distributions, if $E(\mathbf{C}) = \mathbf{AT}_1$, then

$$\mathbf{T} = \mathbf{T}_0 - \mathbf{T}_1\mathbf{B}. \tag{5.3}$$

Hence a homogeneous linear hypothesis involving **T** is not the same as that on $\mathbf{T}_0$ unless the corresponding linear hypothesis on $\mathbf{T}_1$ is given to be true. Thus for testing linear hypotheses on $\mathbf{T}_0$ when the corresponding linear hypotheses on $\mathbf{T}_1$ are given to be true, we have two alternative models (5.1) and (5.2), of which the former ignores the observations **C**. We should

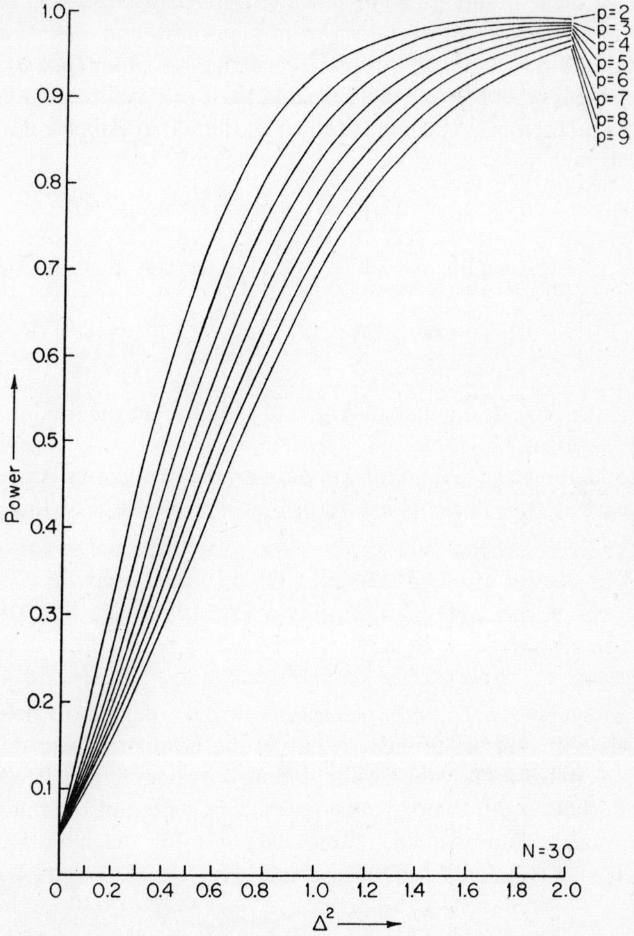

Fig. 3. Power function of the D^2 statistic with $N = 30$.

therefore first examine whether the information provided by **C** is useful for the purpose of examining linear hypotheses on $\mathbf{T}_0$.

For this purpose we first consider the Gauss-Markoff model

$$E(\mathbf{X}) = \mathbf{A}\mathbf{T}_0, \qquad E(\mathbf{C}) = \mathbf{A}\mathbf{T}_1 \tag{5.4}$$

in terms of the matrices $(\mathbf{X} \vdots \mathbf{C})$ of observations and parameters $(\mathbf{T}_0 \vdots \mathbf{T}_1)$:

$$E(\mathbf{X} \vdots \mathbf{C}) = \mathbf{A}(\mathbf{T}_0 \vdots \mathbf{T}_1). \tag{5.5}$$

Let us consider the hypothesis, $\mathbf{R}(\mathbf{T}_0 \vdots \mathbf{T}_1) = \mathbf{0}$, where the rank of $\mathbf{R}$ is s.

Starting with the model (5.5) for $p+q$ correlated variables, let us obtain an analysis of dispersion for deviation from hypothesis and due to residual. The corresponding S.P. (sum of products) matrices of order $(p+q)$ are given in partitioned form separating the elements for the p main and q concomitant variables and their cross products. Thus, let the S.P. matrix for deviation from hypothesis be

$$\mathbf{D}=\begin{pmatrix}\mathbf{D}_{11} & \mathbf{D}_{12}\\ \mathbf{D}_{21} & \mathbf{D}_{22}\end{pmatrix} \qquad \text{with } s \text{ d.f.}$$

and the S.P. matrix due to residual be

$$\mathbf{W}=\begin{pmatrix}\mathbf{W}_{11} & \mathbf{W}_{12}\\ \mathbf{W}_{21} & \mathbf{W}_{22}\end{pmatrix} \qquad \text{with } (n-r) \text{ d.f.,}$$

where r is the rank of the matrix $\mathbf{A}$. Let $(\mathbf{T}_{ij})$ represent the total matrix, where $\mathbf{T}_{ij}=\mathbf{W}_{ij}+\mathbf{D}_{ij}$.

The concomitants yield no information on the hypotheses concerning $\mathbf{T}_0$ if all the regression coefficients are zero, that is, if $\mathbf{B}=\mathbf{0}$. For this purpose we use Wilk's Λ criterion,

$$\Lambda_1=\frac{|\mathbf{W}_{11}-\mathbf{W}_{12}\mathbf{W}_{22}^{-1}\mathbf{W}_{21}|}{|\mathbf{W}_{11}|}=\frac{\begin{vmatrix}\mathbf{W}_{11} & \mathbf{W}_{12}\\ \mathbf{W}_{21} & \mathbf{W}_{22}\end{vmatrix}}{|\mathbf{W}_{11}|\,|\mathbf{W}_{22}|} \tag{5.6}$$

with parameters $(q, p, n-r-q)$ (representing the degrees of freedom of the hypothesis with respect to each variable, the number of variables, and the degrees of freedom for the residual matrix, respectively). If Λ_1 is small, indicating that not all the regression coefficients are null, we may proceed to make covariance adjustment. The Wilk's test for the hypothesis $\mathbf{RT}_0=\mathbf{0}$ given $\mathbf{RT}_1=\mathbf{0}$ is

$$\Lambda_2=\frac{|\mathbf{W}_{11}-\mathbf{W}_{12}\mathbf{W}_{22}^{-1}\mathbf{W}_{21}|}{|\mathbf{T}_{11}-\mathbf{T}_{12}\mathbf{T}_{22}^{-1}\mathbf{T}_{21}|}=\frac{\begin{vmatrix}\mathbf{W}_{11} & \mathbf{W}_{12}\\ \mathbf{W}_{21} & \mathbf{W}_{22}\end{vmatrix}}{\begin{vmatrix}\mathbf{T}_{11} & \mathbf{T}_{12}\\ \mathbf{T}_{21} & \mathbf{T}_{22}\end{vmatrix}}\div\frac{|\mathbf{W}_{22}|}{|\mathbf{T}_{22}|} \tag{5.7}$$

with the parameters $(s, p, n-r-q)$. An alternative test similar to T_3 of Section 2 is the difference

$$\Lambda_3=\frac{\begin{vmatrix}\mathbf{T}_{11} & \mathbf{T}_{12}\\ \mathbf{T}_{21} & \mathbf{T}_{22}\end{vmatrix}}{\begin{vmatrix}\mathbf{W}_{11} & \mathbf{W}_{12}\\ \mathbf{W}_{21} & \mathbf{W}_{22}\end{vmatrix}}-\frac{|\mathbf{T}_{22}|}{|\mathbf{W}_{22}|}, \tag{5.8}$$

whose distribution is unknown except in the case $s=1$.

Suppose that it is required to estimate linear functions $\mathbf{P}'\mathbf{T}_0$ given that $\mathbf{P}'\mathbf{T}_1 = \mathbf{0}$, where $\mathbf{P}$ is a column vector. If we ignore the information $\mathbf{P}'\mathbf{T}_1 = \mathbf{0}$, the least-squares estimate of $\mathbf{P}'\mathbf{T}_0$ is

$$\mathbf{P}'\hat{\mathbf{T}}_0 = \mathbf{P}'(\mathbf{A}'\mathbf{A})^{-1}\mathbf{A}'\mathbf{X}, \tag{5.9}$$

where the inverse matrix in (5.9) is a generalized inverse (as defined in Rao [7],[8]), when the rank $\mathbf{A}$ is less than m. The dispersion matrix of (5.9) is

$$D(\mathbf{P}'(\mathbf{A}'\mathbf{A})^{-1}\mathbf{A}'\mathbf{X}) = \mathbf{P}'(\mathbf{A}'\mathbf{A})^{-1}\mathbf{P}\mathbf{\Sigma}_{11}, \tag{5.10}$$

and an estimate of $\mathbf{\Sigma}_{11}$ is $(n-r)^{-1}\mathbf{E}_{11}$, where

$$\mathbf{E}_{11} = \mathbf{X}'(\mathbf{I} - \mathbf{A}(\mathbf{A}'\mathbf{A})^{-1}\mathbf{A}')\mathbf{X}. \tag{5.11}$$

The confidence interval for any component of $\mathbf{P}'\mathbf{T}_0$ and simultaneous intervals for all the components of $\mathbf{P}'\mathbf{T}_0$ can be obtained using formulas (5.9) to (5.11).

The estimate of $\mathbf{P}'\mathbf{T}_0$ using the concomitant variables $\mathbf{C}$ is

$$\mathbf{P}'\hat{\hat{\mathbf{T}}}_0 = \mathbf{P}'(\mathbf{A}'\mathbf{A})^{-1}\mathbf{A}'\mathbf{X} - \mathbf{P}'(\mathbf{A}'\mathbf{A})^{-1}\mathbf{A}'\mathbf{C}\hat{\mathbf{B}}, \tag{5.12}$$

where $\hat{\mathbf{B}}$ is a solution of the equation $\mathbf{E}_{22}\mathbf{B} = \mathbf{E}_{21}$ and $\mathbf{E}_{21}$ and $\mathbf{E}_{22}$ are defined as

$$\begin{aligned}\mathbf{E}_{21} &= \mathbf{C}'(\mathbf{I} - \mathbf{A}(\mathbf{A}'\mathbf{A})^{-1}\mathbf{A}')\mathbf{X},\\ \mathbf{E}_{22} &= \mathbf{C}'(\mathbf{I} - \mathbf{A}(\mathbf{A}'\mathbf{A})^{-1}\mathbf{A}')\mathbf{C}.\end{aligned} \tag{5.13}$$

The dispersion matrix of the estimates (5.12) is $e\mathbf{\Sigma}_{11\cdot 2}$, where

$$e = \mathbf{P}'(\mathbf{A}'\mathbf{A})^{-1}\mathbf{P} + \mathbf{P}'(\mathbf{A}'\mathbf{A})^{-1}\mathbf{A}'\mathbf{C}\mathbf{E}_{22}^{-1}\mathbf{C}'\mathbf{A}(\mathbf{A}'\mathbf{A})^{-1}\mathbf{P} \tag{5.14}$$

and $\mathbf{\Sigma}_{11\cdot 2} = \mathbf{\Sigma}_{11} - \mathbf{\Sigma}_{12}\mathbf{\Sigma}_{22}^{-1}\mathbf{\Sigma}_{21}$ is estimated by

$$\hat{\mathbf{\Sigma}}_{11\cdot 2} = (n-r-q)^{-1}(\mathbf{E}_{11} - \mathbf{E}_{12}\mathbf{E}_{22}^{-1}\mathbf{E}_{21}) \tag{5.15}$$

on $(n-r-q)$ d.f. Inference on the parametric functions $\mathbf{P}'\mathbf{T}_0$ can be drawn using formulas (5.12) to (5.15). Such inference is of the conditional type, given the values of the concomitant variables. When variations in the concomitant variables are considered, one uses the distribution (2.1) instead of the F distribution.

To compare the alternative estimators (5.9) and (5.12) of $\mathbf{P}'\mathbf{T}_0$ we examine the corresponding dispersion matrices of the estimators $\mathbf{P}'\mathbf{A}\mathbf{P}\mathbf{\Sigma}_{11}$ and $e\mathbf{\Sigma}_{11\cdot 2}$. It is seen from (5.14) that $e \geq \mathbf{P}'\mathbf{A}\mathbf{P}$, and consequently covariance adjustment leads to higher efficiency only if the elements of $\mathbf{\Sigma}_{11\cdot 2}$ are somewhat smaller than those of $\mathbf{\Sigma}_{11}$. Of course, when $\mathbf{\Sigma}_{11\cdot 2} = \mathbf{\Sigma}_{11}$, that is, when $\mathbf{\Sigma}_{12} = 0$, there is always loss of efficiency.

To investigate this problem a little further, we shall consider the simple case of estimating the mean of a variable adjusting for q concomitant variables which are uncorrelated with the main variable. Let us suppose that n independent observations are available on $(q+1)$ variables, one main variable y, and q concomitants $z_1, \dots, z_q$. Further, let

$$(\bar{y} \vdots \bar{\mathbf{z}}') = (\bar{y}, \bar{z}_1, \dots, \bar{z}_q) \tag{5.16}$$

be the observed mean values and

$$\mathbf{S} = \begin{pmatrix} S_{00} & \mathbf{S}_{01} \\ \mathbf{S}_{10} & \mathbf{S}_{11} \end{pmatrix} \tag{5.17}$$

be $(q+1) \times (q+1)$ matrix of the corrected sum of products. The length of the confidence interval for the mean of y based on the observations on y alone is the square root of

$$c_1^2 = \frac{4S_{00}}{n(n-1)} t_1^2, \tag{5.18}$$

where t_1 is the upper $\alpha/2$ point of the t distribution on $(n-1)$ d.f.

When adjustment is made for the concomitant variables $z_1, \dots, z_q$, the corresponding expression is

$$c_2^2 = \frac{4|\mathbf{S}_{11} + n\bar{\mathbf{z}}\bar{\mathbf{z}}'|}{n|\mathbf{S}_{11}|} \frac{S_{00} - \mathbf{S}_{01}\mathbf{S}_{11}^{-1}\mathbf{S}_{10}}{n-q-1} t_2^2, \tag{5.19}$$

where $\bar{\mathbf{z}}' = (\bar{z}_1, \dots, \bar{z}_q)$ and t_2 is the upper $\alpha/2$ point of the t distribution on $(n-q-1)$ d.f. The confidence interval c_1 will be shorter than c_2 if

$$\frac{S_{00} - \mathbf{S}_{01}\mathbf{S}_{11}^{-1}\mathbf{S}_{10}}{S_{00}} > \frac{(n-q-1)t_1^2}{(n-1)t_2^2} \frac{|\mathbf{S}_{11}|}{|\mathbf{S}_{11} + n\bar{\mathbf{z}}\bar{\mathbf{z}}'|}. \tag{5.20}$$

To compute the probability of the event (5.20), let us observe that

$$\frac{S_{00} - \mathbf{S}_{01}\mathbf{S}_{11}^{-1}\mathbf{S}_{10}}{S_{00}} \sim B\left(\frac{n-q-1}{2}, \frac{q}{2}\right) \tag{5.21}$$

(where the symbol $\sim$ is used for "distributed as") and

$$\frac{|\mathbf{S}_{11}|}{|S_{11} + n\bar{\mathbf{z}}\bar{\mathbf{z}}'|} \sim B\left(\frac{n-q}{2}, \frac{q}{2}\right) \tag{5.22}$$

are independently distributed. Hence the desired probability is $P(X_1 > cX_2)$, where X_1 and X_2 are two independent random variables with beta distributions as in (5.21) and (5.22) and c is the constant $(n-q-1)t_1^2/(n-1)\, t_2^2$. Actual computations show that the probability is of the order of 0.80 for $q=1$ and increases with q for values of n of practical interest. The probability will be slightly smaller for large values of n.

6. THE MODEL OF POTTHOFF AND ROY

Potthoff and Roy [3] introduced a model of observations $\mathbf{X}$ such that

$$E(\mathbf{X}) = \mathbf{A}\boldsymbol{\xi}\mathbf{F}, \tag{6.1}$$

where $\mathbf{A}$ and $\mathbf{F}$ are known matrices of orders $n \times m$ and $q \times p$ and $\boldsymbol{\xi}$ is a matrix of order $m \times q$ of unknown parameters. The different rows of $\mathbf{X}$ are distributed independently, while the p components in each row have a p-variate normal distribution with the same dispersion matrix. Starting from the model (6.1) the authors consider the estimation of linear functions of $\boldsymbol{\xi}$ and tests of linear hypotheses on $\boldsymbol{\xi}$. Their approach is summarized below.

Let the rank of $\mathbf{F}$ be q, in which case the rank of $\mathbf{FG}^{-1}\mathbf{F}'$ is q, where $\mathbf{G}$ is any positive definite matrix of order $p \times p$. Multiplying both sides of (6.1) by $\mathbf{G}^{-1}\mathbf{F}'(\mathbf{FG}^{-1}\mathbf{F}')^{-1}$, we have

$$E(\mathbf{Y}) = \mathbf{A}\boldsymbol{\xi}, \tag{6.2}$$

where $\mathbf{Y} = \mathbf{XG}^{-1}\mathbf{F}'(\mathbf{FG}^{-1}\mathbf{F}')^{-1}$. Thus the model (6.1) implies the model (6.2) of the Gauss-Markoff type. The general theory of least squares can then be applied on the model (6.2) for drawing inferences on the parameter $\boldsymbol{\xi}$.

Such a procedure is unsatisfactory, for two reasons. First, the matrix $\mathbf{G}$ is arbitrary. Second, the matrix of observations $\mathbf{X}$ of order $n \times p$ is reduced to a matrix $\mathbf{Y}$ of order $n \times q$, and, if $q < p$, there will be loss of information unless the dispersion matrix of the variables in any row of $\mathbf{X}$ is known and $\mathbf{G}$ is chosen to be this known dispersion matrix. Potthoff and Roy suggest that $\mathbf{G}$ may be chosen on the basis of prior information or estimated from previous data. From a practical point of view, both the suggestions are subject to criticism.

We shall give an alternative reduction of the model (6.1) leading to a conditional model of the type (5.2), in which case the general theory of Section 5 will apply. Construct a $p \times p$ nonsingular matrix $\mathbf{H} = (\mathbf{H}_1 \vdots \mathbf{H}_2)$ such that $\mathbf{FH}_2 = \mathbf{0}$ and the columns of $\mathbf{H}_1$ form a basis of the vector space generated by the rows of $\mathbf{F}$. Such a matrix $\mathbf{H}$ is not necessarily unique. Let r be the number of columns in $\mathbf{H}_1$. Multiplying both sides of (6.1) by $\mathbf{H}$, we find

$$E(\mathbf{XH}_1) = \mathbf{A}\boldsymbol{\xi}\mathbf{FH}_1, \qquad E(\mathbf{XH}_2) = \mathbf{0}. \tag{6.3}$$

The rank of $\mathbf{FH}_1$ is obviously r, and hence $\boldsymbol{\xi}\mathbf{FH}_1$ can be replaced by an $(m \times r)$-order matrix $\boldsymbol{\eta}$ of independent parameters, so that the setup (6.1) is equivalent to

$$E(\mathbf{Y}) = \mathbf{A}\boldsymbol{\eta}, \qquad E(\mathbf{Z}) = \mathbf{0}, \tag{6.4}$$

where $\mathbf{Y} = \mathbf{XH}_1$ and $\mathbf{Z} = \mathbf{XH}_2$. Hence the conditional expectation of $\mathbf{Y}$ given $\mathbf{Z}$ can be written

$$E(\mathbf{Y}|\mathbf{Z}) = \mathbf{F}\boldsymbol{\eta} + \mathbf{ZB}, \tag{6.5}$$

introducing the matrix **B** of unknown regression parameters. Thus we have the observations **Y** and the expectation matrix (6.5) of the Gauss-Markoff type as in (5.2). Then the general theory of analysis of dispersion with adjustment for concomitant variables as given in Section 5 is applicable.

It may be noted that the matrix **H** is not unique but the estimates of parametric functions and test criteria based on analysis of dispersion will be the same for all choices of **H**, satisfying the stated conditions.

When the rank of **F** is q, we can choose $\mathbf{H}_1$ as $\mathbf{G}^{-1}\mathbf{F}'(\mathbf{F}\mathbf{G}^{-1}\mathbf{F}')^{-1}$ and $\mathbf{H}_2$ such that $\mathbf{F}\mathbf{H}_2 = 0$, where **G** is an arbitrary positive-definite matrix. In such a case the conditional expectation (6.5) is

$$E(\mathbf{Y}|\mathbf{Z}) = \mathbf{A}\boldsymbol{\xi} + \mathbf{Z}\mathbf{B}, \tag{6.6}$$

in which the original parameters are retained.

In the method of Potthoff and Roy, the information contained in **Z** is ignored.

7. AN ILLUSTRATIVE EXAMPLE

Let $\mathbf{Y}' = (y_1, \ldots, y_p)$ be observations on a growth curve at p points of time such that

$$E(y_i) = \beta_0 + \beta_1\varphi_{1i} + \cdots + \beta_k\varphi_{ki}, \quad D(\mathbf{Y}) = \boldsymbol{\Sigma} \qquad (i = 1, \ldots, p), \tag{7.1}$$

where φ_{ji} is the value of the jth orthogonal polynomial (in time) at the ith time point. If n independent growth curves each satisfying condition (7.1) are considered, we have an $n \times p$ matrix **X** of observations with the expectation

$$E(\mathbf{X}) = \mathbf{U}\boldsymbol{\beta}\boldsymbol{\Phi}, \tag{7.2}$$

where $\mathbf{U}' = (1, \ldots, 1)$ with all unities, $\boldsymbol{\beta} = (\beta_0, \ldots, \beta_k)$, and $\boldsymbol{\Phi}$ is a $(1 + k) \times p$ matrix of values of orthogonal polynomials of orders 0 to k. The model (7.2) is a special case of (6.1). Let $\boldsymbol{\Phi}_0$ be a $(p - 1 - k) \times p$ matrix of values of orthogonal polynomials of orders $(k + 1)$ to p. Then

$$E[\mathbf{X}(\boldsymbol{\Phi}' \vdots \boldsymbol{\Phi}_0')] = \mathbf{U}\boldsymbol{\beta}\boldsymbol{\Phi}(\boldsymbol{\Phi}' \vdots \boldsymbol{\Phi}_0') = \mathbf{U}\boldsymbol{\beta}(\mathbf{I} \vdots \mathbf{0}), \tag{7.3}$$

giving

$$E(\mathbf{X}\boldsymbol{\Phi}') = \mathbf{U}\boldsymbol{\beta}, \qquad E(\mathbf{X}\boldsymbol{\Phi}_0') = \mathbf{0},$$

a model of the type (6.3). The transformation (7.3) simply implies that if, instead of $(y_1, \ldots, y_p)$ in (7.1), we consider the equivalent variables $(b_0, \ldots, b_{p-1})$ such that

$$b_i = y_1\varphi_{i1} + \cdots + y_p\varphi_{ip}, \tag{7.4}$$

we have a p-dimensional variable $\mathbf{b}$ such that

$$\begin{aligned} E(b_i) &= \beta_i, \qquad i = 0, 1, \ldots, k, \\ &= 0, \qquad i = k+1, \ldots, p-1. \end{aligned} \tag{7.5}$$

We are required to draw inferences on β_i given n sets of independent observations on $\mathbf{b}$ with expectation as in (7.5) and with an unknown dispersion matrix.

We recognize the variables $b_{k+1}, \ldots, b_{p-1}$ as concomitants and proceed to estimate the coefficients β_i using the method outlined in Section 5. Before doing so, it is worthwhile examining whether it is profitable to consider the concomitants. We shall illustrate the procedure by an example given in [3] with $p = 4$ and $n = 16$. The first step is to obtain b_0, b_1, b_2, and b_3 from $y_1, \ldots, y_4$ on each curve and compute the averages and the corrected sum of squares and products from the 16 sets of four b values. The results are summarized in Table II, which also contains individual F tests for testing the significance of each coefficient, and also the correlation matrix in the lower half of matrix on the right side. ($b_0, \ldots, b_3$ are computed using the unstandardized values of the orthogonal polynomials. An adjustment for this is made in Table III, where the estimates of β_i are given.)

TABLE II

Individual Tests and S.P. and Correlation Matrices for $b_0, \ldots, b_3$

$\bar{b}$	$F_{1,\,15}$	S.P. and correlation matrices			
		b_0	b_1	b_2	b_3
$\bar{b}_0 = 99.875$	2982[a]	802.7500	−5.6250	−35.8750	−213.7500
$\bar{b}_1 = 15.687$	59.63[a]	−0.0063	990.4375	−91.4375	105.8750
$\bar{b}_2 = 0.813$	1.88	−0.1383	−0.3162	84.4375	4.6250
$\bar{b}_3 = 1.125$	0.26	−0.2221	0.0987	0.0148	1161.7500

[a] Indicates significance at the 1% level.

It is clear from Table II that b_2 and b_3 are of the nature of concomitants, indicating that the degree of the polynomial to be considered is unity. Further, none of the correlations between (b_0, b_1) and the concomitants (b_2, b_3) is high (not significantly different from zero at 5%), showing that covariance adjustment is not profitable. The point estimates of β_0 and β_1 and the confidence intervals based on the observations on b_0 and b_1 only are given in Table III with the corresponding results of Potthoff and Roy. It is seen from

TABLE III

Estimates and Widths of 95% Confidence Interval

Parameter		Using b_0 and b_1	Method of Potthoff and Roy
β_0	Estimate	24.969	25.111
	Width	1.948	1.941
β_1	Estimate	0.7844	0.7665
	Width	0.429	0.471

Table III that slightly more efficient estimates are obtained by the proposed method. It may be noted that a preliminary analysis led us to decisions on the degree of the polynomial and the use of concomitants, on which the final analysis is based. Does it imply that our computed precisions are over-estimated and need some adjustment because of our preliminary examination of data? This situation must be faced in any statistical analysis of real data where the model used for final analysis is partly determined by a preliminary examination of data. But such difficulties in interpretation arise only if we are considering an isolated case. I imagine that in any experimental investigation a series of growth curves will be studied, possibly under different experimental conditions (treatments), involving the estimation of polynomial growth coefficients in each case and very often a comparison of such estimates. It should be possible to decide on a suitable set of concomitants for such a purpose.

For a discussion of the methods of estimation of polynomial growth curves the reader is referred to [6, 9, 10].

REFERENCES

1. COCHRAN, W. G. (1964). Comparison of two methods of handling covariates in discriminatory analysis. *Ann. Inst. Statist. Math.* **16** 43–53.
2. COCHRAN, W. G. and BLISS, C. I. (1948). Discriminant functions with covariance. *Ann Math. Statist.* **19** 151–176.
3. POTTHOFF, R. F. and ROY, S. N. (1964). A generalized multivariate analysis of variance model useful especially for growth curve problems. *Biometrika* **51** 313–326.
4. RAO, C. R. (1946). Tests with discriminant functions in multivariate analysis. *Sankhyā* **7** 407–414.
5. RAO, C. R. (1949). On some problems arising out of discrimination with multiple characters. *Sankhyā* **9** 343–366.
6. RAO, C. R. (1959). Some problems involving linear hypotheses in multivariate analysis. *Biometrika* **46** 49–58.
7. RAO, C. R. (1962). A note on the generalized inverse of a matrix with applications to problems in mathematical statistics. *J. Roy. Statist. Soc. Ser. B* **24** 152–158.

8. Rao, C. R. (1966). Generalized inverse for matrices and its application in mathematical statistics. *Neyman Festschrift Volume, Research Papers in Statistics* (F. N. David, ed.), pp. 263–279. Wiley, London (in press).
9. Rao, C. R. (1965). The theory of least squares when the parameters are stochastic and it application to the analysis of growth curves. *Biometrika* **52** 447–458.
10. Rao, C. R. (1966). Least square theory using an estimated dispersion matrix and its application to measurement of signals. *Proc. 5th Berkeley Symp. Math. Statist. Prob.* (in press).

Power of the Likelihood-Ratio Test Used in Analysis of Dispersion

J. ROY

RESEARCH AND TRAINING SCHOOL
INDIAN STATISTICAL INSTITUTE
CALCUTTA, INDIA

1. SUMMARY

The power function of Wilks' likelihood-ratio test for general multivariate linear hypothesis when the alternative hypothesis is of unit rank is discussed in detail in this paper. An exact expression is obtained for the case of two variables. For an unrestricted number of variables, two approximations to the power function are obtained; one is based on an expansion in gamma series, the other makes use of Jacobi polynomials. The accuracy of these approximations is examined numerically for the case of two variables.

2. NOTATIONS

Matrices will be denoted by boldface capital letters. An expression like $\mathbf{A}$: $m \times n$ indicates that the matrix $\mathbf{A}$ has m rows and n columns. The following notations will be used for the gamma and beta density functions and the corresponding distribution functions:

$$g(x \mid a) = \frac{1}{\Gamma(a)} e^{-x} x^{a-1}; \qquad 0 \le x < \infty; \quad a > 0, \tag{2.1}$$

$$G(x \mid a) = \int_0^x g(t \mid a)\, dt, \tag{2.2}$$

$$\beta(x \mid a, b) = \frac{\Gamma(a+b)}{\Gamma(a)\Gamma(b)} x^{a-1}(1-x)^{b-1}; \qquad 0 \le x \le 1,\ a, b > 0, \tag{2.3}$$

$$B(x \mid a, b) = \int_0^x \beta(t \mid a, b)\, dt. \tag{2.4}$$

3. GENERAL MULTIVARIATE LINEAR HYPOTHESIS

Consider pN random variables $x_{i\lambda}$, $i = 1, 2, \ldots, p$, $\lambda = 1, 2, \ldots, N$, jointly distributed in a multivariate normal form, with expected values

$$\mathscr{E}(x_{i\lambda}) = a_{1\lambda}\theta_{i1} + a_{2\lambda}\theta_{i2} + \cdots + a_{q\lambda}\theta_{iq} \tag{3.1}$$

and second-order moments

$$\operatorname{Var}(x_{i\lambda}) = \sigma_{ii}, \qquad \operatorname{Cov}(x_{i\lambda}, x_{i'\lambda'}) = \sigma_{ii'} \cdot \partial_{\lambda\lambda'}, \tag{3.2}$$

where $\partial_{\lambda\lambda} = 1$ and $\partial_{\lambda\lambda'} = 0$ for $\lambda \neq \lambda'$. We shall use the following matrix notations:

$$\mathbf{X} = ((x_{i\lambda})), \quad \mathbf{A} = ((a_{j\lambda})), \quad \mathbf{\Theta} = ((\theta_{ij})), \quad \mathbf{\Sigma} = ((\sigma_{ii'})), \tag{3.3}$$

so that (3.1) can be written

$$\mathscr{E}(\mathbf{X}) = \mathbf{\Theta A}.$$

Here $\mathbf{\Theta}$ and $\mathbf{\Sigma}$ are unknown parameter matrices and $\mathbf{A}$ is a matrix of known constants. Let

$$\operatorname{Rank}(\mathbf{A}) = r \leq \min(q, N). \tag{3.4}$$

To avoid triviality, we assume $p \geq 2$ and $N \geq r + p$.

With the above so-called classical fixed-effects model, the basic problem of analysis of dispersion (or, multivariate analysis of variance) is to test a linearly consistent hypothesis of the form

$$\mathscr{H}_0\colon \quad \mathbf{\Theta B} = \mathbf{K}, \tag{3.5}$$

where $\mathbf{B}\colon \ q \times t$ and $\mathbf{K}\colon \ p \times t$ are given matrices.

To reduce the problem to the standard form, we proceed as follows. We call a matrix $\mathbf{G}\colon \ g \times h$ semiorthogonal if $g > h$ and $\mathbf{G}'\mathbf{G} = \mathbf{I}$. Since $\mathbf{A}$ is of rank r, it is possible to find a semiorthogonal matrix $\mathbf{T}_1\colon \ N \times N - r$ such that $\mathbf{AT}_1 = 0$. Again resolving each column vector of $\mathbf{B}$ into two components, one along, and the other orthogonal to, the vector space generated by the column vectors of $\mathbf{AA}'$, we see that there exist matrices $\mathbf{C}\colon \ q \times t$ and $\mathbf{R}\colon \ q \times t$ such that $\mathbf{B} = \mathbf{AA}'\mathbf{C} + \mathbf{R}$, where $\mathbf{RC}'\mathbf{AA}' = \mathbf{0}$. But since $\mathbf{GAA}' = \mathbf{0}$ if and only if $\mathbf{GA} = \mathbf{0}$, we deduce that $\mathbf{C}$ satisfies $(\mathbf{B} - \mathbf{AA}'\mathbf{C})\mathbf{C}'\mathbf{A} = \mathbf{0}$. Let Rank $(\mathbf{A}'\mathbf{CC}'\mathbf{A}) = m$; we can then find a matrix $\mathbf{D}\colon \ N \times m$ such that $\mathbf{T}_2\colon \ N \times m = \mathbf{A}'\mathbf{CC}'\mathbf{AD}$ is semiorthogonal. Obviously $m \leq r$, and $\mathbf{T}_2{}'\mathbf{T}_1 = \mathbf{0}$. We can now find a matrix $\mathbf{T}_3\colon \ N \times r - m$ such that the matrix $[\mathbf{T}_1 \mid \mathbf{T}_2 \mid \mathbf{T}_3]$ is an orthogonal $N \times N$ matrix. We now make the orthogonal transformation $[\mathbf{Y}_1 \mid \mathbf{Y}_2 \mid \mathbf{Y}_3] = \mathbf{X}[\mathbf{T}_1 \mid \mathbf{T}_2 \mid \mathbf{T}_3]$. The second moments are invariant under this transformation, but the expected values are transformed to

$$\mathscr{E}(\mathbf{Y}_1) = \mathbf{0}, \quad \mathscr{E}(\mathbf{Y}_u) = \mathbf{M}_u, \qquad u = 2, 3 \tag{3.6}$$

where $\mathbf{M}_2 = \mathbf{\Theta BC'AD}$ and $\mathbf{M}_3 = \mathbf{\Theta AT}_3$. We note that $\mathscr{H}_0$ specifies that $\mathbf{M}_2 = \mathbf{KC'AD} = \mathbf{M}_{20}$, say, whereas $\mathbf{M}_3$: $p \times r - m$ remains as a matrix of nuisance parameters. Since $\mathbf{Y}_3$ does not supply any useful information, we ignore it, and write for simplicity $n = N - r$, $\mathbf{Z}_1 = \mathbf{Y}_1$: $p \times n$, $\mathbf{Z}_2 = \mathbf{Y}_2 - \mathbf{M}_{20}$: $p \times m$, $\mathbf{M} = \mathbf{M}_2 - \mathbf{M}_{20}$.

In terms of the $p(n+m)$ random variables $\mathbf{Z} = [Z_1 \mid Z_2] = ((z_{i\lambda}))$, $i = 1, 2, \ldots, p$; $\lambda = 1, 2, \ldots, n+m$, which have expected values

$$\mathscr{E}(\mathbf{Z}_1) = \mathbf{0}, \qquad \mathscr{E}(\mathbf{Z}_2) = \mathbf{M} \tag{3.7}$$

and second-order moments

$$\operatorname{Var}(z_{i\lambda}) = \sigma_{ii}, \qquad \operatorname{Cov}(z_{i\lambda}, z_{i'\lambda'}) = \sigma_{ii'} \cdot \partial_{\lambda\lambda'}. \tag{3.8}$$

The problem then is to test the hypothesis

$$\mathscr{H}_0\colon \quad \mathbf{M} = \mathbf{0}. \tag{3.9}$$

4. TEST PROCEDURES

Various procedures are available for testing $\mathscr{H}_0$, of which mention may be made of (a) the likelihood-ratio procedure due to Wilks [32], (b) a generalization of Hotelling's T^2 due to Lawley [12], and Hotelling [8 and 9], (c) the union-intersection procedure due to S. N. Roy [27], and (d) the step-down procedure due to J. Roy [21]. All these procedures make use of two symmetric stochastic matrices of order p, namely,

$$\mathbf{E} = \mathbf{Z}_1\mathbf{Z}_1', \qquad \mathbf{H} = \mathbf{Z}_2\mathbf{Z}_2'.$$

We shall call **E** the error sum of products (S.P.) matrix and we shall call **H** the hypothesis S.P. matrix. The integers $n = N - r$ and m are called the error degrees of freedom (d.f.) and the hypothesis d.f., respectively. The first three procedures are invariant under nonsingular linear transformations, and although the fourth procedure is not invariant, it has certain other advantages.

For a given level of significance α, $(0 < \alpha < 1)$, the rules for rejection of $\mathscr{H}_0$, according to the above three invariant procedures, are given below.

$$\text{Procedure (a):} \quad W \equiv \frac{|\mathbf{E}|}{|\mathbf{E} + \mathbf{H}|} < w, \tag{4.1}$$

$$\text{Procedure (b):} \quad V \equiv \operatorname{tr}(\mathbf{HE}^{-1}) > v, \tag{4.2}$$

$$\text{Procedure (c):} \quad U \equiv \lambda_{\max}[\mathbf{H}(\mathbf{E} + \mathbf{H}^{-1})] > u. \tag{4.3}$$

where "tr" denotes the trace and $\lambda_{\max}$ the maximum latent root of a matrix. Here constants u, v, and w are defined by the equations

$$\begin{aligned} \operatorname{Prob}(W < w \mid \mathscr{H}_0) &= \operatorname{Prob}(V > v \mid \mathscr{H}_0) \\ &= \operatorname{Prob}(U > u \mid \mathscr{H}_0) = \alpha. \end{aligned} \tag{4.4}$$

Let $s = \min(p, m)$, and denote by $1 > l_1 > l_2 > \cdots > l_s > 0$ the positive latent roots of the matrix $\mathbf{H}(\mathbf{E}+\mathbf{H})^{-1}$. Then

$$W = (1 - l_1)(1 - l_2) \cdots (1 - l_s), \tag{4.5}$$

$$V = \frac{l_1}{1 - l_1} + \frac{l_2}{1 - l_2} + \cdots + \frac{l_s}{1 - l_s}, \tag{4.6}$$

$$U = l_1. \tag{4.7}$$

The joint probability function of $l_1, l_2, \ldots, l_s$ under $\mathscr{H}_0$ was obtained independently at about the same time by Fisher [5], Girshick [6], Hsu [10], and S. N. Roy [23]. Under $\mathscr{H}_0$ the random variables $l_1, l_2, \ldots, l_s$ are jointly stochastically independent of the elements of $(\mathbf{E}+\mathbf{H})$. The nonnull distribution of these roots is rather complex, but it is known (Anderson [1]) that if Rank $(\mathbf{M}) = t \le \min(p, m)$, the joint distribution involves at most the t noncentrality parameters $\partial_1, \partial_2, \ldots, \partial_t$, which are the positive latent roots of the matrix $\mathbf{M}'\mathbf{\Sigma}^{-1}\mathbf{M}$. It is also known that the joint distribution is unaffected by altering m, n, and p to $m^* = p$, $n^* = n + m - p$, and $p^* = m$, so that without loss of generality one need consider only values of $m \ge p$.

Except for certain special values of p or m, the exact distributions of the statistics U, V, or W are not yet available in neat closed forms, even in the null case. For the distribution of W in the null case, the moments were obtained by Wilks [32], who also obtained the exact distributions in closed form for the cases $p = 2$, any m; $p = 3$, $m = 3, 4$; and $p = 4$, $m = 4$ [33]. These results with certain corrections are quoted by Anderson [2]. Various approximations to the null distribution of W were given by Bartlett [3] and Rao [17–19]. Asymptotically for large n, the statistic $-[n - (p + m + 1)/2] \log_e W$ follows the chi-square distribution with pm degrees of freedom under $\mathscr{H}_0$. For large n, the statistic nV follows the chi-square distribution with pm degrees of freedom in the null case. The exact null distribution of V for special values of p and m has been investigated by Hotelling [9]. S. N. Roy [25] gave a computational algorithm for the distribution function of U. The same distribution was also obtained by Nanda [13, 14]. Using approximations given by Pillai [15], Heck [7] prepared charts from which the upper 1%, 2.5%, and 5% points of the null distribution of U can be read off for a useful range of values of m, n, and p.

These three tests have certain attractive features. The tests are all uniformly unbiased and consistent. The power function of each test is a monotonic-increasing function[1] of each of the noncentrality parameters [4, 30]. None of

[1] See also [34].

these three tests is uniformly more powerful than either of the other two tests. Very little, however, is known about the actual magnitude of the power. S. N. Roy [26] obtained a computational algorithm for the nonnull distribution of U which is valid when there is just one noncentrality parameter. He also gave [27] a very elegant lower bound for the power of his test. Anderson [1] obtained the moments of W when the number of noncentrality parameters $t = 1, 2$. For the case $t = 1$, J. Roy [22] obtained a gamma-series expansion for the power function of Wilks' test, which is convenient to use when the error d.f. is large and the noncentrality parameter is small. Recently, Posten and Bargmann [16] obtained another approximation.

5. THE NONNULL DISTRIBUTION OF WILKS' CRITERION

We shall refer to the null distribution of W as Wilks' distribution with degrees of freedom p, m, and n. It was shown by J. Roy [22] that the nonnull distribution of W is the same as the product of two independent statistics W_1 and W_2, where W_1 follows Wilks' distribution with degrees of freedom p, $m-t$, and n, and $W_2 = |\mathbf{L}_1\mathbf{L}_1'|/|\mathbf{L}_1\mathbf{L}_1' + \mathbf{L}_2\mathbf{L}_2'|$, where the elements of $\mathbf{L}_1$: $p \times n+m-t$ and $\mathbf{L}_2$: $p \times t$ are all independent random variables each distributed normally with unit variance and expected values $\mathscr{E}(\mathbf{L}_1) = \mathbf{0}$ and $\mathscr{E}(\mathbf{L}_2) = \left[\dfrac{\mathbf{0}}{\mathbf{\Delta}}\right]$, where $\mathbf{\Delta}$ is a $t \times t$ diagonal matrix with diagonal elements $\partial_1, \partial_2, \ldots, \partial_t$, which are the noncentrality parameters.

When $t = 1$, W_2 follows the noncentral beta distribution with indices $(n+m-p)/2$, $p/2$, and noncentrality parameter $\partial = \operatorname{tr} \mathbf{M}'\mathbf{\Sigma}^{-1}\mathbf{M}$, so that its probability density function is

$$\sum_{j=0}^{\infty} p_j(\tfrac{1}{2}\partial)\beta\left(w_2, \frac{n+m-p}{2}, \frac{p}{2}+j\right), \tag{5.1}$$

where $p_j(\theta) = e^{-\theta}\theta^j/j!$ and ∂ is the single noncentrality parameter involved. Consequently, the probability that the product $W = W_1 \cdot W_2$ is less than a preassigned constant x, $(0 < x < 1)$, may be evaluated as

$$\operatorname{Prob}(W < x) = \sum_{j=0}^{\infty} p_j(\tfrac{1}{2}\partial) \cdot P_j(x \mid p, m, n), \tag{5.2}$$

where

$$\mathrm{P}_j(x \mid p, m, n) = \int_{w_1 w_2 < x} f(w_1 \mid p, m-1, n)\beta\left(w_2 \,\middle|\, \frac{n+m-p}{2}, \frac{p}{2}+j\right) dw_1\, dw_2, \tag{5.3}$$

where $f(w_1 \mid p, m-1, n)$ is the probability density function of Wilks' distribution with $p, m-1$, and n degrees of freedom. The following approximation to $P_j(x \mid p, m, n)$ has been derived [22]:

$$P_j(x \mid p, m, n) = G(x_j \mid \tfrac{1}{2}pm + j) + 0(n^{-2}), \tag{5.4}$$

where $x_j = \max(0, -\frac{1}{2}(n - \lambda_j) \log_e x)$, where

$$\lambda_j = \{\tfrac{1}{2}pm(p + m + 1) + j - 2j^2\}/(pm + j). \tag{5.5}$$

The gth moment of W when $t = 1$ was obtained by Anderson [1] as

$$\mathscr{E}(W^g) = C_g(p, m, n) \sum_{j=0}^{\infty} p_j(\tfrac{1}{2}\partial)\left[\Gamma\left(\frac{m+n}{2}+1\right)\Big/\Gamma\left(\frac{m+n}{2}+j+g\right)\right], \tag{5.6}$$

where

$$C_g(p, m, n) = \prod_{i=2}^{p}\left[\Gamma\left(\frac{m+n+1-i}{2}\right)\Big/\Gamma\left(\frac{m+n+1-i}{2}+g\right)\right]$$
$$\times \prod_{i=1}^{p}\left[\Gamma\left(\frac{n+1-i}{2}+g\right)\Big/\Gamma\left(\frac{n+1-i}{2}\right)\right].$$

We shall make use of this expression in obtaining another approximation of the power function using Jacobi polynomials.

6. THE EXACT POWER FUNCTION OF WILKS' TEST WHEN $p = 2$ AND $t = 1$

It is known that if W_1 follows Wilks' distribution with degrees of freedom 2, $m - 1$ and n, then $W_1^* = +W_1^{1/2}$ follows the beta distribution with density function $\beta(w_1 \mid n-1, m-1)$. Thus when $p = 2$ and $t = 1$, Wilks' statistic W is distributed as $(W_1^*)^2 \cdot W_2$, where W_1^* and W_2 are independent random variables, and W_1^* follows the beta distribution with density $\beta(w_1 \mid n-1, m-1)$ and W_2 follows the noncentral beta distribution with indices $\frac{1}{2}(m + n - 2)$, 1, and noncentrality parameter ∂. Thus for any given x, $0 < x < 1$, the distribution function of W is given by (5.2), where we write for simplicity,

$$P(x \mid m, n, j) = P_j(x \mid 2, m, n)$$
$$= \iint \beta(w_1 \mid n-1, m-1)\beta\left(w_2 \,\middle|\, \frac{m+n-2}{2}, j+1\right) dw_1\, dw_2, \tag{6.1}$$

where the integration is to be carried over the region $R(x)$: $w_1{}^2 w_2 \le x$;

$0 \le w_1, w_2 \le 1$. To evaluate the integral we express $R(x)$ as the union of the two disjoint regions

$$R_1(x): 0 \le w_2 \le x, \qquad 0 \le w_1 \le 1,$$

$$R_2(x): x < w_2 \le 1, \qquad 0 \le w_1 \le (x/w_2)^{1/2}.$$

Integrating separately over $R_1(x)$ and $R_2(x)$, we get

$$P(x \mid m, n, j) = B\left(x \,\middle|\, \frac{m+n-2}{2}, j+1\right) + P^*(x \mid m, n, j), \tag{6.2}$$

where

$$P^*(x \mid m, n, j) = \int_x^1 \beta\left(w_2 \,\middle|\, \frac{m+n-2}{2}, j+1\right) B\left(\frac{x^{1/2}}{w_2^{1/2}} \,\middle|\, n-1, m-1\right) dw_2. \tag{6.3}$$

To evaluate P^* we write it as

$$P^* = \tfrac{1}{2}(1-x) \int_{-1}^{1} \beta\left\{\tfrac{1}{2}(1-x)w + \tfrac{1}{2}(1+x) \,\middle|\, \frac{m+n-2}{2}, j+1\right\}$$
$$\times B\left\{\left[\frac{2x}{(1-x)w + (1+x)}\right]^{1/2} \,\middle|\, n-1, m-1\right\} dw \tag{6.4}$$

and apply the eight-point Gaussian quadrature formula:

$$P^* \doteq \tfrac{1}{2}(1-x) \sum_{u=1}^{8} H_u \beta\left(\Psi_u \,\middle|\, \frac{m+n-2}{2}, j+1\right) \cdot B(\Phi_u \mid n-1, m-1), \tag{6.5}$$

where

$$\Psi_u = \tfrac{1}{2}(1-x)K_u + \tfrac{1}{2}(1+x), \qquad \Phi_u = (x/\Psi_u)^{1/2},$$

where $H_u = H_{9-u}$ and $K_u = -K_{9-u}$ are the quadrature constants, quoted below from Kopal [11].

u	K_u	H_u
1	0.960289856497536	0.101228536290376
2	0.796666477413627	0.222381033453374
3	0.525532409916329	0.313706645877887
4	0.183434642495650	0.362683783378362

7. APPROXIMATIONS USING JACOBI POLYNOMIALS

The Jacobi polynomial $J_r(x \mid a, b)$ of degree r in x with parameters $a, b > 0$ is defined by

$$
\begin{aligned}
&J_0(x \mid a, b) = 1, \\
&J_r(x \mid a, b) = \sum_{v=0}^{r} (-1)^v c_v(r \mid a, b) x^v \qquad \text{for} \quad r = 1, 2, \ldots,
\end{aligned}
\tag{7.1}
$$

where

$$
\begin{aligned}
c_0(r \mid a, b) &= a(a+1) \cdots (a+r-1)/r!, \\
c_v(r \mid a, b) &= (r+a+b-1)(r+a+b) \cdots (r+a+b+v-2)/v! \\
&\quad \times (a+v)(a+v+1) \cdots (a+r-1)/(r-v)! \\
&\qquad\qquad \text{for} \quad v = 1, 2, \cdots, r-1, \\
c_r(r \mid a, b) &= (r+a+b-1)(r+a+b) \cdots (2r+a+b-2)/r!.
\end{aligned}
\tag{7.2}
$$

These polynomials are orthogonal with respect to the beta density function $\beta(x \mid a, b)$ in the interval (0, 1), so that

$$\int_0^1 J_r J_s \beta \, dx = k_r(a, b) \partial_{rs}, \tag{7.3}$$

where $\partial_{rs} = 0$ if $r \neq s$ and $\partial_{rr} = 1$ and

$$
\begin{aligned}
&k_0(a, b) = 1, \\
&k_r(a, b) = \frac{a(a+1) \cdots (a+r-1) b(b+1) \cdots (b+r-1)}{r!(2r+a+b-1)(a+b)(a+b+1) \cdots (a+b+r-2)}
\end{aligned}
\tag{7.4}
$$

for $r = 1, 2, \ldots$. Also,

$$
\begin{aligned}
&\int_0^x J_r(t \mid a, b) \beta(t \mid a, b) \, dt \\
&= -\frac{ab}{r(a+b)(a+b+1)} \beta(x \mid a+1, b+1) J_{r-1}(x \mid a+1, b+1)
\end{aligned}
\tag{7.5}
$$

for $r = 1, 2, \ldots$. For proof of these results, the reader is referred to Szegö [31].

Let X be a random variable distributed in the interval (0, 1) with a continuous density function $f(x)$. The quotient $f(x)/\beta(x \mid a, b)$ can be expanded formally in an infinite series in Jacobi polynomials as

$$\frac{f(x)}{\beta(x \mid a, b)} = \sum_{r=0}^{\infty} a_r J_r(x \mid a, b). \tag{7.6}$$

Multiplying both sides by $J_r(x \mid a, b)$ and integrating over x from 0 to 1, we get

$$a_r = \int_0^1 J_r f \, dx / k_r \tag{7.7}$$

formally, by virtue of the orthogonality property of Jacobi polynomials.

What we seek here is an approximation to $f(x)$ using only the first four terms. Thus

$$f(x) \sim \beta(x \mid a, b) \sum_{r=0}^{4} a_r J_r(x \mid a, b). \tag{7.8}$$

This in turn gives the following approximation for the cumulative distribution function $F(x) = \int_0^x f(t)\, dt$:

$$F(x) \sim B(x \mid a, b) - \beta(x \mid a+1, b+1) \sum_{r=1}^{4} a_r^* J_{r-1}(x \mid a+1, b+1), \tag{7.9}$$

where

$$a_r^* = \frac{a_r \cdot ab}{r(a+b)(a+b+1)}. \tag{7.10}$$

Let us write θ_g for the gth moment of X about the origin; thus

$$\theta_g = E(X^g) = \int_0^1 x^g f(x)\, dx, \qquad g = 1, 2, \ldots. \tag{7.11}$$

We now choose a and b to make $a_1 = a_2 = 0$. This gives

$$a = \frac{\theta_1(\theta_1 - \theta_2)}{\theta_2 - \theta_1^2}, \qquad b = \frac{(\theta_2 - \theta_1)(\theta_1 - 1)}{\theta_2 - \theta_1^2}. \tag{7.12}$$

We write $s = a + b$, and then get explicitly

$$a_3^* = \frac{s+5}{(b+1)(b+2)} \left[\frac{a}{3} - (s+2)\theta_1 + \frac{(s+2)(s+3)}{a+1}\theta_2 - \frac{(s+2)(s+3)(s+4)}{3(a+1)(a+2)}\theta_3 \right] \tag{7.13}$$

and

$$a_4^* = \frac{(s+7)(s+2)}{(b+1)(b+2)(b+3)} \left[\frac{a}{4} - (s+3)\theta_1 + \frac{3(s+3)(s+4)}{2(a+1)}\theta_2 - \frac{(s+3)(s+4)(s+5)}{(a+1)(a+2)}\theta_3 + \frac{(s+3)(s+4)(s+5)(s+6)}{(a+1)(a+2)(a+3)}\theta_4 \right]. \tag{7.14}$$

As an illustrative example consider the evaluation of the power function of Wilks' test for the case $p=2$, $m=2$, $n=50$ and deviation parameter $\partial=2.0$, at the 5% level of significance. The first four moments about the origin of the statistic can be computed from (5.6); these turn out to be

$$\theta_1 = 0.890796, \quad \theta_2 = 0.797926, \quad \theta_3 = 0.718370, \quad \theta_4 = 0.649762,$$

respectively. Using (7.12), (7.13), and (7.14) we get

$a = 18.7669$, $b = 2.30065$, $a_3{}^* = 0.517025 \times 10^{-3}$, $a_4{}^* = 0.289055 \times 10^{-3}$, respectively. The lower 5% point of the null distribution of the statistic is

$$x = 0.825557$$

The power function is thus approximated by (7.9) as

$$F \sim B(x \mid a, b) - \beta(x \mid a+1, b+1)(a_3{}^* J_2 + a_4{}^* J_3) = 0.15357.$$

The exact value is 0.16041, so that the relative error in the Jacobi-series approximation is about 4.3%.

8. TABLES

The methods developed in the preceding sections were used in the preparation of the following tables. Table I gives a comparison of the exact value, the gamma approximation, and the Jacobi-series approximation for the power function of Wilks' test at the 5% level of significance for $p = 2$, $m = 1(1)5$; $n = 20, 50, 100$; and $\partial = 2, 10, 20$. Table II gives to five decimal places the exact power of Wilks' test at the 5% level for $p = 2$, $m = 1(1)10$; $n = 10, 20, 50, 100$, inf; and $\beta = 2(2), 20(4)40, 50$. Table III gives to four decimal places the gamma approximation of the power of Wilks' test at the 5% level for $p = 3(1)6$; $m = 1(1)50$; $n = 50, 100, 200$, inf; and $\partial = 2(2), 20(4), 40, 50$.

The computations were carried out on an IBM 1401-8K-4 tape electronic data processing machine system using programs written in FORTRAN II. Because of the small capacity of the system, the computations had to be done in several phases.

TABLE I

COMPARISON OF EXACT VALUES,
GAMMA APPROXIMATION AND JACOBI APPROXIMATION OF
POWER FUNCTION OF WILKS' ANALYSIS OF DISPERSION TEST
AT 5% LEVEL, FOR TWO VARIATES

M	N	D	EXACT	GAMMA	JACOBI
1	20	2	0.19810	0.18993	0.17880
1	20	10	0.74571	0.68794	0.72733
1	20	20	0.96622	0.93231	0.98578
1	50	2	0.21428	0.21139	0.19343
1	50	10	0.78958	0.77371	0.80363
1	50	20	0.97937	0.97391	0.99583
1	100	2	0.21987	0.21849	0.20077
1	100	10	0.80284	0.79596	0.82461
1	100	20	0.98253	0.98054	0.99621
2	20	2	0.14579	0.14150	0.14266
2	20	10	0.60269	0.52802	0.56721
2	20	20	0.90695	0.81374	0.91459
2	50	2	0.16041	0.15926	0.15346
2	50	10	0.67169	0.65107	0.65694
2	50	20	0.94613	0.93147	0.96587
2	100	2	0.16580	0.16534	0.15845
2	100	10	0.69410	0.68536	0.69001
2	100	20	0.95582	0.95073	0.97488
3	20	2	0.12252	0.11988	0.12292
3	20	10	0.50588	0.43094	0.47685
3	20	20	0.84031	0.69895	0.83316
3	50	2	0.13564	0.13540	0.13318
3	50	10	0.58708	0.56633	0.56551
3	50	20	0.90747	0.88397	0.92117
3	100	2	0.14072	0.14077	0.13772
3	100	10	0.61535	0.60679	0.60175
3	100	20	0.92511	0.91714	0.94207
4	20	2	0.10896	0.10686	0.11042
4	20	10	0.43613	0.36585	0.41495
4	20	20	0.77460	0.60272	0.75867
4	50	2	0.12091	0.12116	0.12007
4	50	10	0.52246	0.50327	0.50166
4	50	20	0.86680	0.83605	0.87281
4	100	2	0.12572	0.12607	0.12440
4	100	10	0.55445	0.54685	0.53876
4	100	20	0.89270	0.88244	0.90488
5	20	2	0.09998	0.09774	0.10189
5	20	10	0.38375	0.31901	0.36871
5	20	20	0.71349	0.52530	0.69362
5	50	2	0.11099	0.11147	0.11083
5	50	10	0.47191	0.45420	0.45331
5	50	20	0.82609	0.78994	0.82557
5	100	2	0.11558	0.11612	0.11499
5	100	10	0.50563	0.49925	0.49067
5	100	20	0.85996	0.84805	0.86709

TABLE II

POWER OF WILKS' ANALYSIS OF DISPERSION TEST – WITH TWO VARIATES AT 5% LEVEL AS FUNCTION OF SINGLE DEVIATION PARAMETER 'D', ERROR DEGREES OF FREEDOM 'N' AND NUMBER OF HYPOTHESES 'M'.

	M = 1					M = 2				
N / D	10	20	50	100	INF	10	20	50	100	INF
2	0.17328	0.19810	0.21428	0.21987	0.22554	0.12596	0.14579	0.16041	0.16580	0.17146
4	0.30919	0.36106	0.39352	0.40446	0.41542	0.21459	0.26130	0.29509	0.30734	0.32007
6	0.44112	0.51348	0.55630	0.57027	0.58403	0.30837	0.38232	0.43360	0.45165	0.47010
8	0.55963	0.64289	0.68901	0.70352	0.71756	0.40150	0.49832	0.56172	0.58322	0.60472
10	0.66054	0.74571	0.78958	0.80284	0.81542	0.48990	0.60269	0.67169	0.69410	0.71598
12	0.74314	0.82350	0.86177	0.87286	0.88316	0.57099	0.69223	0.76092	0.78219	0.80242
14	0.80872	0.88015	0.91146	0.92014	0.92802	0.64339	0.76620	0.83016	0.84897	0.86638
16	0.85950	0.92015	0.94451	0.95096	0.95668	0.70665	0.82543	0.88196	0.89770	0.91185
18	0.89805	0.94768	0.96588	0.97047	0.97446	0.76092	0.87166	0.91956	0.93214	0.94311
20	0.92681	0.96622	0.97937	0.98253	0.98521	0.80677	0.90695	0.94613	0.95582	0.96401
24	0.96330	0.98645	0.99278	0.99416	0.99527	0.87652	0.95285	0.97693	0.98217	0.98632
28	0.98216	0.99479	0.99760	0.99814	0.99856	0.92304	0.97709	0.99063	0.99319	0.99510
32	0.99155	0.99807	0.99923	0.99943	0.99958	0.95303	0.98926	0.99636	0.99752	0.99833
36	0.99608	0.99930	0.99976	0.99983	0.99988	0.97184	0.99511	0.99864	0.99913	0.99945
40	0.99821	0.99975	0.99992	0.99995	0.99996	0.98337	0.99783	0.99950	0.99970	0.99982
50	0.99976	0.99998	0.99999	0.99999	0.99999	0.99578	0.99974	0.99996	0.99998	0.99999

TABLE II—*Continued*

N	M = 3					M = 4				
D	10	20	50	100	INF	10	20	50	100	INF
2	0.10611	0.12252	0.13564	0.14072	0.14621	0.09491	0.10896	0.12091	0.12572	0.13105
4	0.17194	0.21208	0.24420	0.25655	0.26979	0.14731	0.18213	0.21215	0.22425	0.23760
6	0.24347	0.31041	0.36257	0.38215	0.40282	0.20480	0.26429	0.31492	0.33493	0.35682
8	0.31727	0.41021	0.47951	0.50465	0.53065	0.26518	0.35040	0.42068	0.44773	0.47658
10	0.39059	0.50588	0.58708	0.61535	0.64384	0.32658	0.43613	0.52246	0.55445	0.58773
12	0.46133	0.59364	0.68075	0.70967	0.73802	0.38745	0.51813	0.61541	0.64988	0.68472
14	0.52802	0.67135	0.75881	0.78636	0.81256	0.44660	0.59404	0.69676	0.73136	0.76524
16	0.58971	0.73817	0.82153	0.84633	0.86917	0.50312	0.66242	0.76549	0.79831	0.82938
18	0.64588	0.79424	0.87039	0.89172	0.91069	0.55637	0.72263	0.82182	0.85155	0.87869
20	0.69633	0.84031	0.90747	0.92511	0.94025	0.60594	0.77460	0.86680	0.89270	0.91546
24	0.78051	0.90695	0.95494	0.96590	0.97465	0.69334	0.85549	0.92874	0.94661	0.96109
28	0.84448	0.94783	0.97918	0.98534	0.98988	0.76513	0.91052	0.96378	0.97491	0.98318
32	0.89165	0.97170	0.99080	0.99400	0.99617	0.82254	0.94624	0.98239	0.98877	0.99311
36	0.92561	0.98508	0.99609	0.99764	0.99861	0.86746	0.96853	0.99176	0.99518	0.99730
40	0.94956	0.99232	0.99839	0.99911	0.99951	0.90200	0.98200	0.99627	0.99801	0.99899
50	0.98178	0.99867	0.99984	0.99993	0.99997	0.95554	0.99590	0.99954	0.99981	0.99992

TABLE II—*Continued*

N / D	M = 5: 10	20	50	100	INF	M = 6: 10	20	50	100	INF
2	0.08761	0.09998	0.11099	0.11558	0.12077	0.08244	0.09353	0.10379	0.10820	0.11328
4	0.13116	0.16182	0.18983	0.20159	0.21489	0.11971	0.14709	0.17330	0.13469	0.19788
6	0.17908	0.23207	0.28040	0.30046	0.32291	0.16071	0.20827	0.25412	0.27394	0.29668
8	0.22987	0.30715	0.37617	0.40415	0.43487	0.20437	0.27446	0.34123	0.36955	0.40151
10	0.28220	0.38375	0.47131	0.50563	0.54242	0.24972	0.34314	0.42981	0.46550	0.50488
12	0.33495	0.45910	0.56124	0.59966	0.63968	0.29591	0.41203	0.51574	0.55689	0.60103
14	0.38716	0.53102	0.64287	0.68297	0.72343	0.34220	0.47926	0.59595	0.64023	0.68626
16	0.43809	0.59797	0.71447	0.75405	0.79262	0.38797	0.54335	0.66839	0.71351	0.75879
18	0.48714	0.65895	0.77545	0.81278	0.84781	0.43271	0.60322	0.73201	0.77594	0.81838
20	0.53388	0.71349	0.82609	0.85996	0.89050	0.47602	0.65821	0.78650	0.82768	0.86588
24	0.61933	0.80308	0.89993	0.92527	0.94626	0.55722	0.75228	0.86972	0.90264	0.93060
28	0.69324	0.86883	0.94518	0.96229	0.97523	0.63009	0.82545	0.92414	0.94791	0.96626
32	0.75564	0.91499	0.97123	0.98188	0.98918	0.69406	0.88002	0.95761	0.97343	0.98447
36	0.80727	0.94621	0.98546	0.99165	0.99550	0.74923	0.91934	0.97717	0.98701	0.99318
40	0.84927	0.96669	0.99289	0.99630	0.99820	0.79609	0.94683	0.98809	0.99388	0.99713
50	0.92075	0.99070	0.99895	0.99958	0.99984	0.88175	0.98259	0.99793	0.99919	0.99972

TABLE II—*Continued*

N / D	M = 7: 10	M = 7: 20	M = 7: 50	M = 7: 100	M = 7: INF	M = 8: 10	M = 8: 20	M = 8: 50	M = 8: 100	M = 8: INF
2	0.07856	0.08864	0.09829	0.10254	0.10753	0.07554	0.08481	0.09394	0.09806	0.10297
4	0.11114	0.13588	0.16050	0.17155	0.18459	0.10447	0.12705	0.15028	0.16099	0.17390
6	0.14692	0.18996	0.23340	0.25285	0.27571	0.13618	0.17543	0.21661	0.23565	0.25852
8	0.18511	0.24893	0.31305	0.34135	0.37412	0.17006	0.22846	0.28981	0.31788	0.35119
10	0.22499	0.31083	0.39546	0.43190	0.47321	0.20556	0.28458	0.36659	0.40334	0.44607
12	0.26589	0.37383	0.47706	0.52004	0.56748	0.24214	0.34231	0.44383	0.48799	0.53805
14	0.30723	0.43632	0.55492	0.60233	0.65305	0.27935	0.40031	0.51887	0.56856	0.62322
16	0.34849	0.49698	0.62692	0.67648	0.72767	0.31675	0.45740	0.58961	0.64265	0.69903
18	0.38924	0.55477	0.69173	0.74127	0.79052	0.35399	0.51263	0.65458	0.70879	0.76425
20	0.42914	0.60893	0.74867	0.79637	0.84189	0.39074	0.56523	0.71290	0.76628	0.81870
24	0.50527	0.70458	0.83903	0.87931	0.91445	0.46181	0.66054	0.80848	0.85570	0.89807
28	0.57534	0.78240	0.90139	0.93215	0.95648	0.52840	0.74095	0.87753	0.91535	0.94608
32	0.63860	0.84327	0.94193	0.96359	0.97903	0.58966	0.80628	0.92459	0.95255	0.97297
36	0.69488	0.88934	0.96698	0.98126	0.99037	0.64527	0.85769	0.95511	0.97447	0.98708
40	0.74432	0.92326	0.98181	0.99071	0.99576	0.69530	0.89713	0.97407	0.98675	0.99409
50	0.84050	0.97133	0.99636	0.99860	0.99953	0.79771	0.95707	0.99414	0.99776	0.99928

TABLE II—*Continued*

N / D	M = 9					M = 10				
	10	20	50	100	INF	10	20	50	100	INF
2	0.07311	0.08170	0.09038	0.09439	0.09924	0.07111	0.07913	0.08742	0.09132	0.09613
4	0.09913	0.11990	0.14191	0.15230	0.16507	0.09475	0.11400	0.13491	0.14502	0.15765
6	0.12757	0.16363	0.20272	0.22132	0.24412	0.12052	0.15384	0.19103	0.20918	0.23189
8	0.15798	0.21169	0.27033	0.29804	0.33166	0.14806	0.19773	0.25376	0.28102	0.31482
10	0.18989	0.26287	0.34200	0.37875	0.42254	0.17700	0.24466	0.32082	0.35735	0.40193
12	0.22290	0.31595	0.41504	0.45987	0.51203	0.20701	0.29362	0.38988	0.43501	0.48884
14	0.25663	0.36979	0.48703	0.53833	0.59629	0.23778	0.34367	0.45878	0.51115	0.57187
16	0.29073	0.42337	0.55600	0.61174	0.67263	0.26902	0.39393	0.52568	0.58345	0.64827
18	0.32489	0.47585	0.62043	0.67846	0.73952	0.30048	0.44362	0.58908	0.65019	0.71628
20	0.35885	0.52649	0.67931	0.73756	0.79642	0.33193	0.49209	0.64791	0.71028	0.77507
24	0.42521	0.62020	0.77850	0.83212	0.88164	0.39400	0.58336	0.74938	0.80884	0.86531
28	0.48830	0.70170	0.85303	0.89779	0.93519	0.45380	0.66480	0.82827	0.87972	0.92395
32	0.54711	0.77002	0.90595	0.94047	0.96635	0.51022	0.73498	0.88633	0.92751	0.95926
36	0.60116	0.82556	0.94174	0.96668	0.98335	0.56256	0.79364	0.92708	0.95798	0.97919
40	0.65042	0.86956	0.96496	0.98201	0.99210	0.61055	0.84141	0.95454	0.97649	0.98981
50	0.75455	0.94026	0.99119	0.99664	0.99896	0.71309	0.92161	0.98747	0.99519	0.99855

TABLE III

GAMMA APPROXIMATION TO POWER OF WILKS' ANALYSIS OF DISPERSION TEST WITH 'P' VARIATES AT 5% LEVEL OF SIGNIFICANCE AS FUNCTION OF SINGLE DEVIATION PARAMETER 'D', ERROR DEGREES OF FREEDOM 'N' AND NUMBER OF HYPOTHESES 'M'.

M = 1

	P = 3				P = 4			
N / D	50	100	200	INF	50	100	200	INF
2	0.1783	0.1853	0.1888	0.1922	0.1579	0.1647	0.1681	0.1715
4	0.3259	0.3425	0.3506	0.3585	0.2864	0.3035	0.3119	0.3201
6	0.4701	0.4949	0.5067	0.5181	0.4176	0.4447	0.4576	0.4701
8	0.5978	0.6274	0.6411	0.6541	0.5396	0.5738	0.5897	0.6047
10	0.7035	0.7343	0.7482	0.7611	0.6456	0.6834	0.7003	0.7160
12	0.7868	0.8160	0.8287	0.8402	0.7335	0.7713	0.7876	0.8024
14	0.8500	0.8757	0.8865	0.8961	0.8035	0.8388	0.8534	0.8664
16	0.8964	0.9179	0.9266	0.9341	0.8577	0.8888	0.9012	0.9119
18	0.9296	0.9468	0.9534	0.9591	0.8985	0.9248	0.9348	0.9431
20	0.9528	0.9661	0.9710	0.9751	0.9286	0.9500	0.9577	0.9640
24	0.9796	0.9868	0.9893	0.9912	0.9659	0.9788	0.9831	0.9863
28	0.9915	0.9951	0.9963	0.9971	0.9844	0.9915	0.9936	0.9951
32	0.9966	0.9983	0.9987	0.9991	0.9931	0.9967	0.9977	0.9983
36	0.9987	0.9994	0.9996	0.9997	0.9970	0.9988	0.9992	0.9995
40	0.9995	0.9998	0.9999	0.9999	0.9987	0.9996	0.9997	0.9998
50	1.0000	1.0000	1.0000	1.0000	0.9999	1.0000	1.0000	1.0000

M = 1

	P = 5				P = 6			
N / D	50	100	200	INF	50	100	200	INF
2	0.1437	0.1504	0.1537	0.1570	0.1332	0.1398	0.1430	0.1462
4	0.2576	0.2750	0.2835	0.2918	0.2354	0.2530	0.2615	0.2698
6	0.3774	0.4061	0.4197	0.4329	0.3453	0.3750	0.3892	0.4028
8	0.4926	0.5304	0.5479	0.5644	0.4536	0.4942	0.5129	0.5307
10	0.5965	0.6400	0.6594	0.6774	0.5541	0.6023	0.6239	0.6438
12	0.6859	0.7313	0.7509	0.7686	0.6431	0.6953	0.7178	0.7380
14	0.7600	0.8042	0.8225	0.8386	0.7192	0.7719	0.7936	0.8126
16	0.8195	0.8603	0.8764	0.8902	0.7824	0.8327	0.8524	0.8692
18	0.8663	0.9022	0.9157	0.9269	0.8336	0.8795	0.8966	0.9107
20	0.9022	0.9327	0.9436	0.9523	0.8743	0.9146	0.9289	0.9403
24	0.9494	0.9695	0.9759	0.9808	0.9305	0.9590	0.9680	0.9747
28	0.9748	0.9869	0.9903	0.9927	0.9628	0.9813	0.9864	0.9899
32	0.9878	0.9946	0.9963	0.9974	0.9807	0.9918	0.9945	0.9962
36	0.9943	0.9979	0.9986	0.9991	0.9902	0.9966	0.9979	0.9986
40	0.9974	0.9992	0.9995	0.9997	0.9952	0.9986	0.9992	0.9995
50	0.9997	0.9999	1.0000	1.0000	0.9992	0.9999	0.9999	1.0000

TABLE III—*Continued*

M = 2

N / D	P = 3: 50	P = 3: 100	P = 3: 200	P = 3: INF	P = 4: 50	P = 4: 100	P = 4: 200	P = 4: INF
2	0.1354	0.1408	0.1435	0.1462	0.1211	0.1261	0.1286	0.1311
4	0.2404	0.2551	0.2625	0.2698	0.2095	0.2236	0.2306	0.2376
6	0.3529	0.3782	0.3906	0.4028	0.3069	0.3322	0.3446	0.3568
8	0.4632	0.4980	0.5146	0.5307	0.4056	0.4421	0.4597	0.4766
10	0.5649	0.6065	0.6257	0.6438	0.5002	0.5461	0.5675	0.5877
12	0.6544	0.6994	0.7195	0.7380	0.5870	0.6394	0.6630	0.6847
14	0.7303	0.7756	0.7951	0.8126	0.6639	0.7196	0.7436	0.7652
16	0.7928	0.8360	0.8537	0.8692	0.7301	0.7861	0.8092	0.8294
18	0.8430	0.8823	0.8976	0.9107	0.7859	0.8397	0.8608	0.8787
20	0.8825	0.9169	0.9297	0.9403	0.8320	0.8817	0.9003	0.9155
24	0.9363	0.9604	0.9685	0.9747	0.8993	0.9383	0.9512	0.9611
28	0.9667	0.9821	0.9866	0.9899	0.9415	0.9694	0.9775	0.9832
32	0.9831	0.9922	0.9946	0.9962	0.9669	0.9854	0.9901	0.9931
36	0.9916	0.9967	0.9979	0.9986	0.9817	0.9933	0.9958	0.9973
40	0.9959	0.9987	0.9992	0.9995	0.9900	0.9970	0.9983	0.9990
50	0.9994	0.9999	0.9999	1.0000	0.9979	0.9997	0.9998	0.9999

M = 2

N / D	P = 5: 50	P = 5: 100	P = 5: 200	P = 5: INF	P = 6: 50	P = 6: 100	P = 6: 200	P = 6: INF
2	0.1114	0.1161	0.1184	0.1208	0.1044	0.1089	0.1111	0.1133
4	0.1881	0.2015	0.2082	0.2149	0.1721	0.1851	0.1915	0.1979
6	0.2736	0.2986	0.3108	0.3229	0.2483	0.2728	0.2848	0.2967
8	0.3624	0.3996	0.4175	0.4349	0.3285	0.3660	0.3840	0.4015
10	0.4496	0.4982	0.5209	0.5424	0.4087	0.4589	0.4825	0.5049
12	0.5319	0.5895	0.6156	0.6397	0.4860	0.5473	0.5752	0.6010
14	0.6071	0.6708	0.6985	0.7234	0.5582	0.6281	0.6587	0.6863
16	0.6740	0.7407	0.7684	0.7926	0.6241	0.6996	0.7311	0.7588
18	0.7324	0.7991	0.8255	0.8478	0.6830	0.7610	0.7920	0.8184
20	0.7823	0.8467	0.8708	0.8905	0.7347	0.8125	0.8418	0.8659
24	0.8593	0.9142	0.9324	0.9463	0.8179	0.8890	0.9126	0.9306
28	0.9114	0.9542	0.9666	0.9752	0.8777	0.9371	0.9543	0.9663
32	0.9454	0.9765	0.9843	0.9892	0.9192	0.9657	0.9772	0.9845
36	0.9669	0.9884	0.9929	0.9955	0.9474	0.9820	0.9891	0.9932
40	0.9802	0.9944	0.9969	0.9982	0.9661	0.9908	0.9950	0.9971
50	0.9948	0.9992	0.9997	0.9998	0.9891	0.9984	0.9994	0.9997

TABLE III—*Continued*

M = 3

N	P = 5				P = 6			
D	50	100	200	INF	50	100	200	INF
2	0.0977	0.1014	0.1033	0.1051	0.0922	0.0957	0.0975	0.0992
4	0.1568	0.1678	0.1734	0.1790	0.1442	0.1546	0.1598	0.1651
6	0.2240	0.2453	0.2560	0.2667	0.2034	0.2237	0.2339	0.2441
8	0.2955	0.3292	0.3458	0.3622	0.2668	0.2995	0.3157	0.3317
10	0.3683	0.4148	0.4373	0.4591	0.3322	0.3783	0.4008	0.4225
12	0.4398	0.4985	0.5261	0.5523	0.3972	0.4569	0.4851	0.5120
14	0.5080	0.5772	0.6087	0.6377	0.4603	0.5324	0.5655	0.5963
16	0.5716	0.6490	0.6827	0.7131	0.5202	0.6030	0.6395	0.6726
18	0.6298	0.7126	0.7471	0.7772	0.5760	0.6672	0.7057	0.7395
20	0.6822	0.7678	0.8016	0.8[illegible]02	0.6273	0.7243	0.7633	0.7964
24	0.7696	0.8536	0.8832	0.9063	0.7157	0.8168	0.8531	0.8816
28	0.8359	0.9115	0.9347	0.9514	0.7859	0.8829	0.9133	0.9352
32	0.8846	0.9484	0.9652	0.9761	0.8403	0.9276	0.9510	0.9664
36	0.9197	0.9708	0.9821	0.9888	0.8815	0.9565	0.9734	0.9834
40	0.9445	0.9840	0.9912	0.9950	0.9124	0.9746	0.9861	0.9921
50	0.9784	0.9968	0.9987	0.9994	0.9590	0.9939	0.9976	0.9990

M = 3

N	P = 3				P = 4			
D	50	100	200	INF	50	100	200	INF
2	0.1164	0.1209	0.1232	0.1255	0.1052	0.1092	0.1112	0.1133
4	0.1993	0.2122	0.2188	0.2254	0.1741	0.1859	0.1919	0.1979
6	0.2914	0.3150	0.3269	0.3387	0.2517	0.2742	0.2854	0.2967
8	0.3858	0.4207	0.4378	0.4545	0.3333	0.3678	0.3848	0.4015
10	0.4775	0.5222	0.5435	0.5639	0.4149	0.4612	0.4834	0.5049
12	0.5628	0.6149	0.6388	0.6613	0.4934	0.5499	0.5762	0.6010
14	0.6394	0.6959	0.7209	0.7437	0.5664	0.6308	0.6597	0.6863
16	0.7064	0.7643	0.7888	0.8106	0.6329	0.7023	0.7321	0.7588
18	0.7637	0.8204	0.8433	0.8631	0.6920	0.7636	0.7930	0.8184
20	0.8117	0.8653	0.8859	0.9030	0.7437	0.8149	0.8427	0.8659
24	0.8836	0.9273	0.9422	0.9538	0.8263	0.8909	0.9132	0.9306
28	0.9302	0.9626	0.9724	0.9793	0.8849	0.9385	0.9547	0.9663
32	0.9591	0.9816	0.9874	0.9913	0.9252	0.9666	0.9774	0.9845
36	0.9765	0.9912	0.9945	0.9965	0.9520	0.9825	0.9892	0.9932
40	0.9867	0.9960	0.9977	0.9986	0.9696	0.9911	0.9950	0.9971
50	0.9970	0.9995	0.9998	0.9999	0.9906	0.9985	0.9994	0.9997

TABLE III—*Continued*

M = 4

D \ N	P = 3: 50	100	200	INF	P = 4: 50	100	200	INF
2	0.1053	0.1092	0.1112	0.1133	0.0960	0.0994	0.1012	0.1030
4	0.1745	0.1860	0.1919	0.1979	0.1531	0.1633	0.1686	0.1739
6	0.2526	0.2744	0.2855	0.2967	0.2180	0.2380	0.2482	0.2585
8	0.3347	0.3682	0.3849	0.4015	0.2874	0.3192	0.3352	0.3512
10	0.4168	0.4617	0.4835	0.5049	0.3584	0.4028	0.4246	0.4461
12	0.4957	0.5504	0.5763	0.6010	0.4285	0.4849	0.5120	0.5381
14	0.5691	0.6314	0.6598	0.6863	0.4957	0.5628	0.5940	0.6232
16	0.6358	0.7029	0.7323	0.7588	0.5587	0.6343	0.6681	0.6990
18	0.6951	0.7642	0.7931	0.8184	0.6166	0.6983	0.7333	0.7643
20	0.7469	0.8155	0.8428	0.8659	0.6691	0.7543	0.7890	0.8187
24	0.8294	0.8914	0.9133	0.9306	0.7575	0.8425	0.8735	0.8981
28	0.8877	0.9389	0.9548	0.9663	0.8252	0.9031	0.9280	0.9461
32	0.9275	0.9669	0.9775	0.9845	0.8757	0.9425	0.9608	0.9730
36	0.9539	0.9827	0.9893	0.9932	0.9124	0.9669	0.9795	0.9871
40	0.9711	0.9912	0.9951	0.9971	0.9387	0.9815	0.9897	0.9941
50	0.9913	0.9986	0.9994	0.9997	0.9753	0.9961	0.9984	0.9993

M = 4

D \ N	P = 5: 50	100	200	INF	P = 6: 50	100	200	INF
2	0.0898	0.0929	0.0945	0.0961	0.0853	0.0882	0.0897	0.0912
4	0.1386	0.1480	0.1528	0.1577	0.1281	0.1369	0.1413	0.1458
6	0.1942	0.2128	0.2223	0.2319	0.1768	0.1943	0.2032	0.2121
8	0.2543	0.2844	0.2996	0.3148	0.2296	0.2582	0.2727	0.2872
10	0.3164	0.3595	0.3808	0.4019	0.2846	0.3262	0.3469	0.3675
12	0.3787	0.4350	0.4624	0.4888	0.3402	0.3957	0.4229	0.4493
14	0.4395	0.5085	0.5411	0.5719	0.3952	0.4646	0.4978	0.5293
16	0.4976	0.5780	0.6146	0.6483	0.4484	0.5311	0.5693	0.6048
18	0.5523	0.6420	0.6812	0.7163	0.4992	0.5938	0.6358	0.6739
20	0.6030	0.6998	0.7401	0.7751	0.5470	0.6516	0.6962	0.7352
24	0.6915	0.7953	0.8341	0.8653	0.6325	0.7508	0.7963	0.8333
28	0.7630	0.8654	0.8991	0.9240	0.7041	0.8275	0.8695	0.9008
32	0.8194	0.9143	0.9412	0.9593	0.7627	0.8841	0.9197	0.9439
36	0.8631	0.9470	0.9671	0.9792	0.8100	0.9240	0.9524	0.9698
40	0.8964	0.9680	0.9822	0.9898	0.8477	0.9513	0.9727	0.9844
50	0.9484	0.9917	0.9966	0.9986	0.9111	0.9852	0.9940	0.9974

TABLE III—*Continued*

M = 5

	P = 3				P = 4			
N / D	50	100	200	INF	50	100	200	INF
2	0.0980	0.1015	0.1033	0.1051	0.0899	0.0930	0.0945	0.0961
4	0.1577	0.1681	0.1735	0.1790	0.1390	0.1481	0.1528	0.1577
6	0.2256	0.2457	0.2561	0.2667	0.1950	0.2130	0.2224	0.2319
8	0.2981	0.3298	0.3459	0.3622	0.2554	0.2847	0.2997	0.3148
10	0.3720	0.4157	0.4376	0.4591	0.3181	0.3599	0.3810	0.4019
12	0.4445	0.4996	0.5264	0.5523	0.3809	0.4356	0.4625	0.4888
14	0.5136	0.5785	0.6090	0.6377	0.4423	0.5092	0.5412	0.5719
16	0.5780	0.6504	0.6830	0.7131	0.5009	0.5788	0.6147	0.6483
18	0.6368	0.7141	0.7474	0.7772	0.5561	0.6429	0.6814	0.7163
20	0.6896	0.7692	0.8019	0.8302	0.6072	0.7006	0.7403	0.7751
24	0.7774	0.8549	0.8835	0.9063	0.6962	0.7961	0.8343	0.8653
28	0.8434	0.9125	0.9349	0.9514	0.7680	0.8662	0.8992	0.9240
32	0.8915	0.9492	0.9653	0.9761	0.8244	0.9150	0.9413	0.9593
36	0.9257	0.9714	0.9822	0.9888	0.8679	0.9475	0.9672	0.9792
40	0.9495	0.9843	0.9912	0.9950	0.9009	0.9684	0.9822	0.9898
50	0.9813	0.9969	0.9987	0.9994	0.9518	0.9919	0.9967	0.9986

M = 5

	P = 5				P = 6			
N / D	50	100	200	INF	50	100	200	INF
2	0.0845	0.0873	0.0887	0.0902	0.0807	0.0833	0.0846	0.0859
4	0.1265	0.1348	0.1390	0.1434	0.1175	0.1251	0.1291	0.1330
6	0.1742	0.1908	0.1993	0.2080	0.1592	0.1745	0.1824	0.1904
8	0.2260	0.2532	0.2672	0.2813	0.2044	0.2299	0.2430	0.2562
10	0.2801	0.3198	0.3399	0.3600	0.2519	0.2895	0.3087	0.3279
12	0.3350	0.3881	0.4146	0.4406	0.3004	0.3516	0.3772	0.4026
14	0.3894	0.4561	0.4885	0.5198	0.3488	0.4142	0.4464	0.4777
16	0.4423	0.5220	0.5595	0.5950	0.3963	0.4760	0.5142	0.5505
18	0.4928	0.5843	0.6259	0.6640	0.4422	0.5356	0.5790	0.6191
20	0.5404	0.6420	0.6864	0.7258	0.4859	0.5920	0.6394	0.6821
24	0.6260	0.7418	0.7876	0.8255	0.5660	0.6926	0.7443	0.7878
28	0.6980	0.8197	0.8624	0.8950	0.6351	0.7750	0.8261	0.8656
32	0.7571	0.8776	0.9144	0.9399	0.6936	0.8394	0.8861	0.9190
36	0.8050	0.9190	0.9487	0.9672	0.7423	0.8879	0.9279	0.9533
40	0.8433	0.9476	0.9703	0.9828	0.7824	0.9232	0.9558	0.9742
50	0.9080	0.9837	0.9933	0.9971	0.8540	0.9722	0.9884	0.9950

ACKNOWLEDGMENTS

It is a pleasure to acknowledge programming assistance received from my colleagues G. Kalyanasundaram, S. Panchapakesan, and P. Dasgupta.

REFERENCES

1. ANDERSON, T. W. (1946). The non-central Wishart distribution and certain problems of multivariate statistics. *Ann. Math. Statist.* **17** 409–431.
2. ANDERSON, T. W. (1958). *An Introduction to Multivariate Statistical Analysis.* Wiley, New York.
3. BARTLETT, M. A. (1938). Further aspects of the theory of multiple regression. *Proc. Cambridge Philos. Soc.* **3** 33–40.
4. DASGUPTA, S., ANDERSON, T. W. and MUDHOLKAR, G. S. (1964). Monotonicity of the power functions of some tests of multivariate linear hypotheses. *Ann. Math. Statist.* **35** 200–205.
5. FISHER, R. A. (1939). The sampling distribution of some statistics obtained from non-linear equations. *Ann. Eugenics* **9** 238–249.
6. GIRSHICK, M. A. (1939). On the sampling theory of roots of determinantal equations. *Ann. Math. Statist.* **10** 203–224.
7. HECK, D. L. (1958). Some uses of the distribution of the largest root in multivariate analysis. Inst. Statist. Mimeo. Ser. 19. Univ. North Carolina, Chapel Hill, N.C.
8. HOTELLING, H. (1947). Multivariate quality control, illustrated by the air testing of sample bomb sights. *Techniques of Statistical Analysis*, Chapter II. McGraw-Hill, New York.
9. HOTELLING, H. (1951). A generalized *T* test and measure of multivariate dispersion. *Proc. Second Berkeley Symp. Math. Statist. Prob.*, Univ. California Press, Berkeley, California.
10. HSU, P. L. (1939). On the distribution of the roots of certain determinantal equations. *Ann. Eugenics* **9** 250–258.
11. KOPAL, Z. (1961). *Numerical Analysis.* Chapman & Hall, London.
12. LAWLEY, D. N. (1938). A generalization of Fisher's *z*-test. *Biometrika* **30** 180–187.
13. NANDA, D. N. (1948). Distribution of a root of a determinantal equation. *Ann. Math. Statist.* **19** 47–57.
14. NANDA, D. N. (1950). Probability distribution tables of the largest root of a determinantal equation with two roots. *J. Indian Soc. Agric. Statist.* **3** 175–177.
15. PILLAI, K. C. S. (1956). On the distribution of the largest or the smallest root of a matrix in multivariate analysis. *Biometrika* **43** 122–127.
16. POSTEN, H. O. and BARGMANN, R. E. (1964). Power of the likelihood-ratio of the test general linear hypothesis in multivariate analysis. **51** 467–476.
17. RAO, C. R. (1948). Tests of significance in multivariate analysis. *Biometrika* **35** 58–79.
18. RAO, C. R. (1951). An asymptotic expansion of the distribution of Wilks' criterion. *Bull. Inst. Internat. Statist.* **33** (2) 177–180.
19. RAO, C. R. (1952). *Advanced Statistical Methods in Biometric Research.* Wiley, New York.
20. ROY, J. (1951). The distribution of a certain class of likelihood-ratio criteria useful in multivariate analysis. *Bull. Inst. Internat. Statist.* **33** (2) 219–230.
21. ROY, J. (1958). Step-down procedure in multivariate analysis. *Ann. Math. Statist.* **29** 1177–1187.
22. ROY, J. (1960). Non-null distribution of the liklihood-ratio in analysis of dispersion. *Sankhya* **22** 289–294.

23. Roy, S. N. (1939). *p*-statistics or some generalisations in analysis of variance appropriate to multivariate problems. *Sankhyā* **4** 381–396.
24. Roy, S. N. (1942). Analysis of variance for multivariate normal populations. The sampling distribution of the requisite *p*-statistics on the null and non-null hypothesis. *Sankhyā* **6** 35–50.
25. Roy, S. N. (1945). The individual sampling distribution of the maximum, minimum and any intermediate of the *p*-statistics on the null hypothesis. *Sankhyā* **7** 133–138.
26. Roy, S. N. (1946). Multivariate analysis of variance: the sampling distribution of the numerically largest of the *p*-statistics on the non-null hypothesis. *Sankhyā* **8** 15–52.
27. Roy, S. N. (1953). On a heurestic method of test construction and its use in multivariate analysis. *Ann. Math. Statist.* **24** 220–238.
28. Roy, S. N. (1957). *Some Aspects of Multivariate Analysis.* Wiley, New York.
29. Roy, S. N. and Roy, J. (1958). Analysis of variance with univariate or multivariate, fixed or mixed classical models. Inst. Statist. Mimeo. Ser. 208. Univ. North Carolina, Chapel Hill. N.C.
30. Roy, S. N. and Mikhail, W. F. (1961). On the monotonic character of the power functions of two multivariate tests. *Ann. Math. Statist.* **32** 1145–1151.
31. Szegö, G. (1939). *Orthogonal polynomials.* Amer. Math. Soc. Colloquium Publ. **33**.
32. Wilks, S. S. (1932). Certain generalizations in the analysis of variance. *Biometrika* **24** 471–494.
33. Wilks, S. S. (1935). On the independence of *K* sets of normally distributed variables. *Econometrica* **3** 309–326.
34. Srivastava, J. N. (1964). On the monotonicity property of three main tests for multivariate analysis of variance. *J. Roy. Statist. Soc. Ser. B* **26** 77–81.

Some Generalizations of Multivariate Analysis of Variance

*J. N. SRIVASTAVA**
DEPARTMENT OF MATHEMATICS
UNIVERSITY OF NEBRASKA
LINCOLN, NEBRASKA

1. SUMMARY

After a brief review of the standard MANOVA,[1] certain applications and generalizations of the same, which enable one to deal (at least partially) with various situations arising in the analysis and design of multiresponse experiments (i.e., experiments in which more than one characteristic is measured on each experimental unit) are discussed. These include the following: (a) multivariate block designs, in which the block systems corresponding to the different variates are not necessarily identical; (b) hierarchical designs, in which the responses are arranged in a fixed order $R_1, R_2, \ldots, R_p$, such that the sets U_j of units in which R_j is measured is such that $U_j \supseteq U_{j+1}$; (c) general incomplete multiresponse designs, which are characterized by the situation that not all responses are measured on each unit; (d) situations which do not fall under the standard MANOVA, although each response is measured on each experimental unit; and (e) a problem in multiresponse surface analysis, which consists of finding the set Δ of points in the factor space such that if $x \in \Delta$, then the expected value of each response at x lies between specified limits.

In each case, the discussion is limited to the analysis of designs, rather than their comparative suitability in various situations.

2. INTRODUCTION

The present paper, or more generally, the branch of statistics called "design and analysis of multiresponse experiments" to which it belongs, was born out of the interaction and the synthesis between the disciplines of

* Present address: Department of Mathematics and Statistics, Colorado State University, Fort Collins, Colorado

[1] Multivariate analysis of variance.

multivariate analysis and experimental design. It concerns the planning and analysis of experiments and investigations where more than one response (or characteristic) is observed (or measured) on each unit. Since most scientific studies involve more than one response, a wide class of problems arising here calls for attention. The major results of multivariate analysis and design of experiments do provide a solution to some of these problems. However, until now, not much consideration has been given to the multiresponse aspect of experimentation, the choice of the design being usually made as if there were *only one response under study*. As will be seen later, the choice of an appropriate multiresponse design would in general involve models more general than the standard MANOVA. However, the author also believes that even the existing (e.g., [1, 2, 10, 13, 14, 16]) large body of statistical techniques associated with MANOVA have not been utilized as much as they should have been. It is expected that the availability of the procedure for analysis under the generalized models would provide enough flexibility to the techniques to suit the needs of diverse experimental and other situations.

Information relating to background material for this paper may be found in [1, 3–6, 17].

3. STANDARD MANOVA

The standard model is

$$E(X) = A\xi, \tag{1}$$

$$V(X) = I_n \otimes \Sigma, \tag{2}$$

where $X(n \times p)$ is the matrix of observations, $A(n \times m)$ a known design matrix, $\xi(m \times p)$ a set of unknown parameters, and $\Sigma(p \times p)$ the variance-covariance matrix of any row of X, and I_n is the $n \times n$ identity matrix.

Equation (2) then implies that if $\mathbf{x}_i^*$ is the ith row of X, then for $i \neq j$, $\mathbf{x}_i^*$ and $\mathbf{x}_j^*$ are uncorrelated. Thus there are n experimental units, the set of observations from two distinct units being independent. Write

$$\Sigma = ((\sigma_{ij})), \qquad X = [\mathbf{x}_1, \mathbf{x}_2, \ldots, \mathbf{x}_p], \qquad \xi = [\xi_1, \xi_2, \ldots, \xi_p],$$

where $\mathbf{x}_i$ and ξ_i are, respectively, the ith columns of X and ξ. Then (1) and (2) could be written as

$$E(\mathbf{x}_i) = A\xi_i, \tag{3}$$

$$\mathrm{Cov}(\mathbf{x}_i, \mathbf{x}_j) = (\sigma_{ij})I_n, \tag{4}$$

for all permissible i and j. Note that (3) and (4) imply a univariate model for each response, such that the design matrix A is the same for all responses.

For purposes of testing hypotheses, we assume that each $\mathbf{x}_i^*$ possesses a multivariate normal distribution with the appropriate mean [given implicitly in (1)] and the dispersion matrix.

Finally, one may recall that some of the customary (see, e.g., [16]) estimation and testing problems considered under the above model are (a) estimation of a given linear parametric function $\mathbf{c}'\xi_i$, and (b) testing a hypothesis of the form

$$H_0: \quad C\xi = 0, \tag{5}$$

where $C(s \times u)$ is a given matrix. But $H_0 = \bigcap_i H_{0i}$, where

$$H_{0i}: \quad C\xi_i = 0, \tag{6}$$

which shows that the same C is supposed to be of interest for the case of each response. If each H_{0i} is tested using the usual F-acceptance region ($F_i \leq \mu$), the acceptance region of H_0 may be taken as

$$F_{\max} \leq \mu, \tag{7}$$

where $F_{\max} = \max(F_1, \ldots, F_p)$. Many experimenters who perform a separate analysis of variance for each response, and reject H_0 if any particular H_{0i} is rejected, implicitly use (7). However, the distribution of $F_{\max}$ under H_0 is not known yet, and it involves the elements of R, were R is the (population) correlation matrix corresponding to the covariance matrix Σ. Attempts are being made by Srivastava and Krishnaiah to obtain bounds (free of nuisance parameters) on the distribution function of $F_{\max}$.

Although the above $F_{\max}$ test is not in general a similar-region test, other similar-region tests for H_0 are well known. These include tests [1, 16, 19] based on $c_1, \sum c_i, \prod (1 + c_i)$, etc., where $c_1 \geq c_2, \ldots, \geq c_p$ are the roots of $(S_0 S_e^{-1})$, S_0 and S_e being, respectively, the sum of products matrices due to the hypothesis and error. Tests based on $\sum_i c_i(1 + c_i)^{-1}$ and $\prod_i c_i(1 + c_i)^{-1}$, recently [8] included in certain Monte Carlo studies by Gnanadesikan *et al.*, have been found to have more power than the first three tests. A valid test, not based on the c's, is the so-called stepdown procedure [15].

The power functions of the first three tests are known to have the monotonicity property [7, 11, 21] with respect to the noncentrality parameters which are measures of deviations from the null hypothesis. By the method used in the proof of these, it can also be easily shown that the following "all-roots test" also has this property. The acceptance region of this test is

$$(c_1 \leq \mu_1, c_2 \leq \mu_2, \ldots, c_p \leq \mu_p), \tag{8}$$

where $\mu_1 \geq \mu_2 \geq \cdots \geq \mu_p \geq 0$ are prechosen constants. When all μ's are equal, this reduces to the c_1 test (which is known to be admissible among scale-invariant tests [11]).

The main feature in which this test differs from the other tests (based on

c's) mentioned above is that in general its acceptance region is not symmetrical with respect to the c's.

It is conjectured that the available choice of several μ's may enable one to give special desirable properties to the all-roots test.

4. PATTERNS OF HETEROGENEITY DIFFERENT FOR DIFFERENT RESPONSES: MULTIVARIATE BLOCK DESIGNS

We now study situations in which the standard MANOVA model is not directly applicable. Consider the familiar block designs in the case of a single response. It is well known that the main purpose for introduction of blocks is to stratify the experimental material in such a way that within each block the units are relatively more homogeneous (with respect to the response under consideration) than between blocks. Thus the pattern of heterogeneity with respect to the given response is of prime importance. When two responses R_1 and R_2 are studied, the pattern of heterogeneity may differ from R_1 to that for R_2. Thus, in order to reduce the error variance for each response, one system of blocks may be required for R_1, and a possibly different system for R_2. In general, for p responses, p block systems may be required. Such designs are called multivariate block designs.

As an example, consider the arrangement of 7 treatments in 28 experimental units shown in Table I. Take two responses R_1 and R_2. Suppose the

TABLE I

Two-Variate Block Design

	Column block			
Row block	I	II	III	IV
I	3	6	7	2
II	1	3	4	6
III	5	7	1	3
IV	2	5	6	1
V	7	1	2	4
VI	4	2	3	5
VII	6	4	5	7

pattern of heterogeneity corresponding to R_1 is such that the 7 row blocks constitute a good block system for R_1. For R_2, suppose the pattern of heterogeneity is different, so that a good block system is provided by the four column blocks rather than by the row blocks. The two-variate block design then consists of the designs D_1 and D_2 corresponding, respectively, to R_1 and

R_2; D_2 is a randomized block, and D_1 a BIB[2] with parameters $v = b = 7$, $r = k = 4$, $\lambda = 2$. The standard MANOVA model is clearly not applicable.

Note that both block systems could possibly be used for each response for two-way elimination of heterogeneity, bringing the situation under standard MANOVA. (A similar remark applies to any multivariate block design.) However, it may be recalled that a block system should be used only if the expected reduction in error variance more than offsets the loss in power due to the decrease in the number of error degrees of freedom as a result of the increase in the number of blocks. Hence it is possible that a two-way block system may not be desirable for either of the responses, and the design described in the last paragraph may be called for.

5. RESPONSES WITH UNEQUAL DEGREES OF IMPORTANCE: HIERARCHICAL MULTIRESPONSE DESIGNS

Many situations occur where considerations of relative cost or difficulty of measurement, or other considerations based on *a priori* information about the nature of responses and their relative importance in the investigation at hand enable the experimenter to decide which one, among a given pair of responses, needs to be measured on a larger number of experimental units. In such a case he could arrange the responses in an ascending order (R_1, $R_2, \ldots, R_p$), such that if n_i is the number of units on which R_i is observed, then $n_i > n_{i+1}$.

Let U_i be the set of n_i units on which R_i is measured. The sets $U_1, U_2, \ldots,$ U_p need not be disjoint. The multiresponse design so formed is called hierarchical if $U_i \supseteq U_{i+1}$. Clearly in this case R_1 is observed on each unit, and for $i > j$, R_j is observed on any unit only if R_i is.

The set U_i could have its own block system appropriate to the ith response. If D_i is the design over U_i with respect to R_i, then the resulting total design ($D_1, D_2, \ldots, D_p$) is called *hierarchical multivariate block design* (HMBD).

The nature and analysis of these designs has been discussed in [18], wherein it has been implicitly assumed that no response is supposed *a priori* to be insensitive to differences between treatments. The analysis (under the assumption of fixed block and treatment effects) is carried out by a generalization of the stepdown procedure for the MANOVA, since the standard MANOVA model is no longer applicable. The model arising here will be termed the GMANOVA, type I, where G stands for *generalized.*

When the number of responses is more than two, and the heterogeneity pattern is similar for the various responses, the cyclic PBIB[3] designs seem to

[2] Balanced incomplete block.

[3] Partially balanced incomplete block.

be specially suitable for use as HMBD's, the reason being that the hierarchical BIB designs with $p > 2$ are more difficult to construct. With $p(= 4)$ responses and $v(= 9)$ treatments, the design of Table II is an example. As indicated, U_1 consists of all the 45 units, U_2 the 36 units after dropping off the last treatment of each block, and so on. Clearly, such a design is available for any of p and v and in various block sizes.

TABLE II

Cyclic PBIBD as HMBD

Block	Column				
	1	2	3	4	5
I	1	2	3	4	5
II	2	3	4	5	6
III	3	4	5	6	7
IV	4	5	6	7	8
V	5	6	7	8	9
VI	6	7	8	9	1
VII	7	8	9	1	2
VIII	8	9	1	2	3
IX	9	1	2	3	4

$$[\text{------------}]$$
$$U_4$$
$$[\text{----------------}]$$
$$U_3$$
$$[\text{----------------------}]$$
$$U_2$$
$$[\text{--------------------------}]$$
$$U_1$$

One could possibly have BIB's for the designs D_1, D_2, etc., particularly when p is small. An HMBD in which each D_i is a BIBD will be called an HBIBD or hierarchical BIB design. An example of such a design is provided by Table I. As mentioned earlier, this design (say D_1), over-all units using the row blocks, is the BIBD $v = b = 7$, $r = k = 4$, $\lambda = 2$. Now suppose that R_2 is not measured on the 7 units in the first column, so that U_2 is the remaining set of 21 units. If rows are used as blocks for R_2 also, then D_2 is a BIBD, $v = b = 7$, $r = k = 3$, $\lambda = 1$.

6. POOLING OF MULTIRESPONSE EXPERIMENTS: GENERAL INCOMPLETE MULTIRESPONSE DESIGNS

In this section we shall consider general classes of multiresponse designs (called *incomplete*) which are characterized by the fact that not all the variates are measured on each experimental unit. Such situations arise often when it is either physically impossible, or uneconomic, or otherwise inadvisable to study all characteristics on each unit. Although a large number of interesting examples are given in [12, 22, 24], a few additional ones are worth mentioning:

(a) A simple example is provided by two sets of skulls dug out in an anthropological investigation. Since the skulls may not all be in good shape, all the different characteristics of interest will in general not be measurable on each skull.

(b) Suppose there are two responses R_1 and R_2 such that the measurement of either of them involves the destruction of the experimental unit itself. Clearly then, both R_1 and R_2 cannot be observed on any unit.

(c) Suppose u experiments are conducted involving the same set of v treatments, one at each of u different places. At the ith place, a subset of p_i out of a total of p responses is studied, all the selected responses being measured on each unit.

The total set of u experiments, considered as a whole, is then clearly an example of a general incomplete multiresponse design (GIMD). The theory of GIM designs thus enables one to pool the data of several experiments in such a way that a single analysis could be carried out.

We now present the outlines of a class of GIMD's called *strongly regular*, for which the procedure of analysis was developed by the author in [22]. The structure of these designs is as follows:

(a) There are u disjoint sets of experimental units, the ith set S_i having N_i units. Let $N = \sum N_i$.

(b) The total of p responses $(R_1, R_2, \ldots, R_p)$ is arranged in an arbitrary but fixed order. Let a subset of p_i responses $(R_{l_{i1}}, \ldots, R_{l_{ip_i}})$ be observed on *each* unit in S_i; the rule D_1 by which these p_i responses for S_i $(i = 1, 2, \ldots, p)$ are selected is called the *response design*.

(c) There are t treatments. For each S_i, the set of treatments is the same, but the block system is different. Let D_{2i} be the block-treatment design defined over the N_i units in S_i. The total multiresponse design D is then the $(u+1)$-plet $D = (D_1; D_{21}, D_{22}, \ldots, D_{2u})$. It is incomplete if $p_i < p$, for some i.

(d) Let ξ_l be the $(t \times 1)$ vector of treatment effects for the lth response R_l. Consider the usual analysis of D_{2i} as a block-treatment design. If R_l is measured on S_i, the normal equations for estimating ξ_l from S_i can be written

$$C_i \xi_l = \mathbf{Q}_{il}, \tag{9}$$

the notation used being in accordance with the standard one $(C\mathbf{t} = \mathbf{Q})$

introduced by Kempthorne [9]. The dimension of C_i and $\mathbf{Q}_{il}$ is, respectively, $(t \times t)$ and $(t \times 1)$. Let $C_{ijj'}$ denote the element in all (j, j') of C_i.

(e) The design D is called "homogeneous," provided there exists a positive integer m, known real numbers α_{ir} $(i = 1, \ldots, u;\ r = 1, \ldots, m)$, and known real linearly independent $(t \times t)$ matrices $F_1, F_2, \ldots, F_m$ such that

$$C_i = \alpha_{i1}F_1 + \cdots + \alpha_{im}F_m \qquad (i = 1, 2, \ldots, u). \tag{10}$$

The trivial case when $m = u$, $F_i = C_i$, for all i, is excluded. Furthermore, D is said to be *nonsingular* if one can choose a set of real numbers $\sigma_1, \sigma_2, \ldots, \sigma_m$, such that the $(m \times m)$ matrices Δ_l $(l = 1, 2, \ldots, p)$ defined below are all nonsingular.

$$\Delta_l = \begin{bmatrix} \sum_r'(\alpha_{r1} + \sigma_r)^2 & \cdots & \sum_r'(\alpha_{r1} + \sigma_r)(\alpha_{rm} + \sigma_r) \\ \cdots & \cdots & \cdots \\ \sum_r'(\alpha_{rm} + \sigma_r)(\alpha_{r1} + \sigma_r) & \cdots & \sum_r'(\alpha_{rm} + \sigma_r)^2 \end{bmatrix}. \tag{11}$$

Here r in $\sum_r'$ runs over the set U_l of integers which is such that, if $i \in U_l$, then the lth response is measured on each unit in S_i.

(f) Let

$$\Pi_l = ((\pi^l_{\theta'\theta})) = \Delta_l^{-1}, \tag{12}$$

$$g^l_{i\theta} = \sum_{\theta'=1}^{m} (\alpha_{i\theta'} + \sigma_i)\pi^l_{\theta'\theta} \tag{13}$$

$(l = 1, 2, \ldots, p;\ i = 1, 2, \ldots, u;\ \theta = 1, 2, \ldots, m)$, where clearly Π_l is $(m \times m)$.

(g) Finally, a nonsingular homogeneous design D is called *strongly regular* (SR), provided that there exists a $(p \times p)$ positive-definite matrix $\Gamma = ((\gamma_{ll'}))$, such that for all $j, j' = 1, 2, \ldots, t$; $l, l' = 1, 2, \ldots, p$; and $\theta, \theta' = 1, 2, \ldots, m$; the following factorization is permissible:

$$\sum_{i \in (U_{ll'})} c_{ijj'} g^l_{i\theta} g^{l'}_{i\theta'} = \gamma_{ll'} \cdot w^{jj'}_{\theta\theta'}, \tag{14}$$

where $W = ((w^{jj'}_{\theta\theta}))$ is an $(mt \times mt)$ positive-semidefinite matrix of rank $m(t-1)$, and $U_{ll'} = U_l \cap U_{l'}$.

The following result on strongly regular incomplete multiresponse (SRIM) designs is implicitly established in [22].

Theorem. *For a SRIM design D, there exist (known) linear transformations such that the total of $(\sum_{i=1}^n N_i p_i)$ observations is transformed into a new set of mtp variables $Y(mt \times p)$, to which the standard MANOVA model* (3 *and* 4) *applies*:

$$E(Y) = B\xi, \qquad V(Y) = I_{mt} \otimes \Sigma^*, \tag{15}$$

where

$$\xi = [\xi_1, \ldots, \xi_p],$$

and $B(mt \times t)$ *is known, and* Σ^* *is an unknown positive-definite matrix. Problems of inference regarding* ξ *can then be tackled in the usual manner.*

In the same paper, some necessary and/or sufficient conditions for strong regularity are also studied. A completely worked out example of an SRIMD is presented in [20].

We now consider more general classes of designs. An IMD will be called *regular* if it is reducible to the generalized MANOVA model given by (19). Finally, a weakly regular design is one in which for any estimable (in the usual sense) linear function $\lambda(=\sum_{i=1}^{p} \mathbf{c}_i'\xi_i$, say) of the parameters there exists a linear unbiased estimate (LUE) ϕ which has minimum variance in the class of all LUE's of λ.

To illustrate the above discussions and definitions, we prove the following

Theorem. *Let* $p = 2$, $u = 3$, *and suppose each* D_{2i} *is a BIBD. Let* R_i $(i = 1, 2)$ *be observed on* S_i *and* S_3; *this gives* D_1. *Let* $D = (D_1; D_{21}, D_{22}, D_{23})$. *Then D is not strongly regular.*

Proof. Let the parameters of the BIBD for D_{2i} be $(v, b_i, r_i, k_i, \lambda_i)$. Then it can be easily checked that for each i,

$$c_{ijj} = r_i\left(1 - \frac{1}{k_i}\right) = \frac{\lambda_i}{k_i}(v-1) = \rho_i(v-1), \quad \text{say},$$

$$c_{ijj'} = -\lambda_i/k_i = -\rho_i \qquad (j \neq j'),$$

$$F_1 = I_v, \qquad F_2 = J_{vv} - I_v,$$

$$\alpha_{il} = \rho_i(v-1), \qquad \alpha_{i2} = -\rho_i.$$

Write

$$w_i = \sigma_i - \rho_i,$$

and suppose σ_i have been so chosen that $|\Delta_l| \neq 0$, $l = 1, 2$. Then

$$\Pi_l = \frac{1}{|\Delta_l|}\begin{bmatrix} \sum'_{r\in U_l} w_r^2 & -\sum'_{r\in U_l} w_r(w_r + v\rho_r) \\ -\sum'_{r\in U_l} w_r(w_r + v\rho_r) & \sum'_{r\in U_l}(w_r + v\rho_r)^2 \end{bmatrix}.$$

Then it can be checked that for $i = 1, 2, 3$,

$$g_{i1}^l = v\sum_{r\in U_l} w_r \zeta i_r = v[w_l\zeta_{il} + w_3\zeta_{i3}],$$

$$g_{i2}^l = -v\sum_{r\in U_l}\zeta_{ir}(w_r + v\rho_r) = -v[\zeta_{il}(w_l + v\rho_l) + \zeta_{i3}(w_3 + v\rho_3)].$$

where $\zeta_{ir} = \rho_i w_r - \rho_r w_i$. Let

$$L(j, j'; \theta, \theta'; l, l') = \sum_{i\in U_{ll'}} c_{ijj'} g_{i\theta}^l g_{i\theta'}^{l'}.$$

Then one obtains

$$L(j,j;1,1;l,l) = (v-1)v^2\zeta_{3l}^2[\rho_l w_3{}^2 + \rho_3 w_l{}^2],$$
$$L(j,j;1,1;l,l') = (v-1)v^2\rho_3\zeta_{3l}\zeta_{3l'}w_l w_{l'} \qquad (l \neq l'),$$
$$L(j,j;2,2;l,l) = (v-1)v^2\zeta_{3l}^2[\rho_l(w_3+v\rho_3)^2 + \rho_3(w_l+v\rho_l)^2],$$
$$L(j,j;2,2;l,l') = (v-1)v^2\rho_3\zeta_{3l}\zeta_{3l'}(w_l+v\rho_l)(w_{l'}+v\rho_{l'}),$$
$$L(j,j;1,2;l,l) = (v-1)v^2\zeta_{3l}^2[\rho_l w_3(w_3+v\rho_3) + \rho_3 w_l(w_l+v\rho_l)],$$
$$L(j,j;1,2;l,l') = (v=1)v^2\rho_3 w_l\zeta_{3l}\zeta_{3l'}(w_{l'}+v\rho_{l'}),$$
$$L(j,j';\theta,\theta';l,l') = -(v-1)^{-1}L(j,j;\theta,\theta';l,l') \qquad (j \neq j').$$

Now (14) requires that the ratio $[L(j,j';\theta,\theta';l,l')]/[L(j,j';\theta,\theta',l,l)]$ be a constant $(\gamma_{ll'}/\gamma_{ll})$, independent of j,j' and θ,θ'. This gives two equations, which on combining yield

$$(w_3{}^2\rho_l + w_l{}^2\rho_3)[\rho_l(w_3+v\rho_3)^2 + \rho_3(w_l+v\rho_l)^2]$$
$$= [\rho_l w_3(w_3+v\rho_3) + \rho_3 w_l(w_l+v\rho_l)]^2,$$

which simplifies to

$$w_l(w_3+v\rho_3) = w_3(w_l+v\rho_l) \qquad (l=1,2).$$

It can be shown, however, that the restriction on w_1, w_2, and w_3 implied by the last equation is such that the matrices Δ_l will be singular. Thus D is not strongly regular.

7. MANOVA INAPPLICABLE, ALTHOUGH EACH RESPONSE OBSERVED ON EACH UNIT

A common notion is that if one has a block-treatment design involving say, n experimental units, such that each of the p responses is measured on each of the n units, then the MANOVA model, given by (1), is applicable. One illustration of the fact that this notion is not true in general is clearly given by the multivariate block designs of Section 4. Another example, arising in an altogether different but important context, is discussed below.

Consider a fractional factorial design (without blocks) with 8 units involving the following 8-treatment combinations from a 2^5 factorial:

(a) 00000	(c) 00101	(e) 10110	(g) 10011
(b) 01010	(d) 01111	(f) 11100	(h) 11001

Denote the factors by $A, B, \ldots, E$, and let there be two responses R_1 and R_2. Suppose it is known that R_1 is insensitive to levels of D and E, and R_2 to B and C. Also suppose that interest lies in estimating, for each response, the general mean μ, the main effects, and the two-factor interactions involving factors to which the response is not insensitive. These effects can in an obvious notation be denoted respectively by μ_1; A_1, B, C; A_1B, A_1C, BC; and μ_2; A_2, D, E; A_2D, A_2E, DE; where the subscripts refer to the responses. Let y_{ij} denote the observed yield for response i under treatment j; and $\mathbf{y}_i' = (y_{i1}, \ldots, y_{i8})$, $i = 1, 2$. Then it can be verified that

$$\begin{aligned} E(\mathbf{y}_1) &= kL(\mu_1, A_1, B, C, A_1B, A_1C, BC)' \\ E(\mathbf{y}_2) &= kL^*(\mu_2, A_2, D, E, A_2D, A_2E, DE)', \end{aligned} \tag{16}$$

where the prime denotes transpose of the vector, k is a constant, and where

$$L = \begin{bmatrix} + & - & - & - & + & + & + \\ + & - & + & - & - & + & - \\ + & - & - & + & + & - & - \\ + & - & + & + & - & - & + \\ + & + & - & + & - & + & - \\ + & + & + & + & + & + & + \\ + & + & - & - & - & - & + \\ + & + & + & - & + & - & - \end{bmatrix}, \tag{17}$$

$$L^* = \begin{bmatrix} + & - & - & - & + & + & + \\ + & - & + & - & - & + & - \\ + & - & - & + & + & - & - \\ + & - & + & + & - & - & + \\ + & + & + & - & + & - & - \\ + & + & - & - & - & - & + \\ + & + & + & + & + & + & + \\ + & + & - & + & - & + & - \end{bmatrix}. \tag{18}$$

Since L and L^* are distinct, (16) is not a special case of (1).

The model applicable here is a special case of the generalized MANOVA model of Type II, which requires that for all $i, j = 1, 2, \ldots, p$,

$$E(\mathbf{x}_j) = A_j\xi_j, \qquad \operatorname{Cov}(\mathbf{x}_i, \mathbf{x}_j) = \sigma_{ij}I_n, \tag{19}$$

where the A_j ($n \times m_j$, say) are not necessarily identical, and the parameters $\xi_j (j = 1, 2, \ldots, p)$ are all independent. Comparing this with the standard model in (3) and (4), one finds that here the design matrices for the different responses need no longer be the same.

We now show that, by reparametrization, the above model is reducible to an equivalent one in which the A_j's are identical, although the new parameters may not always be independent. Let rank $(A_j) = r_j$, and, without loss of generality, write $A_j = (A_{j1} \mid A_{j2})$, where $A_{j1}(n \times r_j)$ is a set of r_j linearly independent columns of A_j. This then induces the partitioning $\xi_j' = (\xi_{j1}' \mid \xi_{j2}')$.

Thus

$$E(\mathbf{x}_j) = A_{j1}\xi_{j1} + A_{j2}\xi_{j2}. \tag{20}$$

Now A_j is $n \times m_j$. Then there exists $K_j(r_j \times \overline{m_j - r_j})$ such that $A_{j2} = A_{j1}K_j$. Let $\mathbf{V}$ be the vector space generated by the set of all the $(\sum_{j=1}^{p} m_j)$ columns of the matrices $A_1, A_2, \ldots, A_p$; let $R(V) = m$. Let $A_{j3}(n \times \overline{m - r_j}), j = 1, \ldots, p$, be a set of matrices such that $A_{j0} = (A_{j1} \mid A_{j3})$ has rank m $(\leq n)$ and has the same column space V for all j. Then

$$E(\mathbf{x}_j) = [A_{j1} \mid A_{j3}]\left[\frac{\xi_{j0}^*}{0}\right] = A_{j0}\xi_{j0}, \quad \text{say}, \tag{21}$$

where $\xi_{j0}^* = \xi_{j1} + K_j\xi_{i2}$, and where 0 is a zero vector of appropriate order and A_{j0} is $(n \times m)$. Let A $(n \times m)$ be such that its columns form a basis of V, and let $A_{j0} = AH_j$. Put $\xi_j^* = H_j\xi_{j0}$. Then

$$E(\mathbf{x}_j) = A\xi_j^*, \qquad \operatorname{Cov}(\mathbf{x}_i, \mathbf{x}_j) = \sigma_{ij}I_n, \qquad R(A) = m, \tag{22}$$

where $\xi_{j0}^* = H_{j1}(I \mid K_j)\xi_j$, H_{j1} $(m \times r_j)$ being the first r_j columns of H_j, and I the identity matrix.

Note, however, that unlike the standard model, the parameters ξ_j^* in (22) obey $(m - r_j)$ linearly independent restrictions. Thus a necessary and sufficient condition for (22) to be equivalent to (3) is that $r_j = m$ for all j; i.e., the column space of A_j is the same for all j. An example of the fulfillment of this condition is given by (16), where, although L and L^* are different, their column spaces are the same.

Let $\mathbf{b}_j' = (\mathbf{b}_{j1}' \mid \mathbf{b}_{j2}')$ be a row vector such that $\eta_j = \mathbf{b}_j'\xi_j$ is estimable [under (19)]. Then we must have $\mathbf{b}_{j2}' = \mathbf{b}_{j1}'K_j$. Hence $\eta_j = (\mathbf{b}_{j1}'P_j)\xi_j^*$, where P_j is the matrix of the top r_j rows of H_j^{-1}. Hence the problem of testing [under (19)] the null hypothesis H_0 that $\eta_j = 0$ for all j is equivalent to testing under (22) the null hypothesis H_0^* that $\mathbf{b}_j^{*\prime}\xi_j^* = 0$ for all j, where $\mathbf{b}_j^{*\prime} = \mathbf{b}_{j1}'P_j$.

In case the $\mathbf{b}_j^*$ are not all identical, no test is as yet available for testing H_0^* [under (22)] even under the assumption that the mp parameters ξ_j^* $(j = 1, 2, \ldots, p)$ are all independent. However, some of the estimation problems can be tackled; the following result is a slight generalization of the result in [23].

Theorem. *In* (19) *let us suppose that the column space of A_j is independent of j. Suppose also that* $\mathbf{b}_j'\xi_j$ *is estimable under* (19) *as a univariate problem for the jth response. Then there exists a unique best linear unbiased estimate of* $(\sum_{j=1}^{p} \mathbf{b}_j'\xi_j)$. Note that no assumption of the normality of the distribution of the x_i's is made.

8. MULTIRESPONSE SURFACES

The problem in this section was suggested to the author by Professor R. C.

Bose. It involves the generalization of ordinary response-surface theory to more than one response.

A manufacturer of steel is interested in p responses R_1: hardness, R_2: tensile strength, etc. Consider a factorial experiment with k factors, and let $\xi_i(a_1, \ldots, a_k)$ be the expected value of the ith response under the treatment combination $(a_1, \ldots, a_k)$ in which the lth factor A_l is at level a_l. The problem is to find some treatment combination $(u_1, \ldots, u_k)$, if one exists, such that the value of each response for this treatment is between specified limits, i.e., such that

$$q_{i1} \le \xi_i(u_1, \ldots, u_k) \le q_{i2} \qquad (i = 1, \ldots, p), \tag{23}$$

where the q's are prescribed constants.

Let Δ_i be the set of points $(u_1, \ldots, u_k)$ for which the ith inequality in (23) holds, and put $\Delta = \bigcap_{i=1}^{p} \Delta_i$. Then any point $(u_1, \ldots, u_k) \in \Delta$ is clearly a solution for (23).

The problem sketched above (called the *specification problem*) is an important one and arises frequently. It is out of the scope of this paper to study it in detail. However an outline of a heuristic but general approach is presented.

In general, a sequence of experiments may be required to determine Δ "well enough." We shall assume throughout that all responses are measured on each experimental unit. Suppose there are k factors $F_1, F_2, \ldots, F_k$ and p responses $R_1, R_2, \ldots, R_p$. Consider first the case where R_i is sensitive to F_l for all (i, l), and let

$$\xi_i(u_1, \ldots, u_k) = \sum_{j=1}^{m_i} \{f_{ij}(u_1, \ldots, u_k)\}\xi_{ij}, \tag{24}$$

where ξ_{ij} are unknown parameters, and f_{ij} are known functions. Let $y_i = y_i(u_1, \ldots, u_k)$ be the observed value of the ith response to the treatment $(u_1, \ldots, u_k)$, and let

$$E[y_i(u_1, \ldots, u_k)] = \xi_i(u_1, \ldots, u_k), \tag{25}$$

implying the absence of any block effects. Assume as usual that observations on different experimental units are independent, and that

$$\operatorname{Var}(y_1, \ldots, y_p) = \Sigma, \tag{26}$$

where $(y_1, \ldots, y_p)$ refer to the p responses on the same unit, and Σ is an unknown dispersion matrix. The model expressed by equations (24) to (26) is a special case of the standard MANOVA model, provided m_i and f_{ij} are independent of i, and then

$$E[y_i(u_1, \ldots, u_k)] = \xi_i(u_1, \ldots, u_k) = \sum_{j=1}^{m} [f_j(u_1, \ldots, u_k)]\xi_{ij}. \tag{27}$$

Under the assumption that the standard MANOVA model as expressed in (26) and (27) is valid in each experiment, the specification problem could be attacked on the following lines.

For the first experiment, choose a suitable design D_1. In general the experimental points in D_1 should be "well-scattered" over a part Ω_1 of the factor space Ω, such that the experimenter is sure that $\Omega_1 \supset \Delta$. Furthermore, D_1 should allow the estimability of all ξ_{ij}, which will imply that $\xi_i(u_1, \ldots, u_k)$ is estimable for all $(u_1, \ldots, u_k)$.

Let us now go back to (1) and (2) and consider simultaneous confidence bounds on linear functions of the form $\mathbf{a}'\xi'\mathbf{b}$, where $\mathbf{a}$ $(p \times 1)$ and $\mathbf{b}$ $(m \times 1)$ are any given vectors. Suppose $R(A) = m < n$. Then it is well known [16] that if $\mathbf{b}$ satisfies

$$\mathbf{b}'(A'A)\mathbf{b} = 1, \tag{28}$$

then the following is a set of simultaneous confidence bounds with confidence coefficient $1 - \alpha$:

$$(\mathbf{a}'X'A(A'A)^{-1}\mathbf{b}) - (\mathbf{a}'S\mathbf{a})^{1/2}[mc_\alpha(p, m, n-m)]^{1/2} \leq \mathbf{a}'\xi'\mathbf{b}$$
$$\leq (\mathbf{a}'X'A(A'A)^{-1}\mathbf{b}) + (\mathbf{a}'S\mathbf{a})^{1/2}[mc_\alpha(p, m, n-m)]^{1/2}, \tag{29}$$

where (a) $c_\alpha(p, n_h, n_e)$ is the upper $100\alpha\%$ point of the distribution of Roy's largest root (occurring in the standard MANOVA test) with degrees of freedom p (number of responses) and n_h and n_e (number of degrees of freedom for hypothesis and error, respectively), and (b) S is the usual error dispersion matrix given by $n_h S = X'[I - A(A'A)^{-1}A']X$.

Let the $(1 \times p)$ vector $(0, 0, \ldots, 1, 0, \ldots, 0)$ with 1 in the ith place be called $\mathbf{a}_i'$. For any fixed $(u_1, \ldots, u_k)$ define $b_j^* = f_j(u_1, \ldots, u_k)$, and $\mathbf{b}^{*\prime} = (b_1^*, \ldots, b_p^*)$, $b_0^* = +[\mathbf{b}^{*\prime}(A'A)\mathbf{b}^*]^{1/2}$, $\mathbf{b} = b_0^{*-1}b^*$, so that $\xi_i(u_1, \ldots, u_k) = (\mathbf{a}_i'\xi'\mathbf{b})b_0^*$. Note that $b_0^* = b_0^*(u_1, \ldots, u_k)$. Thus with probability $\geq 1 - a$, we have the set of simultaneous bounds,

$$b_0^* y_{i1\alpha}(u_1, \ldots, u_k) \leq \xi_i(u_1, \ldots, u_k) \leq b_0^* y_{i2\alpha}(u_1, \ldots, u_k), \tag{30}$$

where

$$\begin{aligned} y_{i1}(u_1, \ldots, u_k) &= \mathbf{x}_i'A(A'A)^{-1}\mathbf{b} - (s_{ii})^{1/2}[mc_\alpha(p, m, n-m)]^{1/2}, \\ y_{i2}(u_1, \ldots, u_k) &= \mathbf{x}_i'A(A'A)^{-1}\mathbf{b} + (s_{ii})^{1/2}[mc_\alpha(p, m, n-m)]^{1/2}, \end{aligned} \tag{31}$$

where s_{ii} is the (i, i) element of S.

Now define the region $\Delta_{i\alpha}^1$ as follows: The point $(u_1, \ldots, u_k)$ of Ω is in $\Delta_{i\alpha}^1$ if and only if

$$q_{i1} \leq b_0^* y_{i1\alpha}(u_1, \ldots, u_k), \qquad q_{i2} \geq b_0^* y_{i2\alpha}(u_1, \ldots, u_k). \tag{32}$$

Define $\Delta_\alpha^1 = \Delta_{1\alpha}^1 \cap \Delta_{2\alpha}^1 \cap \cdots \cap \Delta_{p\alpha}^1$. Then we have

Theorem. *The random set* Δ_α^1 *is such that*

$$\text{Prob}[\Delta_\alpha^1 \subseteq \Delta] \geq 1 - \alpha. \tag{33}$$

This then provides a solution to the specification problem, based on design D_1.

A second experiment (with a design D_2, say) may now be conducted. By the above method, we have established that the points in Δ_α^1 lie in Δ with a confidence coefficient $\geq (1 - \alpha)$. For sufficiently small values of α, the set Δ_α^1 may be null. The number of points that one may like to have under D_2 will depend upon the desired accuracy and the available funds. Our main purpose behind this sequence of experiments is to get a set of points Δ_0 which are in Δ with a high level of confidence, say $1 - \alpha = 0.999$, or $\alpha = 0.001$. Now $\Delta_{0,0001}^1$ may be either null or a very small set. If so, for the points of D_2, we may take the set Δ_α^1 with a sufficiently high value α_1 of α (say, $\alpha_1 = 0.05$, or even perhaps $\alpha_1 = 0.20$), such that the set $\Delta_{\alpha_1}^1$ is suitably large. The *experimental points* of D_2 may be scattered well over $\Delta_{\alpha_1}^1$. Since the region $\Delta_{\alpha_1}^1$ would presumably be much smaller compared to Ω_1, the model for this second experiment could perhaps be chosen to fit the actual surface over Δ_{α_1} much better than in the first experiment.

The knowledge obtained from the first experiment may throw some light on the goodness of the model (27). For example, if for some j, ξ_{ij} is negligible for all i, then the corresponding term $f_j(u_1, \ldots, u_k)\xi_{ij}$ could legitimately be dropped from (27). Another kind of change in (27) could consist of changing certain functions f_j to new ones, say f_j^*. The new "sharpened" model obtained by any or both of the two kinds of changes still remains a special case of (1). Although a general discussion of the second kind of change will not be fruitful here, the first is more prone to statistical treatment. Define the null hypotheses

$$H_{j0}: \quad (\xi_{ij} = 0 \quad \text{for all } i) \qquad (j = 1, \ldots, m). \tag{34}$$

Such a set of hypotheses can be tested both individually or jointly by standard MANOVA methods. If H_{j0} is accepted, the terms in ξ_{ij} should be dropped *for each i* in the "sharpened" model.

After the second experiment, one gets, proceeding in a similar manner, a second set Δ_α^2. Since the experimental points in the second stage belong to Δ_α^1, and since Δ_α^1 is in a (heuristic) sense "closer" to Δ than Ω_0 is, and also because of "sharpening" of the model it seems intuitively evident that Δ_α^2 may be "still closer" to Δ. Thus through a sequence of experiments, the sets $\Delta_\alpha^1, \Delta_\alpha^2, \Delta_\alpha^3, \ldots$ are successively obtained. Experimentation may be stopped when successive Δ_α^i and Δ_α^{i+1} seem to be "close enough."

If the f_{ij} in (13) depend upon i, or some of the m_i are unequal, or if some responses are insensitive to certain factors, the experimental situation may fall under the generalized model (19). In this case the problems of tests of hypotheses of the type H_{j0} are yet to be solved.

One remark, suggested by the referee, may be made here. Confidence bounds that are generally shorter than (30) could be obtained by using p sets of univariate confidence bounds, each set corresponding to one response, and each set based on a confidence coefficient of $100(1 - \alpha/p)\%$. The over-all simultaneous confidence coefficient for all p sets will then be $\geq 100(1 - \alpha)\%$.

It may be added that the confidence bounds of the type required are not yet available with an exact confidence coefficient.

Acknowledgments

The author is grateful to the referee for pointing out typographical errors in the original draft and for his suggestions.

REFERENCES

1. Anderson, T. W. (1956). *An Introduction to Multivariate Statistical Analysis.* Wiley, New York.
2. Anderson, T. W. (1957). Maximum likelihood estimates for a multivariate normal distribution when some observations are missing. *J. Amer. Statist. Assoc.* **52** 200–203.
3. Bose, R. C. (1958). Mimeographed notes on analysis of variance. Inst. Statistics, Univ. North Carolina, Chapel Hill, North Carolina.
4. Box, G. E. P. (1954). The exploration and exploitation of response surfaces: Some general considerations and examples. *Biometrics* **10** 16–60.
5. Box, G. E. P. and Hunter, J. S. (1957). Multifactor experimental designs. *Ann. Math. Statist.* **28** 195–241.
6. Cox, D. R. (1960). *Planning of Experiments*, Wiley. New York.
7. Dasgupta, S., Anderson, T. W. and Mudholkar, G. S. (1964). Monotonicity of the power functions of some tests of multivariate linear hypothesis. *Ann. Math. Statist.* **35** 200–206.
8. Gnanadesikan, R., Lauh, E., Snyder, M., and Yao, Y. (1965). Efficiency comparisons of certain multivariate analysis of variance test procedures (abstract). *Ann. Math. Statist.* **36** 356.
9. Kempthorne, O. (1952). *The Design and Analysis of Experiments.* Wiley, New York.
10. Lord, F. M. (1955). Estimation of parameters from incomplete data. *J. Amer. Statist. Assoc.* **50** 870–876.
11. Mikhail, W. (1960). Monotonicity and admissibility of some multivariate test procedures. Ph.D. dissertation. Univ. North Carolina, Chapel Hill, North Carolina.
12. Monahan, I. P. (1961). Incomplete-variable designs. Unpublished thesis. Virginia Polytechnic Institute, Blacksburg, Virginia.
13. Rao, C. R. (1955). Analysis of dispersion for multiply classified data with unequal numbers in cells. *Sankhyā* **15** 253–280.
14. Rao, C. R. (1956). Analysis of dispersion with incomplete observations on one of the characters. *J. Roy. Statist. Soc. Ser. B* **18** 259–264.
15. Roy, J. (1958). Step-down procedure in multivariate analysis. *Ann. Math. Statist.* **29** 1177–1187.
16. Roy, S. N. (1957). *Some Aspects of Multivariate Analysis.* Wiley, New York.

17. Roy, S. N., Gnanadesikan, R., and Srivastava, J. N. (1964). *Analysis and Design of Multiresponse Experiments*. Unpublished monograph.
18. Roy, S. N. and Srivastava, J. N. (1964). Hierarchical and p-block multiresponse designs and their analysis. *Mahalanobis Dedicatory Volume*. Pergamon Press, New York.
19. Smith, H., Gnanadesikan, R., and Hughes, J. B. (1962). Multivariate analysis of variance. *Biometrics* **18** 22–41.
20. Srivastava, J. N. (1962). Incomplete multiresponse designs (submitted for publication). (Also circulated as a handout for an invited talk at IMS Annual Meetings, Minneapolis, Minnesota, September 1962.)
21. Srivastava, J. N. (1964). On the monotonicity property of the three main tests for multivariate analysis of variance. *J. Roy. Statist. Soc. Ser. B* **26** 77–81.
22. Srivastava, J. N. (1964). On a general class of designs for multiresponse experiments. Inst. Statistics Mimeo Series 402. Univ. North Carolina, Chapel Hill, North Carolina.
23. Srivastava, J. N. (1965). A multivariate extension of Gauss-Markov theorem. *Ann. Inst. Statist. Math.* **17** 63–66.
24. Trawinski, I. M. and Bargmann, R. E. (1964). Maximum likelihood estimation with incomplete multivariate data. *Ann. Math. Statist.* **35** 647–658.

PART III

Classification

Predictive Discrimination[1]

SEYMOUR GEISSER

DEPARTMENT OF MATHEMATICAL STATISTICS
STATE UNIVERSITY OF NEW YORK AT BUFFALO
BUFFALO, NEW YORK

INTRODUCTION

Investigators in sundry areas are often confronted with the problem of rationally assigning individuals or objects to categories based on one or more observational characteristics. In many cases the classification has to be made on the basis of imperfect information expressed in terms of a joint probability distribution of certain variables with known or unknown parameters, modified by prior probabilities of the various populations, and costs of misclassification.

The classical approach to this problem, with all its inherent distributional difficulties except in the simplest situation, is superbly presented by Anderson [1, Chap. 6]. However, it is our view that the Bayesian framework adopted in this paper is more attuned to the investigator's query: "To which population does this particular observation belong?" Apart from the fact that the Bayesian solution is generally simpler to come by, and often just as easily applicable for a broad range of assumptions (e.g., unequal covariance matrices are no more difficult to handle than the more restricted case), it is also flexible enough so that a classification program can be tailored to a temporal imperative.

In what follows, for convenience, we shall ignore the question of differential costs of misclassification, although when these costs are known, they are readily incorporated into the mathematics. Similarly, we shall restrict ourselves to the case where the prior probabilities are known, although the extension to the case where they are unknown, on which we have already commented in detail [3], is easily managed.

Several related classification schemes, each appropriate for special circumstances, are described in Section 1 and are developed in greater detail for

[1] The work was initiated while the author was employed at the National Institutes of Health and was partially supported by this same institution during its very last phase under Research Grant No. GM-14031-01.

normal populations in the succeeding sections. Under the marginal assignment scheme, each of n observations is classified independently of the remaining $n-1$ observations. The application of this scheme to normal populations, and the associated use, in some instances, of linear discriminators are considered in Section 2. In Section 3 we apply to normal populations a joint classification scheme, under which all n observations are simultaneously classified—the assignment of any particular observation depending in part on the remaining $n-1$ observations. Under sequential classification, delineated for normal populations in Section 4, the n observations are considered to be obtained and assigned sequentially, and the classification of the jth observation depends on the previous $j-1$ observations. The practical aspects, and similarities and differences of the three methods, including a simple and interesting illustrative example, are discussed in Section 5.

1. GENERAL OUTLINE

Suppose we have k populations Π_i, $i = 1, \ldots, k$, each specified by a continuous density $f(\cdot \mid \theta_i, \psi_i)$, where θ_i is the set of distinct unknown parameters of Π_i; ψ_i is the set of distinct known parameters of Π_i; X_i are the data obtained on Π_i based on N_i independent (vector) observations; and z is a new (vector) observation to be assigned which has prior probability q_i of belonging to Π_i, $\sum_{i=1}^{k} q_i = 1$.

Further, let $\theta = \bigcup_{i=1}^{k} \theta_i$, $\psi = \bigcup_{i=1}^{k} \psi_i$, i.e., the total set of distinct unknown and known parameters, respectively, and $g(\theta \mid \psi)$ be the joint prior density of θ for known ψ. Let $L(X_i \mid \theta_i, \psi_i)$ be the likelihood of the sample obtained from Π_i with the joint likelihood obtained on $\Pi_1, \ldots, \Pi_k$ given by

$$L(X \mid \theta, \psi) = \prod_{i=1}^{k} L(X_i \mid \theta_i, \psi_i), \tag{1.1}$$

where X represents the set of all the data samples $X_1, \ldots, X_k$. Hence the posterior density, when it exists, is

$$P(\theta \mid X, \psi) \propto L(X \mid \theta, \psi) g(\theta \mid \psi), \tag{1.2}$$

from which we may obtain the predictive density of z on the hypothesis that it was obtained from Π_i, which results in

$$f(z \mid X, \psi, \Pi_i) = \int f(z \mid \theta_i, \psi_i, \Pi_i) P(\theta \mid X, \psi) \, d\theta. \tag{1.3}$$

Occasionally it is more convenient to express the above equation in the following manner:

$$f(z \mid X, \psi, \Pi_i) = \int f(z \mid \theta_i, \psi_i, \Pi_i) P(\theta_i \mid X, \psi) \, d\theta_i, \tag{1.4}$$

where

$$P(\theta_i \mid X, \psi) = \int P(\theta \mid X, \psi)\, d\theta_i^c \tag{1.5}$$

and θ_i^c is the complement of θ_i, $\theta_i^c \cup \theta_i = \theta$. In any event, we then calculate the posterior probability that z belongs to Π_i,

$$\Pr\{z \in \Pi_i \mid X, \psi, q\} \propto q_i f(z \mid X, \psi, \Pi_i), \tag{1.6}$$

where q stands for $q_1, \ldots, q_k$. For classification purposes we may choose to assign z to that Π_i for which (1.6) is a maximum. We could also divide up the observation space of z into sets of regions $R_1, \ldots, R_k$, where R_i is the set of regions for which $u_i(z) = q_i f(z|X, \psi, \Pi_i)$ is maximum and use these as classifying regions for future observations. We may also compute "classification errors," based on the predictive distributions, which are in a sense a measure of the discriminatory power of the variables or characteristics. If we let $\Pr\{\Pi_j \mid \Pi_i\}$ represent the predictive probability that z has been classified as belonging to Π_j when in fact it belongs to Π_i, then we obtain

$$\Pr\{\Pi_i|\Pi_i\} = q_i \int_{R_i} f(z \mid X, \psi, \Pi_i)\, dz, \tag{1.7}$$

$$\Pr\{\Pi_j|\Pi_i\} = q_i \int_{R_j} f(z \mid X, \psi, \Pi_i)\, dz \qquad (i \neq j), \tag{1.8}$$

$$\Pr\{\Pi_i^c|\Pi_i\} = q_i\left(1 - \int_{R_i} f(z \mid X, \psi, \Pi_i)\, dz\right), \tag{1.9}$$

where Π_i^c stands for all the populations with the exception of Π_i. Then the predictive probability of a misclassification is

$$\sum_{i=1}^{k} \Pr\{\Pi_i^c \mid \Pi_i\} = 1 - \sum_{i=1}^{k} \Pr\{\Pi_i \mid \Pi_i\}. \tag{1.10}$$

Prior to observing z, the smaller the predictive probability of a misclassification the more confidence we have in the discriminatory variables. However, once z has been observed and if our interest is only in the particular observed z, the misclassification errors are relatively unimportant, but what is important is (1.6), i.e., the posterior probability that z belongs to Π_i. For a poignant and detailed exposition of this view to statistical inference in general see Dempster [2]. Nevertheless, before any observations are inspected for assignment, the error of misclassification can be of value in determining whether the addition of new variables or the deletion of old ones is warranted.

Suppose we wish to classify jointly n independent observations $z_1, \ldots, z_n$, each having prior probability q_i of belonging to Π_i. We can then compute the joint predictive density on the hypothesis that $(z_1 \in \Pi_{i_1}, \ldots, z_n \in \Pi_{i_n})$, where $i_1, \ldots, i_n$ are each some integer such that $1 \le i_j \le k$, $j = 1, \ldots, n$. Therefore,

$$f(z_1, \ldots, z_n \mid X, \psi, \Pi_{i_1}, \ldots, \Pi_{i_n})$$

$$= \int P(\theta \mid \psi, X) \prod_{j=1}^{n} f(z_j \mid \theta_{i_j}, \psi_{i_j}, \Pi_{i_j})\, d\theta$$

or

$$= \int P\left(\bigcup_{j=1}^{n} \theta_{i_j} \mid \psi, X\right) \prod_{j=1}^{n} f(z_j \mid \theta_{i_j}, \psi_{i_j}, \Pi_{i_j})\, d \bigcup_{j=1}^{n} \theta_{i_j}, \tag{1.11}$$

where

$$P\left(\bigcup_{j=1}^{n} \theta_{i_j} \mid \psi, X\right) = \int P(\theta \mid \psi, X)\, d\left[\bigcup_{j=1}^{n} \theta_{i_j}\right]^c. \tag{1.12}$$

This then yields the joint posterior probability

$$\Pr\{z_1 \in \Pi_{i_1}, \ldots, z_n \in \Pi_{i_n} \mid X, \psi, q\}$$

$$\propto \left(\prod_{j=1}^{n} q_{i_j}\right) f(z_1, \ldots, z_n \mid X, \psi, \Pi_{i_1}, \ldots, \Pi_{i_n}). \tag{1.13}$$

It is to be noted that while the joint density of $z_1, \ldots, z_n$ given $\theta_{i_1}, \ldots, \theta_{i_n}$ factorizes to $\prod_{j=1}^{n} f(z_j \mid \theta_{i_j}, \psi_{i_j}, \Pi_{i_j})$, this will not be generally true for the predictive density; i.e.,

$$f(z_1, \ldots, z_n \mid X, \psi, \Pi_{i_1}, \ldots, \Pi_{i_n}) \neq \prod_{j=1}^{n} f(z_j \mid X, \psi_{i_j}, \Pi_{i_j}). \tag{1.14}$$

Hence the results of a joint assignment will be in principle different from the previous type, which we may refer to as a marginal assignment, although perhaps not often in practice.

It is sometimes convenient to write

$$\Pr\{z_1 \in \Pi_{i_1}, \ldots, z_n \in \Pi_{i_n} \mid X, \psi, q\} = \Pr\{Z_1 \in \Pi_1, \ldots, Z_k \in \Pi_k \mid X, \psi, q\}, \tag{1.15}$$

where Z_i represents the set of n_i observations assumed from Π_i and $\sum_{i=1}^{k} n_i = n$, since the set of observations $z_1, \ldots, z_n$ is apportioned among the k populations such that the n_i belong to Π_i. The reason for using (1.15) is that under certain conditions we do have a useful factorization such that

$$\Pr\{Z_1 \in \Pi_1, \ldots, Z_k \in \Pi_k \mid X, \psi, q\} = \prod_{j=1}^{k} \Pr\{Z_j \in \Pi_j \mid X, \psi, q\}. \tag{1.16}$$

Another form of predictive classification would be one wherein "decisions" or assignments need be made as soon as possible, i.e., as soon as z_i is observed. Hence, if $z_1, z_2, \ldots$ are observed sequentially, we may wish, when we are ready to observe and classify z_n, to make our assignment as precise as possible by incorporating the previous observations $z_1, \ldots, z_{n-1}$ in our predictive machinery. We need now compute the sequential predictive density of z_n on the hypothesis that it belongs to Π_i conditional on ψ and on the observations X (whose population origin is known), and on the observations $z_1, \ldots, z_{n-1}$ (whose population origin is uncertain). We then obtain the sequential predictive density of z_n on the hypothesis that it belongs to Π_i.

$$f(z_n \mid X, \psi, z_1, \ldots, z_{n-1}, \Pi_i)$$

$$\propto \sum_{i_{n-1}=1}^{k} \cdots \sum_{i_1=1}^{k} q_{i_1} \cdots q_{i_{n-1}} f(z_1, \ldots, z_n \mid X, \psi, \Pi_{i_1}, \ldots, \Pi_{i_{n-1}}, \Pi_i), \tag{1.17}$$

i.e., a mixture of joint predictive densities with z_n fixed unto Π_i. Further,

$$\Pr\{z_n \in \Pi_i \mid X, \psi, z_1, \ldots, z_{n-1}\} \propto q_i f(z_n \mid X, \psi, z_1, \ldots, z_{n-1}, \Pi_i). \tag{1.18}$$

This same result can also be obtained from the product of the likelihoods and the prior density,

$$L(X \mid \theta, \psi) L(z_1, \ldots, z_{n-1} \mid \theta, \psi) g(\theta \mid \psi) \propto P(\theta \mid X, \psi, z_1, \ldots, z_{n-1}), \tag{1.19}$$

where

$$L(z_1, \ldots, z_{n-1} \mid \theta, \psi) = \prod_{j=1}^{n-1} \sum_{i_j=1}^{k} q_{i_j} f(z_j \mid \theta_{i_j}, \psi_{i_j})$$

and, finally,

$$f(z_n \mid X, \psi, z_1, \ldots, z_{n-1}, \Pi_i) = \int f(z_n \mid \theta_i, \psi_i) P(\theta \mid X, \psi, z_1, \ldots, z_{n-1})\, d\theta,$$

which is equivalent to (1.17).

2. MULTIVARIATE NORMAL DISCRIMINATION

In a previous paper (Geisser [3]) this Bayesian approach was used specifically to obtain posterior odds for classifying a single multivariate normal observation. A variety of cases, although by no means exhaustive, involving normal populations was considered, as well as other points concerning Bayesian and fiducial classification and unknown prior probabilities $q_1, \ldots, q_k$. In this section we shall restrict ourselves to only several of the previously discussed cases and assume q_i is known. We shall use a particular convenient prior density to reflect an initial diffuseness or vagueness about the unknown parameters. It is to be noted that in classification applications our interest focuses primarily on a statement concerning the relative likelihood or probability that an observation belongs to one or another of the populations, as a basis for assignment, and not the more customary Bayesian application of making a probability statement about where a parameter lies. The prior densities here will then be of the type previously given in [3–5] and in essence are for an unknown p-component vector mean μ and $p \times p$ covariance matrix Σ,

$$g(\mu, \Sigma)\, d\mu\, d\Sigma^{-1} \propto |\Sigma|^{(P+1)/2}\, d\mu\, d\Sigma^{-1}; \tag{2.1}$$

for μ unknown and Σ known,

$$g(\mu \mid \Sigma)\, d\mu \propto d\mu; \tag{2.2}$$

for μ known and Σ unknown,

$$g(\Sigma \mid \mu)\, d\Sigma^{-1} \propto |\Sigma|^{(P+1)/2}\, d\Sigma^{-1}. \tag{2.3}$$

Let $x'_{i\alpha} = (x_{1i\alpha}, \ldots, x_{pi\alpha})$ be the αth observation obtained from Π_i, which is $N(\mu_i, \Sigma_i)$, $i = 1, \ldots, k$, $\alpha = 1, \ldots, N_i$. Predictive densities obtained in the manner of Section 1 and based on prior densities of the type (2.1), (2.2), and (2.3) will be considered for some of the cases previously presented in Ref. 3.

Define

$$\bar{x}_i = N_i^{-1} \sum_{\alpha=1}^{N_i} x_{i\alpha}, \qquad (N_i - 1)S_i = \sum_{\alpha=1}^{N_i} (x_{i\alpha} - \bar{x}_i)(x_{i\alpha} - \bar{x}_i)',$$

$$N_i T_i = \sum_{\alpha=1}^{N_i} (x_{i\alpha} - \mu_i)(x_{i\alpha} - \mu_i)'.$$

In presenting the predictive density we include only those constants which are relevant to the computation of the posterior odds.

Case A. Σ_i is known, μ_i is unknown:

$$f(z \mid \bar{x}_i, \Sigma_i, \Pi_i) \propto \left(\frac{N_i}{N_i + 1}\right)^{p/2} |\Sigma_i|^{-1/2} \exp\left\{-\frac{N_i}{2(N_i + 1)} \operatorname{tr} \Sigma_i^{-1}(\bar{x}_i - z)(\bar{x}_i - z)'\right\}. \tag{2.4}$$

Case B. Σ_i is unknown, μ_i is known:

$$f(z \mid T_i, \Pi_i) \propto \left[\Gamma\left(\frac{N_i + 1}{2}\right) \Big/ \Gamma\left(\frac{N_i + 1 - p}{2}\right)\right] \frac{|N_i T_i|^{N_i/2}}{|N_i T_i + zz'|^{(N_i+1)/2}} \tag{2.5}$$

Case C. Σ_i is unknown, μ_i is unknown:

$$f(z \mid \bar{x}_i, S_i, \Pi_i) \propto \left(\frac{N_i}{N_i + 1}\right)^{p/2}$$

$$\times \left\{\Gamma\left(\frac{N_i}{2}\right)\left[1 + \frac{N_i(\bar{x}_i - z)'S^{-1}(\bar{x}_i - z)}{N_i^2 - 1}\right]^{-N_i/2} \Big/ \Gamma\left(\frac{N_i - p}{2}\right) |(N_i - 1)S_i|^{1/2}\right\}. \tag{2.6}$$

Case D. $\Sigma_i = \Sigma$ but unknown, μ_i known:

$$f(z \mid \mu_i, T, \Pi_i) \propto [1 + N^{-1}(z - \mu_i)'T^{-1}(z - \mu_i)]^{-(N+1)/2}, \tag{2.7}$$

where $N = \sum_{j=1}^{k} N_j$, $T = N^{-1} \sum_{j=1}^{k} N_j T_j$.

Case E. $\Sigma_i = \Sigma$ but unknown, μ_i unknown:

$$f(z \mid \bar{x}_i, S, \Pi_i) \propto \left(\frac{N_i}{N_i + 1}\right)^{p/2} \left[1 + \frac{N_i(\bar{x}_i - z)'S^{-1}(\bar{x}_i - z)}{(N_i + 1)(N - k)}\right]^{-(N-k+1)/2}, \tag{2.8}$$

where $S = (N - k)^{-1} \sum_{j=1}^{k} (N_j - 1)S_j$.

As mentioned before we may use $u_i(z) = q_i f(z \mid X, \psi, \Pi_i)$ for discrimination purposes by calculating the set of regions denoted by R_i such that for $z \in R_i$, $u_i(z)$ is a maximum. We may also inquire under what circumstance linear functions of z with regard to cases A to E will serve as predictive linear discriminants. Let

$$u_{ij}(z) = \frac{u_i(z)}{u_j(z)} = \frac{q_i f(z \mid X, \psi, \Pi_i)}{q_j f(z \mid X, \psi, \Pi_j)}. \tag{2.9}$$

Case A. For $\log u_{ij}(z)$ to be linear we require that

$$\frac{N_i + 1}{N_i} \Sigma_i = V \qquad \text{for} \quad i = 1, \ldots, k, \tag{2.10}$$

which will be certainly satisfied if $\Sigma_i = \Sigma$ and $kN_i = N$ for all i. We then obtain

$$\log u_{ij}(z) = \log \frac{q_i}{q_j} + z'V^{-1}(\bar{x}_i - \bar{x}_j) + \bar{x}_j'V^{-1}\bar{x}_j - \bar{x}_i'V^{-1}\bar{x}_i, \tag{2.11}$$

and Π_i is preferred to Π_j in the assignment of z for all z such that $\log u_{ij}(z) > 0$. Let us suppose, for the sake of exposition, that $k = 2$, i.e., we have only Π_1 and Π_2. Then we may determine the distribution of $\log u_{12}(z)$ from the density of z in (2.4). Hence $\log u_{12}(z)$ is normally distributed with

$$E \log u_{12}(z) = \log \frac{q_1}{q_2} + \tfrac{1}{2}(\bar{x}_1 - \bar{x}_2)'V^{-1}(\bar{x}_1 - \bar{x}_2) \qquad \text{if} \quad z \in \Pi_1 \tag{2.12}$$

and

$$E \log u_{12}(z) = \log \frac{q_1}{q_2} - \tfrac{1}{2}(\bar{x}_1 - \bar{x}_2)V^{-1}(\bar{x}_1 - \bar{x}_2) \qquad \text{if} \quad z \in \Pi_2, \tag{2.13}$$

and in either case

$$\mathrm{Var}[\log u_{12}(z)] = (\bar{x}_1 - \bar{x}_2)'V^{-1}(\bar{x}_1 - \bar{x}_2). \tag{2.14}$$

We shall skip cases B and C, since linear results are obtainable there only under conditions which are entirely unrealistic; i.e., although the Σ_i's are presumed different their sampled estimates are exactly equal.

Case D. Here we have that

$$u_{ij}(z) = \frac{q_i}{q_j}\left[\frac{1 + N^{-1}(z - \mu_j)'T^{-1}(z - \mu_j)}{1 + N^{-1}(z - \mu_i)'T^{-1}(z - \mu_i)}\right]^{(N+1)/2} > 1 \qquad (2.15)$$

implies that Π_i is preferred to Π_j for the assignment of z. Hence if $q_i = k^{-1}$ for $i = 1, \ldots, k$, we find that (2.15) implies that

$$v_{ij}(z) = 2z'T^{-1}(\mu_i - \mu_j) + (\mu_i - \mu_j)'T^{-1}(\mu_i + \mu_j) > 0. \qquad (2.16)$$

From the predictive density given by (2.7) we can show that if $z \in \Pi_i$, then

$$\frac{(z - \mu_i)'(NT)^{-1}(\mu_i - \mu_j)}{(\mu_i - \mu_j)'(NT)^{-1}(\mu_i - \mu_j)^{1/2}} \qquad (2.17)$$

is $(N-p+1)^{-1/2}t_{N-p+1}$, where t_{N-p+1} is Student's t with $N - p + 1$ degrees of freedom [5]. If $k = 2$, then $v_{12}(z)$ is

$$2N^{1/2}[(\mu_1 - \mu_2)'\,T^{-1}(\mu_1 - \mu_2)]^{1/2}(N - p + 1)^{-1/2}t_{N-p+1} + (\mu_1 - \mu_2)'\,T^{-1}(\mu_1 - \mu_2) \qquad (2.18)$$

when $z \in \Pi_1$ and $v_{12}(z)$ is

$$2N^{1/2}[(\mu_1 - \mu_2)'\,T^{-1}(\mu_1 - \mu_2)]^{1/2}(N - p + 1)^{-1/2}t_{N-p+1} + (\mu_1 - \mu_2)'\,T^{-1}(\mu_2 - \mu_1) \qquad (2.19)$$

when $z \in \Pi_2$.

Case E. Here we may also obtain a function $v_{ij}(z)$ linear in z if $kN_i = N$, $q_i = k^{-1}$ for $i = 1, \ldots, k$. Then

$$v_{ij}(z) = 2z'W^{-1}(\bar{x}_i - \bar{x}_j) + (\bar{x}_i - \bar{x}_j)'W^{-1}(\bar{x}_i + \bar{x}_j), \qquad (2.20)$$

where $W = N^{-1}(N^2 - k^2)S$. Similar to the previous case when $k = 2$ we find that v_{12} is

$$2[(\bar{x}_1 - \bar{x}_2)'W^{-1}(\bar{x}_1 - \bar{x}_2)]^{1/2}(N - p - 1)^{-1/2}t_{N-p-1} + (\bar{x}_1 - \bar{x}_2)'W^{-1}(\bar{x}_1 - \bar{x}_2) \qquad (2.21)$$

if $z \in \Pi_1$ and v_{12} is

$$2[(\bar{x}_1 - \bar{x}_2)'W^{-1}(\bar{x}_1 - \bar{x}_2)]^{1/2}(N - p - 1)^{-1/2}t_{N-p-1} + (\bar{x}_1 - \bar{x}_2)'W^{-1}(\bar{x}_2 - \bar{x}_1) \qquad (2.22)$$

if $z \in \Pi_2$.

3. JOINT NORMAL CLASSIFICATION

We now develop the particular normal predictive machinery for the joint classification of a set of observations $z_1, \ldots, z_n$. The cases listed here are identical to those of Section 2 with regard to the assumptions.

Case A.

$$f(z_1, \ldots, z_n \mid X, \Sigma_{i_1}, \ldots, \Sigma_{i_n}, \Pi_{i_1}, \ldots, \Pi_{i_n})$$
$$\propto \int \exp\left\{-\frac{1}{2}\sum_{j=1}^{n} \operatorname{tr} \Sigma_{i_j}^{-1}(z_j - \mu_{i_j})(z_j - \mu_{i_j})' - \frac{N_i}{2}\sum_{i=1}^{k} \operatorname{tr} \Sigma_i^{-1}(\bar{x}_i - \mu_i)(\bar{x}_i - \mu_i)'\right\} \prod_{i=1}^{k} d\mu_i. \tag{3.1}$$

Now as in (1.15) we let Z_i be the $p \times n_i$ matrix of those n_i vectors out of the n which are assumed to belong to Π_i, so that the set of variables $Z_1, \ldots, Z_k$ represents a reassembly of the variables $z_1, \ldots, z_n$ and

$$f(z_1, \ldots, z_n \mid X, \Sigma_{i_1}, \ldots, \Sigma_{i_n}, \Pi_{i_1}, \ldots, \Pi_{i_n}) = f(Z_1, \ldots, Z_k \mid X, \Sigma_1, \ldots, \Sigma_k, \Pi_1, \ldots, \Pi_k). \tag{3.2}$$

In this case, because of the assumed distinctness of all the parameters, we also find that

$$f(Z_1, \ldots, Z_k \mid X, \Sigma_1, \ldots, \Sigma_k, \Pi_1, \ldots, \Pi_k) = \prod_{i=1}^{k} f(Z_i \mid X, \Sigma_i, \Pi_i), \tag{3.3}$$

since by (3.1),

$$f(Z_1, \ldots, Z_k \mid X, \Sigma_1, \ldots, \Sigma_k, \Pi_1, \ldots, \Pi_k)$$
$$\propto \int \exp\left\{-\frac{1}{2}\sum_{i=1}^{k} \operatorname{tr} \Sigma_i^{-1}\left[(Z_i - \mu_i e_i')(Z_i - \mu_i e_i')' + \frac{N_i}{2}(\bar{x}_i - \mu_i)(\bar{x}_i - \mu_i)'\right]\right\} \prod_{i=1}^{k} d\mu_i, \tag{3.4}$$

where e_i is the $n_i \times 1$ vector all of whose elements are unity.

From (3.4) we easily find that

$$f(Z_1, \ldots, Z_k \mid X, \Sigma_1, \ldots, \Sigma_k, \Pi_1, \ldots, \Pi_k) = \prod_{i=1}^{k} N(Z_i \mid \bar{x}_i e_i', \Omega_i \otimes \Sigma_i), \tag{3.5}$$

where the $n_i \times n_i$ matrix

$$\Omega_i = I - (n_i + N_i)^{-1} e_i e_i' \tag{3.6}$$

and $N(\cdot\mid\cdot)$ represents the joint multivariate normal density of the $p \times n_i$ variables denoted by Z_i such that $EZ_i = \bar{x}_i e_i'$ and $\operatorname{Cov} Z_i = \Omega_i \otimes \Sigma_i$ ($\otimes$ is the Kronecker direct product) with the convention that $N(\cdot\mid\cdot) = 1$ if $n_i = 0$.

Hence

$$\Pr\{Z_1 \in \Pi_1, \dots, Z_k \in \Pi_k \mid X, \Sigma_1, \dots, \Sigma_k, q\} \propto \prod_{i=1}^{k} q_i^{n_i} N(Z_i \mid \bar{x}_i e_i', \Omega_i \otimes \Sigma_i) \quad (3.7)$$

with the appropriate norming factor (i.e., the denominator that converts the right side to a probability) consisting of the sum of the k^n terms, each similar to the numerator representing a particular assignment of $z_1, \dots, z_n$ to $Z_1, \dots, Z_k$ and a particular partition of n into $n_1, \dots, n_k$.

Case B. Here

$$\begin{aligned} f(Z_1, \dots, Z_k \mid X, \mu_1, \dots, \mu_k, \Pi_1, \dots, \Pi_k) &\propto \prod_{i=1}^{k} \int |\Sigma_i|^{-(N_i+n_i-p-1)/2} \\ &\quad \times \exp\{-\tfrac{1}{2} \operatorname{tr} \Sigma_i^{-1}[N_i T_i + (Z_i - \mu_i e_i')(Z_i - \mu_i e_i')']\}\, d\mu_i \\ &\propto \prod_{i=1}^{k} D(Z_i \mid \mu_i e_i', I, T_i, N_i, n_i, p), \end{aligned} \quad (3.8)$$

where

$$\begin{aligned} D(Y \mid \Lambda, \Omega, A, M, m, p) &= 1 \qquad \text{if} \quad m = 0, \\ &= \frac{(2\pi)^{-pm/2} K(p, M) |MA|^{M/2} |\Omega|^{p/2}}{K(p, M+m) |MA + (Y - \Lambda)\Omega(Y - \Lambda)'|^{(M+m)/2}} \\ &\qquad \text{otherwise}, \end{aligned} \quad (3.9)$$

and $M \geq p$, $m \geq 1$, A is $p \times p$ and positive-definite, Ω is $m \times m$ and positive-definite, Y and Λ are $p \times m$,

$$K^{-1}(p, \nu) = 2^{p\nu/2} \pi^{[p(p-1)]/4} \prod_{j=1}^{p} \Gamma\left(\frac{\nu + 1 - j}{2}\right). \quad (3.10)$$

Hence

$$\Pr\{Z_1 \in \Pi_1, \dots, Z_k \in \Pi_k \mid X, \mu_1, \dots, \mu_k, q\} \propto \prod_{i=1}^{k} q_i^{n_i} D(Z_i \mid \mu_i e_i', I, T_i, N_i, n_i, p). \quad (3.11)$$

Case C. Here

$$\begin{aligned} f(Z_1, \dots, Z_k \mid X, \Pi_1, \dots, \Pi_k) &\propto \prod_{i=1}^{k} \int |\Sigma_i|^{-(N_i+n_i-p-1)/2} \\ &\quad \times \exp\{-\tfrac{1}{2} \operatorname{tr} \Sigma_i^{-1}[(N_i - 1)S_i + N_i(\bar{x}_i - \mu_i)(\bar{x}_i - \mu_i)' \\ &\quad + (Z_i - \mu_i e_i')(Z_i - \mu_i e_i')']\}\, d\Sigma_i^{-1}\, d\mu_i \\ &\propto \prod_{i=1}^{k} D(Z_i \mid \bar{x}_i e_i', \Omega_i, S_i, N_i - 1, n_i, p). \end{aligned} \quad (3.12)$$

Therefore,

$$\Pr\{Z_1 \in \Pi_1, \ldots, Z_k \in \Pi_k \mid X, q\} \propto \prod_{i=1}^{k} q_i^{n_i} D(Z_i \mid \bar{x}_i e_i', \Omega_i, S_i, N_i - 1, n_i, p). \tag{3.13}$$

Case D. Here it is convenient to define

$$Z - \mu = (z_1 - \mu_{i_1}, \ldots, z_n - \mu_{i_n}) \tag{3.14}$$

as a $p \times n$ matrix. Hence the predictive density

$$\begin{aligned}(z_1, \ldots, z_n \mid X, \mu, \Pi_{i_1}, \ldots, \Pi_{i_n})& \\ \propto \int |\Sigma|^{-(N+n-p-1)/2} \exp\{-\tfrac{1}{2} \operatorname{tr} \Sigma^{-1}[(Z-\mu)(Z-\mu)' + NT]\}\, d\Sigma^{-1}& \\ \propto |NT + (Z-\mu)(Z-\mu)'|^{-(N+n)/2}& \qquad (3.15\end{aligned}$$

and

$$\Pr\{z_1 \in \Pi_{i_1}, \ldots, z_n \in \Pi_{i_n}\} \propto \left(\prod_{j=1}^{n} q_{i_j}\right) |NT + (Z-\mu)(Z-\mu)'|^{-(N+n)/2} \tag{3.16}$$

where there are k^n possibilities for μ depending on the assignment of $i_1, \ldots, i_n$.

Case E. Here it is more convenient to revert back to the notation involving $Z_1, \ldots, Z_k$ and

$$\begin{aligned}&f(Z_1, \ldots, Z_k \mid X, \Pi_1, \ldots, \Pi_k) \\ &\propto \int f(Z_1, \ldots, Z_k \mid \Sigma, \mu_1, \ldots, \mu_k) P(\Sigma^{-1}, \mu_1, \ldots, \mu_k \mid X)\, d\Sigma^{-1} \prod_{i=1}^{k} d\mu_i \\ &\propto \left(\prod_{i=1}^{k} \frac{N_i}{N_i + n_i}\right)^{p/2} |(N-k)S + \sum_{i=1}^{k} (Z_i - \bar{x}_i e_i')\Omega_i (Z_i - \bar{x}_i e_i')'|^{-(N+n-k)/2}\end{aligned} \tag{3.17}$$

and

$$\Pr\{Z_1 \in \Pi_1, \ldots, Z_k \in \Pi_k \mid X, q\} \propto \left(\prod_{i=1}^{k} q_i^{n_i}\right) f(Z_1, \ldots, Z_k \mid X, \Pi_1, \ldots, \Pi_k). \tag{3.18}$$

4. SEQUENTIAL NORMAL CLASSIFICATION

We now assume that the observations are sequentially obtained and for one reason or another it is necessary that they be classified immediately upon receipt. The sequential mechanism has been given in Section 1, and here we adapt it to the cases A to E of normal populations considered in Sections 2 and 3. To ease the cumbersomeness of the formulas we shall write the sequential predictive density for $z_n \in \Pi_i$ as

$$f(z_n \mid X, \psi, z^{(n-1)}, \Pi_i) \propto \textstyle\sum' q_{i_1} \cdots q_{i_{n-1}} f(z_1, \ldots, z_n \mid X, \psi, \Pi^{(n-1)}, \Pi_i), \quad (4.1)$$

where $z^{(n-1)}$ and $\Pi^{(n-1)}$ represent $z_1, \ldots, z_{n-1}$ and $\Pi_{i_1}, \ldots, \Pi_{i_{n-1}}$, respectively, and

$$\textstyle\sum' = \sum_{i_1=1}^{k} \cdots \sum_{i_{n-1}=1}^{k} . \quad (4.2)$$

In several cases, as in the previous section, it is convenient to denote the joint predictive density, on the assumption that $(z_1 \in \Pi_{i_1}, \ldots, z_{n-1} \in \Pi_{i_{n-1}}, z_n \in \Pi_i)$, as

$$f(z_1, \ldots, z_n \mid X, \psi, \Pi^{(n-1)}, \Pi_i) = f(Z_1, \ldots, Z_k \mid X, \psi, \Pi), \quad (4.3)$$

where Π represents $\Pi_1, \ldots, \Pi_k$ and $z_n \in \Pi_i$. In this event we can write for the posterior sequential probability

$$\Pr\{z_n \in \Pi_i \mid X, \psi, z^{(n-1)}, q\} \propto \textstyle\sum'' \left(\prod_{j=1}^{k} q_j^{n_j} \right) f(Z_1, \ldots, Z_k \mid X, \psi, \Pi), \quad (4.4)$$

where $\sum''$ stands for the sum over all assignments of $z_1, \ldots, z_{n-1}$ to $Z_1, \ldots, Z_k$ with z_n always assigned to Z_i and then summed over all partitions of n such that $\sum_{j=1}^{k} n_j = n$ for $n_j \geq 0, j \neq i$, but $n_i \geq 1$.

We now briefly enumerate the results for the same cases as before based on the densities obtained in the previous section.

Case A.

$$\Pr\{z_n \in \Pi_i \mid X, \Sigma_1, \ldots, \Sigma_k, z^{(n-1)}, q\} \propto \textstyle\sum'' \prod_{j=1}^{k} q_j^{n_j} N(Z_j \mid \bar{x}_j e_j', \Omega_j \otimes \Sigma_j). \quad (4.5)$$

Case B.

$$\Pr\{z_n \in \Pi_i \mid X, \mu_1, \ldots, \mu_k, z^{(n-1)}, q\} \propto \textstyle\sum'' \prod_{j=1}^{k} q_j^{n_j} D(Z_j \mid \mu_j e_j', I, T_j, N_j, n_j, p). \quad (4.6)$$

Case C.

$$\Pr\{z_n \in \Pi_i \mid X, z^{(n-1)}, q\} \propto \textstyle\sum'' \prod_{j=1}^{k} q_j^{n_j} D(Z_j \mid \bar{x}_j e_j', \Omega_j, S_j, N_j - 1, n_j, p). \quad (4.7)$$

Case D. Here it is more convenient to revert back to the notation of (4.1) and (4.2), so that

$$\Pr\{z_n \in \Pi_i \mid X, \mu_1, \ldots, \mu_k, z^{(n-1)}, q\}$$
$$\propto q_i \textstyle\sum' q_{i_1} \cdots q_{i_{n-1}} | NT + (Z - \mu)(Z - \mu)' |^{-(N+n-k)/2}, \quad (4.8)$$

where $Z - \mu$ is defined as in (3.13), except that $\mu_{i_n} = \mu_i$.

Case E.

$$\Pr\{z_n \in \Pi_i \mid X, z^{(n-1)}, q\} \propto \sum{}'' \left(\prod_{j=1}^{k} q_j^{n_j}\right)\left(\prod_{j=1}^{k} \frac{N_j}{N_j + n_j}\right)^{p/2}$$

$$\times \left|(N-k)S + \sum_{i=1}^{k} (Z_i - \bar{x}_i e_i')\Omega_i(Z_i - \bar{x}_i e_i')'\right|^{-(N+n-k)/2}. \quad (4.9)$$

5. REMARKS

There still remain at least two questions of interest. Which procedure should we use in practical situations? How different will the procedures be in such situations?

If we consider the cases where observations make their appearance sequentially and the assignment must be made immediately upon receipt, it would appear that the procedure of choice is the sequential one. There are, however, two circumstances that might tend to restrict the use of this alternative. First, the calculation of the posterior sequential probability appears to become quite burdensome, as n increases relative to the posterior marginal-probability calculation.

Second, the sequential assignment, although optimum for the setup, is in a sense "unfair." By this we mean that two successive observations, although identical, may be assigned to different populations. This could certainly render an uninitiated, but alert, consumer a bit uneasy about such a procedure. On the other hand, another consumer might very well regard this and the burdensome calculations as an inconsequential price to pay for the continual improvement of his classification machinery. Of course, the "improvement" derives from the increased precision in the estimation of the parameters by utilizing $z_1, \ldots, z_{n-1}$. However, it is also quite possible that this "improvement" is so gradual that its neglect will have little or no effect in most practical situations on the eventual assignment of the observation. This is certainly a point for further investigation.

If there is no need for immediate assignment and one could just as well wait until all n observations are at hand, then certainly the most appropriate procedure is the joint assignment scheme. Again the calculation may be more burdensome than the marginal scheme, although not nearly so involved as the sequential method. However, if by chance another observation came along, a new joint classification based on $n+1$ observations could obviously differ from the previous one in the populations to which one or another of the first n observations was assigned. But if the consumer can wait until the nth observation, he can probably wait until the next one as well and use the joint optimum assignment for the $n+1$ observations. Of course, if the original decision or assignment is irreversible, the $(n+1)$st observation may be assigned on the basis of the sequential scheme. At any rate, if these and other contingencies are a source of confusion, the user can always opt for the marginal scheme, generally with little or no loss.

We shall now show that these three methods can in actuality lead to differential assignment by means of a simple, concocted example.

Suppose we have only two univariate normal populations Π_1 and Π_2 which are, respectively, $N(\mu, 1)$ and $N(0.8, 1)$, with equal prior probabilities of an observation z occurring from either Π_1 or Π_2. Let us also assume, as is customary in many Bayesian applications, that the prior density of μ is uniform. Further, suppose that on Π_1 we have a single observation x_1. Then the predictive densities of z on the assumption that z belongs to Π_1 or Π_2, respectively, are

$$f(z \mid x_1, \Pi_1) = [1/(4\pi)^{1/2}] \exp\{-(\tfrac{1}{4})(z - x_1)^2\}, \tag{5.1}$$

$$f(z \mid \Pi_2) = [1/(2\pi)^{1/2}] \exp\{-(\tfrac{1}{2})(z - 0.8)^2\}. \tag{5.2}$$

Suppose now there are two observations, z_1 and z_2. Then the four predictive densities necessary for joint classification are

$$f(z_1, z_2 \mid x_1, \Pi_1, \Pi_2) = f(z_1 \mid x_1, \Pi_1) f(z_2 \mid \Pi_2), \tag{5.3}$$

$$f(z_1, z_2 \mid x_1, \Pi_2, \Pi_1) = f(z_1 \mid \Pi_2) f(z_2 \mid x_1, \Pi_1), \tag{5.4}$$

$$f(z_1, z_2 \mid x_1, \Pi_2, \Pi_2) = f(z_1 \mid \Pi_2) f(z_2 \mid \Pi_2), \tag{5.5}$$

$$f(z_1, z_2 \mid x_1, \Pi_1, \Pi_1) = (2\pi)^{-1} |V|^{1/2} \exp\{-\tfrac{1}{2} w' V w\}, \tag{5.6}$$

where $w' = (z_1 - x_1, z_2 - x_1)$ and

$$V = \frac{1}{3}\begin{pmatrix} 2 & -1 \\ -1 & 2 \end{pmatrix}. \tag{5.7}$$

For sequential classification, (5.1) and (5.2) would obtain for the assignment of z_1. For z_2 we have the sequential predictive densities

$$f(z_2 \mid x_1, z_1, \Pi_1) \propto f(z_1, z_2 \mid x_1, \Pi_1, \Pi_1) + f(z_1, z_2 \mid x_1, \Pi_2, \Pi_1), \tag{5.8}$$

$$f(z_2 \mid x_1, z_1, \Pi_2) \propto f(z_1, z_2 \mid x_1, \Pi_1, \Pi_2) + f(z_1, z_2 \mid x_1, \Pi_2, \Pi_2). \tag{5.9}$$

Now suppose, *mirabile dictu*, that $x_1 = z_1 = z_2 = 0$. We then find if we make the necessary calculations that the marginal, joint, and sequential assignment are, respectively,

$$(z_1 \in \Pi_2), (z_2 \in \Pi_2), \qquad (z_1 \in \Pi_1, z_2 \in \Pi_1), \qquad (z_1 \in \Pi_2), (z_2 \in \Pi_1 \mid z_1). \tag{5.10}$$

However, it is only fair to relate that this optimum assignment based on the maximum posterior probability, in all these cases, won out over the other alternatives by very small amounts. Hence an inspection of these probabilities by the classifier would surely cause him to hesitate in making an assignment, unless perforce he must.

Now it is clear that if all the parameters are known, there is absolutely no difference among the three methods, since the joint predictive density is just the original density, which is a product of the marginal densities. Further, new observations in this case obviously do not yield any more information on the known parameters, so that the sequential density is equivalent to the joint density as well. With this in mind, the three methods should not differ by very much, especially whenever the sample sizes $N_1, \ldots, N_k$ are large enough, so that the predictive densities are getting closer to the original densities. On the basis of vague information on the parameters, it would seem reasonable and desirable to use prior densities such that

$$\lim_{N_i \to \infty} f(z \mid X, \psi, \Pi_i) = f(z \mid \theta_i, \psi, \Pi_i). \tag{5.11}$$

It can easily be shown that the prior densities used in Section 2 lead to predictive densities that exhibit this property.

REFERENCES

1. ANDERSON, T. W. (1958). *An Introduction to Multivariate Statistical Analysis.* Wiley, New York.
2. DEMPSTER, A. P. (1964). On the difficulties inherent in the fiducial argument. *J. Amer. Statist. Assoc.* **59** 56–66.
3. GEISSER, S. (1964). Posterior odds for multivariate normal classifications. *J. Roy. Statist. Soc. Ser. B* **26** 69–76.
4. GEISSER, S. (1965). Bayesian estimation in multivariate analysis. *Ann. Math. Statist.* **36** 150–159.
5. GEISSER, S. and CORNFIELD, J. (1963). Posterior distributions for multivariate normal parameters. *J. Roy. Statist. Soc. Ser. B* **25** 368–376.

Discrimination and Classification

M. G. KENDALL
C-E-I-R LTD.
LONDON, ENGLAND

1. INTRODUCTION

The two subjects discussed in this paper are clearly interrelated; so closely, indeed, that they are often confused.

Discrimination. We are given a sample of members from each of two populations. The values of a certain number p of variables are determined for each member. Required: to construct a method of assigning a new member to the correct population of origin on the basis of the values of the p variables which it exhibits. As an extension, we may be given data for k populations and require to discriminate among them. An important problem, which has not been much considered, arises when some or all of the variables are qualitative, for example, dichotomies into attributes.

Classification. We are given a sample of members which may or may not emanate from the same population. The value of p variables are given for each member. Required: to set up a method of deciding whether the members fall into groups, and if so to delineate the groups. As with discrimination, the data may be measurable variables or qualitative observations, or a mixture of the two. We may note in passing a third related subject, *dissection.*

Dissection. We are given a sample of members from a single population, and the values, for each member, of p variables. Required: to set up a method of dissecting the population into sectors with predetermined properties.

Example. An example may make the distinction clear. Suppose we are given two groups of seedlings, one known to be from stock A and the other known to be from stock B. If we find further seedlings, knowing them to come from either A or B, but not knowing which, we require to assign them to the correct stock on the basis of observations made on the seedlings of known origin. This is a problem in discrimination. It is part of the data of the problem that A and B exist and are different.

We may, however, have a group of seedlings of unknown origin, perhaps from one stock, perhaps from many. The problem now is to see whether they form clusters with some internal similarity, or alternatively, whether there is no significant clustering and they can be regarded as a homogeneous group. This is a problem of classification into groups.

Third, suppose we have a set of students taking an examination. We are prepared to regard them as homogeneous, and their scores on examination papers support this conclusion. Where and how do we draw the line to distinguish classes of performance, say first, second, third, and fail? This is a problem in dissection.

2. DISCRIMINATION

The classical work on discrimination is described in Chapter 9 of my *Course in Multivariate Analysis* [4]. It is almost entirely based, following Fisher [1], on the production of a discriminant function of the variables $x_1, x_2, \dots, x_p$:

$$X = \sum_{j=1}^{p} l_j x_j . \tag{1}$$

The coefficients l are derived on the assumption that the two populations A and B are multivariate normal *with identical dispersion matrices.* Smith [6] considered the case of different dispersions, which leads to a quadratic discrimination, but there appears to have been very little attention paid to nonlinear functions.

In biological material, perhaps, the assumptions of multivariate normality and homoscedasticity are acceptable, but they are obviously unduly restrictive for general use. I have therefore sought a method which should be distribution-free, or at least approximately so. Two different methods were tried, but before I describe them it is desirable to say a few words about the discrimination problem itself.

Among the circumstances of the problem we are "given" two samples which are known, without possibility of error, to belong respectively to two populations. The mathematician frequently does not enquire into the reasons for assumptions on which he is to work, but the statistician is entitled to ask how these two samples were separated into A and B in the first place. If there is some unambiguous way of deciding between the populations, why do we not always use it? Why waste our time on discriminant functions? There are at least three classes of cases which provide an answer to this question:

(1) *Lost information.* It would have been very easy to distinguish between different races at the time when their bones were in the living body, but if all that we have to go on today are archaeological remains, we may need indirect observations on surviving material to provide a method of discriminating between alternative attributions of newly discovered data.

(2) *Diagnosis.* Nature may provide us with information about the hidden presence of disease, by surgical necessity or postmortem. But we really require to diagnose from external symptoms the presence of the disease in suspected sufferers, and the methods which enable presence or absence unambiguously to be determined are not, in general, available, In fact, it is often our object to detect the condition without being driven to employ such methods.

(3) *Prediction.* It may be possible to differentiate two conditions without error when they occur, but we may want to discriminate before they occur. For example, if movements up or down in unemployment rates were found to be correlated with certain economic movements which lead them in time, such as capital investment, it would be desirable to discriminate in advance so that remedial measures can be put in hand.

The problem of discrimination therefore exists and has a certain importance, especially, perhaps, in diagnosis. I suspect, however, that a number of problems which are really of classification or dissection are treated incorrectly as discrimination.

Consider first of all the case when p variables $x_1, x_2, \ldots, x_p$ are given for n_1 members of the A population and n_2 members of the B population. We may plot the points corresponding to the n_1 and n_2 members, in theory at least, in a Euclidean space of p dimensions. Figure 1 represents a possible situation in two dimensions, crosses representing the A points and circles, the B points. Our problem is to set up some boundary, such as CC' in the figure, which separates the crosses from the circles in some optimal way. We can, of course, always draw some boundary which will exactly include the crosses to the complete exclusion of the circles, but to do so would require a twisted artificiality which would satisfy nobody. We impose on our boundary CC' the necessity of being reasonably smooth and simply connected, and in doing so we have to accept the possibility of error. In the diagram, if we assert that any point falling on the left of CC' is a cross and every point on the right is a circle, we make no errors for the circles but incur three for the crosses. As Welch [8] has pointed out, the boundary can be determined according to the relative importance of misclassifying circles or crosses. If errors of misclassification are equally important, the appropriate boundary CC' is one for which the ratio f_1/f_2 is constant, f_1 and f_2 being the probability densities of the distributions of x in the two populations. Such a boundary minimizes the amount of misclassification.

It has been a standard assumption in most previous work, by statisticians, although not by taxonomists, that any new member arising from allocation *must* be assigned to either A or B. The theories make little provision for the allocator to say "I am doubtful" or "I don't know." This appears to me to

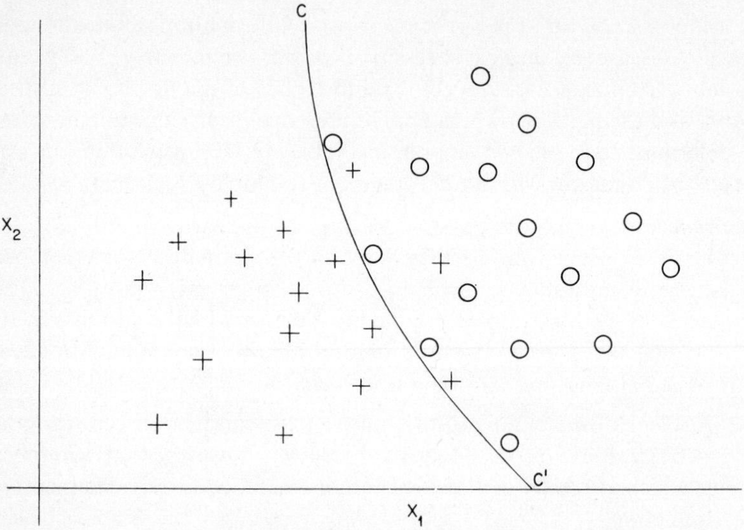

Fig. 1. Example of a discrimination problem in two dimensions (see text).

be a defect, and in the methods to be described I shall divide the sample space into three regions, one for A, one for B, and one for an area of indecision. Any method which fails to do so, in my opinion, is unlikely to stand the test of practical experience.

3. CONVEX-HULL METHOD

The crosses in Fig. 1 have a convex hull which is sketched in Fig. 2. Likewise, the circles have a convex hull, also sketched in. The two hulls will, in general, overlap. If they do not, so much the better. For convenience I continue the exposition in two dimensions, but it will be understood that the method applies generally to p dimensions.

Let us consider the following rule of discrimination:

(a) If a point falls in the A hull but not in the B hull we assign it to A.
(b) If the point falls in the B hull but not in the A hull we assign it to B.
(c) If the point falls into both hulls we shall not assign it to either.

The method is, I hope, plausible but it suffers from certain shortcomings:

(1) How do we determine the hulls?
(2) What do we do if a point falls outside both hulls?

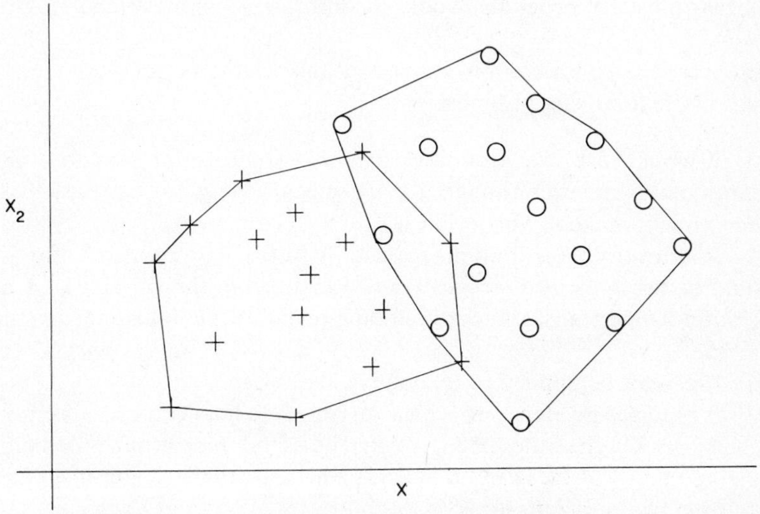

Fig. 2. Convex hulls imposed on data of Fig. 1 (see text).

The problem of finding the convex hull of a set of points in p dimensions is one of linear programming, although of a rather unusual type. It may be solved as follows:

Let the coordinates of n points in p dimensions be x_{ij}, $i = 1, 2, \ldots, p$; $j = 1, 2, \ldots, n$. A new point $y_1, y_2, \ldots, y_p$ will lie in the convex hull determined by the x's if there is a feasible solution to

$$\sum_{j=1}^{n} t_j = 1, \tag{2}$$

$$\sum_{j=1}^{n} x_{ij} t_j = y_i, \qquad (i = 1, 2, \ldots, p). \tag{3}$$

Let

$$\sum_{j=1}^{n} x_{ij} t_j - y_i = \varepsilon_i^{+} \quad \text{or} \quad -\varepsilon_i^{-}, \qquad (\varepsilon_j^{+}, \varepsilon_i^{-} \geq 0) \tag{4}$$

and minimize

$$z = \sum_{i=1}^{p} (\varepsilon_i^{+} - \varepsilon_i^{-}) \tag{5}$$

subject to the constraints (2) and (3). Then y falls in the convex hull of x's if and only if

$$\min z = 0. \tag{6}$$

As problems in linear programming go, this is a relatively simple one, and I think that most LP programs would incorporate a routine which effectively solves it.

However, on consideration I rejected this method, not without some regret, on the following grounds:

(1) It would hardly be economic to apply in practice for the allocation of an occasional member, although a mass screening (e.g., of a large block of patients) might make it worthwhile.

(2) It is not truly distribution-free, although, if the expression be forgiven, it would be nearly so in practice. Transformations of the variable of a nonlinear kind would transform the bounding planes of the hulls into nonplane boundaries.

(3) It cannot be applied to qualitative variables.

(4) It provides no clue as to which variables are important for discriminatory purposes. On the other hand, it might be useful to determine the number of points common to the A and B hulls, as a measure of the degree of entanglement of the two populations.

(5) It makes no provision for points which fall outside both hulls.

On point (5) there arises an interesting theoretical problem which I specify without attempting to solve. It is a generalization of what, in one dimension and with integral variate values, is sometimes referred to as the *bus problem*. The buses in a certain town are known to be numbered consecutively from 1 up to some unknown number N. A visitor arriving at the town for the first time observes buses numbered $a_1, a_2, \ldots, a_k$. What is the best estimator of N?

If we generalize (a) by allowing individuals to bear the values of a continuous variable, (b) by allowing the variable to have an unknown frequency function, (c) by adding $p - 1$ more variables of a similar kind, we arrive at the problem of estimating the parent convex hull from an observed sample. And if, of course, our frequency distributions are unlimited in range, we have to estimate, not the boundaries of the distribution, but some arbitrarily defined boundary such as the locus of a 99 % point. This is indeed a formidable problem, although it might yield to treatment for large samples. If there were to be an attack on it, I should expect success to come rather from an oblique approach by way of examining what restrictions can be placed on the generality of the problem without impairing the usefulness of the solution.

Before proceeding to my second method, I should mention an attempt made some years ago by Fix and Hodges [2]. Their method was simply to allocate a new point to cross or circle, whichever was nearer. But this method fails. For one thing we have to define what we mean by "nearer," and whether we do it simply in terms of distance in the p space, or by reference to a probabilistic metric in terms of the likelihood ratio f_1/f_2, we get some impossibly complicated acceptance and rejection domains in regions where crosses and circles are mixed up—which is the domain of greatest interest. An elaboration of the method, in which the new point is allotted to cross or circle according to whether there is a majority of one or other in the h nearest points ($h > 1$) does not overcome this difficulty.

4. THE ORDER-STATISTIC METHOD

All true distribution-free methods, I contend, must depend on order statistics. Sundrum and I put forward this claim some years ago [5] and, so far as I am aware, no counterexample has been given. It is just conceivable that some method might depend on topological properties, but none has yet been proposed. It follows that any distribution-free method of dealing with the discrimination problem must rely on order properties. One of the distinguishing features of such properties, however, is that they exist only in one dimension. Thus, we have to consider discrimination by one variable at a time. This turns out to be an advantage.

Table I repeats the data for three varieties of *Iris* which Fisher [1] used in his first paper on discriminant functions. For discrimination between *setosa* and *versicolor* he constructed a linear function of the four variables shown. In point of fact, this four-dimensional function is hardly necessary. The petal width of *setosa* has a mean value of 0.246 and a range of 0.2 to 0.6 (variance 0.0109). That of *versicolor* has a mean of 1.326 and a range of 1.0 to 1.8 (variance 0.0383). On this showing, petal width would be a perfectly good discriminator in itself. If we allot a new member to *setosa* or *versicolor* according to petal width is less than or exceeds, say, 0.9, we shall rarely make a mistake, even if the variates are normal.

The method I propose may be illustrated on the discrimination of *versicolor* against *virginica*. A casual inspection of the data shows what can be confirmed by tabulation—that the two differ more on petal length (PL) and petal width (PW) than on sepal length or width. We form a frequency distribution for PL and PW as in Table II.

We observe that on PL the two distributions overlap in the range 4.5 to 5.1. Outside this range there are 29 cases of *versicolor* and 34 cases of *virginica*. On PW there is overlap in the range 1.4 to 1.8, 28 cases of *versicolor* and 34 of *virginica* outside it. The total of cases lying outside the common range

TABLE I

Measurements on Three Varieties of Iris (in cm): *SL, SW, PL, and PW*[a]

Iris setosa				*Iris versicolor*				*Iris virginica*			
SL	SW	PL	PW	SL	SW	PL	PW	SL	SW	PL	PW
5.1	3.5	1.4	0.2	7.0	3.2	4.7	1.4	6.3	3.3	6.0	2.5
4.9	3.0	1.4	0.2	6.4	3.2	4.5	1.5	5.8	2.7	5.1	1.9
4.7	3.2	1.3	0.2	6.9	3.1	4.9	1.5	7.1	3.0	5.9	2.1
4.6	3.1	1.5	0.2	5.5	2.3	4.0	1.3	6.3	2.9	5.6	1.8
5.0	3.6	1.4	0.2	6.5	2.8	4.6	1.5	6.5	3.0	5.8	2.2
5.4	3.9	1.7	0.4	5.7	2.8	4.5	1.3	7.6	3.0	6.6	2.1
4.6	3.4	1.4	0.3	6.3	3.3	4.7	1.6	4.9	2.5	4.5	1.7
5.0	3.4	1.5	0.2	4.9	2.4	3.3	1.0	7.3	2.9	6.3	1.8
4.4	2.9	1.4	0.2	6.6	2.9	4.6	1.3	6.7	2.5	5.8	1.8
4.9	3.1	1.5	0.1	5.2	2.7	3.9	1.4	7.2	3.6	6.1	2.5
5.4	3.7	1.5	0.2	5.0	2.0	3.5	1.0	6.5	3.2	5.1	2.0
4.8	3.4	1.6	0.2	5.9	3.0	4.2	1.5	6.4	2.7	5.3	1.9
4.8	3.0	1.4	0.1	6.0	2.2	4.0	1.0	6.8	3.0	5.5	2.1
4.3	3.0	1.1	0.1	6.1	2.9	4.7	1.4	5.7	2.5	5.0	2.0
5.8	4.0	1.2	0.2	5.6	2.9	3.6	1.3	5.8	2.8	5.1	2.4
5.7	4.4	1.5	0.4	6.7	3.1	4.4	1.4	6.4	3.2	5.3	2.3
5.4	3.9	1.3	0.4	5.6	3.0	4.5	1.5	6.5	3.0	5.5	1.8
5.1	3.5	1.4	0.3	5.8	2.7	4.1	1.0	7.7	3.8	6.7	2.2
5.7	3.8	1.7	0.3	6.2	2.2	4.5	1.5	7.7	2.6	6.9	2.3
5.1	3.8	1.5	0.3	5.6	2.5	3.9	1.1	6.0	2.2	5.0	1.5
5.4	3.4	1.7	0.2	5.9	3.2	4.8	1.8	6.9	3.2	5.7	2.3
5.1	3.7	1.5	0.4	6.1	2.8	4.0	1.3	5.6	2.8	4.9	2.0
4.6	3.6	1.0	0.2	6.3	2.5	4.9	1.5	7.7	2.8	6.7	2.0
5.1	3.3	1.7	0.5	6.1	2.8	4.7	1.2	6.3	2.7	4.9	1.8
4.8	3.4	1.9	0.2	6.4	2.9	4.3	1.3	6.7	3.3	5.7	2.1
5.0	3.0	1.6	0.2	6.6	3.0	4.4	1.4	7.2	3.2	6.0	1.8
5.0	3.4	1.6	0.4	6.8	2.8	4.8	1.4	6.2	2.8	4.8	1.8
5.2	3.5	1.5	0.2	6.7	3.0	5.0	1.7	6.1	3.0	4.9	1.8
5.2	3.4	1.4	0.2	6.0	2.9	4.5	1.5	6.4	2.8	5.6	2.1
4.7	3.2	1.6	0.2	5.7	2.6	3.5	1.0	7.2	3.0	5.8	1.6
4.8	3.1	1.6	0.2	5.5	2.4	3.8	1.1	7.4	2.8	6.1	1.9
5.4	3.4	1.5	0.4	5.5	2.4	3.7	1.0	7.9	3.8	6.4	2.0
5.2	4.1	1.5	0.1	5.8	2.7	3.9	1.2	6.4	2.8	5.6	2.2
5.5	4.2	1.4	0.2	6.0	2.7	5.1	1.6	6.3	2.8	5.1	1.5
4.9	3.1	1.5	0.2	5.4	3.0	4.5	1.5	6.1	2.6	5.6	1.4
5.0	3.2	1.2	0.2	6.0	3.4	4.5	1.6	7.7	3.0	6.1	2.3
5.5	3.5	1.3	0.2	6.7	3.1	4.7	1.5	6.3	3.4	5.6	2.4
4.9	3.6	1.4	0.1	6.3	2.3	4.4	1.3	6.4	3.1	5.5	1.8
4.4	3.0	1.3	0.2	5.6	3.0	4.1	1.3	6.0	3.0	4.8	1.8
5.1	3.4	1.5	0.2	5.5	2.5	4.0	1.3	6.9	3.1	5.4	2.1
5.0	3.5	1.3	0.3	5.5	2.6	4.4	1.2	6.7	3.1	5.6	2.4
4.5	2.3	1.3	0.3	6.1	3.0	4.6	1.4	6.9	3.1	5.1	2.3
4.4	3.2	1.3	0.2	5.8	2.6	4.0	1.2	5.8	2.7	5.1	1.9

[a] SL = sepal length, SW = sepal width, PL = petal length, PW = petal width.

TABLE I—*Continued*

Iris setosa				*Iris versicolor*				*Iris virginica*			
SL	SW	PL	PW	SL	SW	PL	PW	SL	SW	PL	PW
5.0	3.5	1.6	0.6	5.0	2.3	3.3	1.0	6.8	3.2	5.9	2.3
5.1	3.8	1.9	0.4	5.6	2.7	4.2	1.3	6.7	3.3	5.7	2.5
4.8	3.0	1.4	0.3	5.7	3.0	4.2	1.2	6.7	3.0	5.2	2.3
5.1	3.8	1.6	0.2	5.7	2.9	4.2	1.3	6.3	2.5	5.0	1.9
4.6	3.2	1.4	0.2	6.2	2.9	4.3	1.3	6.5	3.0	5.2	2.0
5.3	3.7	1.5	0.2	5.1	2.5	3.0	1.1	6.2	3.4	5.4	2.3
5.0	3.3	1.4	0.2	5.7	2.8	4.1	1.3	5.9	3.0	5.1	1.8

TABLE II

Frequency Distributions of Petal Length and Petal Width for Iris virginica *and* Iris versicolor

Petal length			Petal width		
Variate values	Vers.	Virg.	Variate values	Vers.	Virg.
≤4.3	25				
4.4	4		1.0	7	
4.5	7	1	1.1	3	
4.6	3	—	1.2	5	
4.7	5	—	1.3	13	
4.8	2	2	1.4	7	1
4.9	2	3	1.5	10	2
5.0	1	3	1.6	3	1
5.1	1	7	1.7	1	1
5.2		2	1.8	1	11
5.3		2	1.9		5
5.4		2	2.0		6
5.5		3	2.1		6
5.6		6	2.2		3
5.7		3			8
5.8		3			3
≥5.9		13			3
	—	—		—	—
	50	50		50	50

being 63 for PL and 62 for PW, we shall take PL as our first discriminating variable. We then lay down the rule of discrimination:

$$\begin{array}{ll} PL \leq 4.4 & \text{allot to } \textit{versicolor}, \\ PL \geq 5.2 & \text{allot to } \textit{virginica}, \\ 4.5 \leq PL \leq 5.1 & \text{refer to next variable.} \end{array} \qquad (7)$$

There are 37 cases for which PL lies in the common range 3.5 to 5.1. We take these cases out of Table I and construct a distribution for them in respect of

TABLE III

Frequency Distribution of 37 Cases Not Distinguished by PL

	Petal width	
Variate value	Vers.	Virg.
1.2	1	
1.3	2	
1.4	4	
1.5	9	2
1.6	3	—
1.7	1	1
1.8	1	5
1.9		3
2.0		3
2.1		—
2.2		1
2.3		1
2.4		1
	21	16

TABLE IV

Frequency Distribution of 22 Cases Not Distinguished by PL and PW

	Sepal length			Sepal width	
Variate value	Vers.	Virg.	Variate value	Vers.	Virg.
4.9		1	2.2	1	1
—	—	—	2.3	—	—
5.4	1	—	2.4	—	—
5.5	—	—	2.5	1	1
5.6	1	—	2.6	—	—
5.7	—	—	2.7	1	1
5.8	—	—	2.8	1	2
5.9	1	1	2.9	1	—
6.0	3	2	3.0	3	3
6.1	—	1	3.1	2	
6.2	1	1	3.2	2	
6.3	2	2	3.3	1	
6.4	1	—	3.4	1	
6.5	1	—			
6.6	—	—			
6.7	2	—			
6.8	—	—			
6.9	1	—			
	14	8		14	8

PW, as in Table III. Proceeding as before, we see that there is a common range for PW of 1.5 to 1.8. We therefore add to the rule (7):

$$4.5 \leq PL \leq 5.1,$$

$$\begin{array}{ll} PW \leq 1.4 & \text{allot to } \textit{versicolor}, \\ PW \geq 1.9 & \text{allot to } \textit{virginica}, \\ 1.5 \leq PW \leq 1.9 & \text{proceed to next variable.} \end{array} \qquad (8)$$

This leaves 22 cases undecided (Table IV). PW has discriminated 63 cases and PL a further 15. We now refer to the 22 undecided cases on sepal length SL and sepal width SW.

For SL there are only 5 cases out of 14 lying outside the common range. For SW there are 6. We therefore take SW as our next discriminator and add to (8):

$$4.5 \leq PL \leq 5.1,$$
$$1.5 \leq PW \leq 1.9,$$

$$\begin{array}{ll} SW \geq 3.1 & \text{allot to } \textit{versicolor}, \\ SW < 3.1 & \text{proceed to next variable.} \end{array} \qquad (9)$$

Our third variable discriminates a further 6, making 84 altogether and leaving 16 undecided. For these 16 the distribution on SL is given in Table V.

TABLE V
Distribution of 16 *Cases Not Distinguished by PL, PW, or SW*

Variate value	Vers.	Virg.
4.9		1
—	—	—
5.4	1	—
5.5	—	—
5.6	1	—
5.7	—	—
5.8	—	—
5.9	—	1
6.0	2	2
6.1	—	1
6.2	1	1
6.3	1	2
6.4	—	—
6.5	1	—
6.6	—	—
6.7	1	—
	8	8

For what it is worth we may now add to (9):

$$4.5 \leq \mathrm{PL} \leq 5.1,$$
$$1.5 \leq \mathrm{PW} \leq 1.9,$$
$$\mathrm{SW} \leq 3.1,$$

$$\begin{array}{ll} \mathrm{SL} \geq 6.4 & \text{allot to } \textit{versicolor}, \\ \mathrm{SL} \leq 5.3 & \text{allot to } \textit{virginica}, \\ 5.4 \leq \mathrm{SL} \leq 6.3 & \text{undecided.} \end{array} \tag{10}$$

This leaves us with 87 cases decided and 13 undecided. No further discrimination is possible.

The procedure to be followed in general will, I hope, be clear. Apart from sampling effects it contains no errors—there is no misclassification, as against which we end with a residuum of cases which are undecided. Personally, I prefer a situation in which I may reserve judgement to one which forces me into mistakes even if I know the probability of making them. The procedure has the following advantages:

(1) It is completely distribution-free.

(2) It involves no arithmetic other than counting. Relatively small amounts of data can be analyzed by hand. For large amounts it would be simple to write a program for an electronic computer.

(3) It shows which variables are the most important in the discrimination. In fact, it proceeds by using the variables in order of importance as measured by degree of overlap.

The procedure is not, however, necessarily optimal. It is possible that more refined methods in special circumstances might leave a smaller residuum of undecided cases. I cannot see where any substantial improvement would be possible without sacrificing something in the distribution-free nature of the inference, except perhaps in the following manner.

Consider first of all Fig. 3, where crosses, and circles fall into two coherent separate groups. Some such boundary as CC' would provide a good discriminator. Our method might operate first on the variable x_2, giving the region A, above KK', as belonging to the crosses, and B, below, LL', as belonging to the circles. The second stage would operate in the zone between KK' and LL' and result in a line such as MM'. The first discriminating boundary would be $LMM'K'$, instead of CC', but it is just as good as a discriminator.

In general, the order-statistic procedure will result in a p-dimensional stepwise boundary, with, perhaps, a zone of indetermination in the interior of a hyperparallelopiped. In many ordinary cases this boundary will not differ, so far as discriminating power is concerned, from a smooth surface such as CC, and consequently is not far removed from optimality. Sampling effects apart,

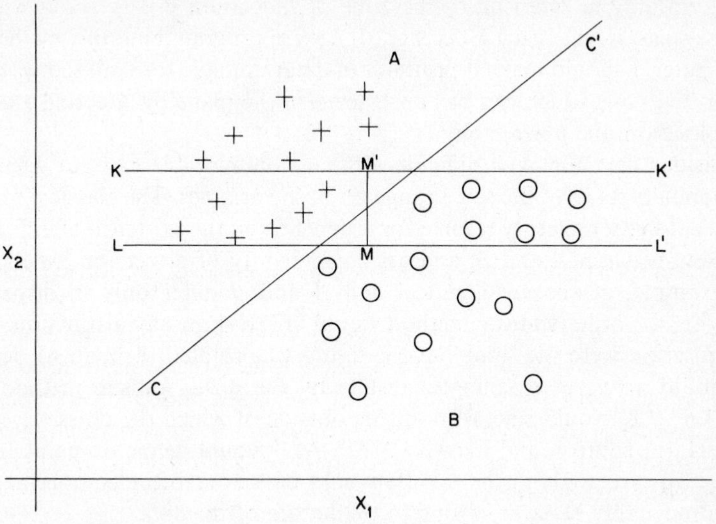

Fig. 3. Discrimination problem in two dimensions; coherent groups treated by distribution-free method (see text).

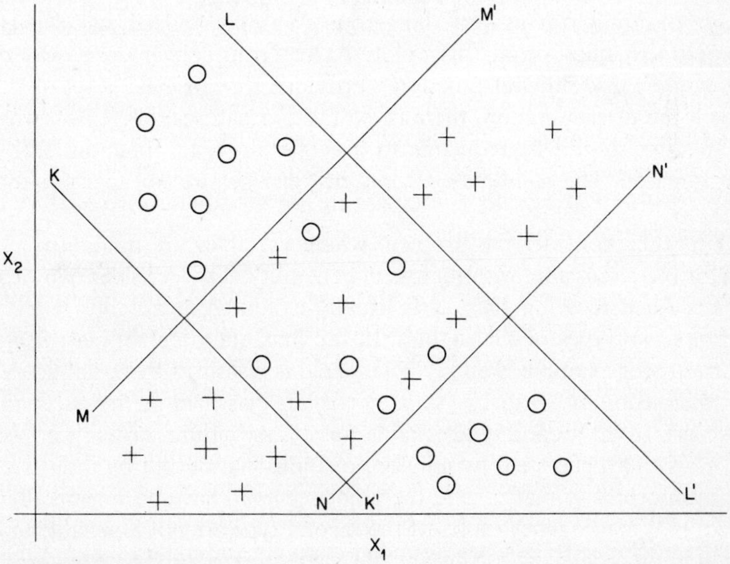

Fig. 4. Discrimination problem in two dimensions; groups with similar means and different dispersions (see text).

it will err only in referring to the zone of indecision points about which a better system might reach a decision. If I were programming this method for a computer, I should make it print out in diagrammatic form all the $\frac{1}{2}p(p-1)$ scatter diagrams which can be constructed in the plane by selecting a pair of variables from the p available.

Consider next Fig. 4, a difficult and very unfavorable case, in which the two populations have the same range on both variables. The classical method here would give nugatory results, for it depends on the existence of differences in means between A and B, and assumes identity of dispersion, whereas, in this example, means are identical and A and B differ only in dispersion. Likewise, the order-statistic method would fail to show any distinction. If the configuration were the same but the figure was rotated through 45 degrees, we should arrive at meaningful results by the order-statistic method. The lines KK', LL' would rule off domains outside of which the crosses were, so to speak, in control, and likewise MM', NN' would define domains for the circles. The rectangle in the middle would be a zone of indecision, and this would inevitably be large, owing to the nature of the data.

Where situations of this kind are suspected of existing, we may be able to improve on the order-statistic method by rotating the axes for measurable variables. I should make a transformation to principal components for one sample and transform all observations to the new variables before applying the order-statistic method. In such cases I should regard any attempt to set up a single discriminator as very dangerous. We may, indeed, ask ourselves a very pertinent question at this point: Apart from convenience, why do we want a *single* discriminant function? Provided that we have a set of rules to perform the discrimination, there is, so far as I can see, no reason whatever why that set should be reducible to a single algebraic function, still less a linear function. The point may become clearer when we consider polytomized data.

Let us then consider the problem where variables are qualitative. It will serve for the discussion, without loss of generality, if we consider two variables in a $k \times l$ classification such as is usually exhibited in a contingency table. There are two types of such tables. In the first, the order of classification is important; for example, we may have persons classified by social grade A to E (in the customary British system), or roads classified as first, second, and third class. In the second type of table there is no natural order; e.g., we may have individuals classified by religion, or industrial output by industry.

It is important to realize, and the point seems to have been generally overlooked, that contingency tables of the second type are not amenable to treatment in multivariate analysis by any of the methods appropriate to correlation or ordered contingency tables. This is not because the methods are defective, but because the unordered contingency table does not contain the information.

It is cast in the form of a table for convenience of presentation, not because of any inherent relation among the cells of the table. Consequently it is an illusion to suppose that unordered contingency tables can be subject to those methods which depend on the structure of ordered tables.

An example may make the point clear. Suppose we have a sample of 100 from each of two populations *A* and *B*, dichotomized by two attributes *P* and *Q* as shown in Table VI. We now have a new member and require to allot it to the appropriate population. Let us suppose it exhibits *P* and not *Q*.

TABLE VI

Examples of Two Double Dichotomies (Imaginary Data)

	A sample				*B* sample		
	P	Not *P*			*P*	Not *P*	
Q	60	20	80	*Q*	40	30	70
Not *Q*	10	10	20	Not *Q*	20	10	30
	70	30	100		60	40	100

In the *A* sample there are 10 such members, in the *B* sample 20 members. We can do nothing better than allot it to the *B* population on the grounds that there are more members like itself in the *B* sample. Only the information in the two cells *P*, not *Q* are relevant to the discrimination, all other information contributing nothing. We may as well, then, dismiss the unordered contingency table from the domain of discussion and consider only ordered tables.

Even with ordered tables we are in a situation quite distinct from that of measurable variables. Frequency distributions do not now overlap in part; except where cells are empty they overlap completely. In terms of the scatter diagram of the type of Fig. 1, we may suppose the place divided into $k \times l$ cells by horizontal and vertical lines, and the numbers of members falling in each cell for *A* and *B* separately specified. In every cell there are, in general, members of both *A* and *B*. We cannot expect to allot a newcomer without the possibility of error. At first sight it looks as if we cannot take matters much further forward than in the unordered case, and consider every cell separately. For completely arbitrary parent populations this is indeed so. It might be possible to use the order properties of the table to set up a single discriminator but again we are entitled to ask, why should we bother?

In Table VII, I have condensed the data for *versicolor* and *virginica*. For petal width "small" means < 1.5. For petal length "small" means < 4.0, "medium" means ≥ 4 and < 5, "large" means ≥ 5. The figures to the left of the colon refer to *versicolor*, those to the right of the colon to *virginica*.

We could attempt to set up a linear discriminator from this table, but there seems no point in doing so. If, for example, we have a new individual with a

TABLE VII

Summary of Data for Iris versicolor *and* Iris virginica *in the Form of an Ordered Contingency Table*

Petal length	Petal width "Small"	"Large"	Totals
"Small"	11 : 0	0 : 0	11 : 0
"Medium"	24 : 0	13 : 6	37 : 6
"Large"	0 : 1	2 : 43	2 : 44
	35 : 1	15 : 44	50 : 50

large petal width and a medium petal length, the odds are 13 to 6 that it is *versicolor* and there seems little more to be said.

There are, however, two reasons why we might wish to go further in the general case:

(1) If p, the number of dimensions, is large, the construction of a multiple contingency table is a nuisance and some reduction in the number of variables is desirable.

(2) Unless the sample is very large, the numbers in individual cells are apt to be small, and are therefore subject to appreciable sampling variation. For this reason some smoothing by rows and columns might be desirable; but I do not know how to attempt it in a purely distribution-free way.

5. CLASSIFICATION

The recent book by Sokal and Sneath [7] gives an excellent account of the problems of taxonomy. They point out that classification, at least in biological contexts, depends on many nonstatistical features which make a taxonomic problem special to individual circumstances. I shall take no account of such background considerations, but consider the purely statistical problem: Given a set of observations on n individuals in p dimensions, is there any evidence that they cluster in groups or can they be regarded as homogeneous variation?

There are two ways of considering a $p \times n$ matrix of observations. The more usual one considers the correlations of p variables over the n observations and leads to such branches of multivariate analysis as component and factor analysis. The other reads the matrix, so to speak, by columns instead of rows and considers the correlations between the $\frac{1}{2}n(n-1)$ pairs of individuals over the p variables. This is known to psychologists as the Q technique. But it presents some problems. The different variables may be measured in quite different units, and correlations of a pair of individuals over p values of noncomparable units does not, in general, make sense. This difficulty is not overcome by standardization, e.g., by reducing each variable to zero mean and unit variance. If we reverse the sign of a given variable, for example (and there is no reason why we should not), we obtain a completely different set of correlations.

I propose to remove this difficulty by working with rank correlations. This will render the analysis distribution-free and at the same time will enable us to deal with measurable variables and with ordered classification. The method is most conveniently explained in terms of an example. I took the data for *Iris versicolor* and *Iris virginica* and imagined that this was a set of 100 individuals of unknown origin. There are four variables. On the first, sepal length, I ranked the 100 individuals. Tied ranks are split in the usual way. Sepal width was treated similarly. For petal length I supposed the variable grouped into four categories as follows: category 1, values < 4 (11 members); category 2, values ≥ 4 and < 5 (43 members); category 3, values ≥ 5 and < 6 (35 members); category 4, values ≥ 6 (11 members). The respective midranks are 6, 33, 72, and 95. For petal width I condensed the data into two categories according to whether the variable was or was not less than 2. There were 71 and 29 members in the two categories, with midranks 36 and 86, respectively. The actual ranks are shown in Table VIII.

The variance of a set of n ranks is $\frac{1}{12}(n^2 - 1)$. When ties are present, this result needs modification, the appropriate formula being

$$\text{var}\, x = \frac{1}{12n}\left[(n^3 - n) - \sum (t^3 - t)\right], \tag{11}$$

where the summation is over all ties of extent t (see Kendall [3]). In our present case the variances are as follows:

x_1 (sepal length)	830.68,	x_3 (petal length)	729.13,
x_2 (sepal width)	821.77,	x_4 (petal width)	514.75.

The data for *Iris versicolor* and *Iris virginica*, 100 members in all, provide 4950 pairs of values. For each pair there was calculated the sum

$$S = \sum_{i=1}^{4} \frac{(x_i - x_i')^2}{\text{var}\, x_i}, \tag{12}$$

where x_i, x_i' are the values of the ith ranking for the pair in question. For instance, for pair 1, 2,

$$S = \frac{(88 - 62)^2}{830.68} + 0 + 0 + 0 = 0.8138$$

The calculations were done on an IBM 7094 and took 1.79 minutes. Owing to the bulk of the resulting data, I do not include them in this paper.

TABLE VIII

Iris versicolor *and* Iris virginica, *Ranked as a Single Group*

Serial No.	x_1	x_2	x_3	x_4	Serial No.	x_1	x_2	x_3	x_4
1	88.	86½.	33	36	51	54.	92½.	95	86
2	62.	86½.	33	36	52	27½.	28.	72	36
3	85½.	79.	33	36	53	89.	65½.	72	86
4	10.	6.	33	36	54	54.	51.	72	36
5	68.	39½.	33	36	55	68.	65½.	72	86
6	21½.	39½.	33	36	56	95.	65½.	95	86
7	54.	92½.	33	36	57	1½.	14½.	33	36
8	1½.	9.	6	36	58	93.	51.	95	36
9	71½.	51.	33	36	59	76½.	14½.	72	36
10	6.	28.	6	36	60	91.	98.	95	86
11	3½.	1.	6	36	61	68.	86½.	72	86
12	32.	65½.	33	36	62	62.	28.	72	36
13	36½.	3.	33	36	63	82.	65½.	72	86
14	42½.	51.	33	36	64	21½.	14½.	72	86
15	15½.	51.	6	36	65	27½.	39½.	72	86
16	76½.	79.	33	36	66	62.	86½.	72	86
17	15½.	65½.	33	36	67	68.	65½.	72	36
18	27½.	28.	33	36	68	97.	99½.	95	86
19	47½.	3.	33	36	69	97.	21.	95	86
20	15½.	14½.	6	36	70	36½.	3.	72	36
21	32.	86½.	33	36	71	85½.	86½.	72	86
22	42½.	39½.	33	36	72	15½.	39½.	33	86
23	54.	14½.	33	36	73	97.	39½.	95	86
24	42½.	39½.	33	36	74	54.	28.	33	36
25	62.	51.	33	36	75	76½.	92½.	72	86
26	71½.	65½.	33	36	76	91.	86½.	95	36
27	82.	39½.	33	36	77	47½.	39½.	33	36
28	76½.	65½.	72	36	78	42½.	65½.	33	36
29	36½.	51.	33	36	79	62.	39½.	72	86
30	21½.	21.	6	36	80	91.	65½.	72	36
31	10.	9.	6	36	81	94.	39½.	95	36
32	10.	9.	6	36	82	100.	99½.	95	86
33	27½.	28.	6	36	83	62.	39½.	72	86
34	36½.	28.	72	36	84	54.	39½.	72	36
35	7.	65½.	33	36	85	42½.	21.	72	36
36	36½.	96.	33	36	86	99.	65½.	95	86
37	76½.	79.	33	36	87	54.	96.	72	86
38	54.	6.	33	36	88	62.	79.	72	36
39	15½.	65½.	33	36	89	36½.	65½.	33	36
40	10.	14½.	33	36	90	85½.	79.	72	86
41	10.	21.	33	36	91	76½.	79.	72	86
42	42½.	65½.	33	36	92	85½.	79.	72	86
43	27½.	21.	33	36	93	27½.	28.	72	36
44	3½.	6.	6	36	94	82.	86½.	72	86
45	15½.	28.	33	36	95	76½.	92½.	72	86
46	21½.	65½.	33	36	96	76½.	65½.	72	86
47	21½.	51.	33	36	97	54.	14½.	72	36
48	47½.	51.	33	36	98	68.	65½.	72	86
49	5.	14½.	6	36	99	47½.	96.	72	86
50	21½.	39½.	33	36	100	32.	65½.	72	36

We can regard S as a kind of distance between the members of a pair. We then have the usual problem: given all the distances, to determine whether any grouping or clustering is present. There are several ways of proceeding here. The one I favor is to pick out the pair which are closest together. Then add the member which increases their average distance the least; then add a fourth member which increases the mean distance the least; and so on until a point is reached at which the addition of a new member adds too much to the mean distance. The amount which is to be considered "too much" is an arbitrary figure. If this procedure does not exhaust the set, proceed to the nearest unused pair and repeat the procedure.

Unfortunately this is a very tedious process, and if it were to be required for samples of any size, I should program for the computer. In the particular example we are considering, I did the analysis by hand, just to get a feel of the kind of thing which was happening, and took a number of short cuts. The values of S range from 0 to 36. To the eye, as it scans the values, there appear to be a lot of values from 0 to 5 and many from 10 to 20. I therefore began with one pair (22, 24) which have $S = 0$ and listed all the members within an S value ≤ 4 from 24. There were 58 of them, with serial numbers (including 24 itself)

2, 4, 5, 6, 7, 10, 12, 13, 14, 15, 16, 17, 18, 19, 20, 21, 22, 23, 24, 25, 26, 27, 29, 30, 31, 32, 33, 34, 35, 36, 37, 38, 39, 40, 41, 42, 43, 45, 46, 47, 48, 49, 50, 52, 54, 57, 62, 67, 70, 74, 77, 78, 84, 85, 89, 93, 97, 100. (A)

There is another coincident pair (55, 98) not included in this set. The 25 points distance ≤ 4 from 98 are

51, 53, 55, 56, 60, 61, 63, 65, 66, 68, 71, 73, 75, 79, 83, 86, 87, 90, 91, 92, 94, 95, 96, 98, 99. (B)

None of these overlaps with those in the first group, and together they account for 83 out of 100 members. The S value of (24, 98) is 8.54, so the two groups are well separated and it seems reasonable to infer that the original data can be classified into two distinct clusters at least. We note, however, that in group (A) there are 15 members of *Iris virginica*, although group (B) contains no member of versicolor.

Of the 17 so far unaccounted for, one group forms a cluster (again based on S values ≤ 4) around 88. They are

1, 2, 3, 7, 9, 12, 14, 16, 21, 25, 26, 28, 29, 34, 36, 37, 42, 48, 54, 58, 62, 67, 76, 78, 80, 81, 84, 88, 89, 100. (C)

Some of these overlap with the members in (A); 9 of them are new, 21 are in common with (A). The S value for (24, 88) is 4.44, and on the whole it seems reasonable to run (A) and (C) together as a single cluster.

We are still left with 8 members, numbers 8, 11, 44, 59, 64, 69, 72, and 82.

We can look at these separately. The S values are given in Table IX. We can group 8, 11, and 44 as a small isolated cluster, and might perhaps be willing to include it with the group centered on 24. The remaining five are fairly remote from any group and from one another.

TABLE IX

"Distances" of 11 *Members Not Falling into Clusters Already Determined (see text)*

	24	88	98	8	11	44	59	64	69	72	82
24											
88	4.44										
98	8.55	5.12									
8	4.16	16.34	20.04								
11	4.64	17.50	20.90	0.08							
44	4.20	16.58	20.15	0.02	0.03						
59	4.24	5.32	8.11	12.78	12.61	12.48					
64	8.23	11.89	5.77	11.35	11.44	11.31	8.50				
69	14.12	11.15	4.15	26.87	26.73	26.52	6.14	7.64			
72	5.73	11.44	6.23	7.22	7.83	7.40	12.18	2.89	13.68		
82	16.68	10.72	7.70	25.69	27.54	26.37	21.42	10.07	18.83	9.94	

It is to be noted that although group (B) contains no members of virginica groups (A) and (C) together contain 19 members as against 47 from versicolor. A classification on this basis would therefore misclassify 19 out of 32 members, and would leave 8 doubtful. In the analogous problem of discrimination, we decided 87 cases and left 13 doubtful. Both results reflect the fact that there is some overlap between the two variates; the numerical differences are in part due to the way in which, for reasons of exemplification, I condensed the grouping in the third and fourth variables.

6. SUMMARY

A distinction is drawn between problems of discrimination and problems of classification. Distribution-free methods are proposed and exemplified for solving both problems. They appear to work reasonably well. They can be applied to data which are measurable or polytomized or are a mixture of both.

REFERENCES

1. Fisher, R. A. (1936). The use of multiple measurements in taxonomic problems. *Ann. Eugenics*. 7 179–188.
2. Fix, E. and Hodges, J. L. (1951). *Discriminatory Analysis*. Project Rept. 21-49-004, Numbers 4 and 11. U.S. Air Force School of Aviation Medicine, Randolph Field, San Antonio, Texas.
3. Kendall, M. G. (1958). *Rank Correlation Methods*. Charles Griffin, London.

4. KENDALL, M. G. (1963). *A Course in Multivariate Analysis.* Charles Griffin, London.
5. KENDALL, M. G. and SUNDRUM, R. M. (1953). Distribution-free methods and order properties. *Rev. Internat. Statist. Inst.* **3** 124–134.
6. SMITH, C. A. B. (1947). Some examples of discrimination. *Ann. Eugenics* **13** 272–282.
7. SOKAL, R. R. and SNEATH, P. H. A. (1963). *Principles of Numerical Taxonomy.* Freeman, San Francisco and London.
8. WELCH, B. L. (1939). Note on discriminant functions. *Biometrika*, **31** 218–220.

A Distance and Related Statistics in Multivariate Analysis

KAMEO MATUSITA
THE INSTITUTE OF STATISTICAL MATHEMATICS
TOKYO, JAPAN

1. INTRODUCTION

Thus far, the author treated various problems by the decision rule based on the notion of distance (see [2] and the bibliography given there). The purpose of this paper is to give an approach to multivariate analysis from the same point of view. As a matter of fact, the decision rule based on the distance is very natural. For instance, consider the problem to be that of choosing one of two given distributions as that of the observed random variable. For this problem it is immediately considered to take the one which lies nearer the empirical distribution, that is, the one which has smaller distance to that empirical distribution. This decision-making is clearly based on the distance.

In this paper, as is often the case in multivariate analysis at present, our consideration will be confined to Gaussian cases. Employing a special distance in the space of Gaussian distributions, we shall introduce a statistic for decision making or simply a "test" statistic by which to deal with problems and give some special forms of that statistic for particular cases. Then we shall discuss their distributions. The generalized T^2 (Hotelling's T^2) will be seen to come out related to a special form of that statistic.

In Section 2 general aspects of decision rules based on distance are sketched. In Section 3 a distance and a related quantity are introduced, and in Section 4 the expression of the latter in multivariate Gaussian cases is given. In Section 5 "test" statistics are presented, and in Section 6 the distributions of the test statistics are treated. Finally, in Section 7, some examples are shown for illustration of the distance method.

2. THE DISTANCE METHOD

Let $d(\cdot, \cdot)$ denote a distance function between two distributions. To fix the idea, let us take up again the above-mentioned example. Given two distributions F_1, F_2, to decide which of F_1, F_2 a random variable under consideration, say X, has as its distribution, provided that one or the other of the two cases is true. Decision is, of course, made on the basis of observations on X. Let S_n denote a distribution determined by n observations on X. As such a distribution, we require that when X has F, $d(F, S_n) \to 0$, with probability 1 as $n \to \infty$. [This means that the form of S_n as a function of n observations on X may depend upon the functional form of the distance $d(\cdot, \cdot)$.] Employing such an S_n, we make a decision according to the magnitudes of $d(F_1, S_n)$ and $d(F_2, S_n)$; i.e., when $d(F_1, S_n) < d(F_2, S_n)$ we decide on F_1, and when $d(F_1, S_n) > d(F_2, S_n)$ we decide on F_2, and when $d(F_1, S_n) = d(F_2, S_n)$ we determine to take, say, F_1, in advance. This decision rule becomes unbiased when

$$P(d(F_1, S_n) \leq d(F_2, S_n) \mid F_1) \geq P(d(F_1, S_n) \leq d(F_2, S_n) \mid F_2)$$

and

$$P(d(F_2, S_n) < d(F_1, S_n) \mid F_2) \geq P(d(F_2, S_n) < d(F_1, S_n) \mid F_1).$$

Then the problem is to evaluate the success rate or error rate of this decision rule, i.e., to evaluate

$$P(d(F_1, S_n) \leq d(F_2, S_n) \mid F_1)$$

and

$$P(d(F_2, S_n) < d(F_1, S_n) \mid F_2).$$

Now,

$$P(d(F_i, S_n) \leq d(F_j, S_n) \mid F_i) \geq P(d(F_i, S_n) \leq \tau, \quad d(F_j, S_n) \geq \tau \mid F_i;$$
$$(\tau \text{ being any fixed positive number}) \quad (i, j = 1, 2, \quad i \neq j).$$

When $d(F_1, F_2) = 2\delta > 0$, and when the distance function $d(\cdot, \cdot)$ satisfies the triangle inequality,

$$d(F_1, S_n) + d(F_2, S_n) \geq d(F_1, F_2),$$

$d(F_1, S_n) \leq \delta$ means $d(F_2, S_n) \geq \delta$, and $d(F_2, S_n) < \delta$ means $d(F_1, S_n) > \delta$. Therefore, we have

$$\begin{aligned} P(d(F_1, S_n) &\leq d(F_2, S_n) \mid F_1) \\ &\geq P(d(F_1, S_n) \leq \delta, \quad d(F_2, S_n) \geq \delta \mid F_1) \\ &= P(d(F_1, S_n) \leq \delta \mid F_1) \end{aligned}$$

and

$$P(d(F_2, S_n) < d(F_1, S_n) \mid F_2) \geq P(d(F_1, S_n) < \delta \mid F_2).$$

Consequently, we can evaluate the success rate by

$$P(d(F_1, S_n) \leq \delta \mid F_1) \qquad \text{or} \qquad P(d(F_2, S_n) < \delta \mid F_2).$$

For example, when we want the success rate greater than or equal to a given positive number α (<1), we take the number of observation, n, so that $P(d(F_i, S_n) < \delta \mid F_i) \geq \alpha$ ($i = 1, 2$). Thus the problem is reduced to evaluating $P(d(F, S_n) < \delta \mid F)$.

From the above procedure it is seen that just in the same way we can treat the problem to decide whether a random variable under consideration has a given distribution F_0 or F with $d(F, F_0) > \delta$, δ being some positive number, provided that for any positive ε we have $P(d(F, S_n) < \varepsilon \mid F) \to 1$ uniformly with respect to F as $n \to \infty$, F being any distribution concerned. The classification problem can also be treated along the same line. Further, a confidence region for an unknown distribution can be obtained from the relation such as $P(d(F, S_n) < \delta) \geq \alpha$. Concerning detailed analysis of the distance method, see [2] and the papers cited there.

3. A DISTANCE AND A RELATED QUANTITY

The distance we employ in this paper is the following. Let F_1 and F_2 be distributions defined in space R and let $p_1(x)$ and $p_2(x)$ be respectively their densities with respect to a measure m in R. Then our distance between F_1 and F_2 is

$$d(F_1, F_2) = \left[\int_R \{[p_1(x)]^{1/2} - [p_2(x)]^{1/2}\}^2 \, dm\right]^{1/2}.$$

So far the author treated this distance in many places (see the references in [2]). This distance satisfies the metric space axioms. Further, we have:

For any (m-measurable) set E,

$$\left|\int_E p_1(x)\, dm - \int_E p_2(x)\, dm\right| \leq 2\, d(F_1, F_2).$$

$d(F_1, F_2) = 0$ means that $\int_E p_1(x)\, dm = \int_E p_2(x)\, dm$ for any E, and vice versa. For a sequence of distributions $\{F_n\}$ $d(F_n, F_0) \to 0$ implies that $\int_E p_n(x)\, dm \to \int_E p_0(x)\, dm$ uniformly in E and vice versa, where $p_n(x)$ is the density of F_n ($n = 0, 1, 2, \ldots$), etc. (See, for instance, [1].)

As a closely related quantity of this distance we consider

$$\rho(F_1, F_2) = \int_R [p_1(x)]^{1/2}[p_2(x)]^{1/2}\, dm.$$

For this ρ we have

$$d^2(F_1, F_2) = 2(1 - \rho(F_1, F_2))$$

and

$$0 \leq \rho(F_1, F_2) \leq 1$$
$$\rho(F_1, F_2) = 1 \leftrightarrow d(F_1, F_2) = 0$$
$$\rho(F_n, F_0) \to 1 \leftrightarrow d(F_n, F_0) \to 0, \qquad \text{etc.}$$

As is seen from these relations, the quantity ρ indicates the closeness between distributions; i.e., the larger $\rho(F_1, F_2)$ is, the closer F_1 and F_2 lie. In this sense the author has called the quantity $\rho(F_1, F_2)$ the *affinity* between F_1 and F_2. This quantity often proves very useful (see the references in [1]).

4. MULTIVARIATE GAUSSIAN CASE

In this section we shall give the affinity a concrete expression when multivariate Gaussian distributions are concerned.

Let F_1 and F_2 be nonsingular k-dimensional Gaussian distributions with density functions

$$\frac{|A|^{1/2}}{(2\pi)^{k/2}} \exp[-\tfrac{1}{2}(A(\mathbf{x} - \mathbf{a}), (\mathbf{x} - \mathbf{a}))]$$

and

$$\frac{|B|^{1/2}}{(2\pi)^{k/2}} \exp[-\tfrac{1}{2}(B(\mathbf{x} - \mathbf{b}), (\mathbf{x} - \mathbf{b}))],$$

respectively, where A, B are positive-definite symmetric matrices of degree k; $|A|$, $|B|$ denote their determinants; $\mathbf{x}, \mathbf{a}, \mathbf{b}$ are k-dimensional column vectors; and $(\mathbf{x}, \mathbf{y})$ denotes the inner product of the vectors $\mathbf{x}$ and $\mathbf{y}$. A^{-1} and B^{-1} are the covariance matrices of F_1 and F_2, respectively. Then we have:

Theorem.

$$\rho(F_1, F_2) = \frac{|AB|^{1/4}}{|\tfrac{1}{2}(A + B)|^{1/2}} \exp\{-\tfrac{1}{4}[-((A + B)^{-1}(A\mathbf{a} + B\mathbf{b}), (A\mathbf{a} + B\mathbf{b})) + (A\mathbf{a}, \mathbf{a}) + (B\mathbf{b}, \mathbf{b})]\}.$$

Proof. By definition, we have

$$\rho(F_1, F_2) = \frac{|A|^{1/4}}{(2\pi)^{k/4}} \frac{|B|^{1/4}}{(2\pi)^{k/4}} \int_{R_k} \exp\{-\tfrac{1}{4}[(A(\mathbf{x} - \mathbf{a}), \mathbf{x} - \mathbf{a}) + (B(\mathbf{x} - \mathbf{b}), \mathbf{x} - \mathbf{b})]\}\, dx_1 \cdots dx_k.$$

Now,

$$(*)\ (A(\mathbf{x} - \mathbf{a}), \mathbf{x} - \mathbf{a}) + (B(\mathbf{x} - \mathbf{b}), \mathbf{x} - \mathbf{b}) = ((A + B)\mathbf{x}, \mathbf{x}) - 2(A\mathbf{a} + B\mathbf{b}, \mathbf{x}) + (A\mathbf{a}, \mathbf{a}) + (B\mathbf{b}, \mathbf{b}).$$

Since A and B are positive-definite and symmetric, so is $A + B$ also, and we can consider the transformation $\mathbf{y} = (A + B)^{1/2}\mathbf{x}$.[1] Then we have

$$\begin{aligned}(*) &= (\mathbf{y}, \mathbf{y}) - 2((A + B)^{-1/2}(A\mathbf{a} + B\mathbf{b}), \mathbf{y}) + (A\mathbf{a}, \mathbf{a}) + (B\mathbf{b}, \mathbf{b}) \\ &= (\mathbf{y} - (A + B)^{-1/2}(A\mathbf{a} + B\mathbf{b}), \mathbf{y} - (A + B)^{-1/2}(A\mathbf{a} + B\mathbf{b})) \\ &\qquad - ((A + B)^{-1}(A\mathbf{a} + B\mathbf{b}), (A\mathbf{a} + B\mathbf{b})) + (A\mathbf{a}, \mathbf{a}) + (B\mathbf{b}, \mathbf{b}),\end{aligned}$$

so we obtain

$$\begin{aligned}\rho(F_1, F_2) &= \frac{|AB|^{1/4}}{(2\pi)^{k/2}} \frac{1}{|A + B|^{1/2}} \\ &\quad \times \int_{R_k} \exp\{-\tfrac{1}{4}(\mathbf{y} - (A + B)^{-1/2}(A\mathbf{a} + B\mathbf{b}), \mathbf{y} - (A + B)^{-1/2} \\ &\quad \times (A\mathbf{a} + B\mathbf{b})) - \tfrac{1}{4}[-((A + B)^{-1}(A\mathbf{a} + B\mathbf{b}), (A\mathbf{a} + B\mathbf{b})) \\ &\qquad + (A\mathbf{a}, \mathbf{a}) + (B\mathbf{b}, \mathbf{b})]\}\, dy_1 \cdots dy_k \\ &= \frac{|AB|^{1/4}}{(2\pi)^{k/2}} \frac{(2\pi)^{k/2} 2^{k/2}}{|A + B|^{1/2}} \\ &\quad \times \exp\{-\tfrac{1}{4}[-((A + B)^{-1}(A\mathbf{a} + B\mathbf{b}), (A\mathbf{a} + B\mathbf{b})) \\ &\qquad + (A\mathbf{a}, \mathbf{a}) + (B\mathbf{b}, \mathbf{b})]\} \\ &= \frac{|AB|^{1/4}}{|\tfrac{1}{2}(A + B)|^{1/2}} \\ &\quad \times \exp\{-\tfrac{1}{4}[-((A + B)^{-1}(A\mathbf{a} + B\mathbf{b}), (A\mathbf{a} + B\mathbf{b})) \\ &\qquad + (A\mathbf{a}, \mathbf{a}) + (B\mathbf{b}, \mathbf{b})]\}.\end{aligned}$$

Corollary 1. *When $A = B$, we have*

$$\rho(F_1, F_2) = \exp[-\tfrac{1}{8}(A(\mathbf{a} - \mathbf{b}), \mathbf{a} - \mathbf{b})].$$

Actually, when $A = B$,

$$\begin{aligned}\rho(F_1, F_2) &= \exp\{-\tfrac{1}{4}[-((2A)^{-1}A(\mathbf{a} + \mathbf{b}), A(\mathbf{a} + \mathbf{b})) + (A\mathbf{a}, \mathbf{a}) + (A\mathbf{b}, \mathbf{b})]\} \\ &= \exp\{-\tfrac{1}{4}[\tfrac{1}{2}(A\mathbf{a}, \mathbf{a}) - (A\mathbf{a}, \mathbf{b}) + \tfrac{1}{2}(A\mathbf{b}, \mathbf{b})]\} \\ &= \exp[-\tfrac{1}{8}((A\mathbf{a}, \mathbf{a}) - (A\mathbf{a}, \mathbf{b}) - (\mathbf{a}, A\mathbf{b}) + (A\mathbf{b}, \mathbf{b}))] \\ &= \exp[-\tfrac{1}{8}(A(\mathbf{a} - \mathbf{b}), \mathbf{a} - \mathbf{b})].\end{aligned}$$

In this case, when we consider

$$d'(F_1, F_2) = -\log \rho(F_1, F_2),$$

[1] Since $A + B$ is positive-definite and symmetric, $A + B$ is transformed into a diagonal form $D^2 = \mathrm{diag}(\lambda_1^2, \ldots, \lambda_k^2)$ $(\lambda_i > 0)$ by an orthogonal transformation T: $T'(A + B)T = D^2$. Define $D = \mathrm{diag}(\lambda_1, \ldots, \lambda_k)$. Then $(A + B)^{1/2}$ is defined as TDT'.

we have

$$8d'(F_1, F_2) = (A(\mathbf{a} - \mathbf{b}), \mathbf{a} - \mathbf{b}).$$

Corollary 2. *When* $\mathbf{a} = \mathbf{b}$, *we have*

$$\rho(F_1, F_2) = \frac{|AB|^{1/4}}{|\frac{1}{2}(A+B)|^{1/2}}.$$

In fact, in this case, we have

$$\begin{aligned} &-((A+B)^{-1}(A\mathbf{a} + B\mathbf{b}), A\mathbf{a} + B\mathbf{b}) + (A\mathbf{a}, \mathbf{a}) + (B\mathbf{b}, \mathbf{b}) \\ &\quad = -((A+B)^{-1}(A+B)\mathbf{a}, (A+B)\mathbf{a}) + (A\mathbf{a}, \mathbf{a}) + (B\mathbf{a}, \mathbf{a}) \\ &\quad = -(\mathbf{a}, (A+B)\mathbf{a}) + ((A+B)\mathbf{a}, \mathbf{a}) \\ &\quad = 0. \end{aligned}$$

5. "TEST" STATISTICS

Let $X_1, X_2, \ldots, X_n$ be n (>1) observed values of a k-dimensional random vector X with a nonsingular Gaussian distribution $N(\mathbf{a}, \Sigma)$. For these $X_1, X_2, \ldots, X_n$ we define, as usual,

$$\bar{X} = \frac{1}{n}\sum_{i=1}^{n} X_i, \qquad V = \frac{1}{n-1}\sum_{i=1}^{n}(X_i - \bar{X})(X_i - \bar{X})',$$

and we consider the Gaussian distribution $N(\bar{X}, V)$ determined by $\bar{X}$, V (V is nonsingular with probability 1 for $n > k$). Then we can consider the distance or affinity between $F = N(\mathbf{c}, C^{-1})$ and $S_n = N(\bar{X}, V)$. That is, we obtain

$$\rho(F, S_n) = \frac{|CU|^{1/4}}{|\frac{1}{2}(C+U)|^{1/2}} \exp\{-\tfrac{1}{4}[-((C+U)^{-1}(C\mathbf{c} + U\bar{X}), (C\mathbf{c} + U\bar{X})) + (C\mathbf{c}, \mathbf{c}) + (U\bar{X}, \bar{X})]\}$$

where $U = V^{-1}$. By this quantity we can make inferences or decisions concerning $N(\mathbf{a}, \Sigma)$ and $N(\mathbf{c}, C^{-1})$, when the former is unknown.

Special Case 1

When it is known beforehand that $\Sigma = C^{-1}$, although Σ itself is unknown, we consider

$$\rho_1(F, S_n) = \exp[-\tfrac{1}{8}(V^{-1}(\bar{X} - \mathbf{c}), \bar{X} - \mathbf{c})],$$

which is the affinity between $N(\mathbf{c}, V)$ and $N(\bar{X}, V)$. Further, when Σ is known, we of course, take

$$\rho_2(F, S_n) = \exp[-\tfrac{1}{8}(\Sigma^{-1}(\bar{X} - \mathbf{c}), \bar{X} - \mathbf{c})].$$

For these ρ_1 and ρ_2, we have

$$-8 \log \rho_1(F, S_n) = (V^{-1}(\bar{X} - \mathbf{c}), \bar{X} - \mathbf{c})$$

and

$$-8 \log \rho_2(F, S_n) = (\Sigma^{-1}(\bar{X} - \mathbf{c}), \bar{X} - \mathbf{c}).$$

These are familiar expressions in multivariate analysis. $-8n \log \rho_1 (F, S_n)$ is the generalized T^2.

Special Case 2

When the problem is concerned only with the covariance matrix, we consider

$$\rho_3(F, S_n) = \frac{|CU|^{1/4}}{|\frac{1}{2}(C + U)|^{1/2}} \quad (U = V^{-1}),$$

which is the affinity between $N(\mathbf{b}, C^{-1})$ and $N(\mathbf{b}, V)$, $\mathbf{b}$ being any vector.

6. DISTRIBUTIONS OF ρ, ρ_1, ρ_2, AND ρ_3

Let S_n be the distribution determined by n observations on a random variable with $F = N(\mathbf{a}, \Sigma)$. In this section we deal with the distributions of $\rho(F, S_n)$, $\rho_1(F, S_n)$, $\rho_2(F, S_n)$, and $\rho_3(F, S_n)$.

Special Case 1

In this case, as mentioned above, we have

$$-8n \log \rho_1(F, S_n) = n(V^{-1}(\bar{X} - \mathbf{a}), \bar{X} - \mathbf{a})$$

and

$$-8n \log \rho_2(F, S_n) = n(\Sigma^{-1}(\bar{X} - \mathbf{a}), \bar{X} - \mathbf{a}),$$

and, as is well known, these quantities have a noncentral F and a χ^2 distribution, respectively.

Special Case 2

In this case, we have

$$\rho_3(F, S_n) = \frac{|\Sigma^{-1}U|^{1/4}}{|\frac{1}{2}(\Sigma^{-1} + U)|^{1/2}}.$$

First, we note that this statistic is invariant under any nonsingular transformation. In fact, for a nonsingular transformation $Y = GX + \mathbf{b}$, the distribution of Y is $F_Y = N(G\mathbf{a} + \mathbf{b}, G\Sigma G')$, and the sample mean and sample covariance matrix become $\overline{Y} = G\overline{X} + \mathbf{b}$ and $Y_Y = GVG'$, respectively. Thus, setting $F_X = F$, $S_{nX} = S_n$ and denoting the distribution based on a sample of Y by S_{nY}, we have

$$\rho_3(F_Y, S_{nY}) = \frac{|(G\Sigma G')^{-1}\cdot(GVG')^{-1}|^{1/4}}{|\frac{1}{2}((G\Sigma G')^{-1} + (GVG')^{-1})|^{1/2}} = \frac{|G'^{-1}\Sigma^{-1}G^{-1}\cdot G'^{-1}UG^{-1}|^{1/4}}{|\frac{1}{2}G'^{-1}(\Sigma^{-1} + U)G^{-1}|^{1/2}}$$

$$= \frac{|\Sigma^{-1}U|^{1/4}\cdot \text{abs. } |G|^{-1}}{\left|\dfrac{\Sigma^{-1}+U}{2}\right|^{1/2}\cdot \text{abs. } |G|^{-1}} = \frac{|\Sigma^{-1}U|^{1/4}}{\left|\dfrac{\Sigma^{-1}+U}{2}\right|^{1/2}} = \rho_3(F_X, S_{nX}).$$

Now, by assumption, Σ is a positive-definite symmetric matrix, so there exists an orthogonal matrix T so that $T\Sigma T'$ has a diagonal form

$$\begin{pmatrix} \lambda_1 & & & 0 \\ & \cdot & & \\ & & \cdot & \\ 0 & & & \lambda_k \end{pmatrix},$$

where $\lambda_i > 0$. Let

$$L = \begin{pmatrix} (\lambda_1)^{1/2} & & & 0 \\ & \cdot & & \\ & & \cdot & \\ 0 & & & (\lambda_k)^{1/2} \end{pmatrix}.$$

Then $L = L'$ and

$$L^2 = \begin{pmatrix} \lambda_1 & & & 0 \\ & \cdot & & \\ & & \cdot & \\ 0 & & & \lambda_k \end{pmatrix}.$$

Further, let $G = L^{-1}T$. Then we have

$$G\Sigma G' = (L^{-1}T)\Sigma(L^{-1}T)' = L^{-1}T\Sigma T'L^{-1} = \begin{pmatrix} 1 & & & 0 \\ & \cdot & & \\ & & \cdot & \\ 0 & & & 1 \end{pmatrix} = I.$$

This with the invariance of ρ_3 implies that, when we are concerned with the distribution of $\rho_3(F, S_n)$, we can consider from the beginning that $F = N(0, I)$.

That is, the distribution of $\rho_3(F, S_n)$ is independent of a particular distribution. For $F = N(0, I)$ we obtain

$$\rho_3(F, S_n) = \frac{|IU|^{1/4}}{|\frac{1}{2}(I + U)|^{1/2}} = \frac{|U|^{1/4}}{|\frac{1}{2}(I + U)|^{1/2}} = \frac{|V^{-1}|^{1/4}}{|\frac{1}{2}(I + V^{-1})|^{1/2}} = \frac{|V|^{1/4}}{|\frac{1}{2}(I + V)|^{1/2}}.$$

Let

$$X_i = \begin{pmatrix} X_{i1} \\ \vdots \\ X_{ik} \end{pmatrix} \qquad (i = 1, \ldots, n).$$

As the matrix V converges to I with probability 1 the distribution of $\rho_3(F, S_n)$ is asymptotically equal to that of

$$\frac{|W|^{1/4}}{|\frac{1}{2}(I + W)|^{1/2}}, \qquad \text{where } W = \begin{pmatrix} \frac{1}{n}\sum_i X_{i1}^2 & & & 0 \\ & \cdot & & \\ & & \cdot & \\ & & & \cdot \\ 0 & & & \frac{1}{n}\sum_i X_{ik}^2 \end{pmatrix}.$$

Put

$$Z_1 = \frac{1}{n}\sum_{i=1}^{n} X_{i1}^2, \ldots, Z_n = \frac{1}{n}\sum_{i=1}^{n} X_{in}^2.$$

Then we obtain

$$\frac{|W|^{1/4}}{|\frac{1}{2}(I + W)|^{1/2}} = \frac{\left(\prod_{i=1}^{k} Z_i\right)^{1/4}}{\left(\prod_{i=1}^{k} \frac{1}{2}(1 + Z_i)\right)^{1/2}} = \left[\prod_{i=1}^{k} \frac{4Z_i}{(1 + Z_i)^2}\right]^{1/4}.$$

$nZ_1, \ldots, nZ_k$ are independent random variables having the chi-square distribution with n degrees of freedom. For an arbitrarily chosen positive number $\alpha < 1$, we have

$$P(\rho_3(F, S_n) > \alpha^k) \risingdotseq P\left(\frac{|W|^{1/4}}{|\frac{1}{2}(I + W)|^{1/2}} > \alpha^k\right) \geq \prod_{i=1}^{k} P\left(\frac{4Z_i}{(1 + Z_i)^2} > \alpha^4\right)$$

$$= \left[P\left(\frac{4Z}{(1 + Z)^2} > \alpha^4\right)\right]^k,$$

Z being a random variable such that nZ has the chi-square distribution with n degrees of freedom. As

$$P\left(\frac{4Z}{(1+Z)^2} > \alpha^4\right)$$

$$= P\left\{n\left[\frac{2}{\alpha^4} - 1 - \frac{2}{\alpha^2}\left(\frac{1}{\alpha^4} - 1\right)^{1/2}\right] < n\,Z < n\left[\frac{2}{\alpha^4} - 1 + \frac{2}{\alpha^2}\left(\frac{1}{\alpha^4} - 1\right)^{1/2}\right]\right\},$$

we can calculate this value. Further, for a given positive number $\gamma < 1$, we can determine n so that the probability value becomes greater than or equal to γ. Hence we can evaluate $P(\rho_3(F, S_n) > \alpha^k)$, or for given positive α and ε (<1) we can determine n so that $P(\rho_3(F, S_n) > \alpha^k) \geq 1 - \varepsilon$. Thus, for given positive δ and ε, both <1, we obtain the relation

$$P(\rho_3(F, S_n) > \delta) \geq 1 - \varepsilon$$

uniformly in F for $n \geq n_0$, n_0 being some integer which depends only on δ and ε. As mentioned in Section 2, this serves well for our purpose.

General Case

In the general case,

$$\rho(F, S_n) = \frac{|\Sigma^{-1}U|^{1/4}}{|\frac{1}{2}(\Sigma^{-1} + U)|^{1/2}} \exp\{-\tfrac{1}{4}[-((\Sigma^{-1} + U)^{-1}$$

$$\times (\Sigma^{-1}\mathbf{a} + U\overline{X}), (\Sigma^{-1}\mathbf{a} + U\overline{X})) + (\Sigma^{-1}\mathbf{a}, \mathbf{a}) + (U\overline{X}, \overline{X})]\}.$$

As mentioned above, our interest is in obtaining a relation such as $P(\rho(F, S_n) > \delta) \geq 1 - \varepsilon$. Now, $\rho(F, S_n)$ is invariant under any orthogonal transformation of the basic variable, and Σ can be transformed into a diagonal form by a suitable orthogonal transformation. We can, therefore, consider that

$$\Sigma = \begin{pmatrix} \lambda_1 & & & 0 \\ & \cdot & & \\ & & \cdot & \\ & & & \cdot \\ 0 & & & \lambda_k \end{pmatrix} \qquad (\lambda_i > 0).$$

For given positive δ take a pair of positive numbers δ_1, δ_2 such that $\delta = \delta_1 \times \exp(-\frac{1}{4}\delta_2)$, $\delta_1 < 1$. Then we obtain

$$P(\rho(F, S_n) > \delta) \geq P\left[\frac{|\Sigma^{-1}U|^{1/4}}{|\frac{1}{2}(\Sigma^{-1} + U)|^{1/2}} > \delta_1,\ -((\Sigma^{-1} + U)^{-1}(\Sigma^{-1}\mathbf{a} + U\overline{X}),\right.$$

$$\left.\times (\Sigma^{-1}\mathbf{a} + U\overline{X})) + (\Sigma^{-1}\mathbf{a}, \mathbf{a}) + (U\overline{X}, \overline{X}) < \delta_2\right]$$

$$= P\left(\frac{|\Sigma^{-1}U|^{1/4}}{|\frac{1}{2}(\Sigma^{-1}+U)|^{1/2}} > \delta_1\right)$$

$$\times P\Big(-((\ ^{-1}+U)^{-1}(\Sigma^{-1}\mathbf{a}+U\bar{X}), \Sigma^{-1}\mathbf{a}+U\bar{X})$$

$$+ (\Sigma^{-1}\mathbf{a}, \mathbf{a}) + (U\bar{X}, \bar{X}) < \delta_2 \,\Big|\, \frac{|\Sigma^{-1}U|^{1/4}}{|\frac{1}{2}(\Sigma^{-1}+U)|^{1/2}} > \delta_1\Big)$$

$$\sim P\left(\frac{|\Sigma^{-1}U|^{1/4}}{|\frac{1}{2}(\Sigma^{-1}+U)|^{1/2}} > \delta_1\right)$$

$$\times P\left((U(\bar{X}-\mathbf{a}), \bar{X}-\mathbf{a}) < 2\delta_2 \,\middle|\, \frac{|\Sigma^{-1}U|^{1/4}}{|\frac{1}{2}(\Sigma^{-1}+U)|^{1/2}} > \delta_1\right)$$

$$\sim P\left(\frac{|\Sigma^{-1}W^{-1}|^{1/4}}{|\frac{1}{2}(\Sigma^{-1}+W^{-1})|^{1/2}} > \delta_1\right)$$

$$\times P\left((W^{-1}(\bar{X}-\mathbf{a}), \bar{X}-\mathbf{a}) < 2\delta_2 \,\middle|\, \frac{|\Sigma^{-1}W^{-1}|^{1/4}}{|\frac{1}{2}(\Sigma^{-1}+W^{-1})|^{1/2}} > \delta_1\right)$$

Here

$$\frac{|\Sigma^{-1}W^{-1}|^{1/4}}{|\frac{1}{2}(\Sigma^{-1}+W^{-1})|^{1/2}} = \frac{\left(\prod_{i=1}^{k}\frac{1}{\lambda_i Z_i}\right)^{1/4}}{\left[\prod_{i=1}^{k}\frac{1}{2}\left(\frac{1}{\lambda_i}+\frac{1}{Z_i}\right)\right]^{1/2}} = \left[\prod_i \frac{4\lambda_i Z_i}{(\lambda_i+Z_i)^2}\right]^{1/4},$$

and as

$$1 \geq \frac{4\lambda Z}{(\lambda+Z)^2},$$

$$\frac{|\Sigma^{-1}W^{-1}|^{1/4}}{|\frac{1}{2}(\Sigma^{-1}+W^{-1})|^{1/2}} > \delta_1 \text{ implies } \frac{4\lambda_i Z_i}{(\lambda_i+Z_i)^2} > \delta_1{}^4 \qquad (i = 1, \ldots, k),$$

from which we have

$$\frac{2}{\delta_1{}^4} - 1 - \frac{2}{\delta_1{}^4}(1-\delta_1{}^4)^{1/2} < \frac{\lambda_i}{Z_i} < \frac{2}{\delta_1{}^4} - 1 + \frac{2}{\delta_1{}^4}(1-\delta_1{}^4)^{1/2} = \beta \quad \text{(say)};$$

that is,

$$\frac{1}{Z_i} < \beta\frac{1}{\lambda_i} \qquad (i = 1, \ldots, k).$$

Consequently, we obtain

$$(W^{-1}(\bar{X}-\mathbf{a}), (\bar{X}-\mathbf{a})) \leq \beta(\Sigma^{-1}(\bar{X}-\mathbf{a}), (\bar{X}-\mathbf{a}));$$

hence

$$P\left((W^{-1}(\bar{X}-\mathbf{a}), (\bar{X}-\mathbf{a})) < 2\delta_2 \,\middle|\, \frac{|\Sigma^{-1}W^{-1}|^{1/4}}{|\frac{1}{2}(\Sigma^{-1}+W^{-1})|^{1/2}} > \delta_1\right)$$
$$\geq P(\beta(\Sigma^{-1}(\bar{X}-\mathbf{a}), (\bar{X}-\mathbf{a})) < 2\delta_2).$$

Since $n^{1/2}\Sigma^{-1/2}(\bar{X}-\mathbf{a})$ obeys $N(0, I)$, we can calculate the value of the last term. From

$$P(\rho(F, S_n) > \delta)$$
$$\geq P\left(\frac{|\Sigma^{-1}W^{-1}|^{1/4}}{|\frac{1}{2}(\Sigma^{-1}+W^{-1})|^{1/2}} > \delta_1\right) P(\beta(\Sigma^{-1}(\bar{X}-\mathbf{a}), \bar{X}-\mathbf{a}) < 2\delta_2),$$

we can evaluate $P(\rho(F, S_n) > \delta)$ by choosing the value of δ_1 (hence δ_2) so as to maximize the right-hand side of this inequality.

To make the value of $P(\rho(F, S_n) > \delta)$ greater than $1 - \varepsilon$, ε being a given positive number less than 1, it is sufficient to let the observation number n be large enough to make the right-hand side greater than $1 - \varepsilon$. For that, let positive numbers α_1 and α_2 be such that $\alpha_1\alpha_2 = 1 - \varepsilon$ and take n so that

$$P\left(\frac{|\Sigma^{-1}U|^{1/4}}{|\frac{1}{2}(\Sigma^{-1}+U)|^{1/2}} > \delta_1\right) > \alpha_1$$

and $P(\beta(\Sigma^{-1}(\bar{X}-\mathbf{a}), \bar{X}-\mathbf{a}) < \delta_2) > \alpha_2$.

7. ILLUSTRATION

For an illustration of the distance method let us consider some problems. As our ρ_1, ρ_2 are related to some familiar statistics in literature, we shall consider here problems concerning the covariance matrix for use of ρ_3.

As is mentioned above, when the random variable under consideration has the distribution F, the relation

$$P(\rho_3(F, S_n) > \delta) \geq 1 - \varepsilon$$

holds uniformly in F, for $n \geq n_0$, n_0 being some integer. Using this property of $\rho_3(F, S_n)$, we can treat various problems.

Problem 1. Decide whether the distribution of the random variable under consideration has the covariance matrix Σ_0 or an unspecified Σ which is distant from Σ_0 by δ (>0) in the sense of ρ_3; i.e.,

$$\rho_3(F_0, F) = \frac{|\Sigma_0^{-1}\Sigma^{-1}|^{1/4}}{|\frac{1}{2}(\Sigma_0^{-1}+\Sigma^{-1})|^{1/2}} < \delta,$$

where F_0 and F denote distributions with Σ_0 and Σ, respectively. It is supposed here that either case holds true.

For this problem we make a decision as follows. When

$$\frac{|\Sigma_0^{-1}U|^{1/4}}{|\frac{1}{2}(\Sigma_0^{-1}+U)|^{1/2}} \geq 1 - \frac{1-\delta}{4},$$

we decide that the distribution has Σ_0, and when

$$\frac{|\Sigma_0^{-1}U|^{1/4}}{|\frac{1}{2}(\Sigma_0^{-1}+U)|^{1/2}} < 1 - \frac{1-\delta}{4},$$

we decide that the distribution has Σ with distance greater than δ from Σ_0.

It is easily seen that, in general, from $\rho(F_0, F) < \delta$ and $\rho(F_0, S_n) \geq 1 - [(1-\delta)/4]$ follows $\rho(F, S_n) < 1 - [(1-\delta) - 4]$. Therefore, the success rate is given by $P(\rho_3(F_0, S_n) \geq 1 - [(1-\delta)/4]$, provided that the random variable has F_0 as its distribution.

Problem 2. Let the k-component vector X be distributed according to $N(\mathbf{a}, \Sigma)$, and let $X^{(1)}, \ldots, X^{(p)}$ be p subvectors of X with $k_1, \ldots, k_p$ components, respectively. Decide whether or not $X^{(1)}, \ldots, X^{(p)}$ are independent.

For this problem we consider the set of positive-definite symmetric matrices of the form

$$\Sigma = \begin{pmatrix} \Sigma_{11} & & & & 0 \\ & \Sigma_{22} & & & \\ & & \cdot & & \\ & & & \cdot & \\ & & & & \cdot \\ 0 & & & & \Sigma_{pp} \end{pmatrix}$$

where Σ_{ii} is a positive-definite symmetric matrix of degree k_i. We denote this set by M_0 and formulate the problem as follows. Decide whether Σ is in M_0 or is distant from M_0 by δ (>0) in the sense of ρ_3. Then for a sample from $N(\mathbf{a}, \Sigma)$, we consider

$$\hat{\rho}_3 = \sup_{\Sigma \in M_0} \frac{|\Sigma^{-1}U|^{1/4}}{|\frac{1}{2}(\Sigma^{-1}+U)|^{1/2}},$$

and decide that $X^{(1)}, \ldots, X^{(p)}$ are independent when $\hat{\rho}_3 \geq 1 - [(1-\delta)/4]$, and decide that $X^{(1)}, \ldots, X^{(p)}$ are not independent when $\hat{\rho}_3 < 1 - [(1-\delta)/4]$.

In the same way, we can treat

Problem 3. Decide whether or not the covariance matrix of a random variable is proportionate to a given positive-definite symmetric matrix.

When we employ the general form ρ, we can, of course, treat more general problems.

ACKNOWLEDGMENT

Thanks are due to M. Siotani, Y. Suzuki, and T. Hayakawa for their useful comments and discussions.

REFERENCES

1. MATUSITA, K. (1955). Decision rules based on the distance, for problems of fit, two samples, and estimation. *Ann. Math. Statist.* **26** 613–640.
2. MATUSITA, K. (1964). Distance and decision rules. *Ann. Inst. Statist. Math.* **16** 305–315.

PART IV

Distribution Theory

A Multiple Behrens-Fisher Distribution

E. A. CORNISH
DIVISION OF MATHEMATICAL STATISTICS
C.S.I.R.O.
ADELAIDE, AUSTRALIA

1. RECAPITULATION OF THE UNIVARIATE CASE

If $\bar{x}_1$, with an estimated variance $s_1{}^2$ based on n_1 degrees of freedom is the mean of a sample of observations from a normal distribution whose mean is ξ, then

$$\xi = \bar{x}_1 + s_1 t_1,$$

where t_1 is distributed in Student's distribution with n_1 degrees of freedom. Similarly, for a sample of observations from a second population with the same mean ξ, the corresponding quantities are related by

$$\xi = \bar{x}_2 + s_2 t_2,$$

and t_2 is distributed in Student's distribution with n_2 degrees of freedom, independently of t_1.

Consequently, on the null hypothesis under consideration, $\bar{x}_1 - \bar{x}_2$ will be distributed as is

$$s_1 t_1 - s_2 t_2,$$

where s_1 and s_2 are independent and have values fixed by the observed data, and t_1 and t_2 have a known simultaneous distribution.

Since $d = \bar{x}_1 - \bar{x}_2$ is known, the null hypothesis may be tested by calculating the probability from the integral

$$\int\int \frac{\Gamma[(n_1+1)/2]}{(\pi n_1)^{1/2}\Gamma(n_1/2)} (1 + t_1{}^2/n_1)^{-(n_1+1)/2}$$

$$\times \frac{\Gamma[(n_2+1)/2]}{(\pi n_2)^{1/2}\Gamma(n_2/2)} (1 + t_2{}^2/n_2)^{-(n_2+1)/2}\, dt_1\, dt_2$$

taken over the domain defined by

$$s_1 t_1 - s_2 t_2 > d$$

(Fisher [1, 2]).

2. A MULTIVARIATE DISTRIBUTION

The above result may be generalized readily to take account of multiple variates. If $\bar{x}_{11}, \bar{x}_{12}, \ldots, \bar{x}_{1p}$, each with estimated variance $s_1{}^2$ based on n_1 degrees of freedom, are independent means of samples from independent normal populations with means $\xi_1, \xi_2, \ldots, \xi_p$, respectively, then

$$\xi_j = \bar{x}_{1j} + s_1 t_{1j} \qquad (j = 1, 2, \ldots, p),$$

where the t_{1j} are distributed in the multivariate Student's distribution

$$\frac{\Gamma[(n_1 + p)/2]}{(\pi n_1)^{p/2}\Gamma(n_1/2)} (1 + \mathbf{t}_1{}'\mathbf{t}_1/n_1)^{-(n_1+p)/2}\, d\mathbf{t}_1$$

with n_1 degrees of freedom, in which $\mathbf{t}_1$ is the column vector with elements $t_{11}, t_{12}, \ldots, t_{1p}$.

Similarly, for samples of observations from a second set of normal populations with the same means ξ_j, the corresponding quantities are related by

$$\xi_j = \bar{x}_{2j} + s_2 t_{2j}$$

and the t_{2j} are distributed independently of the t_{1j} in the multivariate Student distribution

$$\frac{\Gamma[(n_2 + p)/2]}{(\pi n_2)^{p/2}\Gamma(n_2/2)} (1 + \mathbf{t}_2{}'\mathbf{t}_2/n_2)^{-(n_2+p)/2}\, d\mathbf{t}_2,$$

where $\mathbf{t}_2$ is the column vector with elements t_{2j}.

Consequently the $\bar{x}_{1j} - \bar{x}_{2j}$ will be simultaneously distributed, as are the

$$s_1 t_{1j} - s_2 t_{2j},$$

where s_1 and s_2 are known and fixed by the observations and the t_{1j} and t_{2j} have a known simultaneous distribution.

Since the vector $\mathbf{d} = \bar{\mathbf{x}}_1 - \bar{\mathbf{x}}_2$ is known, the null hypothesis may be tested by calculating the probability from the integral

$$\int \cdots \int \frac{\Gamma[(n_1 + p)/2]}{(\pi n_1)^{p/2}\Gamma(n_1/2)} (1 + \mathbf{t}_1{}'\mathbf{t}_1/n_1)^{-(n_1+p)/2} \times \frac{\Gamma[(n_2 + p)/2]}{(\pi n_2)^{p/2}\Gamma(n_2/2)} (1 + \mathbf{t}_2{}'\,\mathbf{t}_2/n_2)^{-(n_2+p)/2}\, d\mathbf{t}_1\, d\mathbf{t}_2$$

taken over the domain defined by

$$s_1 \mathbf{t}_1 - s_2 \mathbf{t}_2 > \mathbf{d}.$$

The generalization may be carried a step further to take account of multiple variates formed by taking linear functions of the original means. Suppose $\bar{\mathbf{x}}_1$ is a column vector with elements $\bar{x}_{11}, \bar{x}_{12}, \ldots, \bar{x}_{1p}$ and $\boldsymbol{\xi}$ is the column vector of population means $\xi_1, \xi_2, \ldots, \xi_p$.

Let

$$\begin{aligned}\mathbf{y}_1 &= \mathbf{H}\bar{\mathbf{x}}_1 \\ &= (h_{ij})\bar{\mathbf{x}}_1\end{aligned} \qquad (i = 1, 2, \ldots, q;\ j = 1, 2, \ldots, p)$$

and

$$\boldsymbol{\eta} = \mathbf{H}\boldsymbol{\xi}$$

be any $q < p$, linearly independent, linear functions of the $\bar{x}_{1j}$ and the ξ_j, respectively; then the elements of $\mathbf{y}_1$ are distributed in a multivariate normal distribution with a vector of means $\boldsymbol{\eta}$. The elements of $\mathbf{H}$ are known constants satisfying the conditions

$$\sum_{j=1}^{p} h_{ij} = 0 \qquad \text{for} \quad i = 1, 2, \ldots, q.$$

If, as before, s_1^2 is the estimated variance of the $\bar{x}_{1j}$ based on n_1 degrees of freedom, distributed independently of the $\bar{x}_{1j}$ and therefore independently of $\mathbf{y}_1$, then

$$\boldsymbol{\eta} = \mathbf{y}_1 + s_1\mathbf{Q}^{-1}\mathbf{t}_1$$

where $\mathbf{Q}$ is a diagonal matrix whose ith diagonal element is $(\mathbf{h}_i\mathbf{h}_i')^{-1/2}$, $\mathbf{h}_i$ being the ith row of $\mathbf{H}$, and the distribution of the t_{1j} takes the form

$$\frac{\Gamma[(n_1+q)/2]}{(\pi n_1)^{q/2}\Gamma(n_1/2)}(1 + \mathbf{t}_1'\mathbf{R}^{-1}\mathbf{t}_1/n_1)^{-(n_1+q)/2}\frac{d\mathbf{t}_1}{|\mathbf{R}|^{1/2}},$$

in which $\mathbf{R} = \mathbf{Q}(\mathbf{HH}')\mathbf{Q}$ is the nonsingular, symmetric correlation matrix of the elements of $\mathbf{y}_1$, the correlation ρ_{ij} being

$$\frac{\mathbf{h}_i\mathbf{h}_j'}{(\mathbf{h}_i\mathbf{h}_i' \,.\, \mathbf{h}_j\mathbf{h}_j')^{1/2}}.$$

Similarly, from the observations of the second set, assuming the original populations have the same means $\xi_1, \xi_2, \ldots, \xi_p$, the corresponding quantities are related by

$$\boldsymbol{\eta} = \mathbf{y}_2 + s_2\mathbf{Q}^{-1}\mathbf{t}_2$$

and the t_{2j} are distributed independently of the t_{1j} in the distribution

$$\frac{\Gamma[(n_2+q)/2]}{(\pi n_2)^{q/2}\Gamma(n_2/2)}(1 + \mathbf{t}_2'\mathbf{R}^{-1}\mathbf{t}_2/n_2)^{-(n_2+q)/2}\frac{d\mathbf{t}_2}{|\mathbf{R}|^{1/2}}.$$

Consequently the elements of $\mathbf{y}_1 - \mathbf{y}_2$ will be distributed simultaneously, as are the elements of

$$s_1\mathbf{Q}^{-1}\mathbf{t}_1 - s_2\mathbf{Q}^{-1}\mathbf{t}_2,$$

in which s_1, s_2, and $\mathbf{Q}$ are known and $\mathbf{t}_1$ and $\mathbf{t}_2$ have a known simultaneous distribution.

Since the vector $\mathbf{d} = \mathbf{y}_1 - \mathbf{y}_2$ is known, the null hypothesis may be tested by calculating the probability from the integral

$$\int \cdots \int \frac{\Gamma[(n_1+q)/2]}{(\pi n_1)^{q/2}\Gamma(n_1/2)} (1 + \mathbf{t}_1'\mathbf{R}^{-1}\mathbf{t}_1/n_1)^{-(n_1+q)/2}$$
$$\times \frac{\Gamma[(n_2+q)/2]}{(\pi n_2)^{q/2}\Gamma(n_2/2)} (1 + \mathbf{t}_2'\mathbf{R}^{-1}\mathbf{t}_2/n_2)^{-(n_2+q)/2} \frac{d\mathbf{t}_1\, d\mathbf{t}_2}{|\mathbf{R}|}$$

taken over the domain defined by

$$s_1\mathbf{Q}^{-1}\mathbf{t}_1 - s_2\mathbf{Q}^{-1}\mathbf{t}_2 > \mathbf{d}.$$

The transformation

$$\begin{bmatrix}\mathbf{t}_1\\ \mathbf{t}_2\end{bmatrix} = \begin{bmatrix}\mathbf{P} & \cdot\\ \cdot & \mathbf{P}\end{bmatrix}\begin{bmatrix}\boldsymbol{\tau}_1\\ \boldsymbol{\tau}_2\end{bmatrix},$$

with $\mathbf{P}'\mathbf{R}^{-1}\mathbf{P} = \mathbf{I}$, reduces this integral to

$$\int \cdots \int \frac{\Gamma[(n_1+q)/2]}{(\pi n_2)^{q/2}\Gamma(n_1/2)} (1 + \boldsymbol{\tau}_1'\boldsymbol{\tau}_1/n_1)^{-(n_1+q)/2}$$
$$\times \frac{\Gamma[(n_2+q)/2]}{(\pi n_2)^{q/2}\Gamma(n_2/2)} (1 + \boldsymbol{\tau}_2'\boldsymbol{\tau}_2/n_2)^{-(n_2+q)/2} d\boldsymbol{\tau}_1\, d\boldsymbol{\tau}_2$$

taken over the domain defined by

$$s_1\mathbf{Q}^{-1}\mathbf{P}\boldsymbol{\tau}_1 - s_2\mathbf{Q}^{-1}\mathbf{P}\boldsymbol{\tau}_2 > \mathbf{d}.$$

At this juncture we may distinguish three important cases which may occur in practice:

(a) The rows of $\mathbf{H}$ are orthogonal, but not normalized, in which case $\mathbf{HH}' = \mathbf{Q}^{-2}$.

(b) The rows of $\mathbf{H}$ are orthogonal, each having the same norm v, in which case $\mathbf{HH}' = v\mathbf{I}$.

(c) The rows of $\mathbf{H}$ are orthogonal and normalized, in which case $\mathbf{HH}' = \mathbf{I}$.

Since $\mathbf{HH}'$ is positive-definite and symmetric, the general case may be reduced to any one of the three forms (a), (b), and (c), and equally either (a) or (b) may be reduced to (c). The course to be followed depends upon the nature of the enquiry; orthogonal comparisons, for example, may not provide just what is wanted.

3. DIFFERENT RESIDUAL VARIANCES IN THE SAME EXPERIMENT

It may happen that in the presence of one element of treatment the residual variance is much less than in its absence. Even in agricultural experiments it is possible, although it is not characteristic, that the experimental area is severely deficient in, for example, nitrogen, so that in portions of the experiment not receiving a nitrogenous manure, there may be much variation from plot to plot, owing to variation in the small amount naturally present, whereas under a nitrogenous dressing this cause of variation may have much less influence. We may imagine a set of varieties of a particular crop to be compared experimentally in respect to their reaction to nitrogen under the conditions mentioned above. In such cases the significance of the effect of nitrogen will be in little doubt. The comparison of the average yield of the dressed plots with that of the undressed plots, will, nonetheless, be essentially a comparison between the means of samples from normal populations with unequal variances, for which the univariate Behrens-Fisher distribution provides the test of significance. The average yield with and without nitrogen will not in such cases generally be of interest.

However, the significance of the interaction of nitrogen with varieties may not be obvious, and only the Behrens-Fisher test will be satisfactory for this. The components of this interaction may be tested individually or jointly, using, for the latter test, the multiple Behrens-Fisher distribution. Moreover, the main effects of varieties and any other factors, and their interactions among themselves, if not judged solely from the plots receiving nitrogenous dressings, may seem to have the error distribution of the weighted mean of two normal samples. Although tests of significance are available for reasonably large numbers of degrees of freedom (say 15 for each sample), the exact formulas are complicated [3] and the experimenter should give consideration to the possibility that his requirements will be best met by ignoring the more variable plots altogether (those without nitrogenous dressing in the illustration being considered).

The *unweighted* mean of the effects of varieties, with and without nitrogen, will, in these cases, have an error distribution given exactly by the Behrens-Fisher test. The use of the weighted mean is appropriate only if, as would not be usual in agricultural trials, the interaction was *known* to be zero.

REFERENCES

1. Fisher, R. A. (1935). The fiducial argument in statistical inference. *Ann. Eugenics* **6** 391–398.
2. Fisher, R. A. (1941). The asymptotic approach to Behren's integral, with further tables for the *d* test of significance. *Ann. Eugenics* **11** 141–172.
3. Fisher, R. A. (1961). The weighted mean of two normal samples with unknown variance ratio. *Sankhyā* **23** 103–114.

Inference on Latent Roots by Calculation of Hypergeometric Functions of Matrix Argument[1]

ALAN T. JAMES
UNIVERSITY OF ADELAIDE
ADELAIDE, AUSTRALIA
UNIVERSITY OF CAMBRIDGE
CAMBRIDGE, ENGLAND

1. SUMMARY

The joint problems of numerical evaluation of the likelihood function of the latent roots of the covariance matrix, and of the statistical inferences to be derived from the results, offer many difficulties, both mathematical and statistical. A combined asymptotic and power-series expansion of the likelihood is proved in Section 10 for the trivariate case and conjectured in Section 9 for the general case. Section 12 has an example which is used to calculate approximate numerical values for the likelihood of adjacent roots, considered two at a time with asymptotic allowance for the influence of the other roots. The inferences supplied by likelihood are compared with those from tests of equality of pairs of adjacent roots. In preparation for this, a detailed review of the bivariate theory is made in Section 6. Distributions of the ratios of roots are given in Section 5 and elsewhere. The use of the marginal distribution of the roots as a basis for inference on the population roots is justified in Section 4, by the quasi sufficiency of the roots, or, alternatively, by assumption of a Bayesian uniform prior distribution of the vectors. Partial confirmation comes in Section 8, where it is shown that maximum marginal likelihood estimates allow for bias. The paper begins with a brief survey of four likelihood functions of canonical analysis which involve similar problems, followed in Section 3 by a definition of the hypergeometric functions required, and by a computational formula for two-variable zonal polynomials.

[1] Part of the work was done at Yale University with support from National Foundation Grant GP-0006.

2. A BRIEF SURVEY OF LIKELIHOOD FUNCTIONS OF CANONICAL ANALYSIS

Four likelihood functions are of importance in multivariate analysis based on normal populations:

(a) In principal components, the likelihood of the latent roots of the covariance matrix, or more conveniently, of the information matrix:

$$\Pi\alpha_i^{(1/2)n}\,{}_0F_0^{(m)}(-\tfrac{1}{2}n(\alpha_1, \ldots, \alpha_m); (l_1, \ldots, l_m)), \tag{2.1}$$

where $l_1, \ldots, l_m$ are the latent roots of the $m \times m$ sample covariance matrix, S, on n degrees of freedom; $\alpha_1, \ldots, \alpha_m$ are the latent roots of the information matrix, Σ^{-1}; and ${}_0F_0^{(m)}$ is a hypergeometric function discussed in Section 3:

$$(\Sigma = E[S], n(\alpha_1, \ldots, \alpha_m) \equiv (n\alpha_1, \ldots, n\alpha_m)).$$

(b) In noncentral means with known covariance, the likelihood of the noncentrality parameters,

$$\exp(-\tfrac{1}{2}\Sigma\omega_i)\,{}_0F_1^{(m)}(\tfrac{1}{2}p; \tfrac{1}{4}(\omega_1, \ldots, \omega_m), (w_1, \ldots, w_m)), \tag{2.2}$$

where $w_1, \ldots, w_m$ are the latent roots of the equation $\det(XX' - w\Sigma) = 0$, X is a $m \times p$ matrix variate whose columns are independently normally distributed with covariance Σ and $E[X] = M$, and the parameters $\omega_1, \ldots, \omega_m$ are the latent roots of $\det(MM' - \omega\Sigma) = 0$.

(c) In noncentral latent roots of multiple discriminant analysis, the likelihood of the noncentrality parameters for $p \geq m$ is

$$\exp\left(-\tfrac{1}{2}\sum_{i=1}^{m}\omega_i\right){}_1F_1^{(m)}(\tfrac{1}{2}(p+n); \tfrac{1}{2}p; \tfrac{1}{2}(\omega_1, \ldots, \omega_m), (w_1, \ldots, w_m)), \tag{2.3}$$

where $w_1 \ldots, w_m$ are the latent roots of $\det(XX' - w(XX' + YY'))$ with X as in (b), Y a $m \times n$ matrix variate whose columns are independently normally distributed, independently of X, with covariance Σ and $E[Y] = 0$, and $\omega_1, \ldots, \omega_m$ are the latent roots of $\det(MM' - \omega\Sigma) = 0$. The likelihood for $p \leq m$ is

$$\exp\left(-\tfrac{1}{2}\sum_{i=1}^{p}\omega_i\right){}_1F_1^{(p)}(\tfrac{1}{2}(p+n); \tfrac{1}{2}m; \tfrac{1}{2}(\omega_1, \ldots, \omega_p), (w_1, \ldots, w_p)), \tag{2.4}$$

where $w_1, \ldots, w_p$ are the nonzero latent roots of the determinental equation for $p \geq m$.

(d) The likelihoods of the canonical correlation coefficients

$$\prod_{i=1}^{p}(1-\rho_i{}^2)^{(1/2)n}\,{}_2F_1^{(p)}(\tfrac{1}{2}n, \tfrac{1}{2}n; \tfrac{1}{2}q; (\rho_1{}^2, \ldots, \rho_p{}^2), (r_1^2, \ldots, r_p^2)), \tag{2.5}$$

where $r_1^2, \ldots, r_p^2$ are the sample and $\rho_1^2, \ldots, \rho_p^2$ the population canonical correlation coefficients between p and q variates on n degrees of freedom, $p \leq q, n > p + q$.

Case (c) arises in a multiple discriminant analysis of a multivariate analysis of variance situation:

	d.f.	S.S. and S.P.
Between classes	p	XX'
Within classes	n	YY'

Case (b) is a limiting case of this when n becomes large, and also a limiting case of (d) when $n \to \infty$, $\rho_i^2 \to 0$ such that $nr_i^2 \to w_i$, $n\rho_i^2 \to \omega_i$ with $0 < \omega_i < \infty$.

For the case of one nonzero population root, the distribution in case (c) from which the likelihood has been obtained was first derived by the late Professor S. N. Roy [22], to whose memory this conference is dedicated.

Further results were obtained by Anderson [2] and Bartlett [4], and the general distributions in cases (c) and (d) are due to Constantine [6]. A survey of them together with their analogues based on the complex normal distribution was given by James [15].

Two major problems associated with each of the four cases are:

(1) To evaluate the likelihood function numerically to an accuracy of three decimal places for its logarithm.

(2) To make inferences about the parameters from the likelihood function.

The first problem is mathematical, the second statistical. This paper is devoted to an attack on these problems in case (a), principal components. Work is still in progress and only partial results can be reported to date.

3. HYPERGEOMETRIC FUNCTIONS OF MATRIX ARGUMENT AND ZONAL POLYNOMIALS

The hypergeometric functions in the latent-roots distributions are functions of the latent roots ω_i, w_i, respectively, of the symmetric matrices Ω and W, given by

$$ {}_pF_q^{(m)}(a_1, \ldots, a_p; b_1, \ldots, b_q; \Omega, W) = \sum_{k=0}^{\infty} \sum_{\kappa} \frac{(a_1)_\kappa \cdots (a_p)_\kappa}{(b_1)_\kappa \cdots (b_q)_\kappa} \frac{C_\kappa(\Omega) C_\kappa(W)}{C_\kappa(I_m) k!}. \quad (3.1) $$

In the likelihood formulas of Section 2, we have, for simplicity, written the actual latent roots rather than the matrices. The index $\kappa = (k_1, \cdots, k_r)$ runs over all partitions of k into $r \leq m$ parts, $k_1 + \cdots + k_r = k$; $C_\kappa(W)$ is a symmetric homogeneous polynomial of degree k in the w_i called a zonal polynomial (see James [14] and [15]) whose value at the identity matrix I_m is given by

$$C_\kappa(I_m) = \frac{2^{2k} k!(m/2)_\kappa \prod_{i<j}^{r} (2k_i - 2k_j - i + j)}{\prod_{i=1}^{r} (2k_i + r - i)!}$$

$$= 2^k \prod_{i=1}^{r} \left(\prod_{j=1}^{k_i} \frac{(k_1 + \cdots + k_{i-1} + j)(m + 2j - i - 1)}{(k_i + j)j} \prod_{j=1}^{r-i} \left(1 - \frac{2k_{i+j}}{2k_i + j}\right)\right). \tag{3.2}$$

The second form is more convenient for programming.

The hypergeometric coefficient is given by

$$(a)_\kappa = \prod_{i=1}^{r} (a - (i-1)/2)_{k_i},$$

where $(a)_k = a(a+1) \cdots (a+k-1)$. Methods of calculating the zonal polynomials were given by James [15], with a table up to $k = 6$. Further calculation has been made up to $k = 11$ (James and Parkhurst [16]). For $m = 2$, we have the explicit formula

$$C_{k_1k_2}(w_1, w_2) = \frac{2^{2k_1} k_1!(k_1+k_2)!(2k_1 - 2k_2 + 1)}{(2k_1+1)!k_2!}$$

$$\times \sum_{\nu_1 + 2\nu_2 = k_1 - k_2} \frac{(-1)^{\nu_2} (\frac{1}{2})_{(\nu_1+\nu_2)}}{\nu_1!\nu_2!} (w_1 + w_2)^{\nu_1} (w_1 w_2)^{\nu_2 + k_2}$$

$$= \frac{2^{2k_1}(2(k_1 - k_2) + 1)}{2k_1 + 1} \prod_{i=1}^{k_1} \frac{k_2 + i}{k_1 + i}$$

$$\times \sum_{\nu_1 + 2\nu_2 = k_1 - k_2} \left(\prod_{i=1}^{\nu_1} (1 - 1/(2i)) \right) \left(\prod_{i=1}^{\nu_2} (1 + (\nu_1 - \tfrac{1}{2})/i) \right) (-1)^{\nu_2}$$

$$\times (w_1 + w_2)^{\nu_1} (w_1 w_2)^{\nu_2 + k_2} \tag{3.3}$$

for purposes of calculation.

Table I provides an example of the numerical values of zonal polynomials of $m = 2$ variables of order $k = 28$, calculated by use of the second formula of (3.3). Two interesting features of this high-order case are:

1. When the variables are markedly unequal, the zonal polynomials corresponding to the low-order partitions are negligibly small, but when the variables are approximately equal, the zonal polynomials are of comparable order of magnitude for all partitions.

TABLE I

Numerical Values of Zonal Polynomials in $m = 2$ Variables of Order $k = 28$

	Zonal polynomial		
Partition	$C_\kappa(81.0, 1.0) \times 10^{-53}$	$C_\kappa(9.0, 1.0) \times 10^{-27}$	$C_\kappa(1.0, 1.0) \times 10^{-7}$
28	2.75630593097	.55572816124	.00000098336
27,1	.93548187407	1.69764977682	.00002486308
26,2	.15275129229	2.49506229670	.00031755374
25,3	.01597110641	2.34813475261	.00257441617
24,4	.00120048753	1.58871983219	.01495384316
23,5	.00006903539	.82238800538	.06612536054
22,6	.00000315519	.33834855729	.23099188979
21,7	.00000011750	.11343164749	.65247721646
20,8	.00000000362	.03150568200	1.51166594768
19,9	.00000000009	.00732621612	2.89232081999
18,10	.0	.00143349958	4.56573500954
17,11	.0	.00023568899	5.87197470275
16,12	.0	.00003216456	5.92843599899
15,13	.0	.00000350651	4.18030743493
14,14	.0	.00000021176	.92563950344
$\Sigma C_\kappa(w_1, w_2)$	3.86178300306	9.99999999924	26.84354554362
$(w_1 + w_2)^{28}$	3.86178300308	10.0	26.84354560010
Difference	−.00000000002	−.00000000076	−.00000005650
Correct to	11 significant figures	10 figures	8 figures

2. The accuracy of the zonal polynomials can be checked from the fact that

$$(\sum w_i)^k = \sum_\kappa C_\kappa(w_i). \tag{3.4}$$

For order $k = 28$, calculated to 11-figures floating point, they appear to be accurate to at least 8 significant figures. Hence it may be possible to calculate the series up to 100 terms using 11 figures, or perhaps 200 using 16 figures. Thus in the two-variate case, power series will be effective for calculating likelihoods over an appreciable part of the range, but asymptotic series, when they can be found, will also be required.

We turn now, for the rest of the paper, to the likelihoods of the latent roots of the covariance matrix and their ratios.

4. PRINCIPAL COMPONENTS

If in the Wishart distribution

$$k_1 \det \Sigma^{-(1/2)n} \exp(-\tfrac{1}{2}n \operatorname{tr}(\Sigma^{-1}S)) \det S^{(1/2)(n-m-1)} (dS), \tag{4.1}$$

where $k_1 = n^{(1/2)mn}/2^{(1/2)mn}\Gamma_m(\frac{1}{2}n)$,

$$\Gamma_m(a) = \pi^{m(m-1)/4} \prod_{i=1}^{m} \Gamma(a - (i-1)/2), \qquad \Sigma = E[S]$$

for the $m \times m$ sample covariance matrix S on n degrees of freedom, we make a transformation to principal axes

$$S = \hat{H}L\hat{H}', \qquad \Sigma = \tilde{H}\Lambda\tilde{H}', \tag{4.2}$$

we obtain the joint distribution of the sample latent roots $L = \text{diag}\,(l_i)$, and the corresponding sample vectors, which are the columns of the orthogonal matrix $\hat{H}$. The joint distribution

$$k_2 \prod_{i=1}^{m} \alpha_i^{(1/2)n} \exp(-\tfrac{1}{2}n \operatorname{tr}(A(\tilde{H}'\hat{H})L(\tilde{H}'\hat{H})'))\,(d\hat{H})$$
$$\times \prod_{i=1}^{m} l_i^{[(1/2)(n-m-1)]} \prod_{i<j}^{m} (l_i - l_j) \prod_{i=1}^{m} dl_i, \tag{4.3}$$

where $k_2 = \pi^{(1/2)m^2} n^{(1/2)mn}/(2^{(1/2)mn}\Gamma_m(\frac{1}{2}n)\Gamma_m(\frac{1}{2}m))$ depends upon the roots, $\Lambda = \text{diag}\,(\lambda_i)$, of the population covariance matrix Σ, but is more conveniently expressed in terms of their inverses, $A = \text{diag}(\alpha_i)$, $\alpha_i = 1/\lambda_i$, which are the latent roots of the information matrix $\Sigma^{-1} = \tilde{H}A\tilde{H}'$. The symbol $(d\hat{H})$ stands for the invariant measure on the orthogonal group $O(m)$, normalized to be unity when integrated over the (2^m)th part of the group. The distribution is essentially due to Roy [21] and Fisher [8], independently.

In the estimation of $\alpha_1, \ldots, \alpha_m$, the matrix $\tilde{H}$ has $\frac{1}{2}m(m-1)$ functionally independent nuisance parameters. Two methods of eliminating them, quasi-sufficiency and Bayesian uniform prior, lead to the same result, the use of the likelihood function obtained from the marginal distribution.

Quasi Sufficiency

In the absence of appreciable information about $\tilde{H}$ outside the sample, we assume that the estimation situation is symmetric in the sense that it is invariant under the group of transformations

$$\left.\begin{array}{l}\tilde{H} \to H\tilde{H}\\ \hat{H} \to H\hat{H}\end{array}\right\} \qquad H \in O(m), \tag{4.4}$$

which acts transitively upon the parameter space of $\tilde{H}$ and the sample space of $\hat{H}$, and leaves the density invariant. Since $(L, \hat{H})$ are jointly sufficient for $(A, \tilde{H})$ and the invariance holds, the statistic L is quasi sufficient for A in the sense of Barnard [3].

Quasi sufficiency requires a symmetry of the concrete estimation situation in the sense of Fraser [10] in his discussion of fiducial inference, not merely a mathematical symmetry of the probability density—that in all practical respects an observed value $H\hat{H}$ of the statistic as an estimate of a possible value $H\tilde{H}$ of the parameter would be equivalent to $\hat{H}$ as an estimate of $\tilde{H}$. The symmetry is only required over a region about $\hat{H}$ of values of $\tilde{H}$, conceivable in practice in the light of the observed value of $\hat{H}$. The region will be smaller or larger according to the accuracy of $\hat{H}$.

The requirement often amounts to much the same thing as that for stable estimation in the Bayesian approach below.

In cases of quasi sufficiency, e.g., estimation of the variance of a univariate normal population, or the correlation coefficient of a bivariate one, it seems appropriate to make inferences from the marginal distribution of the quasi-sufficient statistic.

The marginal distribution of the roots is found by integrating with respect to $\hat{H}$. Putting $H = \tilde{H}'\hat{H}$, we have $(dH) = (d\hat{H})$, and thus the marginal distribution of L is

$$\prod_{i=1}^{m} \alpha_i^{(1/2)n} \int_{O(m)} \exp(-\tfrac{1}{2}n \operatorname{tr}(AHLH'))\,(dH)\; k \prod_{i=1}^{m} l_i^{(1/2)(n-m-1)} \prod_{i=j}^{m} (l_i - l_j) \prod_{i=1}^{m} dl_i, \tag{4.5}$$

where $k = \pi^{(1/2)m^2} n^{(1/2)mn} / (2^{(1/2)mn} \Gamma_m(\tfrac{1}{2}n)\Gamma_m(\tfrac{1}{2}m))$.

Bayesian Uniform Prior

In the absence of prior information comparable to the information supplied by the sample, we may assume a uniform prior distribution for $\tilde{H}$, at least over the range of its values which come into question in the light of the observed $\hat{H}$. We then integrate with respect to a uniform $\tilde{H}$ instead of $\hat{H}$, but it leads to the same result, viz., the likelihood function in the marginal distribution (4.5), which can be written in terms of a hypergeometric function of matrix argument,

$$\prod_{i=1}^{m} \alpha_i^{(1/2)n} {}_0F_0^{(m)}(-\tfrac{1}{2}nA, L), \tag{4.6}$$

where the hypergeometric function ${}_0F_0^{(m)}$ is given by (3.1). It has the obvious properties

$${}_0F_0^{(m)}((\lambda\omega_1, \ldots, \lambda\omega_m), (w_1, \ldots, w_m)) = {}_0F_0^{(m)}((\omega_1, \ldots, \omega_m), (\lambda w_1, \ldots, \lambda w_m)), \tag{4.7}$$

$$\begin{aligned} &{}_0F_0^{(m)}((\lambda + \omega_1, \ldots, \lambda + \omega_m), (\mu + w_1, \ldots, \mu + w_m)) \\ &= \exp\left(m\lambda\mu + \lambda \sum_{i=1}^{m} w_i + \mu \sum_{i=1}^{m} \omega_i \right) {}_0F_0^{(m)}((\omega_1, \ldots, \omega_m), (w_1, \ldots, w_m)). \end{aligned} \tag{4.8}$$

5. RATIOS OF THE ROOTS

More often than not, in practice, interest devolves upon the relative rather than the absolute values of the successive roots. The distribution (4.5) of the latent roots l_i of the covariance matrix is obviously symmetrical with respect to scale transformations,

$$\left.\begin{array}{l} l_i \to \beta l_i \\ \alpha_i \to \beta^{-1}\alpha_i \end{array}\right\} \qquad i = 1, \ldots, m;\ \beta \text{ real}, > 0. \tag{5.1}$$

Provided the estimation situation possesses the symmetry, the ratios of the sample roots will be jointly quasi-sufficient statistics for the ratios of the population roots.

An integration with respect to l_m, performed on the distribution (4.5), establishes the distribution of the ratios u_i $(i = 1, \ldots, m-1)$ of the roots l_i to their mean $\bar{l}$.

Theorem. *If $l_1, \ldots, l_m$ are the latent roots of the sample covariance matrix on n degrees of freedom, whose distribution* (4.5) *depends on the latent roots α_i of the information matrix, and if*

$$\bar{l} = m^{-1}\sum_{i=1}^{m} l_i, \qquad u_i = l_i/\bar{l} \qquad (i = 1, \ldots, m),$$

$$\bar{\alpha} = m^{-1}\sum_{i=1}^{m} \alpha_i, \qquad U = \operatorname{diag}(u_i), \qquad A = \operatorname{diag}(\alpha_i),$$

then the marginal distribution of $u_1, \ldots, u_{m-1}$ is

$$\prod_{i=1}^{m} (\alpha_i/\bar{\alpha})^{(1/2)n} \int_{O(m)} (\operatorname{tr}(m^{-1}UH\bar{\alpha}^{-1}AH'))^{-(1/2)mn}\,(dH)$$
$$\times\, k_3 \prod_{i=1}^{m} u_i^{(1/2)(n-m-1)} \prod_{i<j}^{m} (u_i - u_j) \prod_{i=1}^{m-1} du_i, \tag{5.2}$$

where $k_3 = \pi^{(1/2)m^2}\Gamma(\tfrac{1}{2}mn)/(m^{(1/2)mn}\Gamma_m(\tfrac{1}{2}n)\Gamma_m(\tfrac{1}{2}m))$.

The distribution shows the characteristic form of a likelihood factor in the first row, which becomes unity when all the population roots α_i are equal, multiplied by a null distribution, as given by Bartlett [5], in the second row.

He pointed out that the tth moment of the product

$$L = \prod_{i=1}^{m} u_i = \left(\prod_{i=1}^{m} l_i\right)\Big/\left(\sum_{i=1}^{m} l_i/m\right)^m \tag{5.3}$$

in the null distribution follows immediately as

$$E[L^t] = \frac{m^{mt}\Gamma(\tfrac{1}{2}mn)}{\Gamma(m(t+n/2))} \prod_{i=1}^{m} \frac{\Gamma(t+(n-i+1)/2)}{\Gamma((n-i+1)/2)}. \tag{5.4}$$

But L is the likelihood-ratio statistic for the test of equality of the roots. Hence the distribution of its log can be approximated by χ^2 as follows:

$$\chi^2 = -(n - \tfrac{1}{6}(2m + 1 + 2/m)) \log L \tag{5.5}$$

on $\frac{1}{2}(m-1)(m+2)$ d.f., the multiplier of $\log L$ having been determined from the moments above by the requirement that the means agree to within $O(1/n)$.

Bartlett [5] indicated that as a test of equality of the last $m - r$ roots

$$L = \left(\prod_{i=r+1}^{m} l_i\right) \Bigg/ \left(\sum_{i=r+1}^{m} l_i/(m-r)\right)^{m-r},$$

the χ^2 approximation would still be reasonably good, and Lawley [18] refined the approximation with corrections to the multiplier to make some allowance for the earlier roots.

For nearly equal values of the u_i or α_i, the integral in (5.2) equals

$$\int (1 + \mathrm{tr}(m^{-1}(U - I_m)H(\bar{\alpha}^{-1}A - I_m)H')^{-n}\,(dH)$$

$$= \sum_{k=0}^{\infty} (-1)^k \frac{(n)_k}{k!} \int (\mathrm{tr}(m^{-1}(U - I_m)H(\bar{\alpha}^{-1}A - I_m)H'))^k\,(dH)$$

$$= \sum_{k=0}^{\infty} (-1)^k \frac{(n)_k}{k!\,m^k} \sum_{\kappa} \frac{C_\kappa(U - I_m)C_\kappa(\bar{\alpha}^{-1}A - I_m)}{C_\kappa(I_m)}, \tag{5.6}$$

provided

$$\sum_{i=1}^{m} (u_i - 1)((\alpha_i/\bar{\alpha}) - 1) < m. \tag{5.7}$$

When $m \geq 3$, the expansion only converges in part of the range of the u_i and α_i. An asymptotic formula (7.6) is derived later.

6. THE BIVARIATE CASE

In the special case of $m = 2$, Girshick [13] derived the distribution of the roots and the distribution of their ratio. The likelihood can obviously be expressed as

$$(\alpha_1\alpha_2)^{(1/2)n}\,{}_0F_0^{(2)}(-\tfrac{1}{2}n(l_1, l_2),\ (\alpha_1, \alpha_2))$$

$$= (\alpha_1\alpha_2)^{(1/2)n} \exp(-\tfrac{1}{4}n(l_1 + l_2)(\alpha_1 + \alpha_2))I_0(\tfrac{1}{4}n(l_1 - l_2)(\alpha_2 - \alpha_1)), \tag{6.1}$$

where $I_0(X)$ is the imaginary Bessel function of zero order given by

$$I_0(X) = \pi^{-1} \int_0^{\pi} \exp(X \cos\theta)\,d\theta = {}_0F_1(1; \tfrac{1}{4}X^2) = \sum_{k=0}^{\infty} (\tfrac{1}{4}X^2)^k/(k!)^2. \tag{6.2}$$

The power series need only be used up to $X = 4$. For larger values of X, the well-known asymptotic expansion yields eight-figure accuracy (Erdélyi *et al.* [7], p. 86).

$$I_0(X) = \exp(X)(2\pi X)^{-1/2} \sum_{k=0} \frac{1^2 \cdot 3^2, \ldots, (2k-1)^2}{2^{3k} k! X^k}. \tag{6.3}$$

The sum is taken up to the value of k at which the terms either stop decreasing or have become negligible. Tables II, III, and IV show computer printouts of the likelihood for $l_1 = 1{\cdot}2$, $l_2 = 0.8$, in the cases $n = 10, 55, 100$, respectively.

Girshick's [13] distribution of the ratio $f = l_1/l_2$ of the sample roots depends upon the ratio $\varphi = \alpha_2/\alpha_1$ of the population roots and can easily be obtained from the distribution of the two roots by putting $l_1 = fl_2$ and integrating with respect to l_2 as

$$\varphi^{(1/2)n}((1+\varphi)/2)^{-n} {}_2F_1\left(\tfrac{1}{2}n, \tfrac{1}{2}(n+1); 1; \left(\frac{(f-1)(\varphi-1)}{(f+1)(\varphi+1)}\right)^2\right)$$

$$\times (n-1)\left(\frac{2f^{1/2}}{f+1}\right)^{n-2} d\left(\frac{2f^{1/2}}{f+1}\right) \qquad (1 \leq f \leq \infty). \tag{6.4}$$

The integral from which the hypergeometric function ${}_2F_1$ arises may be used to obtain an asymptotic series for large nx:

$${}_2F_1(\tfrac{1}{2}n, \tfrac{1}{2}(n+1); 1; x^2) = \pi^{-1} \int_0^\pi (1 - x\cos\theta)^{-n}\, d\theta$$

$$\doteqdot \frac{\Gamma(n-\frac{1}{2})}{(2\pi x)^{1/2}\Gamma(n)(1-x)^{n-(1/2)}} \sum_{k<n-1} \frac{((\frac{1}{2})_k)^2 \Gamma(n-\frac{1}{2}-k)}{k!\Gamma(n-\frac{1}{2})} \left(\frac{1-x}{2x}\right)^k$$

$$\doteqdot \frac{1}{(2\pi n x)^{1/2}(1-x)^{n-(1/2)}} \left\{1 + \frac{1}{(8(n-\frac{3}{2})} \frac{1-x}{x} + \frac{9}{128(n-\frac{3}{2})(n-\frac{5}{2})}\right.$$

$$\left. \times \left(\frac{1-x}{x}\right)^2 + \cdots \right\}. \tag{6.5}$$

The likelihood factor in the first line of the distribution (6.4) becomes unity when $\varphi = 1$, yielding the null distribution in the second line, written in the easily integrable form in which it was originally derived by Mauchly [19]. To test the equality of the roots, he obtained the ratio of the geometric to the arithmetic mean of the roots,

$$\frac{(l_1 l_2)^{1/2}}{(l_1 + l_2)/2} = \frac{2f^{1/2}}{f+1} = L_e, \tag{6.6}$$

TABLE II

Log Likelihood of Latent Roots[a]

α_2 \ α_1	0.60	0.70	0.80	0.90	1.0	1.10	1.20	1.30	1.40	1.50	1.60
0.6	−1.11										
0.7	−0.84	−0.57									
0.8	−0.66	−0.40	−0.23								
0.9	−0.56	−0.30	−0.14	−0.05							
1.0	−0.51	−0.26	−0.11	−0.02	−0.00						
1.1	−0.52	−0.27	−0.12	−0.04	−0.02	−0.05					
1.2	−0.55	−0.31	−0.16	−0.09	−0.08	−0.11	−0.18				
1.3	−0.62	−0.38	−0.24	−0.18	−0.17	−0.20	−0.27	−0.38			
1.4	−0.72	−0.48	−0.35	−0.28	−0.28	−0.32	−0.40	−0.50	−0.64		
1.5	−0.83	−0.60	−0.47	−0.41	−0.41	−0.46	−0.54	−0.65	−0.79	−0.95	
1.6	−0.97	−0.74	−0.61	−0.56	−0.56	−0.61	−0.70	−0.82	−0.96	−1.12	−1.30
1.7	−1.12	−0.89	−0.77	−0.72	−0.73	−0.78	−0.87	−1.00	−1.14	−1.31	−1.49
1.8	−1.28	−1.06	−0.94	−0.89	−0.91	−0.97	−1.06	−1.19	−1.34	−1.51	−1.70
1.9	−1.46	−1.24	−1.12	−1.08	−1.10	−1.16	−1.26	−1.39	−1.55	−1.72	−1.92
2.0	−1.65	−1.43	−1.32	−1.28	−1.30	−1.36	−1.47	−1.60	−1.76	−1.95	−2.14

[a] Taken for the latent roots α_1, α_2 of the information matrix for sample roots $l_1 = 1.2$, $l_2 = 0.8$, on $n = 10$ degrees of freedom.

TABLE III

Log Likelihood of Roots for n = 55 d.f.

α_2 \ α_1	0.60	0.70	0.80	0.90	1.00	1.10	1.20	1.30	1.40	1.50
0.6	−11.10									
0.7	−9.53	−8.12								
0.8	−8.40	−7.12	−6.27							
0.9	−7.60	−6.42	−5.71	−5.29						
1.0	−7.08	−5.97	−5.35	−5.07	−5.00					
1.1	−6.79	−5.72	−5.17	−4.99	−5.05	−5.26				
1.2	−6.70	−5.66	−5.16	−5.04	−5.20	−5.54	−5.97			
1.3	−6.79	−5.76	−5.29	−5.22	−5.44	−5.88	−6.45	−7.07		
1.4	−7.02	−6.01	−5.55	−5.51	−5.78	−6.29	−6.95	−7.71	−8.49	
1.5	−7.39	−6.39	−5.94	−5.92	−6.21	−6.76	−7.49	−8.35	−9.27	−10.20
1.6	−7.87	−6.87	−6.44	−6.43	−6.74	−7.32	−8.09	−9.02	−10.04	−11.10
1.7	−8.45	−7.46	−7.03	−7.03	−7.36	−7.96	−8.76	−9.73	−10.81	−11.98
1.8	−9.13	−8.14	−7.72	−7.72	−8.06	−8.67	−9.49	−10.49	−11.62	−12.84
1.9	−9.88	−8.90	−8.48	−8.49	−8.84	−9.45	−10.29	−11.30	−12.36	−13.73
2.0	−10.71	−9.73	−9.32	−9.33	−9.68	−10.31	−11.15	−12.18	−13.45	−14.65

TABLE IV

Log Likelihood of Roots for $n = 100$ d.f.

α_2 \ α_1	0.60	0.70	0.80	0.90	1.00	1.10	1.20	1.30	1.40
0.7	−8.14	−5.67							
0.8	−5.87	−3.76	−2.31						
0.9	−4.22	−2.28	−1.19	−0.54					
1.0	−3.12	−1.25	−0.33	−0.03	−0.00				
1.1	−2.47	−0.64	+0.19	+0.32	−0.00	−0.47			
1.2	−2.22	−0.41	+0.38	+0.43	−0.06	−0.88	−1.77		
1.3	−2.30	−0.51	+0.27	+0.38	−0.30	−1.29	−2.53	−3.76	
1.4	−2.66	−0.88	−0.13	−0.14	−0.75	−1.83	−3.24	−4.82	−6.35
1.5	−3.27	−1.50	−0.76	−0.79	−1.42	−2.54	−4.03	−5.78	−7.67
1.6	−4.10	−2.34	−1.60	−1.64	−2.29	−3.43	−4.96	−6.80	−8.85
1.7	−5.12	−3.36	−2.63	−2.68	−3.34	−4.49	−6.05	−7.93	−10.06
1.8	−6.30	−4.55	−3.82	−3.88	−4.55	−5.72	−7.29	−9.19	−11.36
1.9	−7.64	−5.89	−5.17	−5.23	−5.91	−7.08	−8.66	−10.58	−12.78
2.0	−9.11	−7.37	−6.65	−6.72	−7.40	−8.58	−10.17	−12.10	−14.31

as the nth root of the likelihood ratio, L_e^n, and called it the ellipticity statistic, L_e. From the second line of (6.4), we see that the null distribution of $-2(n-2)\log L_e$ is exactly χ^2 on two degrees of freedom.

7. ASYMPTOTIC FORMULA FOR ${}_0F_0^{(m)}$

If even a single root is large, or if the degrees of freedom, n, are large, the power series will converge very slowly. When n is large and all the roots are well spaced, the asymptotic expansion of Anderson [1] gives good approximations to the likelihood:

$$\prod_{i=1}^{m} \alpha_i^{(1/2)n} {}_0F_0^{(m)}(-\tfrac{1}{2}n(l_1, \ldots, l_m),(\alpha_1, \ldots, \alpha_m))$$
$$= k \prod_{i=1}^{m} \alpha_i^{(1/2)n} \exp\left(-\tfrac{1}{2}n \sum_{i=1}^{m} l_i\alpha_i\right) \prod_{i<j}^{m} C_{ij}^{-1/2}$$
$$\times \left\{1 + (1/(2n)) \sum_{i<j}^{m} C_{ij}^{-1} + (9/(8n^2)) \sum_{i<j}^{m} C_{ij}^{-2} + (1/(4n^2)) \sum C_{ij}^{-1} C_{kl}^{-1} + \cdots\right\}, \tag{7.1}$$

where $k = 2^{(1/4)m(m-1)}\Gamma_m(\tfrac{1}{2}m)/\pi^{(1/4)m(m+1)}$, and $C_{ij} = (l_i - l_j)(\alpha_j - \alpha_i)$.

The last sum is over all possible cross products of the C_{ij}^{-1} without repetition. The last two terms have been proved by Anderson [1] for $m = 4$ and are conjectured for $m > 4$.

The first term of the asymptotic formula is a product of the likelihoods of independent variance estimates

$$\alpha_i^{(1/2)n} \exp(-\tfrac{1}{2}nl_i\alpha_i) \tag{7.2}$$

multiplied by linkage factors

$$(\alpha_j - \alpha_i)^{-1/2}, \tag{7.3}$$

which represent the effects of interactions between roots upon the likelihood.

The asymptotic formula shows that the likelihood function of a group of adjacent roots is sensitive only to those other roots which are close to them.

In considering the likelihood of a single root or a certain group of roots, the remaining population roots are nuisance parameters. One way to eliminate such nuisance parameters is to average the likelihood with respect to some reasonable posterior distribution of the nuisance parameters. For roots somewhat removed from the group, the effect of the averaging would be expected to come out much the same as substitution of the maximum likelihood estimates l_j^{-1} or $\hat{\hat{\alpha}}_j$. The symbol $\hat{\hat{\alpha}}_j$ is the maximum marginal likelihood estimate discussed in Section 8.

This would lead to the formula

$$k + \tfrac{1}{2}n(\log \alpha_i - l_i\alpha_i) - \tfrac{1}{2}\sum_{j>i} \log(\alpha_i/\hat{\hat{\alpha}}_j - 1) - \tfrac{1}{2}\sum_{j>i} \log(1 - \alpha_i/\hat{\hat{\alpha}}_j) \tag{7.4}$$

for the likelihood of a single root or an obvious modification for several roots.

Substituting the asymptotic expansion of the likelihood in the full distribution, we have for the asymptotic expansion of the distribution

$$kn^{(1/4)m(2n-m+1)} \prod_{i=1}^{m} \alpha_i^{(1/2)n} \exp\left(-\tfrac{1}{2}n \sum_{i=1}^{m} l_i\alpha_i\right) l_i^{(1/2)(n-m-1)}$$

$$\times \prod_{i<j} ((l_i - l_j)/(\alpha_j - \alpha_i))^{1/2} \prod_{i=1}^{m} dl_i, \tag{7.5}$$

where $k = \pi^{(1/4)m(m-1)}/(2^{(1/4)m(2n-m+1)}\Gamma_m(\tfrac{1}{2}n))$.

It is a product of χ^2 distributions times a linkage factor $\prod_{i<j}((l_i - l_j)/(\alpha_j - \alpha_i))^{1/2}$.

Anderson [1] has shown that as $n \to \infty$, the factor $\prod_{i<j} ((l_i - l_j)/(\alpha_j - \alpha_i))^{1/2}$ tends to 1 with probability 1, and the χ^2 distributions tend to normality, yielding the asymptotic normality proved by Girshick [12].

An asymptotic formula for the density of the distribution of the ratios, $u_i = l_i/\bar{l}$, of the roots may be obtained by substituting $l_i = u_i\bar{l}$ in the first term of the asymptotic formula (7.1) for the roots density, and integrating with respect to $\bar{l}$.

$$\frac{\prod_{i=1}^{m} (\alpha_i/\bar{\alpha})^{(1/2)n}}{\prod_{i<j}^{m} (\alpha_j/\bar{\alpha} - \alpha_i/\bar{\alpha})^{1/2}(\sum_{i=1}^{m} u_i\alpha_i/\bar{\alpha})^{(1/2)m(n-(1/2)(m-1))}}$$

$$\times\ k \prod_{i=1}^{m} u_i^{(1/2)(n-m-1)} \prod_{i<j}^{m} (u_i - u_j)^{1/2}\, du_1 \cdots du_{m-1}, \tag{7.6}$$

where $k = \pi^{(1/2)m(m-1)} m\Gamma(\tfrac{1}{2}m(n - \tfrac{1}{2}(m-1)))/\Gamma_m(\tfrac{1}{2}n)$. It depends, of course, only on the ratios $\alpha_i/\bar{\alpha}$ of the population roots, and is presumably an asymptotic formula for the density (5.2).

8. MAXIMUM LIKELIHOOD AND BIAS

Confronted with the problems of the sampling distribution of the latent roots, many users of principal components have taken solace in the smooth curve that one ususally get by plotting the roots in descending order (see Fig. 1). The curve gives the impression that sampling errors cannot be too serious, but this is often illusory. First, the curve is monotonic by its very construction, not from any regularity in the data. Second, the sampling errors tend to *smooth* the curve, because the factor $(l_i - l_j)$ in the roots distribution or its square root in the asymptotic distribution tends to spread the sample roots.

The likelihood function of the distribution of the roots allows for this bias, by means of the term $(\alpha_i - \alpha_j)^{1/2}$ in the denominator.

Since the sample covariance matrix S maximizes the likelihood with respect to Σ in the Wishart distribution, it follows that the (l_i^{-1}), $\hat{H}$ are joint maximum-likelihood estimates of the (α_i) and $\hat{H}$. But the (l_i^{-1}) do not maximize the likelihood with respect to the (α_i) in their marginal distribution. (The

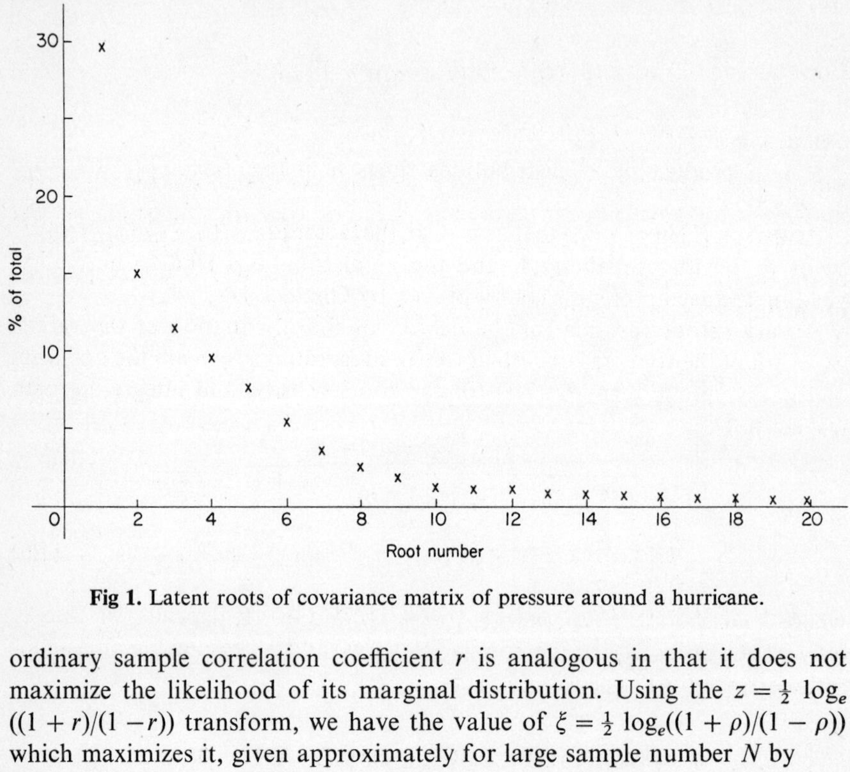

Fig 1. Latent roots of covariance matrix of pressure around a hurricane.

ordinary sample correlation coefficient r is analogous in that it does not maximize the likelihood of its marginal distribution. Using the $z = \frac{1}{2}\log_e((1+r)/(1-r))$ transform, we have the value of $\xi = \frac{1}{2}\log_e((1+\rho)/(1-\rho))$ which maximizes it, given approximately for large sample number N by

$$\hat{\hat{\xi}} = z - r/(2(N-1))$$

(see Fisher [9], Sec. 36).)

The maximum marginal likelihood estimates of the multiple correlation coefficient, and of the Mahalanobis distance in simple discriminant analysis, should similarly show corrections for bias. The marginal likelihoods are, of course, special cases of (c), $p \leq m$, for $p = 1$, and (d) for $m = 1$.

From (7.1) we have asymptotically,

$$\text{log likelihood} = \tfrac{1}{2}n\sum_{i=1}^{m}\log\alpha_i - \tfrac{1}{2}n\sum_{i=1}^{m} l_i\alpha_i - \tfrac{1}{2}\sum_{j\neq i}\log(\alpha_i - \alpha_j),$$

$$\frac{\partial}{\partial\alpha_i} = \tfrac{1}{2}n/\alpha_i - \tfrac{1}{2}nl_i - \tfrac{1}{2}\sum_{j\neq i}\frac{1}{(\alpha_i-\alpha_j)} = 0. \tag{8.1}$$

Hence we obtain Anderson's [1] estimates for the maximum marginal likelihood,

$$\hat{\hat{\alpha}}_i^{-1} = l_i - (l_i/n) \sum_{j \neq i} l_j/(l_i - l_j) + O(1/n^2)$$

or (8.2)

$$\hat{\hat{\alpha}}_i = l_i^{-1}(1 - n^{-1} \sum_{j \neq i} l_j/(l_i - l_j))^{-1} + O(n^{-2}).$$

Comparing (8.2) with Lawley's formula ([18], p. 133),

$$E[l_i] = \lambda_i + (\lambda_i/n) \sum_{j} \lambda_j/(\lambda_i - \lambda_j) + O(1/n^2), \tag{8.3}$$

we see that in going from the joint maximum-likelihood estimate l_i to the maximum marginal likelihood estimate $\hat{\hat{\alpha}}_i^{-1}$, we obtain a correction for the bias. This is further evidence in support of using the marginal distribution of the sample roots with the likelihood function obtained from it as the basis of the inference concerning the population roots.

TABLE V

Largest Latent Roots of a 90 × 90 *Covariance Matrix*[a,b]

Order i	Latent root l_i	Reciprocal l_i^{-1}	Corrected reciprocal $\hat{\hat{\alpha}}_i$ From formula	From likelihood
1	564.2	.00177	.00182	.00182
2	284.5	.00352	.00375	.00375
3	220.9	.0045	.0049	.0049
4	186.1	.0054	.0057	.0050
5	145.0	.0069	.0072	.0065
6	105.3	.0095	.0099	.0093
7	59.6	.0168	.0183	.0188
8	47.8	.0209	.0227	.0199
9	35.8	.0280	.0309	.0290
10	27.3	.0366	.0424	
11	23.6	.0424	.0502	

$m = 90$, $n = 128$, trace = 1902.9

[a] Taken on 128 degrees of freedom, of the atmospheric pressures at 90 grid points about a hurricane as center on 129 days.

[b] Data of K. Veigas.

Table V shows a set of latent roots and the corrected root reciprocals calculated both from the formula above and from a plot of the likelihoods calculated by a method outlined below. The formula gives good corrections for the first three root reciprocals but breaks down for the latter ones because the roots are evidently too close for an asymptotic formula to work.

9. COMBINED ASYMPTOTIC AND POWER-SERIES EXPANSION

In many, if not most, cases in practice some sample roots are too much spread for the power series to be used and some are too close for the asymptotic series. We may also be interested in the likelihood of equality of population roots, in which case the asymptotic formula "blows up." A combination of asymptotic and power series is required. A reasonable method of conjecturing such a formula is to remove the factors in the asymptotic formula which blow up when the certain group of roots become close, and to insert the exact power-series formula for just this group in such a way that, when the power-series formula for the group is replaced by its asymptotic expansion, we shall recover the original asymptotic expansion of all the variables, at least up to a certain order. This leads to the following conjecture:

$$\begin{aligned}
\prod_{i=1}^{m} \alpha_i^{(1/2)n} {}_0F_0^{(m)}(-\tfrac{1}{2}n(l_1, \ldots, l_r, l_{r+1}, \ldots, l_m), (\alpha_1, \ldots, \alpha_r, \alpha_{r+1}, \ldots, \alpha_m)) \\
= {}_0F_0^{(m-r)}(-\tfrac{1}{2}n(l_{r+1}, \ldots, l_m), (\alpha_{r+1}, \ldots, \alpha_m)) \\
\times \prod_{i=1}^{m} \alpha_i^{(1/2)n} \exp\left(-\tfrac{1}{2}n \sum_{i=1}^{r} l_i \alpha_i\right) \\
\times \prod_{i<j}^{r} \{n(l_i - l_j)(\alpha_j - \alpha_i)\}^{-1/2} \prod_{i=1}^{r} \prod_{j=r+1}^{m} \{n(l_i - l_j)(\alpha_j - \alpha_i)\}^{-1/2} \\
\times \left\{1 + (2n)^{-1} \sum_{i<j}^{r} C_{ij}^{-1} + (2n)^{-1} \sum_{i=1}^{r} \sum_{j=r+1}^{m} C_{ij}^{-1} + \cdots\right\},
\end{aligned} \tag{9.1}$$

where $C_{ij} = (l_i - l_j)(\alpha_j - \alpha_i)$.

To compute ${}_0F_0^{(m-r)}$, we can use (4.8) to obtain

$$\begin{aligned}
{}_0F_0^{(m-r)}(-\tfrac{1}{2}n(l_{r+1}, \ldots, l_m), (\alpha_{r+1}, \ldots, \alpha_m)) \\
= \exp\left(-(\tfrac{1}{2}n/(m-r))\left(\sum_{i=r+1}^{m} l_i\right)\left(\sum_{i=r+1}^{m} \alpha_i\right)\right) \\
\times {}_0F_0^{(m-r)}(-\tfrac{1}{2}n(l_{r+1} - l^*, \ldots, l_m - l^*), (\alpha_{r+1} - \alpha^*, \ldots, \alpha_m - \alpha^*)),
\end{aligned} \tag{9.2}$$

where $l^* = (m-r)^{-1} \sum_{i=r+1}^{m} l_i$, $\alpha^* = (m-r)^{-1} \sum_{i=r+1}^{m} \alpha_i$.

For economy of notation, we have written the power series for the last $(m-r)$ roots and the asymptotic series for the first r; but any group of adjacent roots could be used for the power series, provided the nC_{ij} are large, (>10), where the jth root is in the power-series group and the ith root in the asymptotic one.

TABLE VI

Log Likelihood of 3rd- and 4th-Root Reciprocals, α_3 and α_4, for the Hurricane Data of Table V

α_4 \ α_3		0.00428		0.00458		0.00489		0.00520		0.00550	
.00390											
.00408											
.00426	−6.41										
.00444	−6.16	−5.96	−5.78								
.00461	−5.96	−5.77	−5.60	−5.47							
.00479	−5.81	−5.63	−5.48	−5.36	−5.28						
.00497	−5.71	−5.55	−5.41	−5.31	−5.24	−5.21					
.00515	−5.66	−5.51	−5.39	−5.30	−5.25	−5.24	−5.26				
.00532	−5.66	−5.52	−5.41	−5.33	−5.30	−5.30	−5.34	−5.42			
.00550	−5.71	−5.58	−5.48	−5.41	−5.39	−5.41	−5.47	−5.56	−5.68	−5.83	
.00568	−5.80	−5.68	−5.59	−5.54	−5.52	−5.56	−5.62	−5.73	−5.87	−6.03	−6.23
.00586	−5.93	−5.82	−5.74	−5.69	−5.69	−5.74	−5.82	−5.94	−6.09	−6.27	−6.48
.00603	−6.11	−6.00	−5.92	−5.89	−5.89	−5.95	−6.04	−6.17	−6.34	−6.53	−6.76

Numerical values of the log likelihood are given in Table VI, calculated by power series for ranges of values of the 3rd- and 4th-root reciprocals, α_3 and α_4, and asymptotically for the rest of the 90 roots of the hurricane example. The other roots have been set approximately equal to their maximum-likelihood values. A wider range of values of α_3 and α_4 is desirable, but the asymptotic formula breaks down as α_3 approaches α_2 and α_4 approaches α_5.

The formula shows that in the conditional distribution of a group of $m - r$ roots l_j, the influence of the other r roots l_i is approximately via linkage factors $((l_i - l_j)(\alpha_j - \alpha_i))^{-1/2}$.

A proof can be given for the case $m = 3$, $r = 1$.

10. DERIVATION OF THE COMBINED ASYMPTOTIC AND POWER-SERIES APPROXIMATION FOR $m = 3$

Theorem

$$
\begin{aligned}
&{}_0F_0(-\tfrac{1}{2}n(l_1, l_2, l_3); (\alpha_1, \alpha_2, \alpha_3)) \\
&\quad \equiv \int_{O(3)} \exp\left(-\tfrac{1}{2}n \sum_{i,j=1}^{3} l_i\alpha_j h_{ij}^2\right) (dH) \\
&\quad = \exp(-\tfrac{1}{2}nl_1\alpha_1)/(nC_{12}^{1/2}C_{13}^{1/2}) \exp(-\tfrac{1}{4}n(l_2 + l_3)(\alpha_2 + \alpha_3))I_0(\tfrac{1}{4}nC_{23}) \\
&\qquad \times \{1 + 1/(2nC_{12}) + 1/(2nC_{13}) + O(1/(nC_{12}C_{13})) + O(1/n^2)\} \qquad (10.1)
\end{aligned}
$$

when $l_1 \geq l_2 \geq l_3$, $\alpha_1 \leq \alpha_2 \leq \alpha_3$,

$$C_{ij} = (l_i - l_j)(\alpha_j - \alpha_i), \qquad r = (l_2 - l_3)(\alpha_2 - \alpha_1).$$

Proof. A little algebraic calculation will establish the identities

$$\sum_{i,j=1}^{3} l_i\alpha_j h_{ij}^2 = \sum_{i=1}^{3} l_i\alpha_i + \sum_{i<j}^{3} C_{ij}h_{ij}^2 - rd, \qquad (10.2)$$

$$h_{21}^2 - h_{12}^2 = h_{32}^2 - h_{23}^2 = h_{13}^2 - h_{31}^2 \overset{\text{def}}{=} d, \qquad (10.3)$$

and

$$C_{13} - C_{12} - C_{23} = r + C_{12}C_{23}/r. \qquad (10.4)$$

Equation (10.4) shows that r is an algebraic function of the C_{12}, C_{13}, C_{23}, given by the equation

$$r^2 - (C_{13} - C_{12} - C_{23})r + C_{12}C_{23} = 0.$$

Now

$$H = \begin{bmatrix} h_{11} & h_{12} & h_{13} \\ h_{21} & h_{22} & h_{23} \\ h_{31} & h_{32} & h_{33} \end{bmatrix} = \exp\begin{bmatrix} 0 & -s_3 & s_2 \\ s_3 & 0 & -s_1 \\ -s_2 & s_1 & 0 \end{bmatrix} = \exp(S)$$

$$= I_3 + (\sin\theta/\theta)S + ((1-\cos\theta)/\theta^2)S^2, \tag{10.5}$$

where $\theta^2 = s_1{}^2 + s_2{}^2 + s_3{}^2$. Hence

$$\begin{aligned} h_{12} &= -s_3(\sin\theta/\theta) + s_1 s_2((1-\cos\theta)/\theta^2) \\ h_{13} &= s_2(\sin\theta/\theta) + s_1 s_3((1-\cos\theta)/\theta^2) \\ h_{23} &= -s_1(\sin\theta/\theta) + s_2 s_3((1-\cos\theta)/\theta^2) \\ d &= 4 s_1 s_2 s_3(\sin\theta/\theta)((1-\cos\theta)/\theta^2) \end{aligned} \tag{10.6}$$

Since s_2 and s_3 are to be assumed small but s_1 not necessarily so, we expand in terms up to a certain degree in s_2 and s_3:

$$\begin{aligned} \theta &= (s_1{}^2 + s_2{}^2 + s_3{}^2)^{1/2} \\ &= s_1 + \tfrac{1}{2}(s_2{}^2 + s_3{}^2)/s_1 + \cdots \\ &= s_1 + \text{quadratic terms in } s_2 \text{ and } s_3, \end{aligned} \tag{10.7}$$

$$\left.\begin{aligned} h_{12} &= ((1-\cos s_1)/s_1)s_2 - (\sin s_1/s_1)s_3 \\ h_{13} &= (\sin s_1/s_1)s_2 + ((1-\cos s_1)/s_1)s_3 \end{aligned}\right\} \begin{aligned} &+ \text{cubic terms} \\ &\text{in } s_2 \text{ and } s_3, \end{aligned} \tag{10.8}$$
$$h_{23} = -\sin s_1 + \text{quadratic terms in } s_2 \text{ and } s_3.$$

Solving the approximate equations for s_2 and s_3, we have

$$\left.\begin{aligned} s_2 &= \tfrac{1}{2}s_1(h_{12} + (\sin s_1/(1-\cos s_1))h_{13}) \\ s_3 &= \tfrac{1}{2}s_1(-(\sin s_1/(1-\cos s_1))h_{12} + h_{13}) \end{aligned}\right\} \begin{aligned} &+ \text{cubic terms in} \\ &h_{13} \text{ and } h_{23}. \end{aligned} \tag{10.9}$$

$$\begin{aligned} d &= 4 s_1 s_2 s_3(\sin\theta/\theta)((1-\cos\theta)/\theta^2) \\ &= 4 s_2 s_3(\sin s_1)(1-\cos s_1)/s_1{}^2 + \text{quartic terms in } s_2 \text{ and } s_3 \\ &= \sin^2 s_1(h_{13}^2 - h_{12}^2) - 2\sin s_1 \cos s_1 h_{12}h_{13} \\ &\qquad\qquad + \text{quartic terms in } h_{13} \text{ and } h_{23} \\ &= h_{23}^2(h_{13}^2 - h_{12}^2) + 2h_{23}(1-h_{23}^2)^{1/2}h_{12}h_{13} \\ &\qquad\qquad + \text{quartic terms in } h_{13} \text{ and } h_{23}. \end{aligned} \tag{10.10}$$

The volume element of $O(3)$, normalized so that the integral will be 1 when taken over the matrices with positive diagonal elements, is

$$\begin{aligned} (dH) &= (1/(2\pi^2))\, dh_{12}\, dh_{13}\, dh_{23}/(h_{11}h_{33}) \\ &= (1/(2\pi^2))(1 + \tfrac{1}{2}h_{12}^2 + \tfrac{1}{2}h_{13}^2 + \cdots)(1 - h_{23}^2 - h_{13}^2)^{-1/2}\, dh_{12}\, dh_{13}\, dh_{23}. \end{aligned} \tag{10.11}$$

$$
\begin{aligned}
&{}_0F_0(-\tfrac{1}{2}n(l_1, l_2, l_3), (\alpha_1, \alpha_2, \alpha_3)) \\
&\quad = \int_{O(3)} \exp\left(-\tfrac{1}{2}n \sum_{i,j=1}^{3} l_i\alpha_j h_{ij}^2\right) (dH) \\
&\quad = \exp\left(-\tfrac{1}{2}n \sum_{i=1}^{3} l_i\alpha_i\right) \int_{O(3)} \exp\left(-\tfrac{1}{2}n\left(\sum_{i<j}^{3} C_{ij}h_{ij}^2 - rd\right)\right) (dH) \\
&\quad = \exp\left(-\tfrac{1}{2}n \sum_{i=1}^{3} l_i\alpha_i\right) (1/(2\pi^2)) \int \exp(-\tfrac{1}{2}n((C_{12} + rh_{23}^2)h_{12}^2 \\
&\quad\quad - 2rh_{23}(1 - h_{23}^2)^{1/2}h_{12}h_{13} + (C_{13} - rh_{23}^2)h_{13}^2)) \\
&\quad\quad \times \{1 + \tfrac{1}{2}h_{12}^2 + \tfrac{1}{2}h_{13}^2 + O(1/n^2)\} \\
&\quad\quad \times \exp(-\tfrac{1}{2}nC_{23}h_{23}^2)(1 - h_{23}^2 - h_{13}^2)^{-1/2}\, dh_{12}\, dh_{13}\, dh_{23}. \qquad (10.12)
\end{aligned}
$$

Put $h_{23} = u(1 - h_{13}^2)^{1/2}$. Then

$$(1 - h_{23}^2 - h_{13}^2)^{-1/2}\, dh_{13}\, dh_{23} = (1 - u^2)^{-1/2}\, du\, dh_{13}. \qquad (10.13)$$

Since terms in $h_{13}^2h_{12}^2$ will contribute at most $O(1/(nC_{12}C_{13}))$ to the integral they and higher terms will be omitted from the integral.

$$
\begin{aligned}
{}_0F_0 &= (1/(2\pi^2) \exp\left(-\tfrac{1}{2}n \sum_{i=1}^{3} l_i\alpha_i\right) \\
&\quad \times \int \exp(-\tfrac{1}{2}n((C_{12} + ru^2)h_{12}^2 - 2ru(1 - u^2)^{1/2}h_{12}h_{13} \\
&\quad + (C_{13} - (r + C_{23})u^2)h_{13}^2)) \\
&\quad \times \{1 + \tfrac{1}{2}h_{12}^2 + \tfrac{1}{2}h_{13}^2\}\, dh_{12}\, dh_{13} \\
&\quad \times \exp(-\tfrac{1}{2}nC_{23}u^2)(1 - u^2)^{-1/2}\, du. \qquad (10.14)
\end{aligned}
$$

As h_{12} and h_{13} are $O(n^{-1/2})$, the finite range of integration can be replaced by an infinite one with only small error. Hence

$$
\begin{aligned}
{}_0F_0 &= \exp\left(-\tfrac{1}{2}n \sum_{i=1}^{3} l_i\alpha_i\right) \\
&\quad \times (1/(n\pi)) \int \det\begin{bmatrix} C_{12} + ru^2 & -ru(1 - u^2)^{1/2} \\ -ru(1 - u^2)^{1/2} & C_{13} - (r + C_{23})u^2 \end{bmatrix}^{-1/2} \\
&\quad \times \exp(-\tfrac{1}{2}n(C_{23}u^2)(1 - u^2)^{-1/2}\, du \\
&\quad \times \{1 + 1/(2nC_{12}) + 1/(2nC_{13}) + O(n^{-2})\}. \qquad (10.15)
\end{aligned}
$$

Now

$$
\begin{aligned}
(\det)^{-1/2} &= (C_{12}C_{13} - ((C_{12} - C_{13})r + C_{12}C_{13} + r^2)u^2 - rC_{23}u^4)^{-1/2} \\
&= (C_{12}C_{13} + rC_{23}(u^2 - u^4))^{-1/2} \qquad \text{from (10.4)} \\
&= (C_{12}C_{13})^{-1/2}\{1 - (\tfrac{1}{2}rC_{23}/(C_{12}C_{13}))(u^2 - u^4)\} + \cdots \\
&= (C_{12}C_{13})^{-1/2}\{1 + O(1/(nC_{12}C_{13})\} \qquad (10.16)
\end{aligned}
$$

because

$$C_{23}\int \exp(-\tfrac{1}{2}nC_{23})u^2(u^2 - u^4)(1 - u^2)^{-1/2}\, du^2 = O(n^{-1}). \quad (10.17)$$

Hence, since

$$\pi^{-1}\int_{-1}^{1} \exp(-xu^2)(1 - u^2)^{-1/2}\, du = \exp(-\tfrac{1}{2}x)I_0(\tfrac{1}{2}x),$$

$$ {}_0F_0 = \exp\left(-\tfrac{1}{2}n\sum_{i=1}^{3} l_i\alpha_i\right)/(nC_{12}^{1/2}C_{13}^{1/2}) \times \exp(-\tfrac{1}{4}nC_{23})I_0(nC_{23}/4)$$

$$\times \{1 + 1/(2nC_{12}) + 1/(2nC_{13}) + O(n^{-2}) + O(1/(nC_{12}C_{13})\}, \quad (10.18)$$

which, when one substitutes for C_{23} in the exponential, yields the formula of the theorem.

11. INFLUENCE OF DISTANT ROOTS ON THE LIKELIHOOD OF THE RATIO OF ADJACENT ROOTS

The following approach is tentatively suggested. Suppose that the ratios of the root α_j to the adjacent roots α_i, α_{i+1} are both much less than 1 or both much greater than 1. From the combined formula (9.1), we see that the jth root influences the likelihood of the other two by a factor $((\alpha_i - \alpha_j)(\alpha_{i+1} - \alpha_j))^{-1/2}$. To obtain an approximation of the influence of the jth root on the likelihood of the ratio $\varphi = \alpha_{i+1}/\alpha_i$, we multiply by the average $\bar{\alpha} = \frac{1}{2}(\alpha_i + \alpha_{i+1})$, which we take as fixed. The result becomes

$$\tfrac{1}{2}(1 + \varphi)\varphi^{-1/2}(1 - \tau(2 - \tau)(\tfrac{1}{2}(1 + \varphi))^2/\varphi^{-1/2} \quad (11.1)$$

when $\tau = \alpha_j/\bar{\alpha}$.

Multiplying the likelihood factor for two roots of (6.1), we draw the following conclusions. The influence of earlier roots, $j < i$, $\tau \ll 1$, is approximately the loss of one degree of freedom. The influence of later roots, $j > i + 1$, $\tau \gg 1$, is negligible. If τ is closer to 1, the correction (11.1) may be used.

12. NUMERICAL EXAMPLE

Seal [23] quotes Jolicoeur and Mosimann [17] on the length, width, and height in millimeters of the carapaces of 24 male and 24 female specimens of *Chrysemys picta marginata*. The latent roots of the covariance matrix were as follows:

	l_1	l_2	l_3	$\chi_2^{\ 2}$	P_r	Log likelihood ratio
Male	195.28	3.69	1.10	7.236	.027	1.8
Female	680.40	6.50	2.86	3.444	.179	0.3

Tables VII and VIII show the log likelihoods of the last two roots.

TABLE VII

Log Likelihood of 2nd- and 3rd-Root Reciprocals α_2 and α_3 of Principal Components of Chrysemys picta marginata (*Males*)

α_3 \ α_2		.21153		.25577		.30000		.34423		.38847	
.21023	−10.94										
.26921	−9.55	−9.10	−8.72	−8.40							
.32819	−8.46	−8.08	−7.80	−7.59	−7.42	−7.28	−7.15				
.38716	−7.60	−7.26	−7.03	−6.88	−6.79	−6.75	−6.74	−6.75	−6.75		
.44614	−6.94	−6.62	−6.41	−6.29	−6.25	−6.26	−6.32	−6.41	−6.52	−6.63	−6.74
.50512	−6.44	−6.13	−5.93	−5.83	−5.81	−5.85	−5.94	−6.07	−6.24	−6.43	−6.63
.56409	−6.07	−5.77	−5.58	−5.49	−5.47	−5.53	−5.63	−5.79	−5.98	−6.21	−6.46
.62307	−5.81	−5.51	−5.33	−5.24	−5.23	−5.29	−5.41	−5.58	−5.79	−6.03	−6.31
.68205	−5.64	−5.34	−5.16	−5.08	−5.07	−5.14	−5.27	−5.44	−5.66	−5.91	−6.20
.74102	−5.54	−5.24	−5.06	−4.98	−4.99	−5.06	−5.19	−5.37	−5.59	−5.85	−6.15
.80000	−5.50	−5.20	−5.03	−4.95	−4.96	−5.03	−5.17	−5.35	−5.58	−5.85	−6.15
.85898	−5.52	−5.22	−5.05	−4.98	−4.99	−5.06	−5.20	−5.39	−5.62	−5.89	−6.19
.91795	−5.58	−5.29	−5.12	−5.05	−5.06	−5.14	−5.28	−5.46	−5.70	−5.97	−6.28
.97693	−5.69	−5.40	−5.23	−5.16	−5.17	−5.25	−5.39	−5.58	−5.82	−6.09	−6.40
.03591	−5.84	−5.55	−5.38	−5.31	−5.32	−5.40	−5.54	−5.74	−5.97	−6.25	−6.56
.09488	−6.01	−5.73	−5.56	−5.49	−5.50	−5.59	−5.73	−5.92	−6.16	−6.44	−6.75
.15386	− .22	−5.94	−5.77	−5.70	−5.72	−5.80	−5.94	−6.14	−6.38	−6.66	−6.97
.21284	−6.46	−6.17	−6.01	−5.94	−5.95	−6.04	−6.18	−6.38	−6.62	−6.90	−7.21
.27181	−6.72	−6.43	−6.27	−6.20	−6.21	−6.30	−6.45	−6.64	−6.88	−7.16	−7.48
.33079	−7.00	−6.71	−6.55	−6.48	−6.50	−6.58	−6.73	−6.93	−7.17	−7.45	−7.77
.38977	−7.30	−7.01	−6.85	−6.79	−6.80	−6.89	−7.04	−7.23	−7.48	−7.76	−8.08

TABLE VIII

Log Likelihood of 2nd- and 3rd-Root Reciprocals α_2 and α_3 of Principal Components of Chrysemys picta marginata *(Females)*

α_3 \ α_1	.14102		.17051		.20000		.22949		.25898		
.07884											
.10095											
.12307											
.14519	−6.02										
.16730	−5.58	−5.34									
.18942	−5.24	−5.06	−4.94	−4.86							
.21153	−4.97	−4.84	−4.78	−4.76	−4.78						
.23365	−4.77	−4.68	−4.66	−4.69	−4.77	−4.86	−4.96				
.25577	−4.63	−4.56	−4.57	−4.65	−4.77	−4.92	−5.08	−5.25			
.27788	−4.55	−4.50	−4.53	−4.63	−4.78	−4.98	−5.19	−5.42	−5.65	−5.88	
.30000	−4.52	−4.48	−4.52	−4.64	−4.82	−5.04	−5.30	−5.58	−5.87	−6.15	−6.43
.32212	−4.54	−4.50	−4.56	−4.69	−4.88	−5.13	−5.41	−5.72	−6.05	−6.39	−6.73
.34423	−4.60	−4.57	−4.63	−4.77	−4.98	−5.23	−5.54	−5.87	−6.23	−6.61	−7.00
.36635	−4.70	−4.67	−4.74	−4.89	−5.10	−5.37	−5.68	−6.03	−6.41	−6.82	−7.24
.38847	−4.83	−4.81	−4.88	−5.03	−5.25	−5.53	−5.85	−6.21	−6.61	−7.03	−7.47
.41058	−4.99	−4.97	−5.05	−5.21	−5.43	−5.71	−6.04	−6.41	−6.82	−7.25	−7.71
.43270	−5.19	−5.17	−5.25	−5.41	−5.63	−5.92	−6.25	−6.63	−7.04	−7.49	−7.96
.45481	−5.40	−5.39	−5.47	−5.63	−5.86	−6.15	−6.49	−6.87	−7.29	−7.74	−8.22
.47693	−5.64	−5.63	−5.71	−5.88	−6.11	−6.40	−6.74	−7.13	−7.55	−8.01	−8.49
.49905	−5.91	−5.89	−5.98	−6.15	−6.38	−6.67	−7.02	−7.40	−7.83	−8.29	−8.78
.52116	−6.19	−6.18	−6.26	−6.43	−6.67	−6.96	−7.31	−7.70	−8.13	−8.59	−9.08

For reasons of space the log likelihoods are only given to two decimal places, but (10.1), from which they are calculated, would be accurate to at least three decimals, because the n^{-1} terms of the asymptotic series add to less than .001. Inclusion of these terms would increase the accuracy, perhaps by another two or three decimal places. But even without them the log likelihood is accurate enough in this case for ordinary inference purposes. Applying the Mauchly [20], Bartlett [5], and Lawley [18] test for equality of the last two roots, Seal obtained values of χ^2 on two degrees of freedom of 7.263 for males and 3.444 for females. The probabilities of exceeding them are .0265 and .1785, respectively. From Tables VII and VIII one sees that the log marginal likelihood ratios differ only by 1.8 and .3. If the log marginal likelihoods were distributed as $\frac{1}{2}\chi^2$ on 1 d.f., the probabilities would be .057 and .438. From the discrepancy, one can conclude that the log marginal likelihood ratios are nowhere nearly distributed as $\frac{1}{2}\chi^2$ on 1 d.f. in this case. The Mauchley-Bartlett-Lawley probabilities will be accurate, because for the case $m = 2$ we have seen at the end of Section 6 that they are exact, and the first root is too far removed to have much influence.

Acknowledgments

The author is indebted to the Atlas Computing Laboratory, Chilton, U.K., for time and facilities to compute the zonal polynomials listed in Table I, and to Lois Frampton of the Yale Computer Center for calculation of the latent roots in Table V. The likelihoods in Tables II to VIII were calculated on the IBM 7094 at Yale University.

REFERENCES

1. Anderson, G. A. (1965). An asymptotic expansion for the distribution of the latent roots of the estimated covariance matrix. *Ann. Math. Statist.* **36** 1153–1173.
2. Anderson, T. W. (1946). The noncentral Wishart distribution and certain problems of multivariate statistics. *Ann. Math. Statist.* **17** 409–431.
3. Barnard, G. A. (1963). Some logical aspects of the fiducial argument. *J. Roy. Statist. Soc. Ser. B* **25** 111–114.
4. Bartlett, M. S. (1947). The general canonical correlation distribution. *Ann. Math. Statist.* **18** 1–17.
5. Bartlett, M. S. (1951). The effect of standardization on a χ^2 approximation in factor analysis. *Biometrika* **3** 337–344.
6. Constantine, A. G. (1963). Some noncentral distribution problems in multivariate analysis. *Ann. Math. Statist.* **34** 1270–1285.
7. Erdélyi, A., Magnus, W., Oberhettinger, F., and Tricomi, F. G. (1953). *Higher Transcendental Functions*, Vol. II. McGraw-Hill, New York.
8. Fisher, R. A. (1939). The sampling distribution of some statistics obtained from non-linear equations. *Ann. Eugenics* **9** 238–249.
9. Fisher, R. A. (1958). *Statistical Methods for Research Workers.* Oliver & Boyd, Edinburgh and London. 13th ed.
10. Fraser, D. A. S. (1961). Invariance and the fiducial method. *Biometrika* **48** 261–280.
11. Geiser, S. (1965). Bayesian estimation in multivariate analysis. *Ann. Math. Statist.* **36** 150–159.

12. Girshick, M. A. (1939). Roots of determinantal equations. *Ann. Math. Statist.* **10** 203–224.
13. Girshick, M. A. (1941). The distribution of the ellipticity statistic L_e when the hypothesis is false. *Terrestrial Magnetism and Atmospheric Electricity* **46** 455–457.
14. James, A. T. (1961). Zonal polynomials of the real positive definite symmetric matrices. *Ann. Math.* **74** 456–469.
15. James, A. T. (1964). Distributions of matrix variates and latent roots derived from normal samples. *Ann. Math. Statist.* **35** 475–501.
16. James, A. T. and Parkhurst, A. Real zonal polynomials of orders 7 through 11. To be submitted to *Ann. Math. Statist.*
17. Jolicoeur, P. and Mosimann, J. E. (1960). Size and shape variation in the painted turtle. A principal component analysis. *Growth* **24** 339–354.
18. Lawley, D. N. (1956). Test of significance for the latent roots of covariance and correlation matrices. *Biometrika* **43** 128–136.
19. Mauchly, J. W. (1940). A significance test for ellipticity in the harmonic dial. *Terrestrial Magnetism and Atmospheric Electricity* **45** 145–148.
20. Mauchly, J. W. (1940). Significance test for sphericity of a normal n-variate distribution. *Ann. Math. Statist.* **11** 204–209.
21. Roy, S. N. (1939). p-Statistics, or some generalisations in analysis of variance appropriate to multivariate problems. *Sankhyā* **4** 381–396.
22. Roy, S. N. (1942). The sampling distribution of p-statistics and certain statistics on the nonnull hypothesis. *Sankhyā* **61** 15–34.
23. Seal, H. (1964). *Multivariate Statistical Analysis for Biologists.* Methuen, London.

Noncentral Multivariate Beta Distribution and the Moments of Traces of Some Matrices

K. C. SREEDHARAN PILLAI
DEPARTMENT OF STATISTICS
PURDUE UNIVERSITY
LAFAYETTE, INDIANA

1. INTRODUCTION AND SUMMARY

Let A_1 and A_2 be two positive definite symmetric matrices of order p, A_1 having a Wishart distribution [2 and 15] with f_1 degrees of freedom and A_2 having an independent noncentral Wishart distribution with f_2 degrees of freedom, corresponding to the linear case [1 and 3]. Now let

$$A_1 = CLC',$$

where C is a lower triangular matrix such that

$$A_1 + A_2 = CC'.$$

It has been shown [6] that the density function of L is given by

$$f(L) = K \exp(-\lambda^2/2)\,{}_1F_1\{\tfrac{1}{2}(f_1 + f_2), \tfrac{1}{2}f_2, \tfrac{1}{2}\lambda^2(1 - l_{11})\}|L|^{(f_1-p-1)/2}|I - L|^{(f_2-p-1)/2}, \quad (1.1)$$

where

$$K = \pi^{-p(p-1)/4} \prod_{i=1}^{p} \Gamma[\tfrac{1}{2}(f_1 + f_2 + 1 - i)]/\{\Gamma[\tfrac{1}{2}(f_1 + 1 - i)]\Gamma[\tfrac{1}{2}(f_2 + 1 - i)]\},$$

λ^2 is the single noncentrality parameter in the linear case, l_{11} is the element in the top left corner of the L matrix, and ${}_1F_1$ denotes the confluent hypergeometric function.

In this paper the density function of L given by (1.1) has been observed to be a product of density functions of $p(p + 1)/2$ independent beta variables, explicit expressions for these variables being given for $p = 2$, 3, 4, and 5. In view of the independence of the beta variables, it has been shown how the moments of the trace of L (say $W^{(p)}$) and of $I - L$ (say $V^{(p)}$, which is actually Pillai's $V^{(s)}$ criterion with $s = p$ [8]) can be computed from those of the beta variables. Again, if we denote the characteristic roots of $I - L$ by θ_i ($i = 1, 2, \dots, p$), a method has been given for computing the moments of $U^{(2)} = \sum_{i=1}^{2}[\theta_i/(1-\theta_i)] = \sum_{i=1}^{2}\lambda_i$ (a constant times Hotelling's $T_0{}^2$, $s = 2$), [8], also from those of the independent beta variables. The case of $p = 2$ has been considered in detail, deriving the first four moments of $W^{(2)}$, $V^{(2)}$, and $U^{(2)}$ and suggesting approximate distributions for them.

In addition, for tests of the hypothesis $H_0: \lambda = 0$ against $H_1: \lambda > 0$ based on the three criteria $V^{(2)}$, $U^{(2)}$, and Wilks' criterion, $\Lambda = \prod_{i=1}^{2}(1-\theta_i)$, [16], comparison of power functions has been carried out for different values of f_1 and f_2 using the moments of these criteria. Further, such comparison has been extended to include also Roy's largest root criterion in testing the hypothesis H_0: $\rho = 0$ against $H_1: \rho > 0$, where ρ is the single nonnull population canonical correlation coefficient.

2. INDEPENDENT BETA VARIABLES

Let

$$L = TT'$$

where T is a lower triangular matrix $[t_{ij}]$. It has been shown [6] that then the diagonal elements t_{ii} are independently distributed and that t_{ii}^2 ($i = 2, 3, \dots, p$) follows the distribution

$$f_i(t_{ii}^2) = (t_{ii}^2)^{\frac{1}{2}(f_1+1-i)-1}(1-t_{ii}^2)^{\frac{1}{2}f_2-1}/\beta\{\tfrac{1}{2}(f_1+1-i), \tfrac{1}{2}f_2\} \qquad (0 \le t_{ii}^2 \le 1), \tag{2.1}$$

while t_{11}^2 is distributed as

$$f_1(t_{11}^2) = \frac{\exp(-\lambda^2/2)(t_{11}^2)^{\frac{1}{2}f_1-1}(1-t_{11}^2)^{\frac{1}{2}f_2-1}{}_1F_1\{\frac{1}{2}(f_1+f_2), \frac{1}{2}f_2, \frac{1}{2}\lambda^2(1-t_{11}^2)\}}{\beta(\frac{1}{2}f_1, \frac{1}{2}f_2)} \qquad (0 \le t_{11}^2 \le 1). \tag{2.2}$$

(a) $p = 2$. Now, if $p=2$, it can be shown that

$$f(l_{11}, l_{22}, l_{21}) = f_1(u_{11})f_2(u_{22})f_{21}(u_{21}), \tag{2.3}$$

where

$$u_{11} = t_{11}^2,\ u_{22} = t_{22}^2, \qquad \text{and} \qquad u_{21} = t_{21}^2/\{(1-t_{11}^2)(1-t_{22}^2)\}, \tag{2.4}$$

$f_1(u_{11})$ is given by (2.2), $f_2(u_{22})$ by (2.1) with $i = 2$, and

$$f_{21}(u_{21}) = u_{21}^{\frac{1}{2}-1}(1-u_{21})^{\frac{1}{2}(f_2-1)-1}/\beta\{\tfrac{1}{2}, \tfrac{1}{2}(f_2-1)\}, \qquad (0 \le u_{21} \le 1). \tag{2.5}$$

Thus from (2.3) it may be seen that u_{11}, u_{22}, and u_{21} are independently distributed.

(b) $p = 3$. When $p = 3$, it can be shown that

$$f(l_{11}, l_{22}, l_{33}, l_{21}, l_{32}, l_{31}) = f_1(u_{11}) f_2(u_{22}) f_3(u_{33}) f_{21}(u_{21}) f_{21}(u_{32}) f_{31}(v_{31}), \tag{2.6}$$

where u's are defined in a similar manner as in (2.4), v_{31} is defined by

$$v_{31} = [(u_{31})^{1/2} + (u_{21}u_{32}u_{22})^{1/2}]^2/[(1 - u_{21})(1 - u_{32})], \tag{2.7}$$

$f_1(u_{11})$ follows (2.2), $f_i(u_{ii})$ ($i = 2, 3$) is given in (2.1), $f_{21}(u_{21})$ and $f_{21}(u_{32})$ both follow the form as in (2.5), and $f_{31}(v_{31})$ is given by

$$f_{31}(v_{31}) = v_{31}^{\frac{1}{2}-1}(1 - v_{31})^{\frac{1}{2}(f_2-2)-1}/\beta\{\tfrac{1}{2}, \tfrac{1}{2}(f_2 - 2)\}, \qquad (0 \le v_{31} \le 1). \tag{2.8}$$

(c) $p = 4$. Now, if $p = 4$,

$$f(L) = \left[\prod_{i=1}^{4} f_i(u_{ii})\right] f_{21}(u_{21}) f_{21}(u_{32}) f_{21}(u_{43}) f_{31}(v_{31}) f_{31}(v_{42}) f_{41}(w_{41}),$$

where u's are similarly defined as before, v_{31} is given in (2.7), v_{42} is given by

$$v_{42} = [(u_{42})^{1/2} + (u_{43}u_{32}u_{33})^{1/2}]^2/[(1 - u_{32})(1 - u_{43})], \tag{2.9}$$

$$w_{41} = [(v_{41})^{1/2} + (v_{31}z_{42})^{1/2}]^2/[(1 - v_{31})(1 - v_{42})], \tag{2.10}$$

where

$$v_{41} = [(u_{41})^{1/2} + (u_{42}u_{21}u_{22})^{1/2}]^2/[(1 - u_{21})(1 - u_{43})], \tag{2.11}$$

$$z_{42} = [(u_{42}u_{32})^{1/2} + (u_{43}u_{33})^{1/2}]^2/[(1 - u_{32})(1 - u_{43})], \tag{2.12}$$

and where $f_1(u_{11})$ as before is given by (2.2), $f_i(u_{ii})$ ($i = 2, 3, 4$) by (2.1), $f_{21}(u_{21})$, $f_{21}(u_{32})$ and $f_{21}(u_{43})$ follow the form (2.5), $f_{31}(v_{31})$ and $f_{31}(v_{42})$ follow the form (2.8), and

$$f_{41}(w_{41}) = w_{41}^{\frac{1}{2}-1}(1 - w_{41})^{\frac{1}{2}(f_2-3)-1}/\beta(\tfrac{1}{2}, \tfrac{1}{2}(f_2 - 3)), \qquad (0 \le w_{41} \le 1). \tag{2.13}$$

(d) $p = 5$. When $p = 5$,

$$(L) = \left[\prod_{i=1}^{5} f_i(u_{ii})\right]\left[\prod_{i=1}^{4} f_{21}(u_{i+1,i})\right]\left[\prod_{i=1}^{3} f_{31}(v_{i+2,i})\right]\left[\prod_{i=1}^{2} f_{41}(w_{i+3,i})\right] f_{51}(x_{51}), \tag{2.14}$$

where u's are defined as before, v_{31} and v_{42} are given by (2.7) and (2.9) , respectively, v_{53} is given by

$$v_{53} = [(u_{53})^{1/2} + (u_{43}u_{54}u_{44})^{1/2}]^2/[(1 - u_{43})(1 - u_{54})] \tag{2.15}$$

w_{41} is defined in (2.10), w_{52} is given by

$$w_{52} = [(v_{52})^{1/2} + (v_{42}z_{53})^{1/2}]^2/(1 - v_{42})(1 - v_{53}) \tag{2.16}$$

where

$$v_{52} = [(u_{52})^{1/2} + (u_{32}u_{53}u_{33})^{1/2}]^2/[(1 - u_{32})(1 - u_{54})] \tag{2.17}$$

$$z_{53} = [(u_{53}u_{43})^{1/2} + (u_{54}u_{44})^{1/2}]^2/[(1 - u_{43})(1 - u_{54})], \tag{2.18}$$

and where x_{51} is given by

$$x_{51} = \{[(v_{51})^{1/2} + (v_{31}z_{52})^{1/2}](1 - v_{42}) + [(v_{41})^{1/2} + (v_{31}z_{42})^{1/2}] \times [(v_{42}v_{52})^{1/2} + (z_{53})^{1/2}]\}^2/(1 - v_{31})(1 - v_{42})^2(1 - v_{53})(1 - w_{41})(1 - w_{52}) \tag{2.19}$$

and where

$$v_{51} = [(u_{51})^{1/2} + (u_{21}u_{52}u_{22})^{1/2}]^2/[(1 - u_{21})(1 - u_{54})], \tag{2.20}$$

and

$$z_{52} = [(u_{52}u_{32})^{1/2} + (u_{53}u_{33})^{1/2}]^2/[(1 - u_{32})(1 - u_{54})]. \tag{2.21}$$

Here again $f_1(u_{11})$ is given by (2.2), $f_i(u_{ii})(i = 2, 3, 4, 5)$ is given by (2.1), $f_{21}(u_{21}), f_{21}(u_{32}), f_{21}(u_{43})$, and $f_{21}(u_{54})$ follow the form (2.5), $f_{31}(v_{31}), f_{31}(v_{42})$, and $f_{31}(v_{53})$ follow the form (2.8), $f_{41}(w_{41})$ and $f_{41}(w_{52})$ follow the form (2.13), and $f_{51}(x_{51})$ is given by

$$f_{51}(x_{51}) = x_{51}^{\frac{1}{2}-1}(1 - x_{51})^{\frac{1}{2}(f_2 - 4) - 1}/\beta(\tfrac{1}{2}, \tfrac{1}{2}(f_2 - 4)), \qquad (0 \le x_{51} \le 1). \tag{2.22}$$

(e) *General case* (p). In this subsection, for convenience, let us relabel $u_{i+1,i}$ as $u^{(2)}_{i+1,i}$, $i = 1, 2, \ldots, p - 1$; $v_{i+2,i}$ as $u^{(3)}_{i+2,i}$, $i = 1, \ldots, p - 2$; $w_{i+3,i}$ as $u^{(4)}_{i+3,i}$, $i = 1, \ldots, p - 3$; $x_{i+4,i}$, as $u^{(5)}_{i+4,i}$, $i = 1, \ldots, p - 4$; etc. Now from (2.4),

$$1 - u^{(2)}_{21} = |I - L|(p = 2)/[(1 - u_{11})(1 - u_{22})], \tag{2.23}$$

where $L = TT'$. Further, $u^{(2)}_{32}$ is obtained from $u^{(2)}_{21}$ by simultaneously adding unity to both suffixes of each of the t's involved in $u^{(2)}_{21}$, which is reflected in the notation 32, which replaces 21. Similarly, $u^{(2)}_{43}$ is obtained from $u^{(2)}_{32}$, $u^{(2)}_{54}$ from $u^{(2)}_{43}$, etc. Again,

$$1 - u^{(3)}_{31} = \frac{|I - L|(p = 3)}{(1 - u_{11})(1 - u_{22})(1 - u_{33})(1 - u^{(2)}_{21})(1 - u^{(2)}_{32})}. \tag{2.24}$$

Further, $u^{(3)}_{42}$ is obtained from $u^{(3)}_{31}$ by increasing both suffixes in each of the t's in $u^{(3)}_{31}$ by unity, as before. Similarly $u^{(3)}_{53}$ is obtained from $u^{(3)}_{42}$, etc. Following this pattern, it is easy to see that

$$1 - u^{(p)}_{p1} = \frac{|I - L|}{\prod_{i=1}^{p}(1 - u_{ii})\prod_{i=1}^{p-1}(1 - u^{(2)}_{i+1,i})\prod_{i=1}^{p-2}(1 - u^{(3)}_{i+2,i})\cdots\prod_{i=1}^{2}(1 - u^{(p-1)}_{i+p-2,i})}. \tag{2.25}$$

Hence it may be seen that in the case of p variables,[1]

$$f(L)=\left[\prod_{i=1}^{p} f_i(u_{ii})\right]\left[\prod_{i=1}^{p-1} f_{21}(u_{i+1,i}^{(2)})\right]$$
$$\times\left[\prod_{i=1}^{p-2} f_{31}(u_{i+2,i}^{(3)})\right]\cdots\left[\prod_{i=1}^{2} f_{p-1,1}(u_{i+p-2,i}^{(p-1)})\right]f_{p1}(u_{p1}^{(p)}), \quad (2.26)$$

where

$$f_{j1}(u_{i+j-1,i}^{(j)})=(u_{i+j-1,i}^{(j)})^{\frac{1}{2}-1}(1-u_{i+j-1,i}^{(j)})^{\frac{1}{2}(f_2-j+1)-1}/\beta(\tfrac{1}{2},\tfrac{1}{2}(f_2-j+1)),$$
$$(0\le u_{i+j-1,i}^{(j)}\le 1,\quad j=2,3,\ldots,p). \quad (2.27)$$

Further, it may be noted that K in (1.1) equals

$$\prod_{i=1}^{p}\beta(\tfrac{1}{2}(f_1+1-i),\tfrac{1}{2}(f_2))[\beta(\tfrac{1}{2},\tfrac{1}{2}(f_2-i))]^{p-i}. \quad (2.28)$$

3. TRACES OF SOME MATRICES AS FUNCTIONS OF INDEPENDENT BETA VARIABLES

First, consider the trace of L when $p=2$. Noting that

$$l_{11}+l_{22}=t_{11}^2+t_{22}^2+t_{21}^2 \quad (3.1)$$

and using (2.4) we get

$$W^{(2)}=l_{11}+l_{22}=u_{11}+u_{22}+u_{21}(1-u_{11})(1-u_{22}). \quad (3.2)$$

Similarly,

$$V^{(2)}=2-W^{(2)}=(1-u_{11})+(1-u_{22})-u_{21}(1-u_{11})(1-u_{22}). \quad (3.3)$$

When $p=3$,

$$W^{(3)}=u_{11}+u_{22}+u_{33}+u_{21}(1-u_{11})(1-u_{22})+u_{32}(1-u_{22})(1-u_{33})$$
$$+(1-u_{11})(1-u_{33})\{v_{31}(1-u_{21})(1-u_{32})+u_{21}u_{22}u_{32}$$
$$-2[v_{31}(1-u_{21})(1-u_{32})u_{21}u_{22}u_{32}]^{1/2}\} \quad (3.4)$$

and $V^{(3)}=3-W^{(3)}$.

Similarly, $W^{(4)}$, $V^{(4)}$, and $W^{(5)}$ and $V^{(5)}$ can be expressed explicitly as functions of independent beta variables.

Now consider $U^{(2)}=\sum_{i=1}^{2}\lambda_i$. It may be seen that

$$U^{(2)}=\sum_{i=1}^{2}[\theta_i/(1-\theta_i)]=\{[(1-\theta_1)+(1-\theta_2)]/[(1-\theta_1)(1-\theta_2)]\}-2. \quad (3.5)$$

[1] Since this paper was written, a theorem was proved to establish this. [See KHATRI, C. G. and PILLAI, K. C. S. (1965). Some results on the noncentral multivariate beta distribution and moments of traces of two matrices. *Ann. Math. Statist.* **36** 1511–1520.]

Noting that $(1-\theta_1)+(1-\theta_2)=W^{(2)}$ and $(1-\theta_1)(1-\theta_2)=u_{11}u_{22}$, we get

$$U^{(2)} = \frac{1-u_{11}}{u_{11}} + \frac{1-u_{22}}{u_{22}} + \frac{u_{21}(1-u_{11})(1-u_{22})}{u_{11}u_{22}}. \tag{3.6}$$

4. MOMENTS OF $W^{(2)}$, $V^{(2)}$, AND $U^{(2)}$

The first four moments of $W^{(2)}$ will be given by

$$\mu_1'(W^{(2)}) = \{2f_1 \exp(-\lambda^2/2)/(v-1)\} \sum_{i=0}^{\infty} a_i(\tfrac{1}{2}\lambda^2)^i/i!, \tag{4.1}$$

where

$$a_i = (v+i-1)/g_i, \qquad v=(f_1+f_2) \quad \text{and} \quad g_i = v+2i. \tag{4.2}$$

$$\mu_2'(W^{(2)}) = \{4f_1 \exp(-\lambda^2/2)/(v^2-1)\} \sum_{i=0}^{\infty} b_i(\tfrac{1}{2}\lambda^2)^i/i!, \tag{4.3}$$

where

$$b_i = \{f_1 v^2 + 2(i+1)f_1{}^2 + (i^2+3i-1)f_1 + (2i+3)f_1f_2 + f_2{}^2 + (2i-1)f_2 + 2(i^2-1)\}/e_0, \tag{4.4}$$

where $e_0 = g_i(g_i+2)$.

$$\mu_3'(W^{(2)}) = [8f_1 \exp(-\lambda^2/2)/\{(v^2-1)(v+3)\}] \sum_{i=0}^{\infty} c_i(\tfrac{1}{2}\lambda^2)^i/i!, \tag{4.5}$$

where

$$\begin{aligned} c_i &= e_1/e_2, \\ e_1 &= f_1{}^2v^3 + (3i+9)f_1{}^4 + (6i+21)f_1{}^3f_2 + (3i+15)f_1{}^2f_2{}^2 \\ &\quad + (3i^2+21i+25)f_1{}^3 + (3i^2+30i+41)f_1{}^2f_2 \\ &\quad + (i^3+18i^2+44i+15)f_1{}^2 + (9i+18)f_1f_2{}^2 \\ &\quad + 3f_1f_2{}^3 + 2f_2{}^3 + (12i^2+39i+9)f_1f_2 + 6if_2{}^2 \\ &\quad + (6i^3+30i^2+18i-26)f_1 + (12i^2+6i-26)f_2 \\ &\quad + 8i^3 + 12i^2 - 20i - 24, \end{aligned} \tag{4.6}$$

and

$$e_2 = g_i(g_i+2)(g_i+4).$$

$$\mu_4'(W^{(2)}) = [f_1 \exp(-\lambda^2/2)/\{(v^2-1)(v+3)(v+5)\}] \sum_{i=0}^{\infty} d_i(\tfrac{1}{2}\lambda^2)^i/i!, \tag{4.7}$$

where

$$d_i = e_3/e_4, \tag{4.8}$$

$$e_3 = (v+5)[(f_1+2)(f_1+4)(v+1)(v+3)(vf_1+4f_1g_i+23f_1+6v-4g_i-30)$$
$$+4(f_1+2)(v+3)h_i(f_1v+3f_1g_i+19f_1+4v-3g_i-14)$$
$$+2(f_1^2-1)(g_i+4)(g_i+6)(2f_1g_i+3f_1v+13f_1+6v+6g_i+30)$$
$$+12(f_1-1)(g_i+6)h_i(f_1g_i+4f_1+g_i+3h_i+10)$$
$$+6h_i(h_i+2)(3f_1v+9f_1+6v+10h_i+58)]$$
$$+(g_i+5)[(f_1-1)(g_i+6)\{(f_1(g_i+5)+h_i+4)(f_1(g_i+5)$$
$$+12h_i+6)+45h_i(h_i+2)\}+105h_i(h_i+2)(h_i+4)],$$

$$e_4 = g_i(g_i+2)(g_i+4)(g_i+6),$$

and

$$h_i = f_2 + 2i.$$

It may be observed that the moments of $V^{(2)}$ can be obtained from those of $W^{(2)}$ using the relation $V^{(2)} = 2 - W^{(2)}$, which is given in terms of the u's in (3.3).

Now consider the moments of $U^{(2)}$. From (3.6),

$$U^{(2)} = z_1 + z_2 + z_1z_2u_{21}, \tag{4.9}$$

where $z_1 = (1-u_{11})/u_{11}$ and $z_2 = (1-u_{22})/u_{22}$. From (2.2) we get

$$f(z_1)$$
$$= \exp(-\lambda^2/2)z_1^{\frac{1}{2}f_2-1}{}_1F_1\{\tfrac{1}{2}v, \tfrac{1}{2}f_2, (\tfrac{1}{2}\lambda^2 z_1/(1+z_1))\}/\{(1+z_1)^{v/2}\beta(\tfrac{1}{2}f_2, \tfrac{1}{2}f_1)\}. \tag{4.10}$$

Similarly, from (2.1),

$$f(z_2) = z_2^{\frac{1}{2}f_2-1}/\{(1+z_2)^{\frac{1}{2}(v-1)}\beta(\tfrac{1}{2}f_2, \tfrac{1}{2}(f_1-1)\}. \tag{4.11}$$

Now using (4.10), (4.11), and (2.5) we obtain the first four moments of $U^{(2)}$ as follows:

$$\mu_1'(U^{(2)}) = \{2\exp(-\lambda^2/2)/(f_1-3)\}\sum_{i=0}^{\infty}(f_2+i)(\tfrac{1}{2}\lambda^2)^i/i!$$
$$= (2f_2+\lambda^2)/(f_1-3). \tag{4.12}$$

Similarly,

$$\mu_2'(U^{(2)}) = [\lambda^4(f_1-2)+4(\lambda^2+f_2)(f_1+f_2(f_1-3)-1)]$$
$$\times[(f_1-2)(f_1-3)(f_1-5)], \tag{4.13}$$

$$\mu_3'(U^{(2)}) = [\lambda^6(f_1-2) + 3\lambda^4\{(f_1-2)(f_2+4) + f_2(f_1-6)+4\} + (3\lambda^2+2f_2)(f_2+2)\{(f_1-2)(f_2+4) + 3(f_2(f_1-6)+4)\}]/[(f_1-2)(f_1-3)(f_1-5)(f_1-7)], \qquad (4.14)$$

and

$$\mu_4'(U^{(2)}) = [\lambda^8 b + \lambda^6\{(12+s_1)b+4B\} + \lambda^4 \times\{(28+6s_1+s_2)b + 12(f_2+4)B + 6A\} + \lambda^2\{(8+4s_1+2s_2+s_3)b + 16(f_2+2)(f_2+4)B + 12(f_2+2)A\} + 2f_2(f_2+2)\{(f_2+4)(f_2+6)b + 4(f_2+4)B + 3A\}]/[(f_1-2)(f_1-3) \times (f_1-4)(f_1-5)(f_1-7)(f_1-9)], \qquad (4.15)$$

where s_i is the ith ($i = 1, 2, 3$) elementary symmetric function in the arguments f_2, f_2+2, f_2+4, and f_2+6,

$$A = f_2^2(f_1-6)(f_1-8) + 2f_2(f_1-4)(f_1-6) + 16f_1 - 72,$$
$$B = (f_1-4)(f_2(f_1-8)+6) \qquad \text{and} \qquad b = (f_1-2)(f_1-4).$$

It may be observed that when $\lambda = 0$, the moments given in this section reduce to those obtained by Pillai [8–11].

5. APPROXIMATIONS TO THE DISTRIBUTIONS OF $W^{(2)}$, $V^{(2)}$, AND $U^{(2)}$

On the basis of the moments presented in the preceding section, the following approximation to the distribution of $W^{(2)}$ is suggested for small values of λ:

$$g_1(W^{(2)}) = (W^{(2)})^{p_1-1}(1-W^{(2)}/2)^{q_1-1}/[2^{p_1}\beta(p_1, q_1)] \qquad (0 < W^{(2)} < 2), \qquad (5.1)$$

where

$$p_1 = [(2K_1 - K_2)K_1]/[2(K_2 - K_1^2)],$$
$$q_1 = [(2-K_1)(2K_1-K_2)]/[2(K_2-K_1^2)],$$

where

$$K_1 = 2f_1\{1 - (\lambda^2/2)/(v+2)\}/v$$

and

$$K_2 = 4f_1(f_1 v + v - 2)\{1 - \lambda^2/(v+4)\}/\{(v1-)v(v+2)\}.$$

A comparison of the lower-order moments from (5.1) with the respective exact ones may be made from Table I.

TABLE I

Moments (Central) of $W^{(2)}$ from the Exact and Approximate Distributions[a]

Moments	Exact	Approximate	Ratio (A/E)	Exact	Approximate	Ratio (A/E)
	$f_1 = 10,\ f_2 = 5$			$f_1 = 100,\ f_2 = 5$		
μ_1'	1.2134	1.1765	0.9696	1.8708	1.8692	0.9991
μ_2	0.0506	0.0578	1.1404	$0.0^{2}269$	$0.0^{2}284$	1.0560
μ_3	$-0.0^{2}151$	$-0.0^{2}229$	1.5230	$-0.0^{4}919$	$-0.0^{3}113$	1.2319
μ_4	$0.0^{2}731$	$0.0^{2}907$	1.2405	$0.0^{4}255$	$0.0^{4}303$	1.1900
$(\mu_2)^{1/2}$	0.2250	0.2403	1.0679	0.0518	0.0533	1.0276
β_1	0.0175	0.0273	1.5639	0.4350	0.5605	1.2886
β_2	2.8510	2.7192	0.9538	3.5265	3.7632	1.0671
	$f_1 = 20,\ f_2 = 20$			$f_1 = 100,\ f_2 = 80$		
μ_1'	0.9575	0.9543	0.9947	1.0992	1.0989	0.9997
μ_2	0.0229	0.0232	1.0103	$0.0^{2}5419$	$0.0^{2}5425$	1.0012
μ_3	$0.0^{3}112$	$0.0^{3}100$	0.8899	$-0.0^{4}109$	$-0.0^{4}117$	1.0722
μ_4	$0.0^{2}151$	$0.0^{2}154$	1.0148	$0.0^{4}872$	$0.0^{4}874$	1.0020
$(\mu_2)^{1/2}$	0.1514	0.1522	1.0052	0.0736	0.0737	1.0006
β_1	$0.0^{2}105$	$0.0^{3}806$	0.7678	$0.0^{3}748$	$0.0^{3}856$	1.1456
β_2	2.8849	2.8681	0.9942	2.9695	2.9688	0.9997
	$f_1 = 5,\ f_2 = 20$			$f_1 = 5,\ f_2 = 100$		
μ_1'	0.3751	0.3704	0.9875	0.0935	0.0935	0.9991
μ_2	0.0208	0.0203	0.9782	$0.0^{2}162$	$0.0^{2}162$	0.9976
μ_3	$0.0^{2}160$	$0.0^{2}167$	1.0437	$0.0^{4}522$	$0.0^{4}530$	1.0136
μ_4	$0.0^{2}139$	$0.0^{2}136$	0.9806	$0.0^{4}102$	$0.0^{4}103$	1.0075
$(\mu_2)^{1/2}$	0.1442	0.1426	0.9890	0.0403	0.0403	0.9988
β_1	0.2848	0.3314	1.1637	0.6368	0.6591	1.0350
β_2	3.2123	3.2920	1.0248	3.8780	3.9262	1.0124

[a] Computed for different values of f_1 and f_2, with $\lambda = 2$.

Since $V^{(2)} = 2 - W^{(2)}$, an approximation to the distribution of $V^{(2)}$ can be obtained from (5.1) in the following form:

$$g_2(V^{(2)}) = (V^{(2)})^{q_1 - 1}(1 - V^{(2)}/2)^{p_1 - 1}/[2^{q_1}\beta(q_1, p_1)] \qquad (0 < V^{(2)} < 2). \tag{5.2}$$

Again, consider $U^{(2)}$. An approximation to the distribution of $U^{(2)}$ for $f_1 > f_2$, which is good even for very small values of f_2, is given below:

$$g_3(U^{(2)}) = (U^{(2)})^{p_2 - 1}/\{(1 + U^{(2)}/K_3)^{p_2 + q_2 + 1}K_3^{p_2}\beta(p_2, q_2 + 1)\}, \qquad (0 < U^{(2)} < \infty), \tag{5.3}$$

where

$$p_2 = 2q_2/\{q_2(h-1) - 2h\},$$
$$q_2 = 2\{c^2(f_1-5)h - (c+d)^2(f_1-3)\}/\{c^2(f_1-5)(h+1) - 2(c+d)^2(f_1-3)\},$$
$$K_3 = c\{q_2(h-1) - 2h\}/\{2(f_1-3)\},$$
$$h = (c+1.99d)^3(f_1-3)/\{(c+d)^2(f_1-7)c\},$$
$$c = 2f_2 + \lambda^2 \quad \text{and} \quad d = (f_1 - f_2 - 1)/(f_1 - 2).$$

A comparison of the moments from (5.3) with the respective exact ones may be made from Table II.

TABLE II

Moments (Central) of $U^{(2)}$ from the Exact and Approximate Distributions[a]

Moments	Exact	Approximate	Ratio (A/E)	Exact	Approximate	Ratio (A/E)
	$f_1 = 10,\ f_2 = 2,\ \lambda = 1$			$f_1 = 15,\ f_2 = 5,\ \lambda = 5$		
μ_1'	0.7143	0.7143	1.0000	2.9167	2.9167	1.0000
μ_2	0.5041	0.4760	0.9442	2.3937	2.1092	0.8812
μ_3	1.5792	1.5333	0.9709	8.0457	6.8781	0.8549
μ_4	25.7893	27.0736	1.0498	82.9146	67.0244	0.8084
$(\mu_2)^{1/2}$	0.7100	0.6899	0.9717	1.5472	1.4523	0.9387
β_1	19.4703	21.8049	1.1199	4.7198	5.0415	1.0682
β_2'	101.4935	119.5121	1.1775	14.4708	15.0656	1.0411
	$f_1 = 50,\ f_2 = 10,\ \lambda = 1$			$f_1 = 100,\ f_2 = 10,\ \lambda = 1$		
μ_1'	0.4468	0.4468	1.0000	0.2165	0.2165	1.0000
μ_2	0.0258	0.0253	0.9823	0.0^2532	0.0^2522	0.9798
μ_3	0.0^2373	0.0^2407	1.0911	0.0^3295	0.0^3309	1.0467
μ_4	0.0^2296	0.0^2314	1.0616	0.0^3112	0.0^3114	1.0114
$(\mu_2)^{1/2}$	0.1605	0.1591	0.9911	0.0730	0.0722	0.9898
β_1	0.8126	1.0207	1.2561	0.5772	0.6724	1.1648
β_2	4.4566	4.9032	1.1002	3.9610	4.1731	1.0535
	$f_1 = 100,\ f_2 = 20,\ \lambda = 3$			$f_1 = 100,\ f_2 = 20,\ \lambda = 5$		
μ_1'	0.5052	0.5052	1.0000	0.6701	0.6701	1.0000
μ_2	0.0155	0.0140	0.9031	0.0252	0.0209	0.8292
μ_3	0.0^2116	0.0^2106	0.9199	0.0^2236	0.0^2186	0.7886
μ_4	0.0^3874	0.0^3736	0.8417	0.0^2231	0.0^2161	0.6995
$(\mu_2)^{1/2}$	0.1246	0.1184	0.9503	0.1587	0.1446	0.9106
β_1	0.3578	0.4111	1.1488	0.3467	0.3782	1.0907
β_2	3.6295	3.7458	1.0320	0.3631	0.3694	1.0173

[a] Computed for different values of $f_1 > f_2$ and $\lambda = 1$, 3, and 5.

6. POWER FUNCTIONS OF TESTS OF HYPOTHESIS: $\lambda = 0$ AGAINST $\lambda > 0$ BASED ON $V^{(2)}$, $U^{(2)}$, AND Λ

Using the results on the moments of $W^{(2)}$ in Section 4, and the relation $V^{(2)} = 2 - W^{(2)}$, the central moments, μ_2, μ_3, and μ_4, and the moment quotients, β_1 and β_2, were computed for various values of f_1, f_2, and λ. Similar computations were made for $U^{(2)}$ and Wilks' criterion, using the expressions in Section 4 for the moments of the former, and deriving the expressions for the moments of the latter as the product of the respective moments of u_{11} and u_{22}.

For a given size α, using the β_1 and β_2 values computed for fixed f_1 and f_2 for $\lambda = 0$, the critical region was determined for each criterion referring to the tables, "Percentage points of Pearson curves for β_1 and β_2 expressed in standardized measure," in Pearson and Hartley [7]. Further, for the same values of f_1 and f_2 and a value of $\lambda > 0$, the computed values of β_1 and β_2 were used to determine from the same table, by interpolation, the power of the test based on the critical region determined previously. Table III presents the results of these computations.

TABLE III

Powers of Tests of Hypothesis $\lambda = 0$[a]

				Power		
f_1	f_2	α	λ	$V^{(2)}$	$U^{(2)}$	Λ
50	10	0.005	1	0.0076	0.0076	0.0113
50	10	0.005	2	0.0215	0.0217	0.0470
100	10	0.01	1	0.0156	0.0156	0.0217
100	20	0.025	1	0.0306	0.0306	0.0345
100	30	0.025	1	0.0300	0.0300	0.0303
100	50	0.025	1	0.0278	0.0277	0.0280
100	100	0.025	1	0.0270	0.0270	0.0270
50	50	0.005	1	0.0057	0.0056	0.0056
50	50	0.005	2	0.0085	0.0083	0.0085
50	50	0.005	3	0.0151	0.0151	0.0153

[a] Tested against $\lambda > 0$ based on $V^{(2)}$, $U^{(2)}$, and Λ.

Table III shows that (a) there is practically no difference between the powers of tests based on $V^{(2)}$ and $U^{(2)}$, and (b) for small values of f_2 Wilks' criterion seems to have marked power compared to both $V^{(2)}$ and $U^{(2)}$. This point needs further investigation.

7. POWER FUNCTIONS FOR TESTS OF HYPOTHESIS: $\rho = 0$ AGAINST $\rho > 0$ BASED ON $V^{(2)}$, $U^{(2)}$, Λ, AND THE LARGEST ROOT

In the case of the relation between a p set of variates, $x' = (x_1, \dots, x_p)$, and a q set, $y' = (y_1, \dots, y_q)$, from a $(p+q)$-variate normal population, where there is only one nonnull population canonical correlation coefficient, ρ, and $p \le q$, $(p+q) < n'$, where n' is the sample size,

$$\lambda^2 = \rho^2 \sum_{t=1}^{v} y_{1t}^2/(1-\rho^2), \tag{7.1}$$

where y_{1t} $(t = 1 \dots, v)$ are related to the sample observations of y_1, and y, here, is considered fixed [6]. Further, $f_2 = q$ and $f_1 = n' - q - 1$ such that $v = f_1 + f_2$. If, however, y is not fixed, then $\sum_{t=1}^{v} y_{1t}^2$ in λ^2 of (7.1) is a chi square with v degrees of freedom and, therefore, for obtaining the moments of $W^{(2)}$ in this case the following changes may be made in the moments of $W^{(2)}$ given in Section 4:

$$\begin{gathered} \exp(-\tfrac{1}{2}\lambda^2) \to (1-\rho^2)^{v/2}, \qquad (\lambda^2)^i \to (\rho^2)^i, \\ (a_i, b_i, c_i, d_i) \to [v(v+2)\cdots(v+2(i-1))](a_i, b_i, c_i, d_i). \end{gathered} \tag{7.2}$$

Similar changes apply for Wilks' criterion. But for $U^{(2)}$, $(\lambda^2)^i$ is replaced by $(2\rho^2/(1-\rho^2))^i \Gamma(\frac{1}{2}v+1)/\Gamma(v/2)$. Now for the test of the hypothesis: $\rho = 0$ against $\rho > 0$ using $V^{(2)}$, $U^{(2)}$, and Λ, powers were evaluated for $\rho = .05$ and $\rho = .1$ for certain values of f_1 and f_2 using the method discussed in the preceding section. For the largest root, the power was computed using Constantine's form of the distribution of the canonical correlation coefficients [4 and 5] in the following manner:

First the joint distribution for $p = 2$ and a single nonzero ρ was obtained as a series of determinants using a lemma by Pillai [12]. Further, taking into account the first seven terms of the series and integrating out the smallest root by employing Pillai's method [8 and 10], the following expression was obtained for the c.d.f. of the largest canonical correlation coefficient, $r_2{}^2$.

$$\begin{aligned} \Pr\{r_2{}^2 \le x\} \\ = K_4\Big\{ -I_0(m+1, n+1)\Big[& I(x; m, n)\Big\{\sum_{j=0}^{6} (B_j x^{6-j}/(m+n+8-j))\Big\} \\ & - xI(x; m+1, n)\Big\{\sum_{j=0}^{4} (C_j x^{4-j}/(m+n+7-j))\Big\} \\ & - x^2 I(x; m+2, n)\Big\{\sum_{j=0}^{2} (D_j x^{2-j}/(m+n+6-j))\Big\} \\ & - x^3 I(x; m+3, n) E_0/(m+n+5)\Big] \end{aligned}$$

$$+ 2I(x; 2m+7, 2n+1)[\{B_0/(m+n+8)\} - \{C_0/(m+n+7)\}$$

$$- \{D_0/(m+n+6)\} - \{E_0/(m+n+5)\}]$$

$$+ 2I(x; 2m+6, 2n+1)[\{B_1/(m+n+7)\} - \{C_1/(m+n+6)\}$$

$$- \{D_1/(m+n+5)\}]$$

$$+ 2I(x; 2m+5, 2n+1)[\{B_2/(m+n+6)\} - \{C_2/(m+n+5)\}$$

$$- \{D_2/(m+n+4)\}]$$

$$+ 2I(x; 2m+4, 2n+1)[\{B_3/(m+n+5)\} - \{C_3/(m+n+4)\}]$$

$$+ 2I(x; 2m+3, 2n+1)[\{B_4/(m+n+4)\} - \{C_4/(m+n+3)\}]$$

$$+ 2I(x; 2m+2, 2n+1)\{B_5/(m+n+3)\} + 2I(x; 2m+1, 2n+1)$$

$$\times \{B_6/(m+n+2)\}\Big\},$$

where

$$f_1 = 2n+3, \qquad f_2 = 2m+3, \qquad K_4 = (1-\rho^2)^{\nu/2} C(2, m, n),$$

$$C(2, m, n) = \Gamma(2m+2n+5)/\{4\Gamma(2m+2)\Gamma(2n+2)\},$$

$$I_0(m+1, n+1) = x^{m+1}(1-x)^{n+1}, \qquad I(x; c', d') = \int_0^x \theta^{c'}(1-\theta)^{d'}\, d\theta,$$

$$B_0 = 231 A_6, \qquad B_1 = 63 A_5 + (m+7)B_0/(m+n+8),$$

$$B_2 = 35 A_4 + (m+6)B_1/(m+n+7),$$

$$B_3 = 5A_3 + (m+5)B_2/(m+n+6), \qquad B_4 = 3A_2 + (m+4)B_3/(m+n+5),$$

$$B_5 = A_1(m+3)B_4/(m+n+4), \qquad B_6 = 1 + (m+2)B_5/(m+n+3),$$

$$C_0 = 105 A_6, \qquad C_1 = 28 A_5 + (m+6)C_0/(m+n+7),$$

$$C_2 = 15 A_4 + (m+5)C_1/(m+n+6),$$

$$C_3 = 2A_3 + (m+4)C_2/(m+n+5), \qquad C_4 = A_2 + (m+3)C_3/(m+n+4),$$

$$D_0 = 21 A_6, \qquad D_1 = 5A_5 + (m+5)D_0/(m+n+6),$$

$$D_2 = 2A_4 + (m+4)D_1/(m+n+5),$$

$$E_0 = 5A_6, \qquad A_1 = \nu^2\rho^2/2^2 f_2, \qquad A_2 = [\nu(\nu+2)]^2\rho^4/[f_2(f_2+2)2^6],$$

$$A_3 = A_2(\nu+4)^2\rho^2/[(f_2+4)2.3!], \qquad A_4 = A_3(\nu+6)^2\rho^2/\{2^6(f_2+6)\},$$

$$A_5 = A_4(\nu+8)^2\rho^2/\{2^2 \cdot 5(f_2+8)\}, \qquad A_6 = A_5(\nu+10)^2\rho^2/\{2^3 \cdot 6(f_2+10)\}.$$

For $\rho = 0$, the upper 1% points of the largest root were taken from Pillai's tables [11] for values of $m = 2$ and 5 and $n = 10$, 15, 20, 25, 30, 40, and 60. Using these $x_{.99}$ values to determine the critical region, the powers of the largest root test were computed for $\rho = 0.05$ and $\rho = 0.1$ for values of m and n given above. These are shown in Table IV.

TABLE IV

Powers of the Largest Root Test for Testing $\rho = 0^a$

	Power			
	$\rho = 0.05$		$\rho = 0.1$	
n	$m = 2$	$m = 5$	$m = 2$	$m = 5$
10	0.010292	0.010205	0.011222	0.010854
15	0.010441	0.010305	0.011883	0.011288
20	0.010593	0.010406	0.012581	0.011742
25	0.010748	0.010509	0.013315	0.012215
30	0.010905	0.010612	0.014084	0.012707
40	0.011226	0.010823	0.015730	0.013748
60	0.011892	0.011259	0.019467	0.016070

[a] Tested against $\rho = 0.05$ and $\rho = 0.1$ and $\alpha = 0.01$.

A comparison of the powers of the test of hypothesis: $\rho = 0$ against $\rho > 0$ based on $V^{(2)}$, $U^{(2)}$, Λ, and the largest root may be made from Table V.

TABLE V

Powers of the Test $\rho = 0^a$

	Power							f_1
	$f_2 = 7$				$f_2 = 13$			
f_1	$V^{(2)}$	$U^{(2)}$	Λ	Largest root	$V^{(2)}$	$U^{(2)}$	Λ	Largest root
				$\rho = .05$				
53	0.0108	0.0107	0.0118	0.0107	0.0106	0.0106	0.0110	0.0105
83	0.0115	0.0115	0.0140	0.0112	0.0112	0.0109	0.0122	0.0108
123	0.0123	0.0120	0.0155	0.0119	0.0115	0.0115	0.0130	0.0112
				$\rho = 0.1$				
53	0.0135	0.0135	0.0190	0.0133	0.0125	0.0125	0.0135	0.0122
83	0.0165	0.0165	0.0280	0.0157	0.0144	0.0142	0.0180	0.0137
123	0.0202	0.0200	0.0440	0.0195	0.0170	0.0170	0.0240	0.0161

[a] Tested against $\rho > 0$, based on $V^{(2)}$, $U^{(2)}$, Λ, and the largest root for $\rho = 0.05$, $\rho = 0.1$, and $\alpha = 0.01$.

Table V shows that (a) the largest root has comparatively less power than the other test criteria; (b) $V^{(2)}$ and $U^{(2)}$ practically have equal power; and (c) Wilks' criterion, as in the previous case, seems to have greater power for the (small) values of f_2 considered here. Further investigation is being made to clarify this point.

Acknowledgments

The author wishes to thank Mrs. Louise Mao Lui, Statistical Laboratory, Purdue University, for the excellent programming of the material for the computations in this paper carried out on the IBM 7094 Computer in Purdue University's Computer Sciences' Center.

REFERENCES

1. Anderson, T. W. (1946). The non-central Wishart distribution and certain problems of multivariate statistics. *Ann. Math. Statist.* **17** 409–431.
2. Anderson, T. W. (1958). *An Introduction to Multivariate Statistical Analysis.* Wiley, New York.
3. Anderson, T. W. and Girshick, M. A. (1944). Some extensions of the Wishart distribution. *Ann. Math. Statist.* **15** 345–357.
4. Constantine, A. G. (1963). Some non-central distribution problems in multivariate analysis. *Ann. Math. Statist.* **34** 1270–1285.
5. James, A. T. (1964). Distributions of matrix variates and latent roots derived from normal samples. *Ann. Math. Statist.* **35** 475–501.
6. Kshirsagar, A. M. (1961). The non-central multivariate beta distribution. *Ann. Math. Statist.* **32** 104–111.
7. Pearson, E. S. and Hartley, H. O. (1956). *Biometrika Tables for Statisticians* Vol. I. Cambridge Univ. Press (for the Biometrika Trustees), New York and London.
8. Pillai, K. C. S. (1954). On some distribution problems in multivariate analysis. Mimeograph Series 88, Inst. Statist., Univ. North Carolina, Chapel Hill, North Carolina.
9. Pillai, K. C. S. (1955). Some new test criteria in multivariate analysis. *Ann. Math. Statist.* **26** 117–121.
10. Pillai, K. C. S. (1956). Some results useful in multivariate analysis. *Ann. Math. Statist.* **27** 1106–1114.
11. Pillai, K. C. S. (1960). *Statistical Tables for Tests of Multivariate Hypotheses.* The Statistical Center, Manila, The Philippines.
12. Pillai, K. C. S. (1964). On the moments of elementary symmetric functions of the roots of two matrices. *Ann. Math. Statist.* **35** 1704–1712.
13. Pillai, K. C. S. and Mijares, T. A. (1959). On the moments of the trace of a matrix and approximations to its distribution. *Ann. Math. Statist.* **30** 1135–1140.
14. Pillai, K. C. S. and Samson, P. (1959). On Hotelling's generalization of T^2. *Biometrika* **46** 160–168.
15. Roy, S. N. (1957). *Some Aspects of Multivariate Analysis.* Wiley, New York.
16. Wilks, S. S. (1932). Certain generalizations in the analysis of variance. *Biometrika* **24** 471–494.

PART V

Optimum Properties of Test Procedures

Multivariate Optimality Results

J. KIEFER[1]
DEPARTMENT OF MATHEMATICS
CORNELL UNIVERSITY
ITHACA, NEW YORK

1. INTRODUCTION; INVARIANCE AND FORMAL BAYES PROCEDURES

In this article I shall attempt to fulfill Dr. Krishnaiah's request for me to present a survey of optimality results (i.e., mainly of admissibility and minimax results) in multivariate analysis. Hence, aside from a few observations on connections and contrasts among known results and on areas still to be explored, the paper will consist primarily of a list of known results. Even this list will be incomplete and will be accompanied by only brief commentary; it would require too much space and lead too far afield to list all the standard decision-theoretic results which, when specialized, have some bearing on usual multivariate problems. Moreover, as we shall mention, many of the most interesting unanswered optimality questions in multivariate analysis seem likely to have different answers from corresponding questions in the more-explored univariate case, or, in any event, to require different techniques of proof.

I apologize in advance for the inadvertant oversights which have undoubtedly taken place in my list of references, and will try now to indicate some of the conscious omissions which have been dictated by brevity.

In what follows we shall usually forego generality for the sake of brief and simple exposition. Mention will occasionally be made of topics related to those under discussion but not pursued here. We shall not even list sources for all such topics. No distribution theory will be considered (not even the work, quite relevant to our considerations, of Stein, Wijsman, Schwartz, on the distribution of maximal invariants). The vast topic of asymptotic (in sample size) optimality, both nonsequential and sequential, which has been worked on by many authors, will receive no attention at all; perhaps the aspect of that work which has greatest interest from the point of view of this

[1] Work supported by the Office of Naval Research under Contract Nonr-401(03).

survey is Stein's concern with asymptotic optimality questions when the dimension of the multivariate population also goes to infinity.

Uniform optimality properties (e.g., minimaxity or maximum power for a given test on each of a set of contours of alternatives) will usually not receive special mention when we describe optimality results. Power function monotonicity results, such as those of [9], and which are relevant to certain minimax statements, will not be discussed. Conditioning and fiducial inference, for which a considerable literature exists (including certain invariance considerations) will not be mentioned; nor will recent work of Stone's. Characterization of the class of *all* transformations which leave a problem invariant, begun by Lehmann and Stein [39], and work such as that of Brillinger on conditions for a Lie group to leave a problem invariant, will not be mentioned; in our invariance developments we shall take the relevant group to be given. Nor shall we consider the relationship between invariance and almost-invariance (see [35]). When inadmissibility results are mentioned, the wisdom of using various competing procedures will not be discussed.

We will usually restrict attention to parametric, often normal problems. (Nonparametric minimax and admissibility results are commonly proved by reference to a parametric subproblem.) The large literature on intuitively attractive methods for constructing procedures (ML, LR, union-intersection, information, etc.) will not be touched on. We shall deal mainly with estimation and testing results, although most of the discussion applies more generally; Lehmann's work on constructing a "good" multiple decision procedure from a collection of good tests is of interest here.

Although parts of multivariate optimality theory have nothing to do with invariance, the latter concept is involved in many of the developments which have received greatest attention. Aside from the mathematical naturalness of this, there is good practical-historical motivation: many multivariate statistical problems are invariant under large groups of transformations, and, because of intuitive appeal and computational simplicity, invariant procedures were often used in such problems; tests based on Hotelling's T^2 and the same multiple-correlation coefficient R^2 are familiar classical normal examples, while the first systematic study of (scale-location) invariance is due to Pitman [43 and 44]. Thus, attention has often centered around proving or disproving minimax or admissibility properties for these classical invariant procedures, or around finding those invariant procedures which are admissible among all procedures (rather than the full minimal complete class). The role of invariance will perhaps receive more than its due in the present survey. The other principal simplifying structure is the distribution of multivariate exponential (Koopman-Darmois) type.

Minimax and admissibility considerations will be discussed in Sections 2 and 3, respectively.

Notational simplicity is called for in an article of this nature, but the consequent absence of many definitions and explicit expressions will demand some slight background on the part of the reader. We shall use S, Ω, D, and W to denote the sample, state-of-nature, and decision spaces, and the loss function on $\Omega \times D$. (W can also be allowed to depend on the observation X without much additional difficulty, even in invariance considerations.) The loss function can usually be thought of as a simple (zero-one) in testing problems, and, typically, as convex (in the decision) or even quadratic in estimation. The risk function of a statistical procedure (δ, which last is, as usual, a function on $S \times$ subsets of D) will be written r_δ. We write $\bar{r}_\delta = \sup_F r_\delta(F)$. If π is an *a priori* probability measure on Ω, $R_\delta(\pi)$ is the *a priori* (expected) risk of δ. Measurability considerations will be omitted for brevity, but (e.g., p. 400 of [2]) pathologies can arise. In hypothesis-testing problems, β_δ will denote the function of δ, and α_δ the size; minimax testing properties usually refer to the class C_α of tests δ with size $\alpha_\delta \leq \alpha$ (fixed); here $\Omega = \Omega_0 + \Omega_1$ and $\alpha_\delta = \sup_{F \in \Omega_0} \beta_\delta(F)$. A locally compact group G which leaves a problem invariant will be thought of as operating on the left on (S, Ω, D); we shall write g for an element of G, acting on S, and $\bar{g}$ and $\bar{\bar{g}}$ for the homomorphic images of g acting on Ω and D; thus, $P_\theta\{gX \in A\} = P_{\bar{g}^{-1}\theta}\{X \in A\}$ and $W(\theta, d) = W(\bar{g}\theta, \bar{\bar{g}}d)$, and δ is invariant if $\delta(x, B) = \delta(gx, \bar{\bar{g}}B)$ for all x, B, g. The left and right invariant measures on G will be denoted by μ and ν, respectively; and the modular function, by $\Delta(g') = d\mu(gg')/d\mu(g)$. (See Halmos, "Measure Theory," or Loomis, "Abstract Harmonic Analysis," on such topics.) The class of all procedures in a problem will be denoted by C, and those invariant under a group G which leaves the problem invariant will be denoted by $C^{(G)}$. We also write $C_\alpha{}^{(G)} = C^{(G)} \cap C_\alpha$. Words such as "Bayes," "minimax," or "admissible" are meant relative to C or C_α unless further modified; for example, if G is transitive on Ω in an estimation problem, some of the main considerations of this article come down to the C-admissibility or C-minimaxity of a $C^{(G)}$-admissible, Bayes, minimax (namely, best G-invariant) procedure. A Bayes procedure relative to π will be denoted by δ_π. The observed random variable, which can be thought of as the identity function on S, will be denoted by X. When the actual state of nature has (labeled) value θ, the probability measure or density of X with respect to a given σ-finite measure λ will be denoted by P_θ or p_θ, respectively. Where "sample size n" is relevant, X is to be thought of as $(X_1, X_2, \ldots, X_n)$, where the X_i are independent, identically distributed. Where "dimension p" is mentioned, it usually refers to the range of X_1 or, in a typical modification hereafter called the "p-dimensional (or p-variate) translation- (or location-) parameter problem," to that of Z, where $X = (Z, Y)$, Ω is Euclidean p-space E^p (or $\Omega_0 = \Omega_1 = E^p$ in testing), and the P_θ law of $(Z - \theta, Y)$ is independent of θ. Although the few sequential results mentioned are somewhat general, one can think of them in the special case of independent, identically distributed X_i, with each observation costing the same amount. The univariate normal distribution with mean η and variance σ^2 is denoted by $N(\eta, \sigma^2)$.

We conclude this section with a review of the general Wald decision-theoretic results which lead up to the contents of the next two sections. Under fairly general conditions for a statistical problem (e.g., [61 and 32]), the admissible procedures and the minimax procedures (some perhaps inadmissible) are contained in the closure, in an appropriate sense, of the Bayes procedures. (Without suitable compactness of Ω and regularity of W, the Bayes procedures themselves need not suffice.) Thus, restricting ourselves for simplicity to a separable setting, we are faced with studying appropriate limits of sequences $\{\delta_{\pi_i}\}$ of Bayes procedures relative to *a priori* probability measures π_i. (For example, if

$$\bar{r}_{\delta'} = \lim_i R_{\delta_{\pi_i}}(\pi_i), \tag{1}$$

then δ' is minimax.) It is tempting to consider π_i's and positive constants k_i such that $k_i \pi_i \to \pi^*$, a nontrivial and *not necessarily finite* measure on Ω, and then to compute a *formal* Bayes procedure $\delta_\pi{}^*$ relative to this improper π^* by letting $\delta_{\pi^*}(x, \cdot)$ assign measure 1 to decisions d' for which $\int p_\theta(x) W(\theta, d')$ $\pi^*(d\theta)$ (typically finite in important examples, although $R_\delta(\pi^*)$ may be infinite for all δ) is minimized. (For example, if $\Omega = E^1$, π_i is $N(0, i)$, and $k_i = (2\pi i)^{1/2}$, then π^* is Lebesgue measure.) One could then ask: (i) Is the class of such δ_{π^*}, for a suitable class of π^* (proper and improper), complete? (ii) Which improper π^*'s yield an admissible δ_{π^*}? (iii) Can a δ' satisfying (1) be obtained as a δ_{π^*} for appropriate $\{\pi_i\}$? We are trying here to replace sequences $\{\pi_i\}$ by corresponding π^*'s.

Questions (i) and (ii) will be discussed further in Section 3, while question (iii) will be the topic of Section 2. We now indicate the role of invariance in constructing such δ_{π^*}'s.

Suppose that the problem is invariant under a group G which is large enough that the reduced problem in terms of a maximal invariant $X^{(G)}$, its range $S^{(G)}$, possible distributions $\Omega^{(G)}$, decisions D, loss function W, and of course procedures $C^{(G)}$ depending only on $X^{(G)}$, satisfy the regularity assumptions which insure that the $C^{(G)}$-Bayes procedures relative to *proper a priori* laws $\pi^{(G)}$ on $\Omega^{(G)}$ are $C^{(G)}$-complete and contain the $C^{(G)}$-minimax procedures. It is then natural (for reasons indicated later in this paragraph) to modify question (iii) to ask whether some right G-invariant measure π^* (that is, a measure for which $\pi^*(Ag) = \pi^*(A)$ for all g in G and all appropriately measurable subsets A of Ω) yields a δ_{π^*} which is minimax (and which, as a part of question (ii), is admissible). For the simplest general setting which will illustrate certain ideas, suppose S, Ω, and D are all isomorphic to G in an estimation problem, and write e for the identity element of G and $W(\theta, d) = W(e, \theta^{-1}d) \equiv w(\theta^{-1}d)$. (We have identified g, $\bar{g}$, and $\bar{\bar{g}}$ in this notation.) Let $\{p_\theta(x)\}$ be densities relative to left-invariant μ on S. Let π^* be the right-invariant measure ν on $\Omega = \{\theta\}$ (or, equivalently, and what makes this the correct choice, left-invariant measure μ on $\{\theta^{-1}\}$). Then, in minimizing the *a posteriori* risk relative to π^*, we consider

$$\begin{aligned}\int W(\theta, d')p_\theta(x)\pi^*(d\theta) &= \int w(\theta^{-1}d')p_e(\theta^{-1}x)\mu(d\theta^{-1})\\ &= \int w(\theta^{-1}d')p_e(\theta^{-1}x)\mu(d\theta^{-1}x)/\Delta(x)\\ &= \int w(tx^{-1}d')p_e(t)\mu(dt)/\Delta(x) = E_e w(Xx^{-1}d')/\Delta(x). \quad (2)\end{aligned}$$

Suppose for simplicity that $E_e w(Xg)$ is minimized uniquely by $g = g_0$. Then (2) is minimized by taking $d' = xg_0$; that is, $\delta_{\pi^*}(x, xg_0) = 1$, so that δ_{π^*} is the nonrandomized estimator Xg_0. It is easily checked that this procedure is best invariant, i.e., is the essentially unique $C^{(G)}$-admissible procedure.

(This type of computation, as well as that of the next paragraph, can be carried out in the general setting where S, Ω, D need not be isomorphic to G and where, in fact, G need not be transitive on Ω and the subgroup of G leaving a point of Ω fixed need not be trivial; see Stein [58] and Schwartz [50].)

The above computation can be used to obtain the best invariant confidence set of given "shape" and μ-measure (e.g., interval of specified length in the case of a univariate translation parameter): Let B be a fixed subset of G of finite μ-measure, and for each γ in G consider the procedure which makes the confidence statement "$\theta \in X\gamma B$." The μ-measure of the confidence set $X\gamma B$ is $\mu(B)$, and the probability of coverage is

$$P_\theta\{\theta \in X\gamma B\} = P_\theta\{\theta^{-1}X \in B^{-1}\gamma^{-1}\} = P_e\{X \in B^{-1}\gamma^{-1}\}. \quad (3)$$

This is related to our earlier discussion by interpreting decision d' as the confidence set $d'B$ with $w(\theta^{-1}d') = 0$ or 1 according to whether or not $e \in \theta^{-1}d'B$; we obtain r_δ as the probability of not covering. Thus, from the discussion following (2), we see that maximum coverage is obtained by choosing γ to maximize $E_e\{1 - w(X\gamma)\} = P_e\{X \in B^{-1}\gamma^{-1}\}$, in agreement with (3). Moreover, for any γ, dividing all members of (2) by $\int p_\theta(x)\pi^*(d\theta)$, we obtain the equality between (3) and the formal *a posteriori* probability of coverage from using $X\gamma B$, when $X = x$ and π^* is treated as the *a priori* law; this result was obtained first by Pitman [43] and in great generality by Stein [58]. Finally, if we allow B to vary subject to $\mu(B) =$ specified positive constant c (say), maximum coverage among procedures XB is obtained by maximizing

$$\int_{B^{-1}} p_e(g)\mu(dg) \quad \text{subject to} \quad \int_{B^{-1}} \nu(dg) = c,$$

which, by the Neyman-Pearson lemma and the fact that $d\mu(g)/d\nu(g) = \Delta(g)$, yields B^{-1} to be of the form

$$\{g : p_e(g)\Delta(g) > k\} \cup \text{subset of } \{g : p_e(g)\Delta(g) = k\}, \tag{4}$$

for a suitable constant k. When $X = x$, the confidence set xB corresponding to the first part of (4) is thus

$$\{\theta : p_e(\theta^{-1}x)\Delta(\theta^{-1}x) > k\}. \tag{5}$$

If G is unimodular (e.g., compact, abelian, or full linear), then (4) reduces to what has often served as an intuitive choice for the form of a confidence set; to my knowledge, in other cases it has not been made clear as a general prescription that the set (5), where the formal *a posteriori* density *with respect to* μ (given that $X = x$) is $>k$, and which thus also has a natural invariance motivation, is preferable to either of the intuitive choices $xB = \{\theta : p_e(\theta^{-1}x)\,\Delta(x) > k'\}$ where the formal *a posterior* density *with respect to* ν is large, or $xB = \{\theta : p_e(\theta^{-1}x) > k''\}$. (*Added in proof:* I have just become aware of an article by Ishii and Kudo in the 1963 *Osaka J. Math*, treating some such considerations for tolerance regions.) For an example, if G, S, and Ω are the real affine group $(\{(a, b) : -\infty < a < \infty, 0 < b < \infty\}$, with $(a, b)(a', b') = (a + a'b, bb'))$, then $d\mu = da\, db/b^2$, $d\nu = da\, db/b$, and $\Delta((a, b)) = 1/b$. If $X = (U, V)$, where U is the sample mean and V is the sample standard deviation from n independent univariate $N(\theta_1, \theta_2{}^2)$ r.v.'s ($n \geq 2$), so that X is sufficient for $\Omega = \{(\theta_1, \theta_2)\}$, then $e = (0, 1)$ and the Lebesgue density of X is proportional to $v^{n-2}e^{-n(u^2+v^2)/2}$, so that the μ-density $f_e(u, v)$ is proportional to $v^n e^{-n(u^2+v^2)/2}$. Hence B^{-1} is of the form $\{(u, v) : v^{n-1}e^{-n(u^2+v^2)/2} > k\}$. One can object to the use of μ as the measure in the restriction $\mu(B) = c$, but to depart from it requires modification of strict invariance considerations. The role of relatively invariant measures (for which $\lambda(gA) = h(g)\lambda(A)$ for some function h, such as $b^r\, da\, db$ in the above example) should be investigated in this context; their use for π^* has been discussed by Stein [58] in connection with the Pitman-Stein result mentioned above. As we have indicated, the setting $\Omega \cong G$ was chosen for simplicity and brevity, and it is not difficult tn carry out the analogue of the development leading to (4) and (5) when Ω is no longer isomorphic to G but is instead a homogeneous space G/G', where G' (compact) leaves a point of Ω fixed.

We have spent considerable space on the above considerations because a good deal of literature, beginning with Jeffreys [23] and carried on by other authors such as Barnard, Lindley, Cornfield, Geisser (e.g., [14] or possibly the present volume), has been concerned with the construction of such formal

Bayes procedures relative to improper π^*'s; it is thus evidently of interest for further work in this direction to fit particular examples into the general picture, and to make computation-saving use of simple general results such as (2), (4), and that of Pitman-Stein. Moreover, and more important from the point of view of the present survey, the justification (or lack of it) of using such procedures, in terms of desirable risk function properties, is almost never mentioned. We now turn to the description of work in which such justifications in various problems are proved or are shown to be false.

2. MINIMAX QUESTIONS; THE HUNT-STEIN THEOREM

Minimax results have been obtained in the literature for various problems by using (a) the Bayes method indicated in Eq. (1) (including the case where all π_i are the same and thus δ' is genuinely Bayes), (b) the Cramér-Rao inequality method, and (c) the Hunt-Stein theorem.

Many authors, too numerous to list, have used (a) to obtain minimax procedures since Wald first established the Bayes-minimax connection. Most of these results are univariate. A few, beginning with Wald [61] and Wolfowitz [64], gave sequential minimax results. We shall be especially concerned in Section 3 with the results of Lehmann and Stein [37].

Method (b) is due to Hodges and Lehmann [20]; see also [18] for further examples. It actually proves that a certain estimator with *constant* risk is admissible, hence minimax. Stein [53] made a multivariate application in the problem of estimating the mean of a bivariate normal distribution with identity covariance matrix.

Method (c) is approximately twenty years old. It will be discussed in more detail below.

The advantages and disadvantages of these methods are: (a) is always applicable but may require considerable guesswork (in choosing the π_i and δ') and messy computations; (b) yields admissibility as well, but is applicable only in a few estimation problems with a special form of distribution and loss (it is not known whether the inequalities of E. Barankin and M. M. Rao can be used to extend the method, but its usefulness in multivariate problems is in any event limited, since it must yield admissibility as well); method (c) is useful only when a large group G (satisfying the hypothesis of the theorem) leaves the problem invariant, but in such cases, especially when G is transitive on Ω in an estimation problem or on each Ω_i in a testing problem, it eliminates the guesswork and computation of method (a).

Before discussing the Hunt-Stein theorem, we recall the more general question (iii) of Section 1; in particular, if $r_{\delta_{\pi*}}$ is constant for an improper π^*, is δ_{π^*} minimax? As the various counterexamples to the conclusion of the

Hunt-Stein theorem (discussed below) show, the answer is not always affirmative. In addition, even in such a simple setting as that of a univariate translation parameter with π^* not Lebesgue measure, the following type of example (first told to me by Farrell) can occur: Let $S = \Omega = D = E^1$, let X be $N(\theta, 1)$, let $W(\theta, d) = (\theta - d)^2$, and let $d\pi^*(\theta) = e^\theta \, d\theta$; then δ_{π^*} is the estimator $X + 1$, which is even invariant (and thus has constant risk), but which is not admissible or minimax. The minimax question is a less delicate one than that (discussed in Section 3) of admissibility of δ_{π^*} [58]. (Stein also described in his 1961 Wald lectures the varying delicacy required in minimax, conditioning, and admissibility questions in terms of approximating improper π^*'s by proper *a priori* probability measures.) Nevertheless, aside from the invariant setting of the Hunt-Stein theorem, few results have been obtained on the minimax character of such δ_{π^*}. Among the few exceptions are the work of Sacks [46], Katz [27], and Farrell [11] in certain cases of a univariate translation parameter restricted to the half-line.

We now turn to the Hunt-Stein theorem. We have seen in Section 1 that, in the simple context $G = \Omega$ treated there, if $\pi^* = \nu$, then δ_{π^*} (assumed essentially unique here for simplicity) is the best invariant procedure. It has constant risk, and the question of the previous paragraph is whether it is minimax. In general, without the restriction to our simple example, we ask whether a statistical problem which is invariant under a group G has what we hereafter call the *HS* (*Hunt-Stein*) *property*: For any δ in C, there is a δ' in $C^{(G)}$ with $\bar{r}_{\delta'} \leq \bar{r}_\delta$ (or typically in testing problems, the same with C and $C^{(G)}$ replaced by C_α and $C_\alpha^{(G)}$). We have separated off the question of attainment of the minimax risk by a member of C, i.e., of existence of a minimax procedure; this can often be treated by the general decision-theoretic considerations of [61] or [32] (and which are often especially simple for $C^{(G)}$, which is all one need consider if the HS property holds); if the minimax risk is attainable, the HS property asserts that a $C^{(G)}$-minimax procedure exists and is C-minimax.

In terms of the discussion of (1), one can think of π_i as being ν restricted to an appropriate compact set C_i (that is, $\pi_i(A) = \nu(C_i \cap A)/\nu(C_i)$), where $\lim C_i = G$; this may not always be the most convenient way to approximate $\pi^* = \nu$ by a sequence $\{\pi_i\}$, but is helpful intuitively. In our simple example, or more generally when $G \cong \Omega$ (and similarly when G is transitive on Ω), if G is compact ν is finite, and we can take the normalization $\nu(G) = 1$ so that δ_ν becomes a *proper* Bayes procedure with constant risk, which is thus automatically minimax. If G is not compact, we can think of trying to approximate $\pi^* = \nu$ by a sequence $\{\pi_i\}$ (such as that just mentioned) and then (in the case where the minimax risk is attained) of trying to prove (1) with $\delta' = \delta_\nu$. Some of the proofs of the HS theorem proceed in this way.

The version of the HS theorem published by Lehmann [35] is probably close in spirit to the original unpublished one of Hunt and Stein. Another early and independent general approach is due to Peisakoff [42]. Other published proofs are due, in univariate translation parameter settings, to Girshick and Savage [18] and Blackwell and Girshick [3] (with an earlier statement but incomplete proof in Wald [59]), and, in general settings, to Kudô [31], Wesler [62], and Kiefer [28]; the last of these discusses the relationship between some of these methods of proof and the necessity of the various assumptions on S, Ω, D, W, G; under certain restrictions the HS theorem is proved here for groups (called HS groups below) with descending normal chain containing only compact or abelian factor groups (and thus including, in particular, solvable groups). Chen [6, 7] has recently given a presentation of the special cases of location-scale parameter problems, including a repetition of all measurability details outlined in the previous references and consideration of attainability of the minimax risk (for which see also two paragraphs above). Sequential problems are included in the treatment of [28]. Perhaps the best approach to proving the HS theorem (in its elimination of extraneous assumptions, minimizing of considerations such as measurability, etc.) is a streamlined version of the idea used first by Karlin [24] in the context of invariant games; the sketch which follows is of a proof due to Huber; the result is related to work on existence of almost-invariant means (von Neumann, Hewitt, etc.), which has also been noted by Lecam ([33], end of Section 4), who, based on these ideas, also obtained a proof (unpublished) related to that which we now sketch. Suppose first that G is abelian. Let δ_0 be any member of C, hereafter fixed (it suffices to consider $\bar{r}_{\delta_0} < \infty$), and let $K = \{\delta : \bar{r}_{\delta_0} \leq \bar{r}_{\delta_0}\}$. Under fairly general conditions [32], K will be compact in an appropriate topology. (In testing problems, Ω often consists of densities with respect to a fixed σ-finite measure λ, and Wald's "regular convergence" of the sequence

$$\int_A \delta_i(x, d')\lambda(dx)$$

for all A with $\lambda(A) < \infty$, which implies convergence of $\beta_{\delta_i}(F)$, is appropriate; incidentally, K would usually be replaced here and below by $K \cap C_{\alpha\delta_0}$ in testing problems.) For fixed g_1 in G, define the transformation T_{g_1} on C by $(T_{g_1}\delta)(x, \Delta) = \delta(g_1 x, \bar{\bar{g}}_1 \Delta)$. The problem is assumed such that for each g_1 the transformation T_{g_1} is continuous in the above topology. (If $\lambda(gA) < \infty$ whenever $\lambda(A) < \infty$, this is automatic in the testing setting just mentioned parenthetically; examples show that the HS property does not necessarily hold in other problems for HS groups without some such restriction; see [28], examples v and C.) Since T_{g_1} is a continuous linear map of convex compact K into itself, the subset K_1 of K of fixed points under T_{g_1} is nonempty (Schauder-Tychonoff), and one verifies that K_1 is compact and convex. Note that K_1 consists precisely of those δ_1 in K for which $\delta_1(g_1 x, \bar{\bar{g}}_1 \Delta) = \delta_1(x, \Delta)$, i.e., for which δ_1 is invariant under g_1. Next, for fixed g_2 in G, one observes that T_{g_1} maps K_1 into itself (which is where the abelian nature of G is used) and repeats the argument to obtain for the fixed points of K_1 under T_{g_2} a nonempty convex compact set $K_2 \subset K_1$, where K_2 consists of those δ_2 in K which are invariant under both g_1 and g_2. Continuing in this way, for any finite collection $g_1, g_2, \ldots, g_m$, we obtain that $\bigcap_{i=1}^{m}\{\delta : \delta \in K,\ \delta$ invariant under $g_i\}$ is compact and nonempty. Hence by compactness, $\bigcap_{g \in G}\{\delta : \delta \in K,$ δ invariant under $g\}$ is nonempty, and any of its members is a g-invariant δ' in K, proving the HS property. For G_1 a closed normal subgroup of G and $G/G_1 = G_2$ abelian, one proceeds (again as in Karlin [24]) to prove that if the HS property holds for G_1, then because of the validity of the HS theorem for abelian G_2, the result holds for G. This really amounts to invariance in steps as considered by Lehmann [35]. In summary, then, using also the validity of the HS theorem for compact groups (see the previous paragraph), one obtains that if $G = G_0 \supset G_1 \supset G_2 \ldots \supset G_h = \{\text{identity}\}$ with G_{i+1} a closed normal subgroup of G_i and G_i/G_{i+1} compact or abelian for each i (such a G herein being called HS), and if the compactness and continuity conditions on C and T_g are satisfied, then the HS property holds. Using more general fixed-point theorems (Kakutani, Bohnenblust-Karlin, Fan, etc.), one can weaken the continuity assumption.

There are many directions of generalization; to mention only one, first considered in [42], if $g\Omega \subset \Omega$ for only a suitably large subset of elements g of a noncompact G (as in the univariate translation parameter problem with $\Omega =$ half-line), the result still holds; in particular, one can consider transformation semigroups, and the earlier allusion to existence of almost invariant means is relevant.

By now it is well known from several examples of Stein [52, 35, 22][2] that the HS property is not generally valid, even in testing problems, if G is the full linear group of real nonsingular $p \times p$ matrices with $p \geq 2$. (Examples can also be constructed for other Lie groups which are not HS.) In many such examples the solvable group G_T of lower triangular $p \times p$ matrices is transitive on Ω (or on each Ω_i in testing problems) and the unique best G_T-invariant procedure is not G-invariant, so that the best G-invariant procedure cannot be minimax or even admissible. In other settings, such as that of estimating normal multiple regression coefficients [55], the use of a transitive solvable subgroup of the group G of all affine transformations leaving the problem invariant does yield the classical G-invariant procedure as minimax. In still other settings, such as the multivariate normal problems where the Hotelling T^2 test and the R^2 (squared multiple correlation coefficient) test of independence are traditionally used, and where these tests are best G-invariant, G_T is

[2] In terms of the discussion on page 263, this conclusion can also be deduced from Peisakoff's example [42] concerning the free group on two generators, Sanov's result that the latter is isomorphic to a subgroup of the full linear group for $p \geq 2$, and the fact that existence of an invariant mean for a group implies it for a subgroup.

not transitive on the Ω_i, and one is faced with using method (a) for the reduced problem in terms of a G_T-maximal invariant and (in these examples) compact parameter space. This approach was used successfully [15, 17] for only the smallest nontrivial p and n; it seems unprofitable to try for general n and p to obtain analogues of the rather messy unique least-favorable *a priori* distributions obtained in the simplest cases, although a few such cases seem approachable in the same way; there is a good possibility that the use of method (a) on the original problem, rather than on the G_T-reduced problem where much symmetry has been lost, will involve less computational complexity.

Thus, the classical minimax properties of the usual univariate normal tests (e.g., [28, 35]), as well as the results of Wald, Hsu, and Simaika (e.g., [60, 63]), do not have meaningful multivariate counterparts which can be obtained as easily. Incidentally, in contrast with these univariate ANOVA results or the minimax results of [15] and [17], the results of [48], discussed below, make it appear doubtful that any single test is minimax uniformly for a natural set of alternative contours in such settings as MANOVA.

In the absence of easily obtained genuine minimax results in multivariate testing problems, various local and asymptotic (in distance from Ω_0, not in n) results [16, 48] have been obtained, the computational complexity being reduced when one considers only the behavior of the first nonzero derivative of β_δ on the boundary Ω_0 of Ω_1 or the behavior of β_δ far from Ω_0. These generalize some of the classical Neyman-Pearson local considerations [41] and subsequent developments [21, 29, 36]. We mention as an example of the difference between univariate and multivariate problems that, whereas the classical F test both maximizes locally the Gaussian curvature of the power function and also has the well-known minimax property, the T^2 test has a local analogue of the latter but not of the former.

3. ADMISSIBILITY AND COMPLETE CLASSES

The methods which have been used to obtain admissibility results in various settings include (A) the Bayes method, of showing that a procedure is unique Bayes relative to some π, or is Bayes in a setting where all risk functions are continuous and where π gives positive measure to each open set; (B) methods which use exponential type, monotone-likelihood ratio, or similar structure; (C) Cramér-Rao inequality; (D) local properties; and (E) extensions of (A) to formal Bayes procedures relative to improper π^*'s. Method (A) has been used by many authors, of whom we mention Lehmann and Stein [37], Lehmann [35], and Ellison [10] as containing multiparameter examples. We shall also discuss below [30] and [50] in this category. The complete class result of Lehmann [34] for one-parameter exponential-type distributions, and parts of Karlin's extensive investigation of decision procedures for distributions of

Polya type (e.g., [25]) make use of the methods of (A) and (D), in the setting of (B). On the other hand, the work of Birnbaum [1], Stein [54], Nandi [40], Ghosh [19], and Schwartz [49], as well as of Roy and Mikhail [45] (where, however, the method is inapplicable in at least one of the cases treated, for reasons given at the end of this paragraph and discussed in more detail in [30]), makes use of the structure of (B) in a way particularly applicable to convex acceptance regions (in an appropriate reduced sample space) for certain testing problems. For example, suppose in the σ-finite case with λ Lebesgue measure on $S = E^k$ that Ω_0 is a single element θ_0, and that for each half-space H (with bounding hyperplane not necessarily through the origin) of S and subset N of $S - H$ with $P_{\theta_0}\{N\} > 0$, there is a sequence $\{\theta_i\}$ in Ω_1 such that $\lim_i P_{\theta_i}\{N\}/P_{\theta_i}\{H\} \to \infty$ (for which it is easy to give simple sufficient conditions in terms of p_θ). The admissibility of any convex acceptance region A is then proved by noting that if B is any other acceptance region of the same size, then we can find $H \supset A$ and $N \subset B - A$ satisfying the above description, and conclude easily that $\beta_A(\theta_i) > \beta_B(\theta_i)$ for i sufficiently large, so that no such B is better than A and thus A is admissible. Birnbaum considered the case where the p_θ are a k-parameter exponential family and Ω itself is E^k; in some of the multivariate problems considered by the other cited authors, there are restrictions on Ω in this exponential family representation, so that the existence of the sequence $\{\theta_i\}$ is more difficult to establish, and, typically, only certain convex regions A can be handled by the method. Moreover, whereas Birnbaum completely characterized the admissible procedures, in such settings as MANOVA, considered by Schwartz [49], there is a difference between the necessary and the sufficient conditions given for a procedure in $C_\alpha^{(G)}$ to be C_α-admissible, which does not seem easy to eliminate by previously used techniques. We note also that, if Ω_0 is composite, Birnbaum's method as it stands is not applicable to obtain necessary conditions for admissibility. The sufficiency (for admissibility) part of the method is inapplicable in such settings as the normal test of independence (R^2), since the required condition does not hold for any $\{\theta_i\}$, even those approaching degenerate laws ($E_{\theta_i} R^2 \to 1$).

Method (C) has already been discussed in Section 2. Examples of method (D), which goes back to the Neyman-Pearson theory, can be found in Lehmann [35]; the most common occurrence is with unique uniformly or locally most powerful unbiased tests in cases where (local) unbiasedness implies similarity on that part of the boundary of Ω_1 which is in Ω_0. Uniformly most powerful tests can be regarded as a special case of (A), whereas a result like Wald's theorem [60 and 63] can be regarded as an application of (A) to the similar tests obtained from unbiasedness considerations (D). Methods (C) and (D) have not been applied much to classical multivariate problems. In the case of (C), this is because of the limitation to estimation settings, where the desired admissibility conclusion is often false and where, even where it is true (as in [57] for the bivariate normal case), the analysis appears to be much more formidable than in the invariate case. As for (D), it seems to offer greater possibilities; what is often missing is the addition of a *uniqueness* result to local results of the type discussed in Section 2.

The questions (i) and (ii) of Section 1 have already indicated the importance of method (E), which has deservedly received continued attention in the literature for over 10 years, and especially in the last few. Most (but not all) papers have focused on question (ii) for $\pi^* = \nu$ and $G = \Omega$ in estimation or G isomorphic to each of Ω_0 and Ω_1 in testing. The first of these is the classical paper of Blyth [4] in the case $G =$ additive group of reals of estimating a univariate translation parameter for a normal or rectangular density with known scale. (Part of Farrell [11] improves Blyth's sequential results.) Blackwell [2] obtained the first results for a general collection of problems, namely, estimation for discrete univariate location parameter distributions with finite support. Stein [55] considered the univariate location-parameter problem in the absolutely continuous case with squared-error loss, and Farrell [11] considered this problem for more general loss functions, concentrating on the implication of admissibility by the condition of uniqueness of the best invariant estimator, which in turn is a consequence of strict convexity of w. (Lack of uniqueness thus provides one source of counterexamples to admissibility of best invariant procedures.) A scale parameter problem is of course reduced to a location-parameter problem by taking logarithms. Brown [5] considered this univariate location-parameter problem for general loss functions in the sequential case (which is somewhat surprising, since one cannot generally write down a best invariant procedure explicitly there). Perhaps Brown's calculations resemble Blackwell's more than Blyth's, while Stein's and Farrell's are more like Blyth's. Fox and Rubin [13] considered a specific W in detail. For this same group (additive reals), Lehmann and Stein [38] obtained admissibility results in univariate location-parameter testing problems; again, lack of uniqueness of the best invariant procedure can mean inadmissibility. The somewhat different approach of Karlin [26] will be mentioned below.

We shall not discuss here the integrability conditions on W in these references; see [5] for examples which indicate that such conditions are not completely dispensable. Nor shall we discuss the considerations there of proving that almost-admissibility of an invariant procedure δ' (nonexistence of δ with $r_\delta(\theta) \le r_{\delta'}(\theta)$ and strict inequality on a set of positive Lebesgue measure) implies admissibility. The finer nature of almost admissibility of δ' compared with minimaxity is expressed in the fact that the latter can be phrased as $\bar{r}_\delta \le \bar{r}_{\delta'} \Rightarrow \bar{r}_\delta = \bar{r}_{\delta'}$, whereas (for example, again with $G \cong \Omega \cong E^1$) the former can be phrased as $\bar{r}_\delta \le \bar{r}_{\delta'} \Rightarrow r_\delta(\theta) = \bar{r}_{\delta'}$ almost everywhere.

Blyth's approach is to find a sequence of *a priori* Lebesgue densities $\pi_i'(\theta)$ such that, for any compact subset H of Ω, $\pi_i'(\theta) \geq \varepsilon_H/i$ for $i >$ some integer q_H, with $\varepsilon_H > 0$ (the simplest choice being of the form $\pi_i'(\theta) = \pi_1'(\theta/i)/i$ with π_1' suitably smooth); and such that $\bar{r}_{\delta'} - R_{\delta_{\pi_i}}(\pi_i) = o(1/i)$. If there were a δ^* better than δ' with $\bar{r}_{\delta'} - r_{\delta^*}(\theta) > \varepsilon > 0$ on a (bounded) set of positive measure, we would then have $r_{\delta'} - R_{\delta^*}(\pi_i) > \varepsilon'/i$ for i large, with $\varepsilon' > 0$, contradicting the Bayes character of δ_{π_i}. The greater delicacy of this argument than that of Eq. (1) of Section 1 (as discussed under (C) of Section 2) in the present example is evident in the fact that there are many examples where the choice of π_i as uniform on $(-i, i)$ suffices for the minimax but not for the admissibility proof.

The two-dimensional translation-parameter estimation problem ($G \cong \Omega \cong E^2$ under vector addition) is more delicate; the choice $\pi_i'(\theta) = \pi_1'(\theta/i)/i^2$ now yields ε'/i^2 in place of ε'/i in the previous paragraph, and the $o(1/i)$ term there is also at best of order $1/i^2$, yielding no contradiction. A suitable choice of the π_i which can be used to prove admissibility is given by Stein [22] in the case of squared error. A somewhat different approach of Brown (unpublished) treats more general loss functions.

In the case of a three- or higher-dimensional translation-parameter estimation problem, inadmissibility of the best invariant estimator was shown by Stein [54] and by James and Stein [22], quadratic loss normal calculations being given in some detail. It is interesting to note that the latter reference (end of Section 2) shows the inadmissibility of classical best linear unbiased estimators even for certain nonparametric problems. Brown [5] obtains further inadmissibility results. In Stein [56], discussed already in Section 2, Stein's translation-parameter admissibility and inadmissibility results which we have mentioned are used to obtain corresponding results for certain normal multiple regression problems with n sufficiently large. Further work on high-dimensional translation-parameter estimation has been done by Baranchik, Brown, and Srivastava (none as yet published).

In all the above translation-parameter problems, the unknown parameter θ is being estimated. If a subset of the components of θ are being estimated, the situation is somewhat altered. For example, if X and θ are four-dimensional but only one component of θ is being estimated (say with squared error loss), there are examples where the unique best invariant estimator is admissible (the most trivial cases being those where the components of X are independent) and others where it is inadmissible. Blackwell [2] gave the first example of the latter, and the matter is discussed by Stein [22]; the admissible and inadmissible cases are not yet delimited.

Still referring to invariant estimation problems, one would next investigate the nonabelian noncompact groups. For example, in the case of a density depending on unknown real location and positive scale parameter, we are dealing with the real affine group. If only one of these parameters is to be estimated, we have the analogue of the situation described in the previous paragraph. There are few results here, the first being the inadmissibility result of Stein [57] for the problem of estimating the variance of a normal distribution. Inadmissibility of the best invariant estimator of a quantile other than the median in this setting was proved by Brown (unpublished), who has also considered such problems as that of [57] for other distributions. One interesting feature pointed out by Stein is that whereas inadmissibility or nonmaximality results for best invariant procedures can often be proved by showing that no $C^{(G)}$-wide-sense Bayes procedure is C-wide-sense Bayes, the classical estimator considered in [57] has the latter property but not the former!

As for estimation problems involving the full linear group or other non-HS groups, we have already seen in Section 2 that we cannot expect best invariant estimators to be minimax, let alone admissible.

We turn next to the univariate estimation problem where questions (i) and (ii) have been considered in the following cases, other than that of admissibility of best invariant estimators: (I) $\pi^* \neq \nu$ in the translation parameter problems, (II) translation parameter with truncated range, (III) extreme-value densities, and (IV) exponential families. Karlin [26] considers not only the admissibility of the best invariant estimator for the univariate translation-parameter problem (discussed earlier), but also the question of which estimators of the form cx are admissible for squared error loss in cases (III) and (IV). (In [8] linear estimators of linear functions of a multivariate normal mean are considered similarly.) The inadmissibility parts of (III) and (IV) are obtained, as in the examples we have mentioned in earlier paragraphs, by constructing better procedures. The admissibility parts of these (as well as of the location parameter considerations of [26]) are treated by explicitly representing the estimator as a δ_{π^*} and then carrying through the admissibility proof by a Fourier-analysis technique which differs from the admissibility proofs described earlier. Katz [27] and Farrell [11] considered cases of (II), while Farrell [11] also considered (I). Complete class results for the class of δ_{π^*}'s were obtained by Sacks [46, 47] for (IV) and for certain cases of (II); examples which indicate limitations on the validity of such conclusions and the additional complications of (I) over (II) are included, and multiparameter extensions are considered. In Farrell [12], limits of sequences $\{\delta_{\pi_i}\}$ are considered particularly in case (I), and the question of when these limits are δ_{π^*}'s is studied; the possibility that this is not the case and that, for example, some *a priori* probability not absorbed in π^* "escapes to ∞", is treated in detail. The general picture here appears to be quite complicated (as does the extension of some of the work of Katz-Sacks-Farrell to k-variate analogues). Related is the question now being attacked in general settings by Stein [58] of the extent to which various improper π^*'s can be sufficiently well approximated by proper π's (in the sense that there is high π-probability that the formal *a posteriori* law based on *a priori* law π^* is close in an appropriate sense to that based on π); we have mentioned earlier Stein's emphasis on this approximatability point of view. Incidentally, his necessary and sufficient condition for admissibility [51], which had not shown much applicability earlier, is invoked in this study. [*Added in proof:* In the *Fifth Berkeley Symp.* Stein carries out this development in special cases of the univariate translation-parameter problem, and the equivalence of admissibility to nonintegrability of $d\nu/d\pi^*$ is established under certain restrictions.] As yet no analogues of the Katz-Sacks-Farrell considerations for testing problems have been published.

The only general invariant testing result we have mentioned under (E) is that of Lehmann and Stein [38]. Presumably this can be extended to the two-dimensional translation-parameter problem, although this result has not yet appeared in print. There is evidence, however, that a much more general admissibility result for unique best invariant procedures is valid in testing problems than in estimation problems. For example, this seems to be the case for a broad class of p-variate location-parameter problems, even for $p \geq 3$, although I have been unable to obtain a satisfactory general condition; far from there being general inadmissibility results like those of [53], [22], and [5], quite the opposite may be true. The approach of [38], which is similar analytically to those we have mentioned in estimation problems, and which fails in the latter for $p \geq 3$ (where the admissibility conclusion is false), cannot be expected to be modified to work in any testing problems; a new approach seems to be called for. There is no indication yet as to whether or not the approach of [58] will satisfactorily separate the conclusions in estimation from those in testing. A further consideration is that, although some examples (e.g., [35, 52]) show that for non-HS groups best invariant tests need not be minimax, let alone admissible, there are also many examples where such procedures are minimax and admissible. This is very much unlike the estimation situation, where it seems more exceptional that a best G-invariant procedure, for G non-HS, be admissible; the estimation example of [22] appears to be more typical than are the admissible cases of [55], in this respect. One indication of this difference between estimation and testing is that, in such a simple case as that of a translation parameter (of any dimension p), it cannot be that the best invariant procedure is a genuine Bayes procedure, while this can well be the case in corresponding testing examples, where the action of G on D is trivial. (Similar results can hold in other problems where G/J is compact, where J leaves a point of D fixed.) Thus, we return to method (A). Lehmann and Stein [37] presented the first examples of invariant tests which were admissible for the noninvariant reason of being genuinely Bayes. (They were actually concerned with proving most powerful test results which are stronger than admissibility and which we shall not discuss further here.) Kiefer and Schwartz [30] used somewhat different forms of *a priori* distributions to prove that many classical invariant tests (such as those based on T^2 and R^2) are genuinely Bayes; even in cases where admissibility had been proved earlier by method (B), the Bayes approach reflects the goodness of the power function on a different part of the parameter space. These forms of the *a priori* law are to some extent suggested by the structure of the θ_i which enter in method (B) (which, however, as we have remarked, does not actually succeed in the R^2 problem). This Bayes approach, used somewhat at random in [30], has been organized and developed by Schwartz [50] into a theory which shows for certain multivariate problems (usually exponential) that any $C^{(G)}$-Bayes procedure which satisfies an integrability condition involving the *a priori* law, is actually C-Bayes. In MANOVA, for example, the presence of this integrability condition can be exhibited in an alternative form: If, in the space of the maximal invariant (the usual set of latent roots) an acceptance region A is $C^{(G)}$-Bayes for a given n, then A is C-Bayes for slightly larger n. The method clearly has limitations; for example, the "largest root" test in MANOVA, which can be proved admissible by method (B), cannot be Bayes, on grounds of analyticity; as in [1], limits of Bayes procedures are needed. It would be interesting to extend the theory of [50] to include such considerations.

To illustrate what can happen in testing in a much simpler mechanism than that studied in [50], and which merely formalizes the structure observed in the examples of [37], suppose that $X = (Z, Y)$, $\Omega_0 \cong \Omega_1 \cong G \cong$ range (Z), and that the θ density of X with respect to σ-finite $\lambda = \gamma \times \mu$ is, in Ω_i, $g_i(y)h_i(\theta^{-1}z \mid y)$, where g_i is the marginal γ-density of the G-maximal invariant Y under Ω_i. Suppose one can find probability measures π_j on G such that $\int h_1(\theta^{-1}z \mid y)\pi_1(d\theta) = \int h_0(\theta^{-1}z \mid y)\pi_0(d\theta)$. Then the best invariant ($C^{(G)}$-Neyman-Pearson) critical region $\{y : g_1(y)/g_0(y) \geq k\}$ is clearly C-Bayes. (There are clearly many examples for each G. For a simple p-variate location parameter example from [37], let $X_1, \ldots, X_n$ be independent normal p vectors with unknown p-variate mean θ and with covariance matrix I under Ω_1 and $2I$ under Ω_0; here it suffices to concentrate π_0 on a single point and to have π_1 an appropriate multivariate normal law.) This approach can be extended to problems where G is not transitive on the Ω_i and where there is a subgroup G' which leaves a point of Ω fixed. The work of [50] can be viewed as showing in certain of these more complex settings that such π_j do indeed exist for certain multivariate (usually exponential) problems, and of characterizing these π_j's and the resulting $C_\alpha^{(G)}$ tests which are C_α-Bayes (no longer unique if G is not transitive).

REFERENCES

1. Birnbaum, A. (1955). Characterization of complete classes of tests of some multiparametric hypotheses, with applications to likelihood ratio tests. *Ann. Math. Statist.* **26** 21–36.
2. Blackwell, D. (1951). On the translation parameter problem for discrete variables. *Ann. Math. Statist.* **22** 393–399.
3. Blackwell, D. and Girshick, M. A. (1954). *Theory of Games and Statistical Decisions.* Wiley, New York.
4. Blyth, C. R. (1951). On minimax statistical decision procedures and their admissibility. *Ann. Math. Statist.* **22** 22–42.
5. Brown, L. (1964). Admissibility of translation-invariant estimators. Thesis, Cornell Univ.; published in part in *Ann. Math. Statist.*, October 1966.
6. Chen, Hsi-ju. (1964). Minimax estimates of parameter vectors of translation. *Chinese Math.* **5** 300–315.
7. Chen, Hsi-ju (1964). On minimax invariant estimation of scale and location parameters. *Scienita Sinica.* **13** 1569–1586.
8. Cohen, A. (1965). Estimates of linear combinations of the parameters in the mean vector of a multivariate distribution. *Ann. Math. Statist.* **36** 78–87. See also abstract, 1081.
9. Das Gupta, S., Anderson, T. W., and Mudholkar, G. S. (1964). Monotonicity of the power functions of some tests of the multivariate linear hypothesis. *Ann. Math. Statist.* **35** 200–205.
10. Ellison, B. E. (1962). A classification problem in which information about alternative distributions is based on samples. *Ann. Math. Statist.* **35** 213–223.
11. Farrell, R. (1964). Estimators of a location parameter in the absolutely continuous case. *Ann. Math. Statist.* **35** 949–998.
12. Farrell, R. (1965). Weak limits of sequences of Bayes procedures in estimation theory. *Proc. Fifth Berkeley Symp. Math. Statist. Prob.* To be published.
13. Fox, M. and Rubin, H. (1964). Admissibility of quantile estimates of a single location parameter. *Ann. Math. Statist.* **35** 1019–1030.
14. Geisser, S. (1965). Bayesian estimation in multivariate analysis. *Ann. Math. Statist.* **36** 150–159.
15. Giri, N., Kiefer, J., and Stein C. (1963). Minimax character of Hotelling's T^2-test in the simplest case. *Ann. Math. Statist.* **34** 1524–1535.
16. Giri, N. and Kiefer, J. (1964). Local and asymptotic minimax properties of multivariate tests. *Ann. Math. Statist.* **35** 21–35.
17. Giri, N., and Kiefer, J. (1964). Minimax character of the R^2-test in the simplest case. *Ann. Math. Statist.* **35** 1475–1490.
18. Girschick, M. A. and Savage, L. J. (1950). Bayes and minimax estimates for quadratic loss functions. *Proc. Second Berkeley Symp. Math. Statist. Prob.* 53–73.
19. Ghosh, M. N. (1964). On the admissibility of some tests of Manova. *Ann. Math. Statist.* **35** 789–794.
20. Hodges, J. L. Jr. and Lehmann, E. L. (1951). Some applications of the Cramér-Rao inequality. *Proc. Second Berkeley Symp. Math. Statist. Prob.* 13–22.
21. Isaacson, S. L. (1951). On the theory of unbiased tests of simple statistical hypotheses specifying the values of two or more parameters. *Ann. Math. Statist.* **22** 217–234.
22. James, W. and Stein, C. (1960). Estimation with quadratic loss. *Proc. Fourth Berkeley Symp. Math. Statist. Prob.* **1** 361–379.
23. Jeffreys, H. (1939). *Theory of Probability.* Oxford Univ. Press, New York.
24. Karlin, S. (1953). The theory of infinite games. *Ann. Math.* **58** 371–401.

25. KARLIN, S. (1957). Polya type distributions, II. *Ann. Math. Statist.* **28** 281–308.
26. KARLIN, S. (1958). Admissibility for estimation with quadratic loss. *Ann. Math. Statist.* **29** 406–436.
27. KATZ, M. W. (1961). Admissible and minimax estimates of parameters in truncated spaces. *Ann. Math. Statist.* **32** 136–142.
28. KIEFER, J. (1957). Invariance, minimax sequential estimation, and continuous time processes. *Ann. Math. Statist.* **28** 573–601.
29. KIEFER, J. (1958). On the nonrandomized optimality and randomized nonoptimality of symmetrical designs. *Ann. Math. Statist.* **29** 675–699.
30. KIEFER, J. and SCHWARTZ, R. (1959). Admissible Bayes character of T^2, R^2, and other fully invariant tests for classical multivariate normal problems. *Ann. Math. Statist.* **36** 747–770.
31. KUDO, H. (1955). On minimax invariant estimators of the transformation parameter. *Nat. Sci. Rep. Ochanomizu Univ.* **6** 31–73.
32. LECAM, L. (1955). An extension of Wald's theory of statistical decision functions. *Ann. Math. Statist.* **26** 69–81.
33. LECAM, L. (1964). Sufficiency and approximate sufficiency. *Ann. Math. Statist.* **35** 1419–1455.
34. LEHMANN, E. L. (1947). On families of admissible tests. *Ann. Math. Statist.* **18** 97–104.
35. LEHMANN, E. L. (1959). *Testing Statistical Hypotheses.* Wiley, New York.
36. LEHMANN, E. L. 1959). Optimum invariant tests. *Ann. Math. Statist.* **30** 881–884.
37. LEHMANN, E. L. and STEIN, C. (1948). Most powerful tests of composite hypotheses. I. Normal distributions. *Ann. Math. Statist.* **19** 495–516.
38. LEHMANN, E. L. and STEIN, C. (1953). The admissibility of certain invariant statistical tests involving a translation parameter. *Ann. Math. Statist.* **24** 473–479.
39. LEHAMNN, E. L. and STEIN, C. (1953). The totality of transformations leaving a family of normal distributions invariant (abstract). *Ann. Math. Statist.* **24** 142.
40. NANDI, H. K. (1963). On the admissibility of a class of tests. *Calcutta Statist. Assoc. Bull.* **15** 13–18.
41. NEYMAN, J. and PEARSON, E. S. (1938). Contributions to the theory of testing statistical hypotheses, III. *Statist. Res. Mem.* **2** 25–27.
42. PEISAKOFF, M. P. (1950). *Transformation Parameters.* Thesis, Princeton Univ.
43. PITMAN, E. J. G. (1939). The estimation of location and scale parameters of a continuous population of any given form. *Biometrika* **30** 391–421.
44. PITMAN, E. J. G. (1939). Tests of hypotheses concerning location and scale parameters. *Biometrika* **31** 200–215.
45. ROY, S. N. and MIKHAIL, W. F. (1960). On the admissibility of a class of tests in normal multivariate analysis (abstract). *Ann. Math. Statist.* **31** 536.
46. SACKS, J. (1960). Generalized Bayes solutions in estimation problems (abstract). *Ann. Math. Statist.* **31** 246.
47. SACKS, J. (1963). Generalized Bayes solutions in estimation problems. *Ann. Math. Statist.* **34** 751–768.
48. SCHWARTZ, R. (1964). Properties of a test in Manova (abstract). *Ann. Math. Statist.* **35** 939.
49. SCHWARTZ, R. (1964). Admissible invariant tests in Manova (abstract). *Ann. Math. Statist.* **35** 1398.
50. SCHWARTZ, R. (1966). Invariant proper Bayes procedures. This volume. Also Thesis, Cornell Univ.
51. STEIN, C. (1955). A necessary and sufficient condition for admissibility. *Ann. Math. Statist.* **26** 518–522.

52. STEIN, C. (1955). On tests of certain hypotheses invariant under the full linear group (abstract). *Ann. Math. Statist.* **26** 769.
53. STEIN, C. (1955). Inadmissibility of the usual estimator for the mean of a multivariate normal distribution. *Proc. Third Berkeley Symp. Math. Statist. Prob.* **1** 197–206.
54. STEIN, C. (1956). The admissibility of Hotelling's T^2-test. *Ann. Math. Statist.* **27** 616–623.
55. STEIN, C. (1959). The admissibility of Pitman's estimator of a single location parameter. *Ann. Math. Statist.* **30** 970–979.
56. STEIN, C. (1960). Multiple regression. *Hotelling Festschr.* Stanford Univ. Press, 424–443.
57. STEIN, C. (1964). Inadmissibility of the usual estimator for the variance of a normal distribution with unknown mean. *Ann. Inst. Statist. Math.* **16** 155–160.
58. STEIN, C. (1965). Approximation of improper prior measures by prior probability measures. *Bernoulli-Bayes-Laplace Festschr.* Springer-Verlag, New York, 217–240.
59. WALD, A. (1939). Contributions to the theory of statistical estimation and testing hypotheses. *Ann. Math. Statist.* **10** 299–326.
60. WALD, A. (1942). On the power function of the analysis of variance test. *Ann. Math. Statist.* **13** 434–439.
61. WALD, A. (1950). *Statistical Decision Functions.* Wiley, New York.
62. WESLER, O. (1959). Invariance theory and a modified minimax principle. *Ann. Math. Statist.* **30** 1–20.
63. WOLFOWITZ, J. (1949). The power of the classical tests associated with the normal distribution. *Ann. Math. Statist.* **20** 540–551.
64. WOLFOWITZ, J. (1950). Minimax estimates of the mean of a normal distribution with known variance. *Ann. Math. Statist.* **21** 218–230.

Fully Invariant Proper Bayes Tests[1]

RICHARD SCHWARTZ

ELECTRONICS LABORATORY
GENERAL ELECTRIC COMPANY
SYRACUSE, NEW YORK

1. INTRODUCTION

In a variety of problems arising in normal multivariate analysis, Kiefer and Schwartz [3] have constructed fully invariant proper Bayes tests. They treat each problem and each test for a given problem somewhat separately. There is little indication of a general method of constructing *a priori* distributions which yield invariant tests, of the requirements on the problem in order that the method be successful, or of the class of tests which can be constructed in this way.

The present paper concentrates on the multivariate analysis of variance (MANOVA). *A priori* distributions are constructed in such a way that the role of the transformation groups which leave the problem invariant is clarified. Verification that the resulting Bayes tests are fully invariant does not depend on an explicit computation of the tests. In fact, each Bayes test has an interpretation which ensures its invariance, and this interpretation permits the characterization of a wide class of proper Bayes test.

This interpretation of the resulting Bayes tests depends on Stein's representation of the probability density of the maximal invariant as an integral over the appropriate transformation group. Although the result seems to be part of the folklore of the subject, no formal statement and proof has ever appeared. In any given problem it is, of course, possible to give a proof based on direct calculation without appealing to the general result. In the MANOVA problem this is simplified, because of the results of Constantine [1] and James [2].

In a subsequent paper the results of the present paper will be generalized to testing problems concerning the parameter of an exponential family of probability densities when the problem remains invariant under a locally compact group. This forthcoming paper will also include a proof of Stein's

[1] This paper is a portion of the author's doctoral thesis at Cornell University and was written, in part, while the author was a National Science Foundation Pre-Doctoral Fellow.

representation mentioned above. The treatment of the MANOVA problem is specifically designed to provide a clear indication of the methods and results in the more general exponential setting. This is discussed in the concluding section.

Sections 1 to 4 of [3] provide background discussion and references to the literature as well as some specific results which we shall require.

2. NOTATION AND THE MANOVA PROBLEM

If A is a square matrix, the determinant of A, the trace of A, the transpose of A, and the exponential of the trace of A will be denoted by $|A|$, tr A, A', and etr A, respectively. The $p \times p$ identity matrix will be denoted by I_p.

We treat the MANOVA problem in canonical form reduced by sufficiency. The random matrices $Y(p \times r)$, $U(p \times s)$, and $Z(p \times p)$ are independent and distributed as follows: The columns of (Y, U) are independent normal p-vectors with common unknown covariance matrix Σ, and the expectation of (Y, U) is (μ, δ). Z has a probability density $W_m(z)$ on the positive definite $p \times p$ matrices given by

$$W_m(z) = C|\Sigma|^{-m/2}|z|^{(m-p-1)/2} \operatorname{etr}\{-\tfrac{1}{2}\Sigma^{-1}z\},$$

where C is a normalizing constant and $m > p - 1$ is real. (If m is an integer, Z is the usual central Wishart variable. Consideration of all real $m > p - 1$ will permit a more unified statement of the results.)

The hypothesis to be tested is

$$H_0: \mu = 0$$

against the alternative

$$H_1: \mu \neq 0.$$

The MANOVA problem remains invariant under the group $G = GL(p) \times 0(r)$, the direct product of the full linear group of nonsingular $p \times p$ matrices and the group of orthogonal $r \times r$ matrices. An element (A, H) of G acts on a point (y, u, z) of the sample space by

$$(A, H)(y, u, z) = (AyH, Au, AzA').$$

The problem is also invariant under R^{ps} the additive group of the real ps times acting by translation on U. A maximal invariant in the sample space is the latent roots of $Y'(YY' + Z)^{-1}Y$.

Lemma 3.1 of [3] will apply to all the *a priori* distributions constructed below. The import of this lemma is that any test which is Bayes with respect to an *a priori* distribution of appropriate form when $s = 0$ (i.e., U absent) is also Bayes for all values of s. Henceforth we treat the case where U is absent;

the general case then follows from an application of the lemma.

Let

$$S = \{p \times p \text{ symmetric matrices}\}$$
$$S_+ = \{p \times p \text{ positive-definite symmetric matrices}\}$$
$$E^k = \text{Euclidean } k\text{-dimensional space}$$
$$D = S \times E^{pr}$$
$$D_+ = S_+ \times E^{pr}.$$

Let

$$\Gamma = \Sigma^{-1} \qquad \text{and} \qquad \eta = \Sigma^{-1}\mu.$$

In keeping with the exponential structure of the problem we shall denote a parameter point by (Γ, η) instead of (Σ, μ). The induced group, $\bar{G}$, of transformations on the parameter space is isomorphic to G; that is,

$$\bar{G} = GL(p) \times O(r).$$

An element (A, H) of $\bar{G}$ acts on a point (Γ, η) by

$$(A, H)(\Gamma, \eta) = (A'^{-1}\Gamma A^{-1}, A'^{-1}\eta H).$$

Both the sample space and the parameter space are copies of D_+. (Γ, η), in addition to denoting a parameter point, will also denote the linear functional defined on D by

$$(\Gamma, \eta)(v, w) = \operatorname{tr}[-\tfrac{1}{2}\Gamma v + \eta' w].$$

With this notation the joint density $f^{(m)}_{(\Gamma,\eta)}(y, z)$ of (Y, Z) is

$$f^{(m)}_{(\Gamma,\eta)} = C_m h_m(\Gamma, \eta)\, d_m(y, z) \exp\{(\Gamma, \eta)(yy' + z, y)\}, \tag{2.1}$$

where C_m is a normalizing constant,

$$h_m(\Gamma, \eta) = |\Gamma|^{(m+r)/2} \operatorname{etr}\{-\tfrac{1}{2}\eta'\Gamma^{-1}\eta\}$$

and

$$d_m(y, z) = |z|^{(m-p-1)/2}.$$

Finally let M_m denote the MANOVA problem described above when Z has density W_m. Let $M_m{}^*$ denote the same problem reduced by invariance. $M_m{}^*$ is the problem of testing the hypothesis $H_0{}^*$ that the latent roots of $\eta'\Gamma^{-1}\eta$ $(=\mu'\Sigma^{-1}\mu)$ are all zero against the hypothesis $H_1{}^*$ that the latent roots of $\eta'\Gamma^{-1}\eta$ are not all zero, on the basis of observing the latent roots of $Y'(YY' + Z)^{-1}Y$, whose joint probability density will be noted by $f^{(m)*}_{(\Gamma,\eta)}$.

3. IMPROPER BAYES TESTS

Starting with any probability measure $\xi = \xi_0 + \xi_1$ with ξ_j supported on $\{(\Gamma, \eta) | (\Gamma, \eta) \in H_j\}$, there is a formal procedure for constructing improper invariant Bayes tests.

Let

$$\Gamma = A'\gamma A \qquad \text{and} \qquad \eta = A'\theta H,$$

where

$$(\gamma, \theta) \in D_+ \qquad \text{and} \qquad (A, H) \in GL(p) \times O(r).$$

Let $dA\, dH$ denote Haar measure on $GL(p) \times O(r)$; $dA = |AA'|^{-p/2}\, dv$, where v is the Lebesgue measure on E^{p^2}. Then the *improper* Bayes test with critical region

$$\frac{\int_{D+} \int_{O(r)} \int_{GL(p)} f^{(m)}_{(A'\gamma A, A'\theta H)}(y, z)\, dA\, dH\, d\xi_1(\gamma, \theta)}{\int_{D+} \int_{O(r)} \int_{GL(p)} f^{(m)}_{(A'\gamma A, A'\theta H)}(y, z)\, dA\, dH\, d\xi_0(\gamma, \theta)} > K \tag{3.1}$$

is invariant, as we now show.

Let

$$L^{(m)}_{(\gamma,\theta)}(y, z) = \int_{O(r)} \int_{GL(p)} f^{(m)}_{(A'\gamma A, A'\theta H)}(y, z)\, dA\, dH.$$

Since for $(A_0, H_0) \in GL(p) \times O(r)$,

$$f^{(m)}_{(\Gamma,\eta)}((A_0, H_0)(y, z)) = |A_0|^{-(p+r+1)} f^{(m)}_{(A_0'\Gamma A_0, A_0'\eta H)}(y, z),$$

it is immediate using the invariance of $dA\, dH$ that

$$L^{(m)}_{(\gamma,\theta)}((A_0, H_0)(y, z)) = |A_0|^{-(p+r+1)} L^{(m)}_{(\gamma,\theta)}(y, z).$$

The term $|A_0|^{-(p+r+1)}$ appears in both the numerator and denominator of the left side of (3.1), and therefore the test (3.1) is invariant.

Although the verification of the invariance of (3.1) did not depend on the explicit evaluation of $L^{(m)}_{(\gamma,\theta)}$, it is important to what follows to relate $L^{(m)}_{(\gamma,\theta)}$ to the probability density of the maximal invariant. As mentioned in the introduction, this can be accomplished using Stein's representation without the need for explicit evaluation. However $L^{(m)}_{(\gamma,\theta)}$ will be evaluated explicitly using the results of Constantine [1] and James [2]. This is done partly to avoid invoking unpublished results and partly because it was the explicit results of Constantine and James which first suggested the connection between the method used in [3] and Stein's representation (see in particular the test (4.9) of [3]).

First consider,

$$|z|^{(p+1-m)/2}|yy'+z|^{p/2}\,\mathrm{etr}\{\tfrac{1}{2}\theta'\gamma^{-1}\theta\}L^{(m)}_{(\gamma,\theta)}(y,z)$$

$$=\int_{O(r)}\int_{GL(p)}|yy'+z|^{p/2}|A'\gamma A^{(m+r)/2}|$$

$$\times\,\mathrm{etr}\{-\tfrac{1}{2}A'\gamma A(yy'+z)+H'\theta'Ay\}\,dA\,dH$$

$$=\int_{O(r)}\int_{GL(p)}|yy'+z|^{p/2}|BB'^{(m+r)/2}|$$

$$\times\,\mathrm{etr}\{-\tfrac{1}{2}BB'(yy'+z)+H'\theta'\gamma^{-1/2}By\}\,dB\,dH,$$

where we have substituted $B'=\gamma^{1/2}A$.

The integral over B is evaluated by Constantine [1, Eq. 39]. Neglecting the constants the last expression equals

$$\int_{O(r)}\mathrm{etr}\{\tfrac{1}{2}\gamma^{-1/2}\theta Hy'(yy'+z)^{-1}yH'\theta'\gamma^{-1/2}\}$$

$$\times\,{}_1F_1\left(\frac{m+r-p}{2},\tfrac{1}{2}p;\,-\tfrac{1}{2}\gamma^{-1/2}\theta Hy'(yy'+z)^{-1}yH'\theta'\gamma^{-1/2}\right)dH$$

$$=\int_{O(r)}{}_1F_1\left(-\frac{m+r}{2},\frac{p}{2};\,\tfrac{1}{2}\theta'\gamma^{-1}\theta Hy'(yy'+z)^{-1}yH'\right)dH$$

$$={}_1F_1\left(-\frac{m+r}{2},\frac{p}{2};\,\tfrac{1}{2}\theta'\gamma^{-1}\theta,\,y'(yy'+z)^{-1}y\right).$$

We have used the Kummer transformation formula (see Constantine [1], Eq. 40), and the integral over $O(r)$ has been evaluated according to James ([2], Eq. 30). From Eq. 74 of James [2] we see that

$$L^{(m)}_{(\gamma,\theta)}=k^{(m)}f^{(m)*}_{(\gamma,\theta)},\tag{3.2}$$

where $k^{(m)}$ is a function of (y,z) but is independent of (γ,θ) and $f^{(m)*}_{(\gamma,\theta)}$ is the probability density of the latent roots of $Y'(YY'+Z)^{-1}Y$.

Since the factor $k^{(m)}$ appears in both the numerator and denominator of (3.1), the rejection region (3.1) is again seen to be invariant. In fact, (3.1) is identical to the rejection region

$$\frac{\int_{D_+}f^{(m)*}_{(\gamma,\theta)}\,d\xi_1(\gamma,\theta)}{\int_{D_+}f^{(m)*}_{(\gamma,\theta)}\,d\xi_0(\gamma,\theta)}>K.\tag{3.3}$$

Moreover, any Bayes test for the problem $M_m{}^*$ has a rejection region of the form (3.3).

4. PROPER BAYES TESTS

In this section the construction of the previous section is modified to yield *proper* fully invariant Bayes tests.

Let

$$\Gamma = \tilde{\Gamma} + A'\gamma A \qquad \text{and} \qquad \eta = A'\theta H \tag{4.1}$$

where $\tilde{\Gamma} \in S_+$ is fixed, $(\gamma, \theta) \in D_+$, and $(A, H) \in GL(p) \times O(r)$.

As before, let $\xi = \xi_0 + \xi_1$, with ξ_j supported on H_j for $j = 0, 1$, be any probability measure. Define a measure $P_j^{(u)}((A, H), (\gamma, \theta))$ by

$$dP_j^{(u)}((A, H), (\gamma, \theta)) = \frac{h_u(A'\gamma A, A'\theta H)}{h_m(\tilde{\Gamma} + A'\gamma A, A'\theta H)}\, dA\, dH\, d\xi_j(\gamma, \theta). \tag{4.2}$$

Note that if (Γ, η) is defined by (4.1), then the measure induced on $\{(\Gamma, \eta)\}$ by $P_j^{(u)}$ is supported on H_j for $j = 0, 1$. We now determine the values of u for which $P_j^{(u)}((A, H), (\gamma, \theta))$ is a finite measure.

Consider

$$\int_{GL(p)} \frac{h_u(A'\gamma A, A'\theta H)}{h_m(\tilde{\Gamma} + A'\gamma A, A'\theta H)}\, dA$$

$$= \int_{GL(p)} \frac{|A'\gamma A|^{(u+r)/2} \operatorname{etr}\{-\tfrac{1}{2}\theta'\gamma^{-1}\theta\}}{|\tilde{\Gamma} + A'\gamma A|^{(m+r)/2} \operatorname{etr}\{-\tfrac{1}{2}H'\theta' A(\tilde{\Gamma} + A'\gamma A)^{-1}A'\theta H\}}\, dA.$$

Letting $B' = \gamma^{1/2} A \tilde{\Gamma}^{-1/2}$, this last expression becomes

$$|\tilde{\Gamma}|^{(u-m)/2} \int_{GL(p)} \frac{|BB'|^{(u+r)/2}}{|I_p + BB'|^{(m+r)/2}} \operatorname{etr}\{-\tfrac{1}{2}\theta'\gamma^{-1}\theta + \theta'\gamma^{-1/2}B'$$

$$\times (I + BB')^{-1}B\gamma^{-1/2}\theta\}\, dB \le |\tilde{\Gamma}|^{(u-m)/2} \int_{GL(p)} \frac{|BB'|^{(u+r)/2}}{|I_p + BB'|^{(m+r)/2}}\, dB,$$

since the exponential term is bounded by unity because $I_p - B'(I_p + BB')^{-1}B$ is positive-definite. Finally, this last expression is equal to

$$|\tilde{\Gamma}|^{(u-m)/2} \int_{E^{p^2}} \frac{|BB'|^{(u+r-p)/2}}{|I_p + BB'|^{(m+r)/2}}\, dv.$$

From an obvious modification of Eq. (3.7) of [3] and corresponding considerations near $|BB'| = 0$, this last expression is finite if and only if

$$p - r - 1 < u < m - p + 1. \tag{4.3}$$

It is unnecessary to normalize the *a priori* distribution, since any normalizing constant can be incorporated into the critical level.

For u satisfying (4.3), the proper Bayes critical region corresponding to the finite measure $P^{(u)} = P_0^{(u)} + P_1^{(u)}$ is given by

$$\frac{\int_{D_+}\int_{O(r)}\int_{GL(p)} f^{(m)}_{(\tilde{\Gamma}+A'\gamma A, A'\theta H)}(y, z)\, dP_1^{(u)}((A, H), (\gamma, \theta))}{\int_{D_+}\int_{O(r)}\int_{GL(p)} f^{(m)}_{(\tilde{\Gamma}+A'\gamma A, A'\theta H)}(y, z)\, dP_0^{(u)}((A, H), (\gamma, \theta))} > K. \tag{4.4}$$

Substituting from the definitions in (2.1) and (4.2) and performing obvious cancellations, the left side of (4.4) becomes

$$\frac{\int_{D_+}\int_{O(r)}\int_{GL(p)} h_u(A'\gamma A, A'\theta H) \times \exp\{(\tilde{\Gamma} + A'\gamma A, A'\theta H)(yy' + z, y)\}\, dA\, dH\, d\xi_1(\gamma, \theta)}{\int_{D_+}\int_{O(r)}\int_{GL(p)} h_u(A'\gamma A, A'\theta H) \times \exp\{(\tilde{\Gamma} + A'\gamma A, A'\theta H)(yy' + z, y)\}\, dA\, dH\, d\xi_0(\gamma, \theta)}$$

$$= \frac{\int_{D_+}\int_{O(r)}\int_{GL(p)} h_u(A'\gamma A, A'\theta H) \times \exp\{(A'\gamma A, A'\theta H)(yy' + z, y)\}\, dA\, dH\, d\xi_1(\gamma, \theta)}{\int_{D_+}\int_{O(r)}\int_{GL(p)} h_u(A'\gamma A, A'\theta H) \times \exp\{(A'\gamma A, A'\theta H)(yy' + z, y)\}\, dA\, dH\, d\xi_0(\gamma, \theta)}$$

The elimination of $\tilde{\Gamma}$ utilizes the exponential structure. Finally, multiplying the numerator and denominator of this last expression by a factor depending only on (y, z), we find that the critical region (4.4) is identical to

$$\frac{\int_{D_+}\int_{O(r)}\int_{GL(p)} f^{(u)}_{(A'\gamma A, A'\theta H)}(y, z)\, dA\, dH\, d\xi_1(\gamma, \theta)}{\int_{D_+}\int_{O(r)}\int_{GL(p)} f^{(u)}_{(A'\gamma A, A'\theta H)}(y, z)\, dA\, dH\, d\xi_0(\gamma, \theta)} > K. \tag{4.5}$$

A comparison of (4.5) with (3.1) shows that the two expressions are identical except that m in (3.1) has been replaced by u in (4.5). Thus for each ξ the construction of this section yields a proper Bayes test for the problem M_m identical to the improper Bayes test formally obtained starting with ξ and the problem M_u.

We summarize in the following two theorems:

Theorem 1. *Let $\xi = \xi_0 + \xi_1$ be a probability measure on D_+, with ξ_j supported on H_j for $j = 0, 1$. For each u satisfying* (4.3), *the test* (4.5) *is a fully invariant proper Bayes test for the problem M_m. Moreover, the test* (4.5) *is identical to the test* (3.1) *obtained for the problem M_u as an improper Bayes test.*

Theorem 2. *If a test ϕ is Bayes for the problem $M_u{}^*$ and if $m > u + p - 1$, then ϕ is Bayes for the problem M_m.*

Proof. As remarked at the end of Section 3 any Bayes test for $M_u{}^*$ has a critical region of the form

$$\frac{\int_{D_+} f_{(\gamma,\theta)}^{(u)*} \, d\xi_1(\gamma, \theta)}{\int_{D_+} f_{(\gamma,\theta)}^{(u)*} \, d\xi_0(\gamma, \theta)} > K. \tag{4.6}$$

By (3.3) we have that (4.5) is identical to (4.6).

Loosely, Theorem 2 asserts that a test which is Bayes among invariant tests when the error degrees of freedom equals u is Bayes among all tests whenever the error degrees of freedom, m, is greater than $u + p - 1$.

5. REMARKS

(a) All the Bayes tests constructed in Section 4 are essentially unique and therefore admissible. The resulting test does not depend on the choice of $\tilde{\Gamma}$ in (4.1), although two different choices of $\tilde{\Gamma}$ result in two different *a priori* distributions. Similarly, the resulting test depends only on the marginal distribution under ξ of the latent roots of $\eta'\Gamma^{-1}\eta$.

(b) The condition (4.3) implies that $m > 2p - r - 2$, whereas in [3, Section 4] some tests were obtained under the weaker condition $m \geq p$. In (4.1) take $\tilde{\Gamma} = I$ and let

$$\gamma = (\gamma_{ij})$$

be defined by

$$\gamma_{ij} = \begin{cases} 1, & \text{if } j = i \leq r, \\ 0, & \text{otherwise,} \end{cases}$$

and

$$\theta = (\theta_{ij})$$

be defined by

$$\theta_{ij} = \begin{cases} 1, & \text{if } j = i > r, \\ 0, & \text{otherwise.} \end{cases}$$

Then (Γ, η) depends only on the first r columns of A. In [3] the *a priori* distribution was defined only in terms of the first r columns of A by an appropriate density with respect to the Lebesgue measure on E^{pr}. This is a less restrictive construction, requiring only $m \geq p$. However, the construction masks the role of the transformation groups and is believed to be much more limited in the class of tests which it yields. When $r \geq p$, as, for example, in the derivation of (4.9) [3], the present method is not more restrictive.

(c) It may be wondered whether all the tests obtained in [3] can also be obtained by the present methods (perhaps under a more restrictive assumption on the sample size). The affirmative answer to this question follows from Theorem 2. An invariant proper Bayes test is *a fortiori* Bayes among invariant tests, and therefore by Theorem 2 can be obtained as a proper Bayes test by the present methods for a somewhat larger sample size.

(d) We conclude this paper by sketching in a general exponential setting the method of construction used to obtain fully invariant proper Bayes tests. The symbols used below are all newly defined and should not be confused with their use in previous sections.

Let (χ, B, μ) be a measure space and $(f_{(\theta)}^{(m)}(x); \theta \in \Theta)$ an exponential family of probability densities with respect to μ. Let Q_m be the statistical problem of testing

$$H_0 : \theta \in \Theta_0 \subset \Theta \qquad \text{vs.} \qquad H_1 : \theta \in \Theta_1 \subset \Theta$$

when the random observation X has density $f_{(\theta)}^{(m)}$.

Suppose that for $m \in M$, Q_m is invariant under G, a locally compact group of transformations on χ. Let $\bar{G}$ be the induced group of transformations on Θ and let $\bar{g}$ be the image of g under the natural homomorphism from G to $\bar{G}$. Let λ denote a fixed (left) Haar measure on G.

The density function $f_{(\theta)}^{(m)}(x)$ has the form

$$f_{(\theta)}^{(m)}(x) = h_m(\theta)\, d_m(x) \exp\{\theta T(x)\},$$

where θ is a linear functional on the range of T.

Let $\xi = \xi_0 + \xi_1$ be a probability measure with ξ_j supported on Θ_j. Suppose there exists $\tilde{\theta}$, a linear functional on the range of T, and $u \in M$, such that:

(1) $\theta \in \Theta_j$ implies $\tilde{\theta} + \theta \in \Theta_j$ for $j = 0, 1$.

(2) The measure $P_j^{(u)}$ defined by

$$dP_j^{(u)}(g, \theta) = \frac{h_u(\bar{g}^{-1}\theta)}{h_m(\tilde{\theta} + \bar{g}^{-1}\theta)}\, d\lambda(g)\, d\xi_j(\theta)$$

is finite for $j = 0, 1$.

Then writing $\theta = \tilde{\theta} + \bar{g}^{-1}\gamma$, the proper Bayes test for the problem Q_m corresponding to $P^{(u)} = P_0^{(u)} + P_1^{(u)}$ is given by

$$\frac{\int_\Theta \int_G f_{(\tilde{\theta} + \bar{g}^{-1}\gamma)}^{(m)}(x)\, dP_1^{(u)}(g, \gamma)}{\int_\Theta \int_G f_{(\tilde{\theta} + \bar{g}^{-1}\gamma)}^{(m)}(x)\, dP_0^{(u)}(g, \gamma)} > K. \tag{5.1}$$

Substituting and performing obvious cancellations, the left side of (5.1) becomes

$$= \frac{\int_\Theta \int_G h_u(\bar{g}^{-1}\gamma) \exp\{(\tilde{\theta} + \bar{g}^{-1}\gamma)T(x)\} \, d\lambda(g) \, d\xi_1(\gamma)}{\int_\Theta \int_G h_u(\bar{g}^{-1}\gamma) \exp\{(\tilde{\theta} + \bar{g}^{-1}\gamma)T(x)\} \, d\lambda(g) \, d\xi_0(\gamma)}$$

$$= \frac{\int_\Theta \int_G h_u(\bar{g}^{-1}\gamma) \exp\{\bar{g}^{-1}\gamma T(x)\} \, d\lambda(g) \, d\xi_1(\gamma)}{\int_\Theta \int_G h_u(\bar{g}^{-1}\gamma) \exp\{\bar{g}^{-1}\gamma T(x)\} \, d\lambda(g) \, d\xi_0(\gamma)}$$

$$= \frac{\int_\Theta \int_G f^{(u)}_{\bar{g}^{-1}\gamma}(x) \, d\lambda(g) \, d\xi_1(\gamma)}{\int_\Theta \int_G f^{(u)}_{\bar{g}^{-1}\gamma}(x) \, d\lambda(g) \, d\xi_0(\gamma)}$$

$$= \frac{\int_\Theta f^{(u)*}_{(\gamma)} \, d\xi_1(\gamma)}{\int_\Theta f^{(u)*}_{(\gamma)} \, d\xi_0(\gamma)}.$$

The first equation depends on the exponential form of $f^{(m)}_{(\theta)}$ in eliminating $\tilde{\theta}$. The second equation is obtained by multiplying both numerator and denominator by $d_u(x)$. In the last equation $f^{(u)*}_{(\gamma)}$ denotes the probability density of the maximal invariant under G. Thus we are assuming certain restrictions on the problem which ensure the validity of Stein's representation. The final expression shows the invariance of the test and its interpretation as a Bayes test for the problem $Q_u{}^*$ (i.e., the problem Q_u reduced by invariance).

REFERENCES

1. Constantine, A. G. (1963). Some non-central distribution problems in multivariate analysis. *Ann. Math. Statist.* **34** 1270–1285.
2. James, A. T. (1964). Distributions of matrix variates and latent roots derived from normal samples. *Ann. Math. Statist.* **35** 475–501.
3. Kiefer, J. and Schwartz, R. (1965). Admissible Bayes character of T^2-, R^2-, and other fully invariant tests for classical multivariate normal problems. *Ann. Math. Statist.* **36** 747–770.

PART VI

Estimation and Prediction

Multidimensional Information Inequalities and Prediction

M. H. DeGROOT[1] *and M. M. RAO*[2]
CARNEGIE INSTITUTE OF TECHNOLOGY
PITTSBURGH, PENNSYLVANIA

INTRODUCTION

If $F(\cdot \mid \theta)$ is the distribution function of a random variable X, depending on a parameter θ, then one of the fundamental tasks of statistical inference is to obtain "information" about θ from observation on X. The problem is often solved by estimating θ, with a function of X, in an "optimal" way and studying the distribution of the estimator. However, this is often intractable, and one must therefore be content in having certain lower bounds on the relevant "risk" functions. These are the information inequalities provided by $F(\cdot \mid \theta)$. Considerable literature exists on this topic (see the references). These inequalities are typically obtained under certain "standard" regularity conditions but, to our knowledge, the ramifications of these conditions have not yet been fully analyzed. Starting with an analysis of these conditions, we shall consider the related problems for sequential sampling plans as well as Bayes estimation, and then present some general results on nonlinear prediction theory.

In Section 1 we consider in detail the implications of the regularity conditions for the lower bounds, with quadratic loss, when $\theta \in \Theta$, where Θ is a subset of the k-dimensional Euclidean space. Here various characterizations of the distribution functions $F(\cdot \mid \theta)$ are considered. The corresponding results for sequential sampling plans occupy Section 2, where the parameter space Θ is again multidimensional. In Section 3 we consider the distribution functions for which lower bounds of higher order are attained. The study leads to certain problems in differential equations. The results here are fragmentary. In

[1] This research was supported in part under NSF Grant G-25087 and Contract DA-36-061-ORD-477.

[2] This research was supported in part under NSF Grant GP-1349 and Contract DA-36-061-ORD-477.

Section 4 we treat Bayes estimation in the general case when Θ may even be infinite-dimensional, extending an earlier study [9] in which Θ was the real line. Finally, in Section 5, after briefly reviewing the existing work on prediction theory, we consider multidimensional (nonlinear) prediction, with a convex function as the optimality criterion, and present results which subsume all the previously considered cases known to us. Here an attempt is made to bring out the relation between prediction theory and Bayes estimation. Thus the following three sections deal with quadratic loss and the last two consider convex loss. These two parts of the paper can be read independently of each other.

1. ANALYSIS OF THE STANDARD REGULARITY CONDITIONS

Let (Ω, Σ, P) be a fixed probability space to which all the statements, otherwise unspecified, refer. For any random variable (r.v.) X on Ω, $E(X)$ stands for the mathematical expectation of X.

We now prove an auxiliary result which will be useful in what follows. Let $V' = (V_1, \ldots, V_n)$ be a vector (prime for transpose) of r.v.'s with two moments, and let $\mathscr{V}$ be the space spanned by $V_1, \ldots, V_n$. If m is the dimension of $\mathscr{V}$, then $m \leq n$. Define an inner product $(.,.)$ in $\mathscr{V}$ in the usual way by taking for $X, Y \in \mathscr{V}$, $(X, Y) = E(XY)$. Let $\mathscr{A}$ be the class of all linear transformations A such that $A'V = (\varphi_1, \ldots, \varphi_r)'$ is an orthonormal (o.n.) set of r.v.'s. Let $\mathscr{A}^*$ be the subclass of transformations in $\mathscr{A}$ for which $r = m$; i.e., each A in $\mathscr{A}^*$ maps V onto some o.n. basis $(\varphi_1, \ldots, \varphi_m)$ for $\mathscr{V}$. We have

Theorem 1.1. *Let $U' = (U_1, \ldots, U_l)$ and $V' = (V_1, \ldots, V_n)$ be two sets of r.v.'s with finite second moments. Let $M = (E(U_iU_j),\ i, j = 1, \ldots, l)$ and $N = (E(U_iV_j),\ i = 1, \ldots, l,\ j = 1, \ldots, n)$ be the indicated moment matrices. Then (writing $B_1 \leq B_2$ if $B_2 - B_1$ is positive-semidefinite and B_1 and B_2 are symmetric matrices), for any $A \in \mathscr{A}$ and $A_0 \in \mathscr{A}^*$ one has*

$$M \geq NA_0A_0'N' \geq NAA'N'. \tag{1.1}$$

Equality holds in the first inequality of (1.1) *iff $U = CA_0V$ for some nonsingular matrix C and in the second inequality of* (1.1) *iff the components of U are orthogonal to the orthogonal complement relative to $\mathscr{V}$ of the subspace spanned by $A'V$.* [Here and elsewhere, *iff* means if and only if.]

Proof. By definition, for $A \in \mathscr{A}^*$, $A'V$ is an o.n. set. Consider the vector $\begin{pmatrix} U \\ A'V \end{pmatrix}$. The moment matrix of this random vector is clearly

$$\begin{pmatrix} M & NA \\ A'N' & I \end{pmatrix}. \tag{1.2}$$

We claim that the matrix $M - NAA'N'$ is positive-semidefinite. Let X, Y be multidimensional normal (or Gaussian) r.v.'s with zero mean vectors and their (joint) covariance matrix given by (1.2). Then it is well known (cf. [1]) that the conditional distribution of X, given Y, is also normal with its covariance matrix $M - NAA'N'$, so it is positive-semidefinite. This proves the first inequality of (1.1). The condition for equality follows easily from the above argument.

To prove the second half of (1.1), suppose first that $A_0, A_1 \in \mathscr{A}^*$. Then there exists an orthogonal matrix Q such that $A_0'V = QA_1'V$. From this we have $E(UV'A_0) = NA_0 = NA_1Q'$. This gives, since $Q'Q = I$,

$$NA_0A_0'N' = NA_1Q'QA_1'N' = NA_1A_1'N'. \tag{1.3}$$

Now suppose that $A \in \mathscr{A}$ and is such that $A'V$ is an o.n. set of dimension $r < m$ (so it is not a basis). Let $A_0 = [A \,\vdots\, B]$, where B is the completion of the basis, so that $A_0'V$ is an o.n. basis for $\mathscr{V}$, and $A_0 \in \mathscr{A}^*$. Since $A_0A_0' = AA' + BB'$, we have, from (1.3) with this A_0,

$$NA_0A_0'N' = NAA'N' + NBB'N' \geq NAA'N', \tag{1.4}$$

in view of the obvious positive semidefiniteness of $NBB'N'$. Together (1.3) and (1.4) prove the desired result. Finally note that equality holds in (1.4) iff $NB = 0$. This means that the components of U and $B'V$ are orthogonal, which is equivalent to the condition for equality stated in the theorem.

Remarks. 1. The inequalities (1.1) can alternatively be derived from the facts that if X, Y, Z are three random vectors with second moments, and if the moment matrix of X given Y is $M_{X|Y}$, and that of X given Y and Z is $M_{X|Y,Z}$, then $M_{X|Y} \geq M_{X|Y,Z}$. We may then take $M_{X|Y} = M - NAA'N'$ and $M_{X|Y,Z} = M - NA_0A_0'N'$, the vector (Y, Z) being the larger set $A_0'V$ and Y the smaller set $A'V$.

2. The preceding result says that a maximal lower bound is obtained by taking *any* orthonormalizing transformation of maximum dimension. In particular, if the moment matrix W of V is nonsingular, then one such transformation is $A_0 = W^{-1/2}$, the unique positive-definite square root of W^{-1}.

3. The above theorem also holds if $n = \infty$ but $l < \infty$. A somewhat different argument is needed, but the result can be proved by certain linear space methods. Since we do not need this case, we shall not prove it here (for a proof see [26]). If $l = n$ ($< \infty$) in the above, the result was proved differently by Barankin [3]. The first part is the lemma (p. 2-12) of the unpublished notes on estimation (1950) by E. L. Lehmann, generalized slightly to the case where the components of V can be linearly dependent. (Lehmann states that the lemma is due to J. L. Hodges, Jr., and is an extension of a result of Cramér.)

Definition 1.1. *A set of r.v.'s $Z_1, \dots, Z_n$ is said to be linearly independent if there is no nontrivial set of constants $a_1, \dots, a_n$ such that $P\{a_1Z_1 + \cdots + a_nZ_n = 0\} = 1$.*

In deriving the information inequalities, a certain set of regularity conditions on the family of distributions is assumed. The conditions given below are usually employed, and they are referred to as the *standard regularity conditions.* We now state them and analyze their implications. We consider $F(\cdot \mid \theta)$ to be absolutely continuous, relative to a σ-finite measure μ with density $f(\cdot \mid \theta)$. (The undominated case has not been treated in these problems.) Let $\theta = (\theta_1, \dots, \theta_k)'$ lie in I, a nonempty open convex set in the Euclidean k-space, and let S_θ be the carrier of $f(x \mid \theta)$. Here x may be a vector observation.

Condition I. The sets S_θ remain the same ($= S$, say) for all $\theta \in I$.

Condition II. For each x in S and all θ in I, $\partial f(x \mid \theta)/\partial\theta_i$, $i = 1, \dots, k$, exist.

Condition III. For each i and all θ in I, $|\partial f(x \mid \theta)/\partial\theta_i| < M_i(x)$ such that M_i and TM_i are integrable for $i = 1, \dots, k$, where T is the estimator introduced below.

Condition IV. If $D_i(x, \theta) = (\partial/\partial\theta_i)[\log f(x \mid \theta)]$, then $\int_S D_i^2 f \, d\mu < \infty$, $i = 1, \dots, k$, and the r.v.'s $D_1, \dots, D_k$ are linearly independent.

These conditions are variants of those originally given by Cramér [7]. We remark that from conditions II and III it follows that if T is an estimator and $g(\theta) = \int_S Tf \, d\mu$, where $g(\theta) = (g_1(\theta), \dots, g_k(\theta))'$, then $\partial g_i(\theta)/\partial\theta_j$, $i, j = 1, \dots, k$, also exist for all $\theta \in I$. This will be used below.

Definition 1.2. *Let $f(\cdot \mid \theta)$ be the density function (relative to μ) of a r.v. X, where $\theta' = (\theta_1, \dots, \theta_k)$, and let $T' = (T_1, \dots, T_l)$ be a vector estimator whose components have finite second moments. Let M, Λ, and N be the covariance matrices of T, $D = (D_1, \dots, D_k)'$ (cf. condition IV for the definition of D_i), and of T and D, respectively. Then the inequality $M \geq N\Lambda^{-1}N'$ is called the information inequality (following [31]), and if there is equality here, then T is said to be an efficient estimator (globally) of its expectation.*

We remark that in the one-dimensional case (i.e., $l = k = 1$) the information inequality is also known as the Cramér-Rao inequality.

Theorem 1.2. *Suppose $T' = (T_1, \dots, T_l)$ is an l-vector of estimators of a vector θ-function, the T_i having finite second moments. If $f(\cdot \mid \theta)$ satisfies the regularity conditions I to IV above, then the following conclusions hold:*

(a) *There exist at most $k + 1$ linearly independent components, $(T_1, \dots, T_{k+1})$ say, of the l-vector T that are (jointly) efficient estimators.*

(b) *If the l-vector T itself is efficient, then at most $k + 1$ components are linearly independent.*

(c) *The $(k+1)$-vector $(T_1, \ldots, T_{k+1})$ of efficient estimators, if linearly independent, will estimate $k+1$ linearly independent functions of θ, $(a_1(\cdot), \ldots, a_{k+1}(\cdot))$ say, unbiasedly.*

Proof. (a) The linear independence of $(D_1, \ldots, D_k)$ implies that of $(1, D_1, \ldots, D_k)$. Identifying this $(k+1)$ set and the l-vector T with the V and U vectors of Theorem 1.1, respectively, the result is an immediate consequence of that theorem and Remark 2 following it.

(b) This is immediate from part (a).

(c) If $T' = (T_1, \ldots, T_{k+1})$ is a linearly independent efficient set, then it follows from Theorem 1.1 that the T set and the set $D' = (1, D_1, \ldots, D_{k+1})$ span the same space (relative to $f\,d\mu$). So there exists a nonsingular matrix $A(=A(\theta))$ such that

$$T = AD = [\tilde{a}_1 | A_1] \left[\frac{1}{D^*} \right], \tag{1.5}$$

where $\tilde{a}_1(\theta) = (a_1(\theta), \ldots, a_{k+1}(\theta))'$ is the first column of A, and A_1 and D^* are defined by the context. From (1.5) and conditions III and IV it follows that $E_\theta(T) = \tilde{a}_1(\theta)$, so that T estimates $\tilde{a}_1$ unbiasedly. [Here E_θ indicates that the probability measure is $f(x \mid \theta) d\mu$.] We now show that the $a_i(\cdot)$ are linearly independent.

Suppose that the $a_i(\cdot)$ are linearly dependent. Then there is a vector $(c_1, \ldots, c_{k+1}) \neq 0$ such that $\sum_{i=1}^{k+1} c_i a_i(\theta) = 0$, $\theta \in I$. Now writing (1.5), with $A_1 = (\alpha_{ij})$, as

$$T_i - a_i(\theta) = \sum_{j=1}^{k} \alpha_{ij}(\theta) D_j(x, \theta) \qquad (i = 1, \ldots, k+1), \tag{1.6}$$

we note that $\varphi(x) = \sum_{i=1}^{k+1} c_i(T_i - a_i)$ is independent of θ, by our supposition. Setting $\beta_i(\theta) = \sum_{j=1}^{k+1} c_j \alpha_{ij}(\theta)$, (1.6) can be written

$$\varphi(x) = \sum_{j=1}^{k} \beta_j(\theta) D_j(x, \theta). \tag{1.7}$$

Thus $E_\theta(\varphi(X)) = 0$, $\theta \in I$. By the regularity conditions II to IV, we may differentiate under the integral (relative to θ_i) to obtain

$$E_\theta(\varphi(X) D_i(X, \theta)) = 0 \qquad (i = 1, \ldots, k, \quad \theta \in I). \tag{1.8}$$

This implies $0 = E_\theta(\varphi(X) \sum_{i=1}^{k} \beta_i(\theta) D_i(X, \theta)) = E_\theta(\varphi^2(X))$, using (1.7). So $\varphi = 0$, a.e., and (1.7) implies that the D_i are linearly dependent [recall that not all the $\beta_i = 0$, since in (1.5) A is nonsingular], which contradicts the linear independence assumption of D_i. This completes the proof.

As an immediate consequence, we have

Corollary 1.2.1. *If $T' = (T_1, \ldots, T_l)$ and $R' = (R_1, \ldots, R_m)$ are two sets of* *estimators of a (vector) θ-function, and* $\tilde{P}' = (T', R')$, *then* $\tilde{P}$ *is an efficient set iff both T and R are efficient.*

It suffices to recall that a set T of estimators is efficient if it lies in the subspace spanned by the D vector of the theorem. The above statements are supplemented by the following theorem.

Theorem 1.3. *There exists a linearly independent set of efficient estimators* $T^* = (T_1^*, \dots, T_r^*)'$ *with* $1 \le r \le k+1$ *such that any set* $T = (T_1, \dots, T_l)'$ *is efficient iff* $T = AT^*$ *for some linear transformation A.*

Proof. By (b) of Theorem 1.2, the class of all efficient estimators is a linear space of dimension r, $1 \le r \le k+1$. If $(T_1^*, \dots, T_r^*)$ is a basis for this subspace, and if any vector T is also efficient, then it must lie in this subspace. So $T = AT^*$ for some A. The converse is trivial.

We now investigate the properties of θ functions that can be efficiently estimated by linearly independent (unbiased) estimators.

Theorem 1.4. *Let* $T = (T_1, \dots, T_k)'$ *be a k-vector of (nonconstant) linearly independent unbiased estimators of* $a(\theta) = (a_1(\theta), \dots, a_k(\theta))'$, *where the density function* $f(\cdot \mid \theta)$ *satisfies the regularity conditions I to IV for* $\theta \in I$, *an open convex subset of the k-space. Then*

(a) $a(\theta)$ *is one-to-one; i.e.,* $a_i(\theta) = a_i(\theta^*)$, $i = 1, \dots, k$, *iff* $\theta = \theta^*$.

(b) *There exists a function* $b(\cdot)$ *which is inverse to* $a(\cdot)$ *such that b is continuously differentiable and takes its values in I.*

Proof. (a) Let $\theta^0, \theta^* \in I$ and $\theta^0 \ne \theta^*$. We shall show that $a(\theta^0) \ne a(\theta^*)$. Suppose this is false. Then $a_i(\theta^0) = a_i(\theta^*)$, for $i = 1, \dots, k$. In the *present* notation (1.6) can be written

$$T(X) - a(\theta) = A_1(\theta)D(X, \theta).$$

Note that A_1 is a square $(k \times k)$ matrix now. We remark that the linear independence of T_i implies that of $(T_i - a_i)$. This evidently implies the nonsingularity of $A_1(\theta)$ for $\theta \in I$. In particular, for an arbitrary $\bar{\theta} \in I$, we have

$$D(X, \bar{\theta}) = A_1^{-1}(\bar{\theta})(T(X) - a(\bar{\theta})). \tag{1.9}$$

Moreover,

$$E_\theta(D(X, \bar{\theta})) = A_1^{-1}(\bar{\theta})(a(\theta) - a(\bar{\theta})). \tag{1.10}$$

Because of the regularity conditions, we may differentiate (1.10) under the integral sign relative to θ_i, $i = 1, \dots, k$, so that

$$\Lambda(\bar{\theta}, \bar{\theta}) = [E_\theta(D_i(X, \bar{\theta}))D_j(X, \theta)] = A_1^{-1}(\bar{\theta})B(\theta), \tag{1.11}$$

where $B(\theta) = (\partial a_i(\theta)/\partial\theta_j,\ i, j = 1, \dots, k)$, which exists by conditions II and III.

Recall that the multidimensional Rolle's theorem states: If a vector function $a(\cdot)$ is continuously differentiable in an open set in R_k, the k-space, containing the line segment $\alpha\theta^0 + (1-\alpha)\theta^*$, $0 \le \alpha \le 1$ with $\theta^0 \ne \theta^*$, and if $a(\theta^0) = a(\theta^*)$, then there is a $\delta(0 < \delta < 1)$ such that the determinant det $B(\tilde{\theta}) = 0$ for $\tilde{\theta} = \delta\theta^0 + (1-\delta)\theta^*$, where $B(\theta)$ is defined above.

Since, by hypothesis, I is convex, it follows that det $B(\tilde{\theta}) = 0$ for at least one $\tilde{\theta} \in I$. Thus (1.11) gives $\Lambda(\tilde{\theta}, \bar{\theta}) = A_1^{-1}(\bar{\theta})B(\tilde{\theta})$. Since $\bar{\theta} \in I$ is arbitrary we may take $\bar{\theta} = \tilde{\theta}$, so that det $\Lambda(\tilde{\theta}, \tilde{\theta}) = 0$. But $\Lambda(\tilde{\theta}, \tilde{\theta})$ is the covariance matrix of $D(X, \tilde{\theta})$ relative to $f(\cdot \mid \tilde{\theta})$. Since the $D_i(X, \theta)$ are linearly independent for $\theta \in I$, det $\Lambda(\tilde{\theta}, \tilde{\theta}) > 0$. The contradiction contained between this and the preceding statement proves that $a(\theta^0) \ne a(\theta^*)$, if $\theta^0 \ne \theta^*$. The converse implication is trivial.

(b) Note that proving (b) is equivalent to showing that for $\theta^0 \in I \subset R_k$ (I open convex) and $b = a(\theta^0)$ the following conclusions hold:

(1) There exist open sets Θ and Θ^* such that (α) $\theta^0 \in \Theta$, $b \in \Theta^*$; (β) for every $\theta \in \Theta$, $a(\theta) \in \Theta^*$; (γ) for every $\theta^* \in \Theta^*$ there is one and only one $\theta \in \Theta$, such that $\theta^* = a(\theta)$.

(2) If a^* is the inverse of a [which exists by (1)] on Θ^* defined by $a^*(a(\theta)) = \theta$ for $\theta \in \Theta$, then $a^*(\cdot)$ is continuously differentiable.

Since I is a nonempty open set, let $\theta^0 \in I$. Then by (a) [cf. (1.11)] det $B(\theta^0) = \det(A_1(\theta^0)\Lambda(\theta^0, \theta^0)) = \det A_1(\theta^0) \det \Lambda(\theta^0, \theta^0) \ne 0$. Hence (1) and (2) above are immediate consequences of the well-known *inverse function theorem* of classical analysis. Thus part (b), and with it the theorem, is proved.

To note more clearly the implications of the above result, we first state a lemma which enables us to discuss the distribution problem for efficient estimators.

Lemma. *Suppose $f(\cdot \mid \theta)$ satisfies the regularity conditions I to IV above, and let $(D_1, \ldots, D_k)$ be linearly independent. If $T' = (T_1, \ldots, T_k)$ are linearly independent, efficient, nonconstant, unbiased estimators of $a(\theta) = (a_1(\theta), \ldots, a_k(\theta))'$, then $f(\cdot \mid \theta)$ belongs to the generalized exponential family, namely,*

$$f(x \mid \theta(a)) = \exp\left\{\sum_{j=1}^{k} \psi_j(a)T_j(x) - h(a) + g(x)\right\},$$

where θ can be considered as a function of a [*due to part* (*b*) *of Theorem* 1.4)].

Remark. In ([5], p. 210) Bhattacharyya has sketched a plausible argument of this fact. Since it can be made rigorous, we omit the proof.

Theorem 1.2 and the above lemma yield the following restatement of the preceding results in terms of sufficiency and maximum-likelihood estimation, which may be more revealing.

Theorem 1.5. *Let the density $f(\cdot \mid \theta)$ satisfy conditions I to IV. Then*

(a) *A linearly independent efficient k-vector $(T_1, \ldots, T_k)$ of nonconstant estimators of $(a_1(\theta), \ldots, a_k(\theta))$, where $E_\theta(T_i) = a_i(\theta)$, is jointly (minimal) sufficient for θ.*

(b) *The estimators* $(T_1, \ldots, T_k)$ *of* (a) *are maximum-likelihood estimators of* $(a_1(\theta), \ldots, a_k(\theta))$.

(c) *If* $b_i(X) = a_i^{-1}(T_1, \ldots, T_k)$, *from* (b), *then* $(b_1, \ldots, b_k)$ *are maximum-likelihood estimators of* $(\theta_1, \ldots, \theta_k)$.

Remark. The above result includes as a special case a result of Fend ([13], Theorem 1). Note also that if the dimensionality of $(D_1, \ldots, D_k)$ is less than k, and $\theta = (\theta_1, \ldots, \theta_k)'$, then there is a degeneracy in the distributions. We do not consider that case here.

2. SEQUENTIAL SAMPLING PLANS

In this section we assume that $X_1, X_2, \ldots$ is a sequence of independent r.v.'s with a common d.f., whose density is $f(\cdot \mid \theta)$, where θ is again a k-dimensional vector parameter. In this section we consider sequential sampling plans and efficient estimation. Accordingly, let $X_1, \ldots, X_N$ be a sequential random sample obtained from the above distribution according to a given sampling plan; i.e., a well-defined rule that specifies for any given set of observations $(X_1, \ldots, X_n)$ whether sampling terminates and $N = n$ or whether the observation X_{n+1} should be taken. Thus, N is a r.v.

Guided by the work of the preceding section, we assume that the density $f(\cdot \mid \theta)$ belongs to the exponential family; i.e.,

$$f(x \mid \theta) = c(\theta) \exp\left[\sum_{i=1}^{k} \theta_i h_i(x)\right] \qquad (\theta \in I), \tag{2.1}$$

where I is an open cell in the Euclidean k space, and $c(\theta) > 0$. We let

$$\begin{aligned} T_i(X_1, \ldots, X_N) &= \sum_{j=1}^{N} h_i(X_j) \qquad (i = 1, \ldots, k), \\ D_i(X_1, \ldots, X_N, \theta) &= \frac{\partial}{\partial \theta_i} \log f(X_1, \ldots, X_N \mid \theta) \\ &= T_i(X_1, \ldots, X_N) + N[c_i(\theta)/c(\theta)], \end{aligned} \tag{2.2}$$

where $c_i(\theta) = \partial c(\theta)/\partial \theta_i$. Assuming $E_\theta(N) < \infty$, from (2.2) we have with the regularity conditions, $E_\theta(D_i) = 0$, $E_\theta(T_i) = E_\theta(N)\xi_i(\theta)$, $i = 1, \ldots, k$, where $\xi_i(\theta) = -c_i(\theta)/c(\theta)$. Hereafter we assume that, for nontriviality, at least one observation is taken under the given sampling plan, so that $E_\theta(N) > 0$, and also that $(D_1, \ldots, D_k)$ are linearly independent. (For a discussion of the regularity conditions, see, e.g., [33].)

Lemma 2.1. *If* $\xi(\theta) = (\xi_1(\theta), \ldots, \xi_k(\theta))'$, *then* ξ *is a one-to-one function of* θ.

Proof. If the statement is false, there exist θ^0 and θ^* ($\theta^0 \neq \theta^*$) such that $\xi(\theta^0) = \xi(\theta^*)$. The form of $f(\cdot \mid \theta)$ and the regularity conditions imply that $\xi(\cdot)$ is a continuously differentiable function of θ_i and by the multidimensional Rolle's theorem there exists a $\tilde{\theta}$ such that $\det B(\tilde{\theta}) = 0$, where $B(\theta) = (\partial \xi_i(\theta)/\partial \theta_j, i, j = 1, \ldots, k)$. This contradicts the linear independence of D_i [cf. (2.2) and the proof of Theorem 1.4], and proves the lemma.

Remark. We can also conclude, as in Theorem 1.4, that the correspondence between ξ and θ is bicontinuous and differentiable.

Because of this lemma, we may, and do, reparametrize $f(x \mid \theta)$ and write $f(x \mid \theta(\xi))$ or $f(x \mid \xi)$. Thus (2.2) may be written $D(X, \theta(\xi)) = D(X, \xi) = (T_i - N\xi_i)$, $i = 1, \ldots, k$. The result of Theorems 1.2 and 1.3 [or (1.5)] can be combined to give the following localized result. We consider real-valued functions of $(\xi_1, \ldots, \xi_k)$ and denote a real-valued estimator by $h(X)$ $(=h(X_1, \ldots, X_N))$.

Theorem 2.2. *An estimator $h(X)$ is an efficient estimator (of its expected value) at $\xi = \xi^*$ iff there exist constants $a_1, \ldots, a_k, b$ (depending on ξ^*) such that*

$$h(X) = b + \sum_{i=1}^{k} a_i(T_i - N\xi_i^*). \tag{2.3}$$

This result shows that a necessary condition for an estimator of a (real) ξ function to be efficient at some $\xi = \xi^*$ is that it be linear in $T_1, \ldots, T_k$ and N. We now consider the structure of (locally or globally) efficient estimators of real parametric functions. As in [8], we introduce

Definition 2.1. *A sampling plan is said to be linear if there exist constants $\alpha_1, \ldots, \alpha_k, \beta, \gamma$, not all zero, such that,*

$$P\left[\gamma + \beta N + \sum_{i=1}^{k} \alpha_i T_i = 0\right] = 1. \tag{2.4}$$

We now establish various properties of linear sampling plans.

Lemma 2.3. *If the sampling plan is linear, then $\beta + \sum_{i=1}^{k} \alpha_i \xi_i \neq 0$ for all admissible ξ (i.e., all $\xi(\theta)$ for $\theta \in I$).*

Proof. By (2.4), $\gamma + \beta N + \sum_{i=1}^{k} \alpha_i T_i = 0$ with probability 1. Taking expectations, we have

$$\beta + \sum_{i=1}^{k} \alpha_i \xi_i = -\gamma / E_\xi(N). \tag{2.5}$$

Since $E_\xi(N) > 0$, if the left side vanishes for some $\xi = \xi^*$, we must have $\gamma = 0$ in (2.5). But then $\beta + \sum_{i=1}^{k} \alpha_i \xi_i = 0$ for all ξ. Consequently $\sum_{i=1}^{k} \alpha_i D_i\ (X, \xi) = \sum_{i=1}^{k} \alpha_i T_i + \beta N$, by (2.2). By (2.4), since $\gamma = 0$, this implies

$P[\sum_{i=1}^{k} \alpha_i D_i(X, \xi) = 0] = 1$. Since the D_i are linearly independent, this means $\alpha_i = 0$, all i, and so $\beta = 0$. This contradicts the fact that all constants of (2.4) are not zero. This completes the proof.

Lemma 2.4. *If the sampling plan is linear, then every linear estimator (i.e., one of the form $c + bN + \sum_{i=1}^{k} a_i T_i$) is (globally) efficient.*

Proof. By Theorem 2.2 an estimator $h(X)$ is efficient (at ξ^*) iff it is of the form (2.3). Let ξ^* be a fixed but arbitrary admissible point. Consider a linear estimator

$$h(X) = c + bN + \sum_{i=1}^{k} a_i T_i.$$

It is to be shown that $h(X)$ can be written as (2.3). Since the plan is linear, we have, using (2.4), for any real λ,

$$h(X) = c + bN + \sum_{i=1}^{k} a_i T_i + \lambda \left[\gamma + \beta N + \sum_{i=1}^{k} \alpha_i T_i \right]. \tag{2.6}$$

Choose $\lambda = -[b + \sum_{i=1}^{k} a_i \xi_i^*]/[\beta + \sum_{i=1}^{k} \alpha_i \xi_i^*]$. In view of Lemma 2.3, this is well defined. Set $b' = c + \lambda\gamma$ and $a_i' = a_i + \lambda\alpha_i$, where λ is given by the above choice. Then a simple computation shows that (2.6) becomes

$$h(X) = b' + \sum_{i=1}^{k} a_i'(T_i - N\xi_i^*),$$

which is of the form (2.4). Since ξ^* is arbitrary, the lemma follows.

Another property we need is given in

Lemma 2.5. *If the sampling plan is not linear, then a linear estimator $h(X) = c + bN + \sum_{i=1}^{k} a_i T_i$ is efficient at $\xi = \xi^*$ iff $b + \sum_{i=1}^{k} a_i \xi_i^* = 0$.*

Proof. Sufficiency is immediate, by Theorem 2.2. Conversely, suppose $h(X)$ is efficient at ξ^*. Then by the necessity part of Theorem 2.2, we have

$$h(X) = c' + \sum_{i=1}^{k} a_i' (T_i - N\xi_i^*)$$

for some constants $c', a_1', \ldots, a_k'$. Since also $h(X) = c + bN + \sum_{i=1}^{k} a_i T$ by hypothesis, we have, on subtraction,

$$(c - c') + \left(b + \sum_{i=1}^{k} a_i' \xi_i^*\right) N + \sum_{i=1}^{k} (a_i - a_i')T_i = 0.$$

Since the plan is not linear, by (2.4), all coefficients must vanish. So $c = c'$, $a_i = a_i'$, and $b + \sum_{i=1}^{k} a_i' \xi_i^* = 0$, as was to be proved.

We now introduce, following [8],

Definition 2.2. *A sampling plan is said to be efficient if it admits a non-constant efficient estimator.*

We now characterize efficient plans in

Theorem 2.6. *A sampling plan is efficient iff it is linear.*

Proof. Suppose the plan is efficient but not linear. Then any nonconstant efficient estimator must be of the form

$$h(X) = b(\xi) + \sum_{i=1}^{k} a_i(\xi)(T_i - N\xi_i), \tag{2.7}$$

for all ξ. Since $b(\xi) = E_\xi(h(X))$, $b(\cdot)$ is not a constant (i.e., not independent of ξ), as the only efficient estimators of constants are constants and $h(X)$ is not a constant. Thus there are ξ^0, ξ^* such that $b(\xi^0) \neq b(\xi^*)$. From (2.7) we have, on subtraction,

$$[b(\xi^0) - b(\xi^*)] + \sum_{i=1}^{k} [a_i(\xi^0) - a_i(\xi^*)]T_i - N \sum_{i=1}^{k} [a_i(\xi^0)\xi_i{}^0 - a_i(\xi^*)\xi_i{}^*] = 0.$$

Since the plan is not linear, by (2.4), all coefficients must vanish. In particular, $b(\xi^0) = b(\xi^*)$, a contradiction.

The converse is precisely Lemma 2.4 together with Theorem 2.2.

The next result generalizes Theorem 5.1 of [8].

Theorem 2.7. *A real parametric function $g(\cdot)$ of ξ is estimable (i.e., there exists an unbiased estimator of g) efficiently at $\xi = \xi^*$ iff there exist constants $(a_1, \ldots, a_k)$ such that*

$$\frac{g(\xi) - g(\xi^*)}{E_\xi(N)} = \sum_{i=1}^{k} a_i(\xi_i - \xi_i{}^*). \tag{2.8}$$

Proof. If g is efficiently estimable at ξ^*, then there exists an estimator $h(X)$ of the form $h(X) = b + \sum_{i=1}^{k} a_i(T_i - N\xi_i{}^*)$, and $E_\xi(h(X)) = g(\xi)$. Hence

$$g(\xi) = b + E_\xi(N) \sum_{i=1}^{k} a_i(\xi_i - \xi_i{}^*).$$

Taking $\xi = \xi^*$ gives $b = g(\xi^*)$, and hence g has the required form.

Conversely if g satisfies (2.8), then

$$h(X) = g(\xi^*) + \sum_{i=1}^{k} a_i(T_i - N\xi_i{}^*)$$

is clearly an unbiased estimator of g and from its form [cf. (2.3)] we see that $h(X)$ is efficient at ξ^*. This completes the proof.

This terminates our study of sequential sampling plans. In the remaining sections we again consider problems of optimal estimation with a sample space of fixed dimension.

3. EFFICIENT ESTIMATION IN THE WIDE SENSE

An estimator is efficient in the wide sense if the density is differentiable n times (relative to θ) and if the nth but not the $(n-1)$th bound in the information inequality is reached (see below). The purpose of this section is to consider such estimators and discuss their relation with Fend's result [13]. We consider only the one-dimensional case here, since the problem has not been completely settled even in that case, and the multiparameter case is much less understood.

Let $f(\cdot \mid \theta)$ be a density function of the r.v. X for $\theta \in (a, b) = I$. As in Section 1, let $D_i(x, \theta) = [f(x \mid \theta)]^{-1}[\partial^i f(x \mid \theta)/\partial\theta^i]$, $i = 1, 2, \ldots$, and assume $D_1, \ldots, D_n$ are linearly independent, dropping the dependent ones and relabeling if necessary. If $T(X)$ is an (unbiased) estimator of θ, it will be said to be *efficient in the wide sense* if, for some value of $n > 1$, the variance of T is $N_n \Lambda_n^{-1} N_n'$, where Λ_n is the covariance matrix of $(D_1, \ldots, D_n)$ and N_n is the covariance vector of T and the D_i.

The regularity conditions of Section 1 (with obvious modifications) will be assumed. Then the following result is a consequence of Theorem 1.1.

Theorem 3.1. *An estimator $T(X)$ is efficient in the wide sense at $\theta = \theta^*$, iff there exist constants $a_0, a_1, \ldots, a_n$ such that*

$$T(X) = a_0(\theta^*) + \sum_{i=1}^{n} a_i(\theta^*) D_i(X, \theta^*), \tag{3.1}$$

and it is efficient in the wide sense if (3.1) *holds for all $\theta^* \in I$.*

This result states that if there exists a choice of $a_0(\theta), \ldots, a_n(\theta)$, such that $a_0(\theta) + \sum_{i=1}^n a_i(\theta) D_i(\cdot, \theta)$ is a function of X alone, for all $\theta \in I$, then it is necessarily an efficient estimator [of $a_0(\cdot)$]. As in Section 1, from the linear independence of $\{D_i\}$ and the regularity conditions, we have

Lemma 3.2. *The $\{a_i(\cdot)\}_0^n$ of* (3.1) *are continuous functions of $\theta (\in I)$.*

Proof. Since $E_\theta(T) = a_0(\theta)$, $\theta \in I$, and the regularity conditions hold, $a_0(\cdot)$ is differentiable at least n times. Let $\theta_0 (\in I)$ be a fixed but arbitrary point. Then from

$$T(X) - a_0(\theta_0) = \sum_{i=1}^{n} a_i(\theta_0) D_i(X, \theta_0)$$

we have, on taking expectations E_θ and differentiating the result i times,

$$a_0^i(\theta) = \sum_{j=1}^{n} a_j(\theta_0) E_\theta(D_j(X, \theta_0) D_i(X, \theta)) \qquad (i = 1, \ldots, n). \tag{3.2}$$

Let $\beta(\theta) = (a_0^{(1)}(\theta), \ldots, a_o^n(\theta))'$, $\alpha(\theta_0) = (a_1(\theta_0), \ldots, a_n(\theta_0))'$, and $\Lambda(\theta)$ be the covariance matrix of D_i's. Since θ is arbitrary, (3.2) gives in particular,

$$\beta(\theta_0) = \Lambda(\theta_0)\alpha(\theta_0). \tag{3.3}$$

By the regularity conditions, the $a_0{}^i(\theta)$ are continuous and $\Lambda(\theta_0)$ is nonsingular. So (3.3) may be written

$$\alpha(\theta_0) = \Lambda^{-1}(\theta_0)\beta(\theta_0), \tag{3.4}$$

so that from the arbitrariness of θ_0 in I, it follows from (3.4) that the components of $\alpha(\theta)$ are continuous, completing the proof.

The above lemma and Theorem 3.1 imply the following result.

Proposition 3.3. *Let the r.v. X have the density $f(\cdot \mid \theta)$, $\theta \in I$, and the regularity conditions hold. For an estimator T of $a_0(\cdot)$ to be efficient, in the wide sense, it is necessary that there exist $a_1(\theta), \ldots, a_n(\theta)$, continuous, ($a_n(\theta) \neq 0$) such that $f(\cdot \mid \theta)$ is a solution of the nth-order differential equation*

$$a_n(\theta)\frac{\partial^n f}{\partial \theta^k} + \cdots + a_1(\theta)\frac{\partial f}{\partial \theta} + (a_0(\theta) - T(x))f = 0, \tag{3.5}$$

subject to the boundary conditions ($f(x \mid \theta) \geq 0$),

$$\int_S T(x) f(x \mid \theta)\, d\mu = a_0(\theta), \quad \int_S \frac{\partial^i f(x \mid \theta)}{\partial \theta^i}\, d\mu = 0, \qquad \textit{and} \qquad \int_S f(x \mid \theta)\, d\mu = 1.$$

Since the boundary conditions are not given at a point (they are averages), it seems a nontrivial problem to solve (3.5) generally. If $f(x \mid \theta) = \exp[\sum_{i=1}^n u^i(x) g_i(\theta) + v(x)]$ is a solution, then it is possible to find further properties of $a_i(\theta)$ and the form of $T(X)$. For this particular choice Fend [13] has shown that $f(x \mid \theta)$ can be expressed as $f(x \mid \theta) = \exp[u(x)g(\theta) + v(x)]$ and that T is a polynomial of degree n in $u(\cdot)$. One of his examples can be used to show that the assumption of an exponential family being a solution of (3.5) is nonvacuous.

The converse problem of determining all probability densities $f(\cdot \mid \theta)$ that are solutions of (3.5) is more difficult, as is the multidimensional case, which leads to a related partial differential equation. At present both these problems are unsolved.

4. MULTIDIMENSIONAL BAYES ESTIMATION

The point of view of this section (and the next) is somewhat different from the preceding ones in that the parameter θ is itself a r.v. We consider the problem from a general point of view and present some extensions of our results in [9]. Here θ will be a multidimensional (even infinite-dimensional) r.v. in contrast to the one-dimensional (real-valued) case of [9]. As seen below, the methods of [9] do not seem to extend to the multidimensional case (even for two dimensions).

Let X be a r.v. on (Ω, Σ, P) with values in an abstract set $\mathscr{X}$ in which an appropriate σ-field is defined. Suppose the distribution of X depends on a parameter Θ which takes its values in $\mathscr{Y}$, a complete normed linear (or Banach) space. Let $W(\cdot)$ be a nonnegative symmetric convex function on the line. If the observed value of X is x and the corresponding (true) value of Θ is θ, then let the estimated value of θ be $T(x)$, where $T(\cdot): \mathscr{X} \to \mathscr{Y}$ is a measurable function of x relative to $\mathscr{Y}$ (i.e., the σ-field of all Borel sets in $\mathscr{Y}$). The loss is $W(|T - \theta|)$, where $|\cdot|$ is the norm in $\mathscr{Y}$. Suppose that $P(\cdot \mid x)$ is the posterior distribution of Θ when the observed value is x [i.e., the conditional probability distribution on the σ-field of Borel sets of $\mathscr{Y}$ given x]. Then a *Bayes estimate* for the given value of x is $T^*(x) \in \mathscr{Y}$, given by

$$\int_{\mathscr{Y}} W(|\theta - T^*(x)|)P(d\theta|x) = \inf_{T\in\mathscr{Y}} \int_{\mathscr{Y}} W(|\theta - T|)P(d\theta \mid x). \tag{4.1}$$

For this to make sense we have to assume that each of the integrals in (4.1) exists for almost all x; i.e., $P(\cdot \mid x)$ exists.

Let $\mathscr{B} \subset \Sigma$ be the σ-field generated by the r.v. X. (Here and in the rest of the paper the measurability of vector-valued functions conforms to the treatment of [11].) If $L(\Sigma)$ is the space of all r.v.'s T from (Ω, Σ, P), the probability space, to $\mathscr{Y}$ such that $\int_\Omega W(k\,|T|)\,dP < \infty$ for some $k > 0$, then $L(\Sigma)$ is a linear space and we let $L(\mathscr{B})$ denote the subset of $L(\Sigma)$ of $\mathscr{B}$-measurable functions. If we introduce a norm $\|\cdot\|$ in $L(\Sigma)$ as

$$\|T\| = \inf\left\{1/k;\ \int_\Omega W(k\,|T|)\,dP \le 1\right\} \qquad [T \in L(\Sigma)], \tag{4.2}$$

then it is known that this is a norm and with it $L(\Sigma)$ becomes a Banach space. (This is proved if $\mathscr{Y}$ is the space of scalars in [35] and the same proof holds in the general case also.) It is then easy to see that $L(\mathscr{B})$ is a closed subspace of $L(\Sigma)$. We now reinterpret the problem as follows: $X: \Omega \to \mathscr{X}$, $T: \mathscr{X} \to \mathscr{Y}$ such that $T(X): \Omega \to \mathscr{Y}$ is $\mathscr{B}$-measurable, while $\Theta: \Omega \to \mathscr{Y}$ is not $\mathscr{B}$-measurable, but only Σ-measurable. Thus a Bayes estimator T^* is an element in $L(\mathscr{B})$ such that $\int_\Omega W(|\Theta - T^*|)\,dP$ is a minimum on $L(\mathscr{B})$. We later translate the problem into one involving conditional distributions.

We first establish a result in the new setup as follows.

Theorem 4.1. *Suppose $L(\Sigma)$ is the class (introduced above) of all Σ-measurable functions from Ω to a uniformly convex Banach space $\mathscr{Y}$. Let $W(\cdot)$ be a nontrivial symmetric convex function such that $W(0) = 0$. Suppose that the norm in $\mathscr{Y}$ is differentiable except at the origin [i.e., $\varphi(t) = |X_0 + tY|$ is differentiable as a function of t for each Y and each $X_0 \neq 0$], and that $W(\cdot)$ satisfies the following growth conditions for all $x > 0$, some $0 < c < \infty$, and for each $a > 1$ and some $k_a > 1$: (1) $W(2x) \le cW(x)$, and (2) $W'(ax) \ge k_a W'(x)$ $(W'(x) = (d/dx)W(x))$. Then,*

(a) *There exists a unique* T^* *in* $L(\mathscr{B})$ *such that* $\int_\Omega W(|\Theta - T^*|)\, dP$ *is a minimum.*

(b) *The* T^* *of* (a) *is the (unique) solution in* $L(\mathscr{B})$ *of the integral equation*

$$\int_\Omega W'(|\Theta - T^*|) \frac{d}{du} [|(\Theta - T^*) + uY|]_{u=0}\, dP = 0, \tag{4.3}$$

for all $Y \in L(\mathscr{B})$, *and the solution does not depend on* Y.

Proof. Consider the convex functional $U(\cdot)$ on $L(\Sigma)$ defined by

$$U(T) = \int_\Omega W(|\Theta - T|)\, dP \qquad [T \in L(\Sigma)].$$

Since U is nonnegative and $L(\mathscr{B}) \subset L(\Sigma)$, we have

$$\alpha_0 = \inf_{T \in L(\mathscr{B})} U(T), \tag{4.4}$$

and that $\alpha_0 > 0$ because $\Theta \notin L(\mathscr{B})$. If $\mathscr{M}$ is the set of elements that yield the infimum (4.4), then it is a closed bounded convex subset of $L(\mathscr{B})$. For the convexity and boundedness (i.e., $\mathscr{M}$ can be enclosed in some sphere) are clear, and the closure property is seen as follows. If $\{T_i\} \subset \mathscr{M}$ is a convergent sequence, relative to the norm (4.2), then let T_0 be its limit. So $|T_n - T_0| \to 0$ in measure also and since $W(\cdot)$ is continuous we have,

$$\begin{aligned}
\alpha_0 \le U(T_0) &= \int_\Omega W(|\Theta - {}_0T|)\, Pd = \int_\Omega \lim_{n\to\infty} W(\Theta| - T_n|)\, dP \\
&\le \lim_{n\to\infty} \int_\Omega W(|\Theta - T_n|)\, dP \qquad \text{(by Fatou's lemma)} \\
&= \lim_{n\to\infty} U(T_n) = \alpha_0 .
\end{aligned}$$

Thus $T_0 \in \mathscr{M}$ and the latter is closed. We now show that $\mathscr{M}$ is nonempty. The conditions (1) and (2) on $W(\cdot)$ imply that it is strictly convex, and the same is true of $U(\cdot)$. Thus $\mathscr{M}$ has at most one point. The conclusion that $\mathscr{M}$ is nonempty [and hence (a)] will now be proved.

The conditions on $W(\cdot)$ imply (by [23] in the nonatomic and [29] in the general case) that $L(\Sigma)$ is uniformly convex when $\mathscr{Y}$ is the space of scalars [i.e., $L(\Sigma)$ is the space of (equivalence classes of) scalar functions]. In general, if $\mathscr{Y}$ is a uniformly convex Banach space and $W(\cdot)$ is such that $L(\Sigma)$ is uniformly convex, then by a result of Halperin [18], the $L(\Sigma)$ of $\mathscr{Y}$-valued functions is also uniformly convex. Since $L(\mathscr{B})$ is a closed (convex) subspace of $L(\Sigma)$, it is also of the same type. If $f(T) = \|\Theta - T\|$, then by ([11], II. 4.29), $f(T)$ assumes its minimum exactly once on $L(\mathscr{B})$ (in fact, on any closed convex subset). Let this minimum point be T_0 in $L(\mathscr{B})$. We claim that $T_0 \in \mathscr{M}$;

i.e., $U(T_0) = \alpha_0$. If this were not true, then $U(T_0) > \alpha_0$ and, by definition of infimum, there exists a T_0' in $L(\mathscr{B})$, $T_0' \neq T_0$, a.e., satisfying $\alpha_0 \leq U(T_0') < U(T_0)$. Now the result on $f(\cdot)$ implies $f(T_0') > f(T_0)$ ($=\alpha$, say). We may assume $\alpha = 1$. Using condition (1) on $W(\cdot)$ and the definition of norm in (4.2), we have

$$U(T_0') = \int_\Omega W(|\Theta - T_0'|)\, d\mu < U(T_0) = \int_\Omega W(|\Theta - T_0|) \leq 1.$$

But again by (4.2), this means that the norm $f(T_0') = \|\Theta - T_0'\| \leq 1$, and at the same time $1 < f(T_0')$. This contradiction proves $U(T_0) = \alpha_0$ and $T_0 \in \mathscr{M}$. Note that the differentiability of norm in $\mathscr{Y}$ was not needed here. This completes the proof of part (a) of the theorem.

We now derive (4.3). We have just seen that $\mathscr{M}$ has a unique element, say T^*. Consider the functional f on $L(\Sigma)$ defined by ($|u| \leq 1$),

$$f_u(Y) = \frac{d}{du}[U(T^* + uY)] \qquad [Y \in L(\Sigma)]. \tag{4.5}$$

That the derivative exists will be shown below. Since $U(T^*) \leq U(T^* + uY)$, for all real u and $Y \in L(\mathscr{B})$, it follows from elementary considerations that $f_0(Y) = 0$, for $Y \in L(\mathscr{B})$. We show that this equation is equivalent to (4.3).

Let $\bar{T} = \Theta - T^*$. Since $d/du[|\bar{T} + uY|]$ exists by hypothesis, we have

$$\frac{d}{du} W[|\bar{T} + uY|] = W'(|\bar{T} + uY|) \frac{d}{du}(|\bar{T} + uY|). \tag{4.6}$$

By ([11], V.9.1), $|\bar{T} + uY|/u$ is a nonincreasing function as $u \to 0^+$, and $d/du[|T + uY|]_{u=0} \leq |\bar{T}| + |Y|$. Hence the right side of (4.6) is dominated by $W'(|\bar{T}| + |Y|)(|\bar{T}| + |Y|)$, which is integrable. So we may integrate (4.6) and interchange the integral and derivative. This shows that $f_u(Y)$ of (4.5) exists and $f_0(Y) = 0$, which is precisely (4.3). The classical results in linear analysis give that $d/du[|\bar{T} + uY|]_{u=0}$ is a linear functional in Y for each $\bar{T}$. This completes (b) and with it the proof of the theorem.

Remark. The functional $U(\cdot)$ is continuous; i.e., $\|T_n - T_0\| \to 0$ implies $U(T_n) \to U(T_0)$.

Proof. Let $Z_n = \Theta - T_n$ and $Z_0 = \Theta - T_0$. Since $T_n \to T_0$ strongly, it follows that $Z_n \to Z_0$ strongly and hence in measure. We have to show that $U(T_n) \to U(T_0)$ which is equivalent to showing $\int_\Omega W(|Z_n|)\, dP \to \int_\Omega W(|Z_0|)\, dP$. The proof is a modification of the familiar techniques for the L^p spaces [11]. Let $f_n = |Z_n|$, $f_0 = |Z_0|$, and $0 < \alpha < 1$ be arbitrary. The preceding statements imply $f_n \to f_0$ strongly [for the scalar $L(\Sigma)$ spaces] and in measure. From the identity

$$f_n = \frac{\alpha}{2}(2f_0) + (1-\alpha)f_0 + \frac{\alpha}{2}\left[\frac{2}{\alpha}(f_n - f_0)\right]$$

and the convexity of $W(\cdot)$, we have

$$\int_\Omega W(f_n)\,dP \le \frac{\alpha}{2}\int_\Omega W(2f_0)\,dP + (1-\alpha)\int_\Omega W(f_0)\,dP$$
$$+ \frac{\alpha}{2}\int_\Omega W\left[\frac{2}{\alpha}(f_n - f_0)\right]dP.$$

Note that the integrals on the right side exist since $W(\cdot)$ satisfies the growth condition (1). The last term tends to zero, since $\|f_n - f_0\| \le \|Z_n - Z_0\| \to 0$. In fact, if $k_n = 2/\alpha\|f_n - f_0\|$, then for large enough n, $k_n \le 1$, and

$$\int_\Omega W\left[\frac{2}{\alpha}\left(\frac{f_n - f_0}{k_n}\right)\cdot k_n\right]dP \le k_n \cdot 1 \to 0.$$

Hence we infer, on first letting $n \to \infty$ and then $\alpha \to 0$,

$$\overline{\lim_{n\to\infty}} \int_\Omega W(f_n)\,dP \le \int_\Omega W(f_0)\,dP \le \underline{\lim_{n\to\infty}} \int_\Omega W(f_n)\,dP.$$

The last inequality is a consequence of Fatou's lemma. This means there is equality throughout, as was to be shown. Note that only condition (1) on $W(\cdot)$ is used; neither condition (2) nor the finiteness of the measure is needed in this argument. This completes the proof.

We now restate the result in a form for comparison with our earlier result in [9]. For convenience set $l(Y) = d/du[|\Theta - T^* + uY|]_{u=0}$ for fixed $\Theta - T^*$. As stated at the beginning of the section, we assume the existence of the conditional distribution $P(\cdot \mid x)$, which is the posterior distribution in $\mathscr{Y}$ for each x. Then the distribution $\pi(\cdot)$ in $\mathscr{X}$ denotes the marginal distribution of the observation X. We have

Theorem 4.2. *An estimator T^* of Θ, with values in a uniformly convex Banach space $\mathscr{Y}$ whose norm is differentiable, is a Bayes estimator relative to the convex (loss) function $W(\cdot)$ satisfying the growth conditions* (1) *and* (2) *of Theorem* 4.1, *iff it satisfies the equation*

$$\int_{\mathscr{Y}} W'(|\theta - T^*(x)|)l(Y(x))P(d\theta \mid x) = 0 \qquad [\text{a.e. } (\pi)]. \qquad (4.7)$$

Here $T^*(\cdot)$ is $\mathscr{B}$-measurable, unique, and the above equation holds for all $\mathscr{B}$-measurable $Y(\cdot)$ such that $\int_{\mathscr{Y}} W(k|Y|)P(dy \mid x) < \infty$ for some $k > 0$. Such a $T^*(\cdot)$ exists. In particular, if $\mathscr{Y}$ is a Hilbert space with inner product denoted by (.,.), then (4.7) *can be written, for almost all x,*

$$\int_{\mathscr{Y}} W'(|\theta - T^*(x)|)[|\theta - T^*(x)|]^{-1}(\theta, y)P(d\theta \mid x)$$

$$= \int_{\mathscr{Y}} W'(|\theta - T^*(x)|)[|\theta - T^*(x)|]^{-1}(T^*(x), y)P(d\theta \mid x). \quad (4.8)$$

Here y is an arbitrary (fixed) element of $\mathscr{Y}$.

Proof. This result is a translation of Theorem 4.1. Since $T^* \in L(\mathscr{B})$, it is $\mathscr{B}$-measurable (recall that $\mathscr{B} \subset \Sigma$ is the σ field generated by the observation X). But then, however, by Lemma 1.5 of Dynkin ([12], p. 6), which also holds for $\mathscr{Y}$-valued functions (in the reference cited $\mathscr{Y}$ was the line, but the proof is seen to hold for a metric space $\mathscr{Y}$), it follows that $T^* = T^*(X)$. Thus (4.7) is just a restatement of (4.3).

In the case that $\mathscr{Y}$ is a Hilbert space, we have

$$\frac{d}{du}(|\overline{T} + uY|^2) = \frac{d}{du}[(\overline{T} + uY, \overline{T} + uY)] = 2u(Y, Y) + 2(\overline{T}, Y).$$

Since the left side is $2|\overline{T} + uY|(d/du)[|\overline{T} + uY|]$, we may write $l(Y)$ as

$$l(Y) = \frac{d}{du}[|\overline{T} + uY|]_{u=0} = [|\overline{T}|]^{-1}(\overline{T}, Y).$$

This is well defined, since $\overline{T} = \theta - T^* \neq 0$, and since $Y \in L(\mathscr{B})$ is arbitrary, we may take it to be a constant element of $\mathscr{Y}$. Hence

$$l(Y) = (|\theta - T^*(x)|)^{-1}[(\theta, y) - (T^*(x), y)].$$

Substituting this in (4.7) we get (4.8) at once, completing the proof.

Remarks. It is of interest to note that (4.8) cannot be simplified appreciably further, even if $\mathscr{Y}$ is two-dimensional. If $\mathscr{Y}$ is the line, we can cancel y, the constant, on both sides of (4.8), and it reduces to (3.3) of [9]. The latter case was proved in [9] under more general conditions on $W(\cdot)$; in fact, the growth conditions of Theorems 4.1 and 4.2 were not needed there. Since the methods of [9] do not seem to extend to the multidimensional case (the proof of measurability of $T^*(\cdot)$ given in [9] does not extend, and the rest of the argument breaks down), it is still an open question whether or not Theorems 4.1 and 4.2 hold without the growth conditions on $W(\cdot)$. It is noted, however, that the above results include $W(x) = |x|^p$, $1 < p < \infty$, and some (convex) polynomial functions as well.

In contrast to the results concerning the existence and determination of the Bayes estimators discussed above, the results of [9] on the lower bounds for the Bayes risk admit an extension to the multidimensional case with essentially the same methods. We now present such an extension of Theorem 4 of [9] when Θ takes it values in $\mathscr{Y}$, a Hilbert space.

Let $D(.,.): \mathscr{Y} \times \mathscr{X} \to \mathscr{Y}$ be a measurable map relative to the product σ-field), such that $|D(\Theta, X)|$ is integrable. Consider the set

$$\mathscr{D} = \{D : \mathscr{E}[D(\Theta, X) \mid x] = 0, \qquad \text{a.e. } (\pi)\}.$$

Here the conditional expectation is one of vector-valued functions, (cf. [32]) which has all the properties that we need, corresponding to the numerical case. Some lower bounds for the Bayes risk $E[W(|\Theta - T^*(X)|)]$ are given in

Theorem 4.3. *Let $W(\cdot)$ be a (nontrivial) symmetric convex function on the line, $W(0) = 0$, and such that for some k (> 1) the function $W^{1/k}(\cdot)$ is also convex. Let $k' = k/(k-1)$. Then for $D \in \mathscr{D}$ with $0 < E|D(\Theta, X)|^{k'}) < \infty$, and any estimator $T(\cdot)$ of Θ, we have [(.,.) is the inner product of $\mathscr{Y}$]*

$$E(W(|\Theta - T(X)|)) \geq W\left\{\frac{E[(D, \Theta)]}{E(|D|)}\right\}\left\{\frac{E(|D|)}{E^{1/k'}(|D|^{k'})}\right\}^{k}. \tag{4.9}$$

For $k = 1$ also (4.9) *holds if $E^{1/k'}(|D|^{k'})$ is interpreted as the essential supremum of $|D(\Theta, X)|$.*

Remark. Note that the growth conditions on $W(\cdot)$ of Theorems 4.1 and 4.2 are not assumed here.

Proof. The proof is on the same lines as in [9], with a judicious use of the inner product in lieu of the products of real functions used there. A sketch is as follows: Let $\overline{W} = W^{1/k}$. Then $\overline{W}(\cdot)$ has the same properties as $W(\cdot)$. So with Jensen's inequality applied to the identity

$$|D|\,\overline{W}(|\overline{T}|) = E(|D|)\left[\frac{|D|}{E(|D|)}\,\overline{W}(|\overline{T}|)\right] \qquad (\overline{T} = \Theta - T),$$

we have

$$\begin{aligned} E[|D|\,\overline{W}(|\overline{T}|)] &\geq E(|D|)\overline{W}\left[\frac{E(|D|\,|\overline{T}|)}{E(|D|)}\right] \\ &\geq E(|D|)\overline{W}\left\{\frac{|E[(D, \overline{T})]|}{E(|D|)}\right\} && \text{by the Schwarz inequality} \\ &= E(|D|)\overline{W}\left\{\frac{E[(D, \overline{T})]}{E(|D|)}\right\} && \text{by symmetry of } W(\cdot). \end{aligned}$$

But $D \in \mathscr{D}$ implies

$$E[(D, \Theta - T)] = E[(D, \Theta)] - E[E(D, T) \mid X] = E((D, \Theta)),$$

since $E((D, T) \mid x) = (\mathscr{E}(D \mid x), T(x)) = 0$ by the relation between $\mathscr{E}$ and E (cf. [32]) and the definition of $\mathscr{D}$. Thus

$$E[|D|\,\overline{W}(|\Theta - T|)] \geq E(|D|)\overline{W}\left(\frac{E[(D, \Theta)]}{E(|D|)}\right). \tag{4.10}$$

If $k>1$, Hölder's inequality applied to the left side of (4.10) yields

$$E[|D|\overline{W}(|\Theta - T|)] \leq E^{1/k}(W(|\Theta - T|))E^{1/k'}(|D|^{k'}). \tag{4.11}$$

Now (4.9) is an easy consequence of (4.10) and (4.11). If $k = 1$, the result follows from the corresponding case of the Hölder inequality. This completes the proof.

Remark. The above proof shows that the same result holds if $\mathcal{Y}$ is an arbitrary Banach space and if we define $D: \mathcal{Y} \times \mathcal{X} \to \mathcal{Y}^*$, the dual of $\mathcal{Y}$, and if $<D, \Theta>$ is the linear functional D evaluated at Θ, instead of the inner product. Since $|<D, \Theta>| \leq |D|\,|\Theta|$, we could use this for the Schwarz inequality above. With this interpretation, the result holds in this case also without change.

It is now clear that the work on Bayes lower bounds presented in [9] completely generalizes to the multidimensional case. The restatements of these results will be omitted.

5. MULTIDIMENSIONAL PREDICTION THEORY

A prediction problem can be described, in the spirit of this paper, as follows. Let $Y, X_1, \ldots, X_n$ be r.v.'s and $g(X_1, \ldots, X_n)$ be a r.v. which is a function of $X_1, \ldots, X_n$ only. If the joint distribution of Y and $(X_1, \ldots, X_n)$ is known, then the problem is to find, among all functions g of a certain class $\mathcal{G}$, a function that minimizes the expected value of a nonnegative convex function $W(\cdot)$ of the error, that is, to find a g_0 such that $E(W(|Y - g_0(X_1, \ldots, X_n)|)) = \inf_{g\in\mathcal{G}} E(W(|Y - g(X_1, \ldots, X_n)|))$. If $\mathcal{G}$ is a set of linear functionals (or operators) g, then the problem is one of *linear prediction*, and in the general case it is one of *nonlinear prediction.* Here n need not be finite, and the X's and Y can be vector-valued. The relation between the prediction problem (in the general case) and Bayes estimation is evidently close. This was long recognized ([34 and 6]), but it does not seem to have been sufficiently exploited in the literature. When $W(x) = x^2$ and the r.v.'s are scalar-valued, Grenander [16] considered the problem in this spirit. When $W(x) = |x|^p$, $1 < p < \infty$, the general case, with X_i, Y vector-valued, was recently considered in [28]. We shall now discuss, briefly, the available work on the prediction problem and, as an application and extension of the results of the preceding section, present the general case (subsuming the known results) if X_i, Y are vector-valued (not necessarily finite-dimensional) and $W(\cdot)$ is a convex function (not necessarily a power). Our treatment centers around nonlinear prediction.

Except for [28], virtually all the work on prediction theory is confined to the case of quadratic loss, $W(x) = x^2$, and most of it is on linear prediction for scalar r.v.'s. This work, with references to earlier contributions to the problems, can be found in [17] and [24]. The early pioneering work is to be found in [21] and [36]. In comparison, there is less work available when the r.v.'s are (finite) vector-valued. A description of this is contained in ([10], Chap. 12) and in [19]. The latter, reviewing the work on the subject, has an essentially complete list of references on finite vector processes. There is an extension of this (again with quadratic loss), when the r.v.'s are Banach-space-valued, in [15]. It should be mentioned that linear least-squares prediction problems are closely related to Hilbert-space methods, particularly so if the process is stationary in the wide sense; i.e., if $E(X_t) = 0$, the covariance function $r(s, t) = E(X_t X_s)$ is $r(s-t)$, a function of one variable only. Essentially all the work described above assumes this additional stationarity condition. In the same spirit, a problem of linear prediction for wide-sense Markov processes has been considered for (finite) vector processes in [4]. A rather general and systematic study of nonlinear prediction when the r.v.'s are vector (function space)-valued was considered in [14] when the process is again stationary (and the loss is quadratic). A simpler problem in the scalar case was treated in ([16], Chap. 5). If the process is Gaussian, the optimal (nonlinear) predictor has been explicitly determined in [20]. There is also some general discussion of the prediction problem (with quadratic loss) in [24]. This seems to be all that is known about prediction theory with a certain degree of generality. Of course, there is much literature on applications and specific cases.

It is characteristic of the least-squares prediction problem that the predictors can be calculated by certain self-adjoint projections given by Fourier transforms (in the linear case) or by conditional expectations (in the nonlinear case). However, both of these cease to be the appropriate tools as soon as one considers the loss function $W(x) = |x|^p$, $p \neq 2$. The difficulties have been discussed at some length in [28]. Here the previous results will be extended to more general loss functions $(W\cdot)$ when the processes are vector-valued. A somewhat related problem, when the r.v.'s are scalar-valued, was considered in [27].

Let $Y, X_1, \dots$ be a sequence of r.v.'s such that $E(W(|X_i|))$, $i \geq 1$, and $E(W(|Y|))$ exist and the joint distribution of Y and $X_1, X_2, \dots$ is known. (Here the X_i and Y are $\mathscr{Y}$-valued strongly measurable functions in E. Hille's terminology; our notation conforms to [11].) The nonlinear prediction problem is to find a functional $g(\cdot)$ on $\{X_i\}$, where g maps Y into $\mathscr{Y}$, such that $E(W(|Y-g|))$ is a minimum. Then g is said to be the best predictor of Y relative to the loss function $W(\cdot)$. Let $\mathscr{B}_n = \mathscr{B}(X_i, 1 \leq i \leq n)$ and $\mathscr{B} = \mathscr{B}(X_i, i \geq 1)$ be the σ fields determined by the r.v.'s shown, and $L(\mathscr{B}_n)$ be the space of $\mathscr{B}_n$-measurable functions f with $\int_\Omega W(\alpha\,|\,f\,|\,)\,dP < \infty$ for some $\alpha > 0$, and define $L(\Sigma)$ and $L(\mathscr{B})$ similarly. The solution to the general prediction problem can now be given as follows:

Theorem 5.1. *Let $L(\Sigma)$ be the Banach space of all Σ-measurable functions from Ω to a uniformly convex Banach space $\mathcal{Y}$ which are integrable relative to $W(\cdot)$ as defined above. Suppose the joint distribution of Y and $\{X_i\}$ is known, and $Y, X_i \in L(\Sigma)$. If the loss function $W(\cdot)$ is a symmetric convex function on the line with $W(0) = 0$ and satisfying* (a) $W(2x) \leq cW(x), 0 < c < \infty$, *and* (b) $W'(ax) \geq k_a W'(x)$ *for each $a > 1$ and some $k_a > 1$ and all $x > 0$, then there exists a unique predictor Y_0, relative to the loss function $W(\cdot)$, based on an observation of the vector $\{X_i\}$ [i.e., $Y_0 \in L(\mathcal{B})$], such that $E[W(|Y - Y_0|)]$ is a minimum. Moreover, if Y_n is the (unique) predictor in $L(\mathcal{B}_n)$, then $Y_n \to Y_0$ strongly, in that $E[W(|Y_0 - Y_n|)] \to 0$, as $n \to \infty$.*

Remark. The last statement of the theorem says that the predictor Y_0 can be approximated in the strong sense by Y_n, the predictor based on the first n r.v.'s, for large enough n. We show later how Y_n (or Y_0) can be calculated in any specific problem. Note that the result implies (trivially) that $Y_n \to Y_0$ in probability; the problem of a.e. convergence is more difficult.

Proof. As in the proof of Theorem 4.1, we consider the convex function U,

$$U(Z) = \int_\Omega W(|Y - Z|)\, dP \qquad [Z \in L(\Sigma)]. \tag{5.1}$$

Since $L(\mathcal{B}_n) \subset L(\mathcal{B}) \subset L(\Sigma)$ and (excluding the trivial case) $Y \notin L(\mathcal{B})$, the proof of the first half of that theorem can be repeated verbatim to conclude that there exists a unique $Y_0 \in L(\mathcal{B})$ $[Y_n \in L(\mathcal{B}_n)]$ such that $U(Y_0)[U(Y_n)]$ is a minimum on $L(\mathcal{B})[L(\mathcal{B}_n)]$, because $W(\cdot)$ and $\mathcal{Y}$ satisfy the same conditions as there. Hence we only need to prove that $Y_n \to Y_0$ in the stated sense.

Since $U(Y_n)$ and $U(Y_0)$ are finite and $0 \leq U(Y_0) \leq U(Y_n) \leq U(Y_1)$ by definition of the $\{Y_n\}$ sequence, it follows that $\{Y_n\}$ is a bounded set [in the $L(\Sigma)$ norm, given by (4.2)]. As shown in the proof of Theorem 4.1, the above statement is also equivalent to the following: $0 \leq \|Y - Y_0\| \leq \|Y - Y_n\| \leq \|Y - Y_1\|$, and $\{\|Y - Y_n\|\}$ converges (monotonely) to a limit α_0 (say). We claim that $\alpha_0 = \|Y - Y_0\|$ itself. The argument here is very similar to that of the proof of ([27], Theorem 5), and we need not repeat it here. Thus, using the uniform convexity of $L(\Sigma)$, we may deduce as in [27], that $\|Y_n - Y_0\| \to 0$. [Even though Y_n's are scalar-valued in [27], the argument on page 110 applies here verbatim.] From this, if $\varepsilon_n = \|Y_n - Y_0\|$, we have, for large n, $0 < \varepsilon_n < 1$ and

$$E[W(|Y_n - Y_0|)] = \int_\Omega W\left(\frac{\varepsilon_n |Y_n - Y|}{\varepsilon_n}\right) d\mu \leq \varepsilon_n \cdot 1, \tag{5.2}$$

by (4.2) and the convexity of $W(\cdot)$. Since $\varepsilon_n \to 0$ as $n \to \infty$, this completes the proof.

The proof of Theorem 4.2 now implies immediately the next result on the calculation of Y_n or Y_0, the nth or the final predictors, as solutions of an integral equation. Hence we state without proof

Theorem 5.2. *Let the hypothesis of Theorem* 5.1 *hold on* $W(\cdot)$ *and the norm in* $\mathcal{Y}$ *be differentiable. If the conditional distribution of* Y *given* $\mathcal{B}_n$ *exists* [*i.e.*, $P(\cdot \mid \mathcal{B}_n) = P(\cdot \mid x_1, \ldots, x_n)$], *then the best predictor* Y_n (*or* Y_0) *is given as a unique solution in* $L(\mathcal{B}_n)$ [*or in* $L(\mathcal{B})$] *of the integral equation*

$$\int_{\mathcal{Y}} W'(|y - Y_n(x)|)l(Z)P(dy \mid x_1, \ldots, x_n) = 0, \tag{5.3}$$

for almost all $(x_1, \ldots, x_n)$, *where* $l(Z) = (d/dt)[|Y - Y_n + tZ|]_{u=0}$ *for* $Z \in L(\mathcal{B}_n)$, (*or of the equation obtained by replacing* Y_n *and* $\mathcal{B}_n$ *by* Y_0 *and* $\mathcal{B}$).

Remark. If $\mathcal{Y}$ is the real line, this equation can be simplified to a corresponding result in [9].

The second part of Theorem 5.1 naturally raises the question of pointwise convergence of the sequence of predictors $\{Y_n\}$. The answer is in the affirmative but the proof is nontrivial. For completeness we present the proof here; the arguments are generalizations of those given in [2] and [30] for the scalar case [and $W(x) = |x|^p$].

Theorem 5.3. *Let the hypothesis of Theorem* 5.1 *hold and let* Y_n, Y_0 *be the predictors on* $L(\mathcal{B}_n)$ *and* $L(\mathcal{B})$. *Then* $Y_n \to Y$, *as* $n \to \infty$, *with probability* 1.

For the proof of this result we need some preliminaries. If f is a bounded $\mathcal{B}_1$-measurable scalar function on Ω with $\int_\Omega W(f)\,dP < \infty$, and e is any element on the unit sphere of $\mathcal{Y}$, then fe is $\mathcal{Y}$-valued and $fe \in L(\mathcal{B}_1)$. With this device the scalar functions satisfying the integrability conditions may be identified as elements of $L(\Sigma)$. Note that if $g \in L(\Sigma)$ and f is a bounded scalar function, then fg is a $\mathcal{Y}$-valued r.v. and $fg \in L(\Sigma)$. With this understanding we have

Lemma 5.4. *Let* $\mathcal{B}_i \subset \Sigma$, $i = 1, \ldots, n$, *be n increasing* σ-*fields and* $X \in L(\Sigma)$, *and let the hypothesis of Theorem* 5.3 *hold. If* Y_i *is the predictor in* $L(\mathcal{B}_i)$ *and* $\{A_i; i = 1, \ldots, n\}$ *is a disjoint sequence with* $\bigcup_{i=1}^n A_i = \Omega$, *with* $A_i \in \mathcal{B}_i$, *then the following inequality holds:*

$$\int_\Omega W(|X - Y_1|)\,dP \geq \sum_{i=1}^n \int_{A_i} W(|X - Y_i|)\,dP \geq \int_\Omega W(|X - Y_n|)\,d\mu. \tag{5.4}$$

If $Z_n = \sum_{i=1}^n \chi_{A_i} Y_i$, then Z_n, $Y_n \in L(\mathcal{B}_n)$, where χ_A is the indicator of A. By definition of Y_n we note that $U(Y_n)$, of (5.1), is the minimum of $U(\cdot)$ in $L(\mathcal{B}_n)$ and hence $U(Z_n) \geq U(Y_n)$. This is just the last inequality. For the first note that (intuitively) Z_n improves upon Y_1 in each $L(\mathcal{B}_i)$, $i = 1, \ldots, n$, by being the closest element on each A_i, so the inequality must hold. The formal argument here needs a little care. It is essentially the same as ([30], Lemma 2) and will be omitted.

The following modification of the above lemma is needed in the proof of the theorem. Let $Z_{n,k} = \sum_{i=1}^{k} Y_{n+i}\chi_{A_i}$, where $A_i \in \mathscr{B}_{n+i}$, $i = 1, \ldots, k$, $\Omega = \bigcup_{i=1}^{k} A_i$. With this notation we may deduce, from Theorem 5.1 and the above lemma,

Lemma 5.5. *Under the hypothesis of the theorem, for each* $\varepsilon > 0$, *there exist an* $\eta_\varepsilon > 0$ *and integers* n_ε *and* k_ε *such that* $n \geq n_\varepsilon$ *and* $k \geq k_\varepsilon$ *imply*

$$\int_\Omega W[|Y_n - Y_0|]\,d\mu < \eta_\varepsilon, \qquad \int_\Omega W[|Y_n - Z_{n,k}|]\,d\mu < \varepsilon. \tag{5.5}$$

The formal details are again obtainable easily from the scalar case [30].

Proof of Theorem 5.3. Let k_1, k_2, and k be integers satisfying $1 \leq k_1$, $k_2 \leq k$. If $Z = \limsup_{n\to\infty} |Y_n - Y_0|$, we must show that $P[Z > 0] = 0$, and this will now be demonstrated.

Let $\varepsilon > 0$ and $\delta > 0$ be given. Choose k_ε and n_ε as in Lemma 5.5, and let $k \geq k_\varepsilon$. Let the partition of Lemma 5.4 be the following (this is a standard partition used in probability theory; e.g., see [10], p. 315, or [22], p. 235):

$$A_1 = \{|Y_n - Y_{n+1}| > \delta\}, \qquad \text{and (inductively)}$$
$$A_i = \{|Y_n - Y_{n+j}| \leq \delta,\ \ j = 1, \ldots, i-1,\ |Y_n - Y_{n+i}| > \delta\}, \quad (i = 2, \ldots, k).$$

Now let $A_{k+1} = \Omega - \bigcup_{i=1}^{k} A_i$. Then $A_i \in \mathscr{B}_{n+i}$, $i = 1, \ldots, k$. We note that on A_{k+1}, $|Y_{n+i} - Y_{n+j}| \leq 2\delta$, $1 \leq i, j \leq k$.

The following computations use the fact that $W(\cdot)$ is a symmetric convex function and certain elementary inequalities, without comment. Since $\bigcup_{i=1}^{k} A_i = \bigcup_{i=1}^{k} \{|Y_n - Y_{n+i}|\chi_{A_i} > \delta\}$, we have

$$P\Big[\max_{1\leq i\leq k_1}\ \max_{1\leq j\leq k_2} |Y_{n+i} - Y_{n+j}| > 2\delta\Big] \leq P\Big[\sum_{i=1}^{k} |Y_n - Y_{n+i}|\,\chi_{A_i} > \delta\Big]$$

$$= P\Big[W\Big(\sum_{i=1}^{k} |Y_n - Y_{n+i}|\chi_{Ai}\Big) > W(\delta)\Big] \leq P\Big[\sum_{i=1}^{k+1} W(|Y_n - Y_{n+i}|\,\chi_{A_i}) > W(\delta)\Big]$$

$$= P[W(|Y_n - Z_{n,k+1}|) > W(\delta)] \leq \frac{1}{W(\delta)} \int_\Omega W[|Y_n - Z_{n,k+1}|]\,dP$$

$$\leq \frac{\varepsilon}{W(\delta)} \qquad \text{by Lemma 5.5.}$$

Now letting $k \to \infty$, and then $k_1 \to \infty$ and finally $k_2 \to \infty$, we get

$$P\Big[\sup_{i,j\geq 1} |Y_i - Y_j| \geq 2\delta\Big] \leq \frac{\varepsilon}{W(\delta)}.$$

This implies immediately $P[Z \geq 2\delta] \leq \varepsilon / W(\delta)$. If we let $\varepsilon \to 0$ and then $\delta \to 0$, the desired conclusion is obtained.

The above results give a complete solution of the multidimensional prediction problem with a convex loss (with growth conditions) when the observations are taken on a discrete parameter process. The results can be extended to the continuous parameter processes. We shall state the extension without proof, since the modification needed is easy (cf. [28]). The concepts of separability and fixed points of discontinuity of a process are standard (cf., e.g., [10] or [12] or [22]).

Theorem 5.6. *Let $\{X_t, t \in T\}$, T a linear interval, be a (strongly measurable) separable $\mathcal{Y}$-valued stochastic process without fixed points of discontinuity, where $\mathcal{Y}$ is a uniformly convex Banach space. Let X_{t_0}, $t_0 \notin T$, also be a $\mathcal{Y}$-valued random variable such that the joint distribution of X_{t_0} and X_t, $t \in T$, is given. Let $W(\cdot)$ be a symmetric convex function on the line, $W(0) = 0$, and satisfy the growth conditions of Theorem 5.1, and $\int_\Omega W(|X_t|)\, dP < \infty$ for $t = t_0$ and $t \in T$. Then the following conclusions hold:*

(a) *There exists a best predictor Y_0 relative to $W(\cdot)$ as loss based on a realization of $\{X_t, t \in T\}$ (or sample path).*

(b) *If $\tilde{T} \subset T$, where $\tilde{T} = \{t_1, t_2, \ldots\}$, is a dense denumerable subset of T and Y_n is the predictor based on n sample points at $(t_1, \ldots, t_n)$ in $\tilde{T}$, then as $n \to \infty$, $E(W(|Y_0 - Y_n|)) \to 0$ and also $Y_n \to Y_0$, with probability 1.*

(c) *If the norm in $\mathcal{Y}$ is differentiable, then the predictor Y_0 is given as a solution of the integral equation*

$$\int_\Omega W'(|X_{t_0} - Y_0|) \frac{d}{du} [|(X_{t_0} - Y_0) + uZ|]_{u=0}\, dP = 0 \tag{5.6}$$

for all $Z \in L(\mathcal{B}_T)$, where $\mathcal{B}_T$ is the σ-field determined by $\{X_t, t \in T\}$. Replacing Y_0 and T above by Y_n and n in (5.6), one can determine Y_n.

Remark. If $W(x) = |x|^p$, $1 < p < \infty$, this theorem reduces to a result of [28], and if $W(x) = x^2$ and $\mathcal{Y}$ is the line, this result may be specialized to obtain certain results of [16] and [20]. Other specializations may be considered.

REFERENCES

1. Anderson, T. W. (1958). *An Introduction to Multivariate Statistical Analysis.* Wiley New York.
2. Andô, T. and Amemiya, I. (1965). Almost everywhere convergence of prediction sequences in $L^p(1 < p < \infty)$. *Z. Wahrscheinlichkeitstheorie* **4** 113–120.
3. Barankin, E. W. (1951). Concerning some inequalities in the theory of statistical estimation. *Skand. Aktuarietidskr.* **34** 35–40.
4. Beutler, F. J. (1963). Multivariate wide-sense Markov processes and prediction theory. *Ann. Math. Statist.* **34** 424–438.

5. Bhattacharyya, A. (1946/47). On some analogues of the amount of information and their use in statistical estimation. *Sankhyā* **8** 1–14, 201–218.
6. Blackwell, D. and Girshick, M. A. (1954). *Theory of Games and Statistical Decision Functions*. Wiley, New York.
7. Cramér, H. (1946). *Mathematical Methods of Statistics*. Princeton Univ. Press, Princeton, New Jersey.
8. DeGroot, M. H. (1959). Unbiased sequential estimation for binomial populations. *Ann. Math. Statist.* **30** 80–101.
9. DeGroot, M. H. and Rao, M. M. (1963). Bayes estimation with convex loss. *Ann. Math. Statist.* **34** 839–846.
10. Doob, J. L. (1953). *Stochastic Processes*. Wiley, New York.
11. Dunford, N. and Schwartz, J. T. (1958). *Linear Operators, Part I*. Wiley (Interscience), New York.
12. Dynkin, E. B. (1961). *Theory of Markov Processes* (translation). Prentice-Hall, Englewood Cliffs, New Jersey.
13. Fend, A. V. (1959). On the attainment of Cramér-Rao and Bhattacharyya bounds for the variance estimate. *Ann. Math. Statist.* **30** 381–388.
14. Furstenburg, H. (1960). *Stationary Processes and Prediction Theory*. Princeton Univ. Press, Princeton, New Jersey.
15. Gangolli, R. (1963). Wide-sense stationary sequences of distributions on Hilbert space and the factorization of operator valued functions. *J. Math. Mech.* **12** 893–910.
16. Grenander, U. (1950). Stochastic processes and statistical inference. *Arkiv. Math.* **1** 195–277.
17. Hájek, J. (1962). On linear statistical problems in stochastic processes. *Čz. Math. J.* **12** (87) 404–444.
18. Halperin, I. (1954). Uniform convexity in function spaces. *Duke Math. J.* **21** 195–204.
19. Helson, H. and Lowdenslager, D. (1961). Vector-valued processes. *Proc. Fourth Berkeley Symp. Math. Statist. Prob.* **2** 203–212.
20. Kallianpur, G. (1959). A problem in optimum filtering with finite data. *Ann. Math. Statist.* **30** 659–669.
21. Kolmogorov, A. N. (1941). Stationary sequences in Hilbert space (in Russian). *Bull. Math. Univ. Moscow* **2** No. 6.
22. Loève, M. (1963). *Probability Theory* (3rd ed.). Van Nostrand, Princeton, New Jersey.
23. Milnes, H. W. (1957). Convexity in Orlicz spaces. *Pacific J. Math.* **7** 1151–1183.
24. Parzen, E. (1962). Extraction and detection problems and reproducing kernal Hilbert spaces. *J. SIAM Control* **1** 35–62.
25. Rao, C. R. (1945). Information and accuracy attainable in the esitmation of statistical parameters. *Bull. Calcutta Math. Soc.* **37** 81–91.
26. Rao, M. M. (1959). Lower bounds for risk functions in estimation. *Proc. Nat. Acad. Sci. U.S.A.* **45** 1168–1171. [See also (1961). *Math. Ann.* **143** 379–398.]
27. Rao, M. M. (1965). Conditional expectations and closed projections. *Indag. Math.* **27** 100–112.
28. Rao, M. M. (to appear). Inference in stochastic processes III: Nonlinear prediction, filtering and sampling theorems.
29. Rao, M. M. (1965). Smoothness of Orlicz spaces. *Indag. Math.* **27** 671–690.
30. Rao, M. M. (1966). Notes on pointwise convergence of closed martingales. *Indag. Math.* **28**.
31. Savage, L. J. (1954). *The Foundations of Statistics*. Wiley, New York.
32. Scalora, F. S. (1961). Abstract martingale convergence theorems. *Pacific J. Math.* **11** 347–374.

33. SETH, G. R. (1949). On the variance of estimates. *Ann. Math. Statist.* **20** 1–27.
34. WALD, A. (1950). *Statistical Decision Functions*. Wiley, New York.
35. WEISS, G. (1956). A note on Orlicz spaces. *Portugal. Math.* **15** 35–47.
36. WIENER, N. (1949). *Extrapolation, Interpolation, and Smoothing of Stationary Time Series*. Wiley, New York.

Estimation in Multivariate Analysis

A. P. DEMPSTER[1]

DEPARTMENT OF STATISTICS
HARVARD UNIVERSITY
CAMBRIDGE, MASSACHUSETTS

1. INTRODUCTION

This paper is concerned with the various methodologies of statistical estimation in the special context of estimating the parameters of a multivariate normal population from a random sample of size n. At the close of Section 2, after comparing these methodologies, a practical approach is suggested which relies on an adaptation of the jackknife method of Tukey. In Section 3 this approach is developed in the particular area of canonical correlation analysis. The discussion of Section 3 is asymptotic in the sense that the aim is to provide satisfactory methods of estimation in moderately large samples.

The term *estimation* is meant in a wide sense to include (a) point estimation without or with corresponding estimates of variability, (b) interval estimation whether from confidence, likelihood, Bayesian, or fiducial reasoning, and (c) full posterior distributions over parameters, whether from Bayesian or fiducial arguments. However, the methods given in Section 3 are limited to category (a).

2. A LABORATORY FOR COMPARING METHODOLOGIES

2.1. The Situation

In sampling from a p-variate normal population there are p parameters governing the means and $p(p + 1)/2$ parameters governing the covariance structure, all of which will be considered unknown. By and large, increasing numbers of parameters pose increasingly serious tests for any theory of estimation. Thus, for moderate p, say from 10 to 50, and moderate sample sizes, say from 50 to 500, the estimation of covariance structure should prove an

[1] Research supported by the United States Navy through the Office of Naval Research under Contract Nonr-1866(37). Reproduction in whole or in part permitted for any purpose of the United States Government.

interesting laboratory setting for the comparison of different conceptual approaches to estimation.

The various standard analyses, such as principal component analysis, canonical correlation analysis, and multiple discriminant analysis, are procedures which strongly involve the covariance structure of the population. When the population mean and population covariance are unknown, the standard practice is to replace them by the sample mean and sample covariance and to carry out the analysis in terms of these sample statistics. This use of simple-minded estimates is justified to some extent by their being maximum likelihood estimates.

Obvious statistical questions concern the errors made in treating various sample eigenvalues as though they were the population eigenvalues, whether these eigenvalues be principal components of variance, canonical correlation coefficients, or among group variance components associated with discriminant analysis. Interest also focuses on the errors in the associated sample eigenvectors which estimate special linear combinations of the original p variates. Inquiry should also be made into the misbehavior of these sample eigenvectors when applied to future data, ignoring the errors in both eigenvalues and eigenvectors. Bias corrections, estimates of mean square error, and future sample properties will be discussed in Sections 3.4, 3.5, and 3.6, respectively, in the case of canonical correlation analysis.

The remainder of Section 2 is concerned with the general strengths and weaknesses of the various schools of statistical inference as they appear in the multivariate normal setting.

2.2. Methods Based on Sampling Theory

Estimates may be based on sample statistics selected on consideration of their sampling distributions given each possible set of parameters. To estimate a specified parameter one seeks a statistic whose sampling distribution is highly sensitive to changes in that parameter in a way relatively free of dependence on the values of the remaining parameters. Such a statistic may be used for point estimation or for interval estimation via a confidence argument.

The approach thus briefly described has weaknesses of several kinds. The choice of what aspects of a sampling distribution shall define optimal estimates is generally somewhat arbitrary. Furthermore, it is only rarely that a principle of estimation (such as minimum variance unbiasedness) leads to a definite choice of estimating statistic. Sampling distributions usually have the awkward feature of depending on unknown parameters and so are themselves unknown. Such difficulties are well recognized within the school and are regarded as providing scope for rational discussion and ingenious mathematical argument.

A more serious difficulty is that sampling theory is concerned with averages over what might have happened rather than with interpretation of the data actually observed. One aspect of this difficulty is reflected in debates over the choice of an appropriate "reference set" or "level of conditioning"; i.e., even given that sampling theory defines the correct approach, there are many different relevant sampling theories, depending on which features of the data are regarded as fixed and which are regarded as random. There exist quite convincing examples, such as that of Savage [18, p. 27], which say that the unconditional sampling model is at least sometimes quite unreasonable, even if the sampling had been physically carried out. The standard Neyman-Pearson theory does not appear to have any internal resources or principles which bear on this difficulty.

In the case of multivariate normal sampling theory the situation is perhaps as nice as possible in the face of so many parameters. There exist sufficient statistics of minimal dimensions and with appealing interpretations. The sampling theory of these statistics is very elegant and highly developed. Still the problem of nuisance parameters often remains acute. Nor does the elegance of the sampling theory help with the question of whether the sampling hypothesis provides an appropriate frame of reference. A nagging doubt remains that someone may recognize in the data a conditional frame of reference, analogous to that in the example of Savage referred to above, which casts doubt on the conclusion based on the raw unconditional theory.

One attractive feature of the sampling theory approach is its ability to provide bias corrections of a qualitatively desirable kind. Consider, for example, the eigenvalues of a sample covariance matrix regarded as estimates of the corresponding eigenvalues of the population covariance matrix. These eigenvalues may also be regarded as sample or population variances of the linear combinations of the p variates defined by their corresponding eigenvectors (properly normalized). The following reasoning suggests that the larger sample eigenvalues are upwardly biased estimates of the corresponding population eigenvalues, and similarly that the smaller sample eigenvalues are downwardly biased. The reasoning assumes that the sample variance of a preselected linear combination of variates is a good estimate of the population variance of that linear combination; i.e., for such an estimate no upward or downward correction is needed. The largest eigenvalue, however, is a sample variance for a linear combination of variates selected among normalized linear combinations to have the largest sample variance. Consequently the largest sample eigenvalue is larger than the estimate of the largest population eigenvalue which could have been based on the corresponding population eigenvector, had that eigenvector been known. Since this latter estimate would have been regarded as acceptable, the largest sample eigenvector must therefore be biased upward.

Similar reasoning applies to the smallest sample eigenvalue and, although less clear, one might expect similar effects to appear for eigenvalues close to the largest or smallest. Moreover, although the above reasoning is given for principal component analysis, similar reasoning applies for other analyses in which eigenvalues appear in different roles.

The sampling theory approach to inference allows these qualitatively apparent biases to be expressed in quantitative terms, and this is no mean achievement for the theory. Such bias computations have been carried out by Lawley [12, 13] for principal component analysis and canonical correlation analysis.

2.3. Bayesian Methods

The ascendancy of the sampling theory school of inference has been increasingly challenged over the past decade by a re-emerging Bayesian school. The Bayesian argument, which yields conditional distributions given the sample data, is strongly appealing in its logic and consistency. In particular it avoids the frame of reference difficulty which troubles the sampling theory approach. The conventional criticism of the Bayesian method is to point out the difficulty of supplying a meaningful prior distribution over all the unknown parameters jointly. This is a considerable task when, as in the p-variate normal sampling situation, a prior distribution over $p + p(p + 1)/2$ parameters is required. For those working within the Bayesian school, this criticism should be regarded as a challenge. After all, one almost always does know something about range of variation of variates under consideration and often about their covariation as well. The greatest need of the Bayesian statistician is for viable methods that transform such knowledge into a prior distribution or a range of prior distributions.

To my knowledge this challenge has not yet been successfully met in the situation of multivariate normal sampling. Instead, the tendency has been to rely on conventional "flat" or "informationless" prior densities. Usually these are not actual densities, since they do not have finite integrals. Often they are derivable by invariance arguments. A considerable catalogue of multivariate estimation methods based on such conventional prior pseudodistributions has been given by Geisser and Cornfield [8] and Geisser [6, 7].

Analogous conventional prior pseudodistributions are generally acceptable in the presence of a single parameter or a small number of parameters, since a fairly small sample generally suffices almost to eliminate the influence of the choice of a prior distribution. With a moderately large number of parameters, however, stereotyped Bayesian methods may yield results severely different from the results of standard sampling theory arguments (Stein [19]). Estimation of a covariance matrix provides an especially good example of difficulties of this kind (Dempster [3]).

It is instructive to analyze how the conventional Bayesian arguments behave with respect to the biases in sample eigenvalues discussed in Section 2.2. Consider again principal component analysis. Suppose that $\mathbf{S}$ is a sample covariance matrix estimating the covariance matrix $\boldsymbol{\Sigma}$ of a multivariate normal population. Then $\mathbf{T} = (n-1)\mathbf{S}$ has the Wishart sampling distribution $W(\boldsymbol{\Sigma}, n-1)$ in the notation of Anderson [1]. On the other hand, Geisser and Cornfield [8] obtain $W(\mathbf{T}^{-1}, n-v-1)$ as the posterior distribution of $\boldsymbol{\Sigma}^{-1}$ when the prior density of $\boldsymbol{\Sigma}^{-1}$ is proportional to $|\boldsymbol{\Sigma}|^{v/2}$.

The discordance between the sampling theory result and the posterior distribution may be exposed as follows. Under sampling theory, the ratio of the largest sample eigenvalue to the smallest has a distribution which indicates an upward bias in this ratio regarded as an estimate of the corresponding population ratio, for the numerator is biased upward and the denominator is biased downward. This concurs with the qualitative bias argument in Section 2.2. The Bayes posterior distribution theory is similar to the sampling theory except that the roles of $\mathbf{T}$ and $\boldsymbol{\Sigma}$ in the latter are played by $\boldsymbol{\Sigma}^{-1}$ and $\mathbf{T}^{-1}$ in the former. Thus, according to the posterior distribution, the ratio of the largest population eigenvalue to the smallest is biased upward relative to the same ratio in the sample. This is just the opposite of the result which the argument of Section 2.2 suggested was plausible. Thus, when samples are sufficiently small that these biases matter, as is often the case in practice, the conventional Bayesian approach has a decidedly questionable property.

2.4. Other Approaches

R. A. Fisher founded two further schools of statistical estimation, each of which retains small groups of devotees. Both of these approaches grew out of the sampling theory milieu in which Fisher did his early work. In retrospect both may be seen as attempts to come closer to inferences made conditional on the data observed.

The first of these approaches says that parameters may be estimated by direct contemplation of the likelihood function of the parameters. The likelihood of a given hypothesis determined from given observed data is proportional to the probability of that particular set of data arising under the sampling distribution associated with the given hypothesis. The likelihood function is essentially all that remains of the sampling theory approach when one insists on dealing with probabilities relevant only to the data actually observed. The role of likelihood as one of two factors in a Bayes posterior density is well known. But, if one attempts a direct interpretation of likelihood alone, the form and appeal of the reasoning is rather unclear. In particular, it is not clear how to disentangle nuisance parameters from a parameter of interest in a multiparameter situation.

Fisher's other contribution is the fiducial argument. The aim of this argument is clear, namely to rely on sampling theory but to try to recognize frames of reference which may be regarded as conditionally valid given observed data. The fiducial argument differs from Neyman's theory of confidence regions in its attempt to face up to the conditioning issue. Unfortunately the internal difficulties in the fiducial canon as expounded by Fisher seem insurmountable (Dempster [4]). In particular, there are many different versions of the fiducial distribution for a covariance matrix, even in the case $p = 2$ (Mauldon [14]). It thus appears that the fiducial argument founders on the rock of covariance estimation, as does the conventional Bayesian approach.

In spite of this, neither the likelihood nor fiducial positions should be rejected out of hand. Recently James [11] has been working with a modification of the likelihood approach, in which he investigates not the likelihood found from the complete sample but rather the likelihood based on the sampling distribution of the sample eigenvalues. He has shown that the maximum likelihood estimates of the eigenvalues of a covariance matrix based on this revised likelihood provide bias corrections on the original maximum likelihood estimates. Asymptotically these bias corrections agree with those of Lawley [12], which come from the sampling theory approach.

My own sympathies lie more in the fiducial direction. I feel a strong need for new incarnations of the fiducial type of argument, where the randomness is based solely on the sampling hypothesis and yet the inferences may be regarded as posterior distributions conditioned by the data in hand. These methods are at the moment theoretical ideals and not practical alternatives for the situation of multivariate normal sampling.

2.5. A Suggested Approach for the Present

Pending the arrival of more satisfying Bayesian or fiducial arguments, it seems temporarily necessary to adopt some variant of the sampling theory approach. A consolation for the pain of accepting such a departure from high principle is the absence of any strong arguments against the resulting methods. In particular, there do not seem to be any natural conditional frames of reference which upset the unconditional averages, and the failure of such frames to appear in such a well studied area suggests that there may not be any. It seems likely that some nontrivial new ideas will be required before the sampling theory approach, however awkward, may be replaced.

The variant of the sampling theory approach which is illustrated in Section 3 is a modification of the jackknife method of Tukey [20]. The essential idea of the jackknife is the computation of the values of an estimator not only for a full sample but also for many subsamples formed by dropping small parts of the full sample. The variation in these additional computed estimates is used to estimate a bias and variance for the original estimate. In this paper the jackknife approach is modified to allow dropping not of sample individuals but rather single degrees of freedom entering an estimated covariance matrix. Thus, along with an estimated covariance matrix, the class of revised estimated covariance matrices based on one fewer degrees of freedom will be considered.

In the original jackknife method, bias corrections and variance estimates can be computed by averaging certain statistics over all subsamples of size $n - 1$ out of a sample of size n. In the modified jackknife method, averaging needs to be carried out over single degrees of freedom dropped. Such a single degree of freedom taken from a total of m may be characterized mathematically as a single direction in an m-dimensional Euclidean space E_m, and the averaging will be carried out using the uniform or invariant distribution over E_m (James [10]). One reason for using this distribution is that it reflects the invariance of multivariate normal sampling theory. Another reason is that it essentially amounts to averaging over reduced statistics given the sufficient statistics. Thus the resulting estimates depend only on the sufficient statistics and have optimality conferred on them by the Blackwell-Rao theory of sufficient estimation. A disadvantage of the modified jackknife is that it leans on the invariance properties of normal samples and so may not retain the robustness properties of the original jackknife.

The jackknife method produces bias corrections and estimates of variance directly, whereas the more standard sampling theory approach would follow the circuitous route of first expressing biases and variances of estimators as functions of unknown parameters and then substituting efficient estimates of the unknown parameters to obtain estimated biases and variances. The two are asymptotic equivalent. References on the jackknife method remain scarce, but see Mosteller and Tukey [16], Brillinger [2], and Miller [15].

3. THE MODIFIED JACKKNIFE APPLIED TO CANONICAL CORRELATION ANALYSIS

3.1. Basic Ideas

In statistical practice a canonical correlation analysis must be based on a covariance matrix computed from sample data. A $p \times p$ sample covariance matrix $\mathbf{S}$ is usually computed from $\mathbf{S} = \mathbf{T}/m$, where $\mathbf{T}$ is a corresponding matrix of sums of squares and products on m degrees of freedom whose sampling distribution is $W(\Sigma, m)$. In particular, if $\mathbf{S}$ is computed from a single sample of size n, then $m = n - 1$.

The matrix $\mathbf{T}$ has a natural interpretation as a matrix of inner products among p vectors in an m-dimensional Euclidean space E_m. These p vectors correspond to the original p variates and will be denoted by their $m \times 1$ coordinate vectors $\mathbf{V}_1, \mathbf{V}_2, \ldots, \mathbf{V}_p$ relative to any fixed orthonormal coordinate system in E_m. *Unless otherwise noted,* $\mathbf{T}$ *and* $\mathbf{V}_1, \mathbf{V}_2, \ldots, \mathbf{V}_p$ *will be regarded as fixed in the following discussion, whose main burden is to show how to produce jackknifed estimates from given data.*

The canonical correlation analysis based on $\mathbf{S}$, or equally well on $\mathbf{T}$, which relates the first s variates to the last $p - s$ variates ($s \leq p - s$), requires finding sets of $1 \times p$ vectors $\mathbf{x}_1, \mathbf{x}_2, \ldots, \mathbf{x}_s$ and $\mathbf{y}_1, \mathbf{y}_2, \ldots, \mathbf{y}_{p-s}$ such that

(a) the last $p - s$ elements of each $\mathbf{x}_i$ are zero,
(b) the first s elements of each $\mathbf{y}_j$ are zero, and
(c)
$$\begin{aligned} &\mathbf{x}_i\mathbf{T}\mathbf{x}_j' = \delta_{ij} && \text{for } i \text{ and } j = 1, 2, \ldots, s, \\ &\mathbf{y}_i\mathbf{T}\mathbf{y}_j' = \delta_{ij} && \text{for } i \text{ and } j = 1, 2, \ldots, p-s, \\ &\mathbf{x}_i\mathbf{T}\mathbf{y}_j' = r_i\delta_{ij} && \text{for } i = 1, 2, \ldots, s \text{ and } j = 1, 2, \ldots, p-s. \end{aligned} \tag{3.1.1}$$

The use of $\mathbf{T}$ rather than $\mathbf{S}$ in (3.1.1) is convenient for later purposes, but it means that the vectors $\mathbf{x}_i$ and $\mathbf{y}_j$ need to be rescaled by $m^{1/2}$ before they denote linear combinations with unit sample variance. Thus

$$\begin{aligned} \mathbf{U}_i &= (\mathbf{V}_1, \mathbf{V}_2, \ldots, \mathbf{V}_p)\mathbf{x}_i' && \text{for } i = 1, 2, \ldots, s, \\ \mathbf{U}_{s+j} &= (\mathbf{V}_1, \mathbf{V}_2, \ldots, \mathbf{V}_p)\mathbf{y}_j' && \text{for } j = 1, 2, \ldots, p-s \end{aligned} \tag{3.1.2}$$

denote a set of vectors in E_m representing linear combinations of the original p variates whose sample inner product matrix has the form

$$\begin{pmatrix} \mathbf{I}_s & \mathbf{r} & \mathbf{0}_{s \times (p-2s)} \\ \mathbf{r} & \mathbf{I}_s & \mathbf{0}_{s \times (p-2s)} \\ \mathbf{0}_{(p-2s) \times s} & \mathbf{0}_{(p-2s) \times s} & \mathbf{I}_{p-2s} \end{pmatrix}, \tag{3.1.3}$$

where $\mathbf{I}$ and $\mathbf{0}$ denote identity and zero matrices of the indicated dimensions and $\mathbf{r}$ is a diagonal matrix with diagonal elements $r_1, r_2, \ldots, r_s$. At the same time, the vectors $m^{1/2}\mathbf{U}_i$ for $i = 1, 2, \ldots, p$ have sample covariance matrix given by (3.1.3).

The pair of linear combinations defined by $(m^{1/2}\mathbf{U}_i, m^{1/2}\mathbf{U}_{s+i})$ is called the ith *pair of sample canonical variates* and their sample correlation coefficient r_i is called the ith *sample canonical correlation coefficient*. It will be assumed that

$$r_1 > r_2 > \cdots > r_s > 0. \tag{3.1.4}$$

The jackknife method requires consideration not only of the canonical correlation analysis of $\mathbf{T}$ but also that of inner product matrices based on reduced samples. Specifically, one needs to consider the removal of single degrees of freedom from $\mathbf{T}$. In geometrical terms this means eliminating a single dimension of E_m in the sense of projecting $\mathbf{V}_1, \mathbf{V}_2, \ldots, \mathbf{V}_p$ into a subspace of dimension $m - 1$ and recomputing the inner product matrix of the resulting components of $\mathbf{V}_1, \mathbf{V}_2, \ldots, \mathbf{V}_p$. The details of this computation are given in Section 3.2.

After revising the matrix $\mathbf{T}$ it is necessary to investigate the corresponding revision of the canonical correlation analysis defined by (3.1.1). When m is moderately large, this revision is like a minor perturbation, so it is natural to consider a Taylor series expansion of the revised canonical correlations and variates about their original values. The details of this Taylor series expansion are presented in Section 3.3.

Finally, certain statistics based on the revised estimates must be averaged over a uniformly random choice of degrees of freedom. A single degree of freedom or direction in E_m may be represented by its direction cosines $l_1, l_2, \ldots, l_m$ relative to a set of orthonormal coordinate axes $\mathbf{W}_1, \mathbf{W}_2, \ldots, \mathbf{W}_m$ in E_m. The uniform distribution over directions may be characterized by considering independent $N(0, 1)$ random variables $Z_1, Z_2, \ldots, Z_m$ and defining

$$l_i = Z_i \Big/ \left(\sum_{i=1}^{m} Z_i^2\right)^{1/2}. \tag{3.1.5}$$

The averaging operations of Sections 3.4, 3.5, and 3.6 require the joint moments of the l_i up to order 4. From (3.1.5) it follows that any such moment involving an odd power of l_i is zero. Also $l_1^2, l_2^2, \ldots, l_m^2$ have the Dirichlet distribution $D(\frac{1}{2}, \frac{1}{2}; \ldots, \frac{1}{2}; \frac{1}{2})$, so named by Wilks [2], whence it follows that

$$E(l_i^2) = 1/m, \tag{3.1.6}$$

$$E(l_i^4) = 3/m(m+2), \tag{3.1.7}$$

$$E(l_i^2 l_j^2) = 1/m(m+2), \tag{3.1.8}$$

for i and $j = 1, 2, \ldots, m$ and $i \neq j$.

3.2. Deleting a Single Degree of Freedom

The task of this section is to describe the effect on the sample inner product matrix of dropping a single degree of freedom. A way to do this which fits well with the expansions developed later is to find the change in the inner product matrix of $\mathbf{U}_1, \mathbf{U}_2, \ldots, \mathbf{U}_p$ rather than that of $\mathbf{V}_1, \mathbf{V}_2, \ldots, \mathbf{V}_p$, where $\mathbf{U}_1, \mathbf{U}_2, \ldots, \mathbf{U}_p$ are regarded as fixed linear combinations of $\mathbf{V}_1, \mathbf{V}_2, \ldots, \mathbf{V}_p$.

Define $t_i = (1 - r_i^2)^{1/2}$ for $i = 1, 2, \ldots, s$ and note that $r_i = \cos\theta_i$ and $t_i = \sin\theta_i$, where θ_i is the angle between $\mathbf{U}_i$ and $\mathbf{U}_{s+i}$. Define

$$\mathbf{W}_i = t_i^{-1}(\mathbf{U}_i - r_i\mathbf{U}_{s+i}) \quad \text{for} \quad i = 1, 2, \ldots, s \tag{3.2.1}$$

and

$$\mathbf{W}_{s+j} = \mathbf{U}_{s+j} \quad \text{for} \quad j = 1, 2, \ldots, p - s. \tag{3.2.2}$$

It follows that $\mathbf{W}_1, \mathbf{W}_2, \ldots, \mathbf{W}_p$ are orthonormal in E_m. Define $\mathbf{W}_{p+1}$ $\mathbf{W}_{p+2}, \ldots, \mathbf{W}_m$ in any way which completes a full orthonormal basis of E_m.

A single degree of freedom may now be expressed by a unit vector $\sum_1^m l_i \mathbf{W}_i$, where $\sum_1^m l_i^2 = 1$. The components of the vectors $\mathbf{U}_1, \mathbf{U}_2, \ldots, \mathbf{U}_p$ along the direction of this single degree of freedom are easily seen to be given by the vector

$$\mathbf{D} = \begin{pmatrix} l_1 t_1 + l_{s+1} r_1 \\ \vdots \\ l_s t_s + l_{2s} r_s \\ \\ l_{s+1} \\ \vdots \\ l_p \end{pmatrix}. \tag{3.2.3}$$

Consequently, the desired change in the inner product matrix of $\mathbf{U}_1, \mathbf{U}_2, \ldots, \mathbf{U}_p$ due to dropping this single degree of freedom is given by $-\mathbf{DD}'$.

3.3. A Taylor-Series Expansion

Suppose that $\mathbf{T}$ is perturbed to $\mathbf{T} + \varepsilon\boldsymbol{\Delta}$. Then there are corresponding perturbations of $\mathbf{x}_i$ to $\mathbf{x}_i + \varepsilon\mathbf{x}_{1i} + \varepsilon^2\mathbf{x}_{2i} + \cdots$, of $\mathbf{y}_i$ to $\mathbf{y}_i + \varepsilon\mathbf{y}_{1i} + \varepsilon^2\mathbf{y}_{2i} + \cdots$, and of r_i to $r_i + \varepsilon r_{1i} + \varepsilon^2 r_{2i} + \ldots$. These expansions are governed by formulas (3.1.1) applied to $\mathbf{T} + \varepsilon\boldsymbol{\Delta}$ instead of $\mathbf{T}$, namely,

$$\begin{aligned}
&(\mathbf{x}_i + \varepsilon\mathbf{x}_{1i} + \varepsilon^2\mathbf{x}_{2i} + \cdots)(\mathbf{T} + \varepsilon\boldsymbol{\Delta})(\mathbf{x}_j + \varepsilon\mathbf{x}_{1j} + \varepsilon^2\mathbf{x}_{2j} + \cdots)' = \delta_{ij} \\
&\qquad \text{for } i \text{ and } j = 1, 2, \ldots, s \\
&(\mathbf{y}_i + \varepsilon\mathbf{y}_{1i} + \varepsilon^2\mathbf{y}_{2i} + \cdots)(\mathbf{T} + \varepsilon\boldsymbol{\Delta})(\mathbf{y}_j + \varepsilon\mathbf{y}_{1j} + \varepsilon^2\mathbf{y}_{2j} + \cdots)' = \delta_{ij} \\
&\qquad \text{for } i \text{ and } j = 1, 2, \ldots, p - s, \\
&(\mathbf{x}_i + \varepsilon\mathbf{x}_{1i} + \varepsilon^2\mathbf{x}_{2i} + \cdots)(\mathbf{T} + \varepsilon\boldsymbol{\Delta})(\mathbf{y}_j + \varepsilon\mathbf{y}_{1j} + \varepsilon^2\mathbf{y}_{2j} + \cdots)' \\
&\quad = (r_i + \varepsilon r_{1i} + \varepsilon^2 r_{2i} + \cdots)\delta_{ij} \qquad \text{for } i = 1, 2, \ldots, s \text{ and } j = 1, 2, \ldots, p - s
\end{aligned} \tag{3.3.1}$$

It is convenient to set

$$\mathbf{x}_{1i} = \sum_{j=1}^{s} a_{ij}^{(1)}\mathbf{x}_j, \qquad \mathbf{x}_{2i} = \sum_{j=1}^{s} a_{ij}^{(2)}\mathbf{x}_j, \tag{3.3.2}$$

and so on for $i = 1, 2, \ldots, s$, and

$$\mathbf{y}_{1i} = \sum_{j=1}^{p-s} b_{ij}^{(1)}\mathbf{y}_j, \qquad \mathbf{y}_{2i} = \sum_{j=1}^{p-s} b_{ij}^{(2)}\mathbf{y}_j, \tag{3.3.3}$$

and so on for $i = 1, 2, \ldots, p - s$.

Comparing the term of (3.3.1) linear in ε and using (3.3.2) and (3.3.3), one finds that

$$r_{1i} = -\tfrac{1}{2}r_i(\mathbf{x}_i\boldsymbol{\Delta}\mathbf{x}_i' + \mathbf{y}_i\boldsymbol{\Delta}\mathbf{y}_i') + \mathbf{x}_i\boldsymbol{\Delta}\mathbf{y}_i' \tag{3.3.4}$$

for $i = 1, 2, \ldots, s$,

$$a_{ii}^{(1)} = -\tfrac{1}{2}(\mathbf{x}_i\,\boldsymbol{\Delta}\mathbf{x}_i'), \tag{3.3.5}$$

$$a_{ij}^{(1)} = \frac{1}{r_i^2 - r_j^2}\,[r_j(\mathbf{x}_i\,\Delta\mathbf{y}_j') + r_i(\mathbf{x}_j\,\Delta\mathbf{y}_i') - r_i^2(\mathbf{x}_i\,\Delta\mathbf{x}_j') - r_ir_j(\mathbf{y}_i\,\Delta\mathbf{y}_j')], \tag{3.3.6}$$

for i and $j = 1, 2, \ldots, s$, and

$$b_{ii}^{(1)} = -\tfrac{1}{2}(\mathbf{y}_i\,\Delta\mathbf{y}_i'), \tag{3.3.7}$$

$$b_{ij}^{(1)} = \frac{1}{r_i^2 - r_j^2}\,[r_i(\mathbf{x}_i\,\Delta\mathbf{y}_j') + r_j(\mathbf{x}_j\,\Delta\mathbf{y}_i') - r_i^2(\mathbf{y}_i\,\Delta\mathbf{y}_j') - r_ir_j(\mathbf{x}_i\,\Delta\mathbf{x}_j')], \tag{3.3.8}$$

for $i = 1, 2, \ldots, s$ and $j = 1, 2, \ldots, p - s$. In (3.3.8) one must set $r_j = 0$ for $j = s + 1, \ldots, p - s$. The remaining coefficients $b_{ij}^{(1)}$ with $i = s + 1, \ldots, p - s$ are not required in what follows.

Comparing the terms of (3.3.1) quadratic in ε and using (3.3.2) and (3.3.3) one finds that

$$\begin{aligned} r_{2i} = {} & \sum_{j=1}^{s} a_{ij}^{(1)}b_{ij}^{(1)}r_j + \sum_{j=1}^{p-s} b_{ij}^{(1)}(\mathbf{x}_i\,\Delta\mathbf{y}_j') + \sum_{j=1}^{s} a_{ij}^{(1)}(\mathbf{x}_j\,\Delta\mathbf{y}_i') \\ & - r_i\left[\frac{1}{2}\sum_{j=1}^{p-s} b_{ij}^{(1)2} + \sum_{j=1}^{p-s} b_{ij}^{(1)}(\mathbf{y}_i\,\Delta\mathbf{y}_j')\right] - r_i\left[\frac{1}{2}\sum_{j=1}^{s} a_{ij}^{(1)2} + \sum_{j=1}^{s} a_{ij}^{(1)}(\mathbf{x}_i\,\Delta\mathbf{x}_j')\right]. \end{aligned} \tag{3.3.9}$$

The quadratic terms would also yield expressions for a_{ij}^2 and b_{ij}^2, but again these are not needed here and so are not reproduced.

In principle the above type of expansion could be carried out recursively to any number of terms, but third- and higher-order terms would sensibly require the aid of a computer programmed to carry out the tedious algebra.

The above formulas will be applied with the role of the matrix

$$\varepsilon\begin{pmatrix}\mathbf{x}_1\\ \mathbf{x}_2\\ \vdots\\ \mathbf{x}_s\\ \mathbf{y}_1\\ \vdots\\ \mathbf{y}_{p-s}\end{pmatrix}\Delta\begin{pmatrix}\mathbf{x}_1\\ \mathbf{x}_2\\ \vdots\\ \mathbf{x}_s\\ \mathbf{y}_1\\ \vdots\\ \mathbf{y}_{p-s}\end{pmatrix}' \tag{3.3.10}$$

played by (3.2.4). Here ε may be regarded as $1/m$. It follows that

$$\varepsilon r_{1i} = \tfrac{1}{2}r_i[(l_it_i + l_{s+i}r_i)^2 + l_{s+1}^2] - (l_it_i + l_{s+i}r_i)l_{s+i} \qquad \text{for} \quad s = 1, 2, \ldots, s. \tag{3.3.11}$$

Also, after a little simplifying, one finds

$$\varepsilon a_{ii}^{(1)} = \tfrac{1}{2}(l_it_i + l_{s+i}r_i)^2, \tag{3.3.12}$$

$$\begin{aligned} \varepsilon a_{ij}^{(1)} = {} & \frac{1}{r_j^2 - r_i^2}\,[l_il_j\{-r_i^2t_it_j\} + l_il_{s+j}\{r_jt_i^3\} \\ & + l_{s+i}l_j\{r_it_jt_i^2\} + l_{s+i}l_{s+j}\{r_ir_jt_i^2\}], \end{aligned} \tag{3.3.13}$$

$$\varepsilon b_{ii}^{(1)} = \tfrac{1}{2} l_{s+i}^2, \tag{3.3.14}$$

$$\varepsilon b_{ij}^{(1)} = \frac{1}{r_j^{\,2} - r_i^{\,2}} [l_i l_j \{-r_i r_j t_i t_j\} + l_i l_{s+j} \{r_i t_i t_j^{\,2}\}$$
$$+ l_{s+i} l_j \{r_j t_j t_i^{\,2}\} + l_{s+i} l_{s+j} \{r_j^{\,2} t_i^{\,2}\}], \tag{3.3.15}$$

these being the specific forms of (3.3.5), (3.3.6), (3.3.7), and (3.3.8).

3.4. Bias Correction

The bias correcting component of the jackknife method was first proposed as a separate technique by Quenouille [17]. Suppose that a method of estimating a parameter θ is defined for each sufficiently large sample size n. Suppose that B denotes the estimator from a sample of size n and that $B_{(i)}$ denotes the estimator from the subsample of size $n - 1$ formed by deleting individual i from the sample. If the ordinary sampling theory bias in the family of estimators is $O(1/n)$, as is the case with the regular maximum likelihood estimators in the situation of this paper, then the bias may be reduced to a smaller order, here $O(1/n^2)$, by using the estimator

$$B_p = \frac{1}{n} \sum_{i=1}^{n} B_{pi}, \tag{3.4.1}$$

where the "pseudoscores" B_{pi} are defined to be

$$B_{pi} = nB - (n - 1)B_{(i)}. \tag{3.4.2}$$

In the present modification of the jackknife the sample size n is replaced by the number of degrees of freedom m used to estimate the covariance. The role of $B_{(i)}$ is played by an estimator with a single degree of freedom omitted. The same device as (3.4.2) is used to eliminate the leading bias term, except that n is replaced by m. The averaging operation of (3.4.1) is replaced by averaging with respect to the uniform distribution over directions in E_m.

The bias corrected estimator for the ith population canonical correlation coefficient is

$$E(mr_i - [m - 1][r_i + \varepsilon r_{1i} + \varepsilon^2 r_{2i} + \cdots]), \tag{3.4.3}$$

whence the bias correction on r_i is

$$E(-[m - 1][\varepsilon r_{1i} + \varepsilon^2 r_{2i} + \cdots]). \tag{3.4.4}$$

From (3.3.11) and (3.1.6), together with the fact that odd moments of the l_i are zero, it follows that

$$E(\varepsilon r_{1i}) = 0. \tag{3.4.5}$$

This shows that the leading term in the bias correction comes from $E(\varepsilon^2 r_{2i})$. The computation of $E(\varepsilon^2 r_{2i})$ requires separate evaluations of the terms $j = i$

and $j \neq i$ in each of the seven parts of (3.3.9). These various terms require fourth moments given by (3.1.7) and (3.1.8). The details are omitted. From $E(\varepsilon^2 r_{2i})$, together with (3.4.4), the leading term in the bias correction is found to be

$$\frac{m-1}{m(m+2)} \frac{1-r_i^2}{r_i} \left[\tfrac{1}{2}(r_i^2 - p + 2s) + \sum_{\substack{j=1 \\ j \neq i}}^{s} \frac{1-r_j^2}{r_j^2 - r_i^2} \right] \tag{3.4.6}$$

for $i = 1, 2, \ldots, s$. Since

$$r_i^2 \sum_{\substack{j=1 \\ j \neq i}}^{s} \frac{1-r_j^2}{r_j^2 - r_i^2} = (1 - r_i^2) \sum_{\substack{j=1 \\ j \neq i}}^{s} \frac{r_j^2}{r_j^2 - r_i^2} - (s-1), \tag{3.4.7}$$

and since for the present purposes $(m-1)/m(m+2)$ may be replaced by $1/m$ an alternative to (3.4.6) is

$$\frac{1}{m} \frac{1-r_i^2}{r_i} \left[\tfrac{1}{2}(r_i^2 - p + 2) + (1 - r_i^2) \sum_{\substack{j=1 \\ j \neq i}}^{s} \frac{r_j^2}{r_j^2 - r_i^2} \right]. \tag{3.4.8}$$

The expression (3.4.8) checks with the bias calculated by Lawley [13] in the sense that (3.4.8) may be obtained by replacing ρ_i in Lawley's bias by r_i and changing the sign of his expression to make it a correction.

The corresponding bias correction to r_i^2 may also be of interest. This requires finding

$$E(r_i + \varepsilon r_{1i} + \varepsilon^2 r_{2i} + \cdots)^2 = r_i^2 + E(\varepsilon^2 r_{1i}^2 + 2\varepsilon^2 r_i r_{2i}) + \cdots. \tag{3.4.9}$$

From (3.3.11) one may easily show that

$$E(\varepsilon^2 r_{1i}^2) = \frac{1}{m(m+2)} (1 - r_i^2)^2, \tag{3.4.10}$$

from which the bias correction for r_i^2 is

$$2r_i(\text{bias correction for } r_i) - \frac{m-1}{m(m+2)}(1 - r_i^2)^2$$

$$= \frac{m-1}{m(m+2)} \left[-(1 - r_i^2)(p-3) + (1 - r_i^2)^2 \left(-2 + 2 \sum_{\substack{j=1 \\ j \neq i}}^{s} \frac{r_j^2}{r_j^2 - r_i^2} \right) \right]. \tag{3.4.11}$$

Similar bias corrections could be found for the elements of the $\mathbf{x}_i$ and $\mathbf{y}_j$ and also for the inverse transformations expressing $\mathbf{V}_1, \mathbf{V}_2, \ldots, \mathbf{V}_p$ in terms of $\mathbf{U}_1, \mathbf{U}_2, \ldots, \mathbf{U}_p$, but these are not pursued here.

3.5. Estimation of Sampling Variance and Covariance

The second component of the jackknife asserts essentially that the sample variance of the pseudoscores B_{pi} in (3.4.2) is a useful estimate of the sampling mean square error of the estimators B or B_p. The justification relies on the leading term of an asymptotic expansion. In general the sampling distributions of B or B_p have a spread of order $n^{-1/2}$ which is of a higher order than the bias in B or the difference $B_p - B$. Consequently the same leading term represents variously the sampling mean square error or sampling variance of B or B_p. Also, one may equally well use either the standard sample variance

$$\frac{1}{n-1}\sum_{i=1}^{n}(B_{pi}-B_p)^2 \tag{3.5.1}$$

or the asymptotically equivalent modification

$$\frac{1}{n}\sum_{i=1}^{n}(B_{pi}-B)^2 \doteqdot n\sum_{i=1}^{n}(B_{(i)}-B)^2 \tag{3.5.2}$$

to estimate this sampling variance or mean square error.

The multiparameter extension of (3.5.2) will now be given, and a justification of its use will be sketched. Suppose that the parameters are represented by a $q \times 1$ vector $\boldsymbol{\theta}$ and that the corresponding estimators are denoted by $q \times 1$ vectors $\mathbf{B}$ based on the full sample and $\mathbf{B}_{(i)}$ based on a reduced sample. Then the appropriate generalization of (3.5.2) is to take

$$n\sum_{i=1}^{n}(\mathbf{B}_{(i)}-\mathbf{B})(\mathbf{B}_{(i)}-\mathbf{B})' \tag{3.5.3}$$

as estimating the sampling covariance matrix of $\mathbf{B}$ or the corresponding $\mathbf{B}_p$.

Suppose that $\mathbf{B}$ is a maximum-likelihood estimator for $\boldsymbol{\theta}$. Suppose that $L(\boldsymbol{\theta})$ denotes the log of the likelihood of a sample of size n. Suppose that $\mathbf{L}'(\boldsymbol{\theta})$ denotes the $q \times 1$ vector of first-order partial derivatives with respect to the parameters and that $\mathbf{L}''(\boldsymbol{\theta})$ denotes the $q \times q$ symmetric matrix of second-order partial derivatives. Then, under sufficient regularity conditions, $\mathbf{B}$ satisfies

$$\mathbf{L}'(\mathbf{B}) = \mathbf{0}, \tag{3.5.4}$$

and the asymptotic sampling covariance matrix $\boldsymbol{\kappa}_2(\boldsymbol{\theta})$ given $\boldsymbol{\theta}$ may be determined from

$$\begin{aligned}\boldsymbol{\kappa}_2(\boldsymbol{\theta})^{-1} &= E(\mathbf{L}'(\boldsymbol{\theta})\mathbf{L}'(\boldsymbol{\theta})') \\ &= -E(\mathbf{L}''(\boldsymbol{\theta}))\end{aligned} \tag{3.5.5}$$

where the expectation operator refers to averages over sampling distributions.

Suppose that L_i, $\mathbf{L}_i'$, and $\mathbf{L}_i''$ denote the log likelihood and its derivatives for the ith sample observation alone, and that $L_{(i)} = L - L_i$, $\mathbf{L}'_{(i)} = \mathbf{L}' - \mathbf{L}'_i$, and $\mathbf{L}''_{(i)} = \mathbf{L}'' - \mathbf{L}''_i$ denote the same quantities for the sample omitting the ith observation. From (3.5.4),

$$\mathbf{L}'_i(\mathbf{B}) = -\mathbf{L}'_{(i)}(\mathbf{B}). \tag{3.5.6}$$

Now $\mathbf{B}_{(i)}$ is that vector of values $\boldsymbol{\theta}$ which maximizes $L_{(i)}(\boldsymbol{\theta})$. To the first-order approximation adopted here, one may set

$$L_{(i)}(\theta) \doteqdot L_{(i)}(\mathbf{B}) + (\theta - \mathbf{B})'\mathbf{L}'_{(i)}(\mathbf{B}) + \tfrac{1}{2}(\theta - \mathbf{B})'\mathbf{L}''_{(i)}(\mathbf{B})(\boldsymbol{\theta} - \mathbf{B}), \tag{3.5.7}$$

whence, to a first approximation,

$$\begin{aligned} \mathbf{B}_{(i)} - \mathbf{B} &\doteqdot -\mathbf{L}''_{(i)}(\mathbf{B})^{-1}\mathbf{L}'_{(i)}(\mathbf{B}) \\ &= \mathbf{L}''_{(i)}(\mathbf{B})^{-1}\mathbf{L}_i'(\mathbf{B}). \end{aligned} \tag{3.5.8}$$

Averaging over the sampling distributions, one finds

$$\begin{aligned} E([\mathbf{B}_{(i)} - \mathbf{B}][\mathbf{B}_{(i)} - \mathbf{B}]') &= E(\mathbf{L}''_{(i)}(\mathbf{B})^{-1}\mathbf{L}'_i(\mathbf{B})\mathbf{L}_i'(\mathbf{B})'\mathbf{L}''_{(i)}(\mathbf{B})^{-1}) \\ &\doteqdot \boldsymbol{\kappa}_2(\boldsymbol{\theta})\frac{1}{n}\boldsymbol{\kappa}_2(\boldsymbol{\theta})^{-1}\boldsymbol{\kappa}_2(\boldsymbol{\theta}) = \frac{1}{n}\boldsymbol{\kappa}_2(\boldsymbol{\theta}). \end{aligned} \tag{3.5.9}$$

The reasoning in (3.5.9) is that the terms $\mathbf{L}''_{(i)}(\mathbf{B})^{-1}$ are converging probabilistically to their mean values $\boldsymbol{\kappa}_2(\boldsymbol{\theta})$, and so these expected values may be substituted in, leaving only $E(\mathbf{L}_i'(\boldsymbol{\theta})\mathbf{L}_i(\boldsymbol{\theta})')$ which has mean $(1/n)\boldsymbol{\kappa}_2(\boldsymbol{\theta})^{-1}$.

Thus asymptotically unbiased estimators for $\boldsymbol{\kappa}_2(\boldsymbol{\theta})$ may be found by averaging $n(\mathbf{B}_{(i)} - \mathbf{B})(\mathbf{B}_{(i)} - \mathbf{B})'$ over the sample observations, as in (3.5.3), or by averaging over the uniform continuous distribution of deleted degrees of freedom, as in the modified jackknife of this paper.

The first application of the foregoing theory will be to estimate the variance of r_i. This estimate is given by $mE(\varepsilon^2 r_{1i}^2)$, taking as usual only the first term of the expansion. Here the expectation is with respect to the random choice of omitted degrees of freedom. Thus from (3.4.10) the estimate of variance is

$$\frac{1}{m+2}(1 - r_i^2)^2. \tag{3.5.10}$$

Similarly the covariance of the estimates r_i and r_j may be estimated to be

$$mE(\varepsilon r_{1i}\varepsilon r_{1j}) = 0 \tag{3.5.11}$$

for $i \neq j$. Formulas (3.5.10) and (3.5.11) check with the asymptotic sampling theory of Hsu [9].

In a similar way, one could associate estimated variances with the elements of the matrices relating the set $U_1, U_2, \ldots, U_p$ with the set $V_1, V_2, \ldots, V_p$. This will not be done here. Instead a measure of the angular deviation of sample canonical variates from the population canonical variates will be estimated. The measure used will be the squared sine of the angle defined using the population covariance as Euclidean inner product. This criterion is asymptotically equivalent to the sum of squared errors in a set of parameters defining the direction cosines of the canonical variates relative to a coordinate system which is orthonormal with respect to the population covariance inner product.

The original estimate of the ith canonical variate in the first set is defined by $m^2\mathbf{x}_i$. After dropping a single degree of freedom, this estimate is revised to $(m-1)^{1/2}(\mathbf{x}_1 + \varepsilon\mathbf{x}_{1i} + \cdots)$. The leading terms in the coordinates of the difference between these estimates relative to the basis $m^{1/2}\mathbf{x}_1, m^{1/2}\mathbf{x}_2, \ldots, m^{1/2}\mathbf{x}_s$ are

$$\left(1-\frac{1}{m}\right)^{1/2}[1+\varepsilon a_{ii}^{(1)}]-1, \tag{3.5.12}$$

corresponding to the coordinate axis $m^{1/2}\mathbf{x}_i$, and

$$\left(1-\frac{1}{m}\right)^{1/2}\varepsilon a_{ij}^{(1)}, \tag{3.5.13}$$

corresponding to the coordinate axis $m^{1/2}\mathbf{x}_j$ for $j \neq i$. The appropriate estimate of the chosen error criterion is found by squaring the above coordinates, adding them, multiplying by m, and finally averaging over the random choice of degrees of freedom. The expression (3.5.12) is asymptotically equivalent to

$$-\frac{1}{2}\frac{1}{m}+\varepsilon a_{ii}^{(1)}=\frac{1}{2}\left[(l_i t_i + l_{s+i} r_i)^2-\frac{1}{m}\right]. \tag{3.5.14}$$

Squaring (3.5.14), multiplying by m, and averaging via (3.1.6), (3.1.7), and (3.1.8) yields

$$\frac{1}{2}\frac{1}{m+2}. \tag{3.5.15}$$

Applying similar operations to (3.5.15) yields

$$\frac{m-1}{m(m+2)}\frac{(1-r_i^2)(r_i^2+r_j^2-2r_i^2r_j^2)}{(r_j^2-r_i^2)^2}. \tag{3.5.16}$$

Summing and replacing the leading coefficients by $1/m$ yields

$$\frac{1}{m}\left[\frac{1}{2}+\sum_{\substack{j=1\\ j\neq i}}^{s}\frac{(1-r_i^2)(r_i^2+r_j^2-2r_i^2r_j^2)}{(r_j^2-r_i^2)^2}\right], \tag{3.5.17}$$

as the estimate of the angular mean square error criterion for the ith canonical variate in the first set. Similarly,

$$\frac{1}{m}\left[\frac{1}{2}+\sum_{\substack{j=1\\ j\neq i}}^{p-s}\frac{(1-r_i^2)(r_i^2+r_j^2-2r_i^2r_j^2)}{(r_j^2-r_i^2)^2}\right] \tag{3.5.18}$$

estimates the angular mean-square error for the ith canonical variate in the second set, where, as usual, $r_j = 0$ for $j = s + 1, \ldots, p$.

3.6. Bias Corrections Related to the Use of Estimated Canonical Variates in Future Samples

The original motivation for r_i was estimation of the population correlation coefficient ρ_i between the ith pair of population canonical variates. Alternatively, r_i may be regarded as an estimate of the population correlation coefficient between the ith pair of *sample* canonical variates. The latter interpretation may be important in statistical practice when sample canonical variates are treated as acceptable substitutes for the population variates and their use with future samples is contemplated or carried out. The errors of estimation associated with r_i are different under the two interpretations. The purpose of this section is to develop bias corrections for r_i and several other quantities related to the use of estimated canonical variates in future samples.

The device used to find these corrections is an extension of the jackknife idea, in which the single degree of freedom deleted from the original estimator is regarded as simulating a future sample observation. The sample canonical variates estimated from the remaining $m - 1$ degrees of freedom may then be applied to the simulated future sample observation. The glimpses of future sample behavior thus obtained may then be averaged over all choices of a single degree of freedom. The resulting bias corrections are, strictly speaking, applicable to estimation based on $m - 1$ rather than m degrees of freedom, but a fractional correction factor such as $m/(m - 1)$ is generally disregarded in this paper.

The sample canonical variates based on $m - 1$ degrees of freedom are linear combinations of the original variables given by the vectors

$$(m-1)^{1/2}[\mathbf{x}_i + \varepsilon\mathbf{x}_{1i} + \cdots] = (m-1)^{1/2}\left[\mathbf{x}_i + \sum_{j=1}^{s} \varepsilon a_{ij}^{(1)}\mathbf{x}_j + \cdots\right] \tag{3.6.1}$$

for $i = 1, 2, \ldots, s$ and

$$(m-1)^{1/2}[\mathbf{y}_i + \varepsilon\mathbf{y}_{1i} + \cdots] = (m-1)^{1/2}\left[\mathbf{y}_i + \sum_{j=1}^{p-s} \varepsilon b_{ij}^{(1)}\mathbf{y}_j + \cdots\right] \tag{3.6.2}$$

for $i = 1, 2, \ldots, p - s$. At the same time, the single degree of freedom dropped from the sample has components along $\mathbf{x}_1, \mathbf{x}_2, \ldots, \mathbf{x}_s, \mathbf{y}_1, \ldots, \mathbf{y}_{p-s}$ given by $(l_1 t_1 + l_{s+1} r_1, \ldots, l_s t_s + l_{2s} r_s, l_{s+1}, \ldots, l_{p-s})$. Thus the dropped degree of freedom has scores

$$(m-1)^{1/2}\left[(l_i t_i + l_{s+i} r_i)(1 + \varepsilon a_{ii}^{(1)}) + \sum_{\substack{j=i \\ j \neq i}}^{s} (l_i t_i + l_{s+i} r_i)\varepsilon a_{ij}^{(1)}\right] \tag{3.6.3}$$

$$(m-1)^{1/2}\left[l_{s+i}(1+\varepsilon b_{ii}^{(1)})+\sum_{\substack{j=1\\j\neq i}}^{p-s} l_{s+j}\varepsilon b_{it}^{(1)}\right] \tag{3.6.4}$$

on the ith pair of canonical variates computed from $m-1$ degrees of freedom. The product of (3.6.3) and (3.6.4) minus $r_i + \varepsilon r_{1i} + \cdots$ estimates the bias in regarding the sample canonical correlation coefficient as an estimate of the covariance between the ith pair of sample canonical variates when applied to a future sample. Averaging over the random choice of degrees of freedom yields an estimated correction to r_i of

$$\frac{1}{m}\left[2r_i-(p-2)\frac{1-r_i^2}{r_i}+2\frac{1-r_i^2}{r_i}\sum_{\substack{j=1\\j\neq i}}^{s}\frac{r_j^2}{r_j^2-r_i^2}\right]. \tag{3.6.5}$$

Note that the correction (3.6.5) is roughly double the correction (3.4.8) relevant to the other interpretation of r_i.

All the sample canonical variates are estimated in a simple-minded way to have variance unity in future samples. In the case of the ith pair of canonical variates a pair of bias corrections on the estimates of unity may be found by squaring (3.6.3) and (3.6.4), subtracting unity from each, and averaging over the choice of degree of freedom deleted. The resulting bias corrections are

$$\frac{1}{m}\left[2+2(1-r_i^2)\sum_{\substack{j=1\\j\neq i}}^{s}\frac{r_j^2}{r_j^2-r_i^2}\right] \tag{3.6.6}$$

for both members of the ith pair of sample canonical variates.

Either member of a pair of population canonical variates may be used as a linear predictor for the other member, with the corresponding canonical correlation coefficient ρ_i as regression coefficient. The predictor thus defined has variance ρ_i^2 and is uncorrelated with the error of prediction which has variance $1-\rho_i^2$. Thus the unit variance of each canonical variate has a natural decomposition into $\rho_i^2 + (1-\rho_i^2)$. If the sample predictor $r_i\mathbf{U}_i$ is used to predict $\mathbf{U}_{s+i}$, it is of interest to know how the naïve estimated decomposition,

$$1 = r_i^2 + (1-r_i^2) \tag{3.6.7}$$

will hold up on future data. Bias corrections for the terms in (3.6.7) will now be found. For this purpose (3.6.7) should be written

$$1 = r_i^2 + 2(0) + (1-r_i^2), \tag{3.6.8}$$

where the zero terms represents the estimated covariance between the predictor and the prediction error. Note that the bias correction for the left side of (3.6.7) is already displayed in (3.6.6).

The bias correction for the first term on the right side of (3.6.8) is found by multiplying (3.6.3) by $(r_i + \varepsilon r_{1i} + \cdots)$, squaring the product, averaging, and subtracting r^2. Following similar prescriptions, bias corrections may also be found for the covariance term zero and the residual variance term $1 - r_i^2$ on the right side of (3.6.8). The bias corrections thus found for r_i^2, 0, and $1 - r_i^2$ are, respectively,

$$\frac{1}{m} 2r_i^2 \left[r_i^2 + (1 - r_i^2) \sum_{\substack{j=1 \\ j \neq i}}^{s} \frac{r_j^2}{r_j^2 - r_i^2} \right], \tag{3.6.9}$$

$$\frac{1}{m} (1 - r_i^2) \left[2r_i^2 - p + 2(1 - r_i^2) \sum_{\substack{j=1 \\ j \neq i}}^{s} \frac{r_j^2}{r_j^2 - r_i^2} \right], \tag{3.6.10}$$

and

$$\frac{1}{m} 2(1 - r_i^2) \left[(1 - r_i^2) + p - (1 - r_i^2) \sum_{\substack{j=1 \\ j \neq i}}^{s} \frac{r_j^2}{r_j^2 - r_i^2} \right]. \tag{3.6.11}$$

The formulas are the same whether the second variate in the ith pair is predicted from the first or vice versa.

ACKNOWLEDGMENTS

The author would like to thank John Chambers and Samprit Chatterjee for their helpful discussions.

REFERENCES

1. ANDERSON, T. W. (1957). *An Introduction to Multivariate Statistical Analysis.* Wiley, New York.
2. BRILLINGER, D. R. (1964). The asymptotic behavior of Tukey's general method of setting approximate confidence limits (the jackknife) when applied to maximum likelihood estimates. *Rev. Inst. Internat. Statist.* **31**.
3. DEMPSTER, A. P. (1963). On a paradox concerning inference about a covariance matrix. *Ann. Math. Statist.* **34** 1414–1418.
4. DEMPSTER, A. P. (1964). On the difficulties inherent in Fisher's fiducial argument. *J. Amer. Statist. Assoc.* **59** 56–66.
5. DEMPSTER, A. P. *Elements of Multivariate Statistical Analysis.* To be published by Addison-Wesley, Reading, Mass.
6. GEISSER, S. (1964). Posterior odds for multivariate normal classifications. *J. Roy. Statist. Soc. Ser. B* **26** 69–76.
7. GEISSER, S. (1965). Bayesian estimation in multivariate analysis. *Ann. Math. Statist.* **36** 150–159.
8. GEISSER, S. and CORNFIELD, J. (1963). Posterior distributions for multivariate normal parameters. *J. Roy. Statist. Soc. Ser. B* **25** 368–376.
9. HSU, P. L. (1941). On the limiting distribution of the canonical correlations. *Biometrika* **32** 38–45.

10. JAMES, A. T. (1954). Normal multivariate analysis and the orthogonal group. *Ann. Math. Statist.* **25** 40–75.
11. JAMES, A. T. (1964). Personal communication.
12. LAWLEY, D. N. (1956). Tests of significance for the latent roots of covariance and correlation matrices. *Biometrika* **43** 128–136.
13. LAWLEY, D. N. (1959). Tests of significance in canonical analysis. *Biometrika* **46** 59–66.
14. MAULDON, J. G. (1955). Pivotal quantities for Wishart's and related distributions, and a paradox in fiducial theory. *J. Roy. Statist. Soc. Ser. B* **17** 79–90.
15. MILLER, R. G. Jr. (1964). A trustworthy jackknife. *Ann. Math. Statist.* **35** 1594–1605.
16. MOSTELLER, F. and TUKEY, J. W. Data analysis including statistics. To appear in the revised *Handbook of Social Psychology* (G. Lindzey and E. Aronson, eds.). Addison-Wesley, Reading, Mass.
17. QUENOUILLE, M. H. (1956). Notes on bias in estimation. *Biometrika* **43** 353–360.
18. SAVAGE, L. J. and other contributors. (1962). *The Foundations of Statistical Inference.* Methuen, London.
19. STEIN, C. (1959). An example of wide discrepancy between fiducial and confidence intervals. *Ann. Math. Statist.* **30** 864–876.
20. TUKEY, J. W. (1958). Bias and confidence in not-quite large samples (abstract). *Ann. Math. Statist.* **29** 614.
21. WILKS, S. S. (1962). *Mathematical Statistics.* Wiley, New York.

On the Fix-Point Property of Wold's Iterative Estimation Method for Principal Components

EJNAR LYTTKENS

UNIVERSITY INSTITUTE OF STATISTICS
UPPSALA, SWEDEN

1. THE METHOD

The iterative method established by Wold [6, 7] for estimating principal components makes use of the least-squares principle in two ways, with the result that the principal components are obtained as regression coefficients for given values of the direction cosines, and at the same time the direction cosines come out as regression coefficients for given values of the principal components.

The underlying model is as follows:

$$\begin{aligned} \eta_1 &= \beta_1 \xi + \varepsilon_1, \\ \eta_2 &= \beta_2 \xi + \varepsilon_2, \\ &\vdots \\ \eta_p &= \beta_p \xi + \varepsilon_p, \end{aligned} \tag{1.1}$$

where $\eta_1, \eta_2, \ldots, \eta_p$ are random variables; ξ the first principal component; $\beta_1, \beta_2, \ldots, \beta_p$ the direction cosines of the first principal axis; and $\varepsilon_1, \varepsilon_2, \ldots, \varepsilon_p$ the residuals, which are assumed to have zero mean and no correlation with ξ. The moments up to the second order of $\eta_1, \eta_2, \ldots, \eta_p$ are assumed to exist. The direction cosines fulfill the condition

$$\sum_{i=1}^{p} \beta_i^2 = 1. \tag{1.2}$$

Multiplying (1.1) by $\beta_1, \beta_2, \ldots, \beta_p$, respectively, and adding, we get

$$\xi = \sum_{i=1}^{p} \beta_i \eta_i - \sum_{i=1}^{p} \beta_i \varepsilon_i. \tag{1.3}$$

Now the model can be looked upon in two ways:

a. Principal-Components Model

The residual vector $(\varepsilon_1, \varepsilon_2, \ldots, \varepsilon_p)$ is orthogonal to the principal component. Thus

$$\sum_{i=1}^{p} \beta_i \varepsilon_i = 0, \tag{1.4}$$

so that

$$\xi = \sum_{i=1}^{p} \beta_i \eta_i \tag{1.5}$$

and

$$E(\zeta^2) = \sum_{i=1}^{p} \sum_{j=1}^{p} \beta_i \beta_j E(\eta_i \eta_j). \tag{1.6}$$

In this model ε_i can be looked upon as the combined effect of the second- and higher-order principal components.

b. Factor-Analysis Model with Equal Residual Variances

The residuals have equal variances and are uncorrelated with each other. With this specification we denote the residuals by $\varepsilon_1{}^*, \varepsilon_2{}^*, \ldots, \varepsilon_p{}^*$, the first factor by ξ^*, while the direction cosines $\beta_1, \beta_2, \ldots, \beta_p$ of the first principal axis is the same in both models (cf. Whittle [5]).

Then the first factor ξ^* is given by (1.3) written in the new notations so that

$$\xi^* = \sum_{i=1}^{p} \beta_i \eta_i - \sum_{i=1}^{p} \beta_i \varepsilon_i{}^*, \tag{1.7}$$

and if the common residual variance is denoted by σ^2 we obtain

$$E(\xi^{*2}) = \sum_{i=1}^{p} \sum_{j=1}^{p} \beta_i \beta_j E(\eta_i \eta_j) - \sigma^2. \tag{1.8}$$

If two principal components are retained, (1.1) is replaced by

$$\eta_i = \beta_i \xi + \beta_i^{\mathrm{II}} \xi^{\mathrm{II}} + \varepsilon_i, \tag{1.9}$$

where β_i^{II} is the ith-direction cosine of the second principal axis and ξ^{II} the second principal component. Remembering that the principal axes are orthogonal, we have for the principal-components model,

$$E(\xi^2) = \sum_{i=1}^{p} \sum_{j=1}^{p} \beta_i \beta_j E(\eta_i \eta_j), \qquad E\{(\xi^{\mathrm{II}})^2\} = \sum_{i=1}^{p} \sum_{j=1}^{p} \beta_i^{\mathrm{II}} \beta_j^{\mathrm{II}} E(\eta_i \eta_j), \tag{1.10}$$

and for the factor-analysis model with equal residual variances:

$$E(\xi^{*2}) = \sum_{i=1}^{p} \sum_{j=1}^{p} \beta_i \beta_j E(\eta_i \eta_j) - \sigma^2, \qquad E\{(\xi^{\mathrm{II}*})^2\} = \sum_{i=1}^{p} \sum_{j=1}^{p} \beta_i^{\mathrm{II}} \beta_j^{\mathrm{II}} E(\eta_i \eta_j) - \sigma^2, \tag{1.11}$$

where $\xi^{\mathrm{II}*}$ denotes the second factor and σ^2 denotes the common residual variance in the two-factor case. The developments here immediately extend to the case of more than two factors.

Furthermore, it should be noted that a factor-analysis model with k factors and equal residual variances corresponds to a principal-components model, where the $p - k$ smallest eigenvalues are equal.

It will be shown in Section 2 that Wold's iterative method is equivalent to a classical iterative method for the eigenvalue problem of the matrix of the second-order moments of $\eta_1, \eta_2, \ldots, \eta_p$, and, consequently, Wold's iterative method gives consistent estimates of the principal components. Regularity conditions for this consistency are given by Wold [7].

A random sample of size n from the above-mentioned p-dimensional distribution is considered. Let y_{iv} be the vth observation of the ith variable. Starting with the first principal axis, let b_i be the estimate of the ith direction cosine and x_v the estimate of the first principal component of the vth observation.

Since we have the side condition

$$\sum_{i=1}^{p} b_i^2 = 1, \tag{1.12}$$

the function to be minimized is[1]

$$\sum_{i=1}^{p} \sum_{v=1}^{n} (y_{iv} - b_i x_v)^2 + \gamma\left(\sum_{i=1}^{p} b_i^2 - 1\right), \tag{1.13}$$

where γ is a Lagrange multiplier. The condition that the derivatives with respect to x_v and b_i vanish together with the side condition (1.12) leads to the following relations:

$$x_v = \sum_{i=1}^{p} b_i y_{iv} \qquad (v = 1, 2, \ldots, n) \tag{1.14}$$

and

$$b_i = \frac{\sum_{v=1}^{n} x_v y_{iv}}{\sum_{v=1}^{n} x_v^2 - \gamma} \qquad (i = 1, 2, \ldots, p). \tag{1.15}$$

If the last expression is multiplied by b_i and the sum over i is taken, and (1.14) and the side condition (1.12) are used, it is found that the multiplier γ has the value zero. Hence

$$b_i = \frac{\sum_{v=1}^{n} x_v y_{iv}}{\sum_{v=1}^{n} x_v^2}. \tag{1.16}$$

Another way of obtaining b_i is to start with quantities proportionate with b_i and then use the side condition (1.12). By introducing c_i as given by

$$c_i = \sum_{v=1}^{n} x_v y_{iv}, \tag{1.17}$$

[1] Whittle [5] starts with the factor analysis model, but as mentioned before, consistent estimates of the principal components are obtained. In other words, the estimates of the factor analysis model have a bias which persists when the sample size tends to infinity.

we get

$$b_i = \frac{c_i}{(\sum_{j=1}^{p} c_j^{\,2})^{1/2}}. \tag{1.18}$$

For future reference we shall introduce the notation λ for the common value of the denominator of expressions (1.16) and (1.18) for b_i. Thus

$$\lambda = \sum_{\nu=1}^{n} x_\nu^{\,2} = \left(\sum_{i=1}^{p} c_i^{\,2}\right)^{1/2}. \tag{1.19}$$

Wold's iterative procedure runs as follows:

(1) Suppose that the values $b_1^{(s)}, b_2^{(s)}, \ldots, b_p^{(s)}$ have been reached in approximation number s. Then for each observation, that is, for each value of ν, we take the regression over the variables and treat $x_\nu^{(s)}$ as the regression coefficient. If $x_\nu^{(s)}$ denotes the value of x_ν in approximation number s, we then have

$$x_\nu^{(s)} = \sum_{i=1}^{p} b_i^{(s)} y_{i\nu}, \tag{1.20}$$

which corresponds to (1.14).

(2) For each variable, that is, for each value of i, we take the regression over the observations and treat $b_i^{(s+1)}$ as a regression coefficient. Then, since the side condition (1.12) should be fulfilled, we calculate in an intermediate step the quantities $c_i^{(s+1)}$ as

$$c_i^{(s+1)} = \sum_{\nu=1}^{n} x_\nu^{(s)} y_{i\nu} \tag{1.21}$$

and obtain

$$b_i^{(s+1)} = \frac{c_i^{(s+1)}}{[\sum_{j=1}^{p} (c_j^{(s+1)})^2]^{1/2}}, \tag{1.22}$$

which corresponds to (1.17) and (1.18). The iteration is continued until two successive sets of values agree sufficiently well.

The starting values of the direction cosines are arbitrary. It is not even necessary that the side condition (1.12) is fulfilled for the starting values, for it will in any case be satisfied after the first iteration. Only in the case when we happen to start with a direction exactly orthogonal to the correct one, the procedure does not give the first principal axis. Alternatively, it is possible to choose starting values for the principal components. Then it is not necessary to choose values which can be written in the form (1.20), because after the first iteration such a relation will always be fulfilled.

To find the second principal axis we subtract from every observed value the projection of the first principal component. The observed values, reduced for the effect of the first principal component in this way, are denoted by $y_{i\nu}^{\text{II}}$. Thus

$$y_{i\nu}^{\text{II}} = y_{i\nu} - b_i x_\nu . \tag{1.23}$$

The procedure is now repeated with $y_{i\nu}^{\text{II}}$ instead of $y_{i\nu}$, and then the direction cosines of the second principal axis and the corresponding principal components are obtained. Let these quantities be denoted by b_i^{II} and x_ν^{II}, respectively. The third principal axis is found if the procedure is repeated for the quantities $y_{i\nu}^{\text{III}}$ as defined by

$$y_{i\nu}^{\text{III}} = y_{i\nu}^{\text{II}} - b_i^{\text{II}} x_\nu^{\text{II}}, \tag{1.24}$$

and in the same way all principal axes are found successively.

2. THE RELATION TO OTHER PROCEDURES

Most earlier methods take their starting point not in (1.1) but in the second-order moments of the observed values. For simplicity we shall not use moments but the corresponding totals. Let m_{ij} denote the sum of the products of the ith and jth variable; that is,

$$m_{ij} = \sum_{\nu=1}^{n} y_{i\nu} y_{j\nu} . \tag{2.1}$$

Then if expression (1.20) for $x_\nu^{(s)}$ is introduced in expression (1.21) for $c_i^{(s+1)}$ the following relation is obtained:

$$c_i^{(s+1)} = \sum_{j=1}^{p} m_{ij} b_j^{(s)}, \tag{2.2}$$

and from this formula together with (1.22) we obtain $b_i^{(s+1)}$ without explicit use of the principal components $x_\nu^{(s)}$. Let $\mathbf{b}^{(s)}$ denote the column vector of the directions $b_1^{(s)}, b_2^{(s)}, \ldots, b_p^{(s)}$ and $\mathbf{c}^{(s)}$ the column vector of the intermediate quantities $c_1^{(s)}, c_2^{(s)}, \ldots, c_p^{(s)}$. Further, let $\mathbf{M}$ be the symmetric matrix of the sums of squares and products m_{ij}, where $i, j = 1, 2, \ldots, p$. Then (2.2) and (1.22) can be written in matrix form in the following way:

$$\mathbf{c}^{(s+1)} = \mathbf{M}\mathbf{b}^{(s)} \tag{2.3}$$

and

$$\mathbf{b}^{(s+1)} = \frac{\mathbf{c}^{(s+1)}}{[\mathbf{c}'^{(s+1)}\mathbf{c}^{(s+1)}]^{1/2}}, \tag{2.4}$$

where the prime means that the matrix is transposed. $\mathbf{c}'^{(s+1)}$ is thus a row vector.

Letting $\lambda^{(s+1)}$ denote the first eigenvalue of the matrix $\mathbf{M}$ as obtained in approximation $s+1$, we get the following expression, which in the limit coincides with (1.19):

$$\lambda^{(s+1)} = [\mathbf{c}'^{(s+1)}\mathbf{c}^{(s+1)}]^{1/2}. \tag{2.5}$$

A proof of the convergence of this procedure is given by Anderson [1]. Since it can be considered as a combination of two steps in Wold's procedure, the latter will also converge.

A related method is known as the power method (see, e.g., Bodewig [2], p. 270). Starting from a column vector $\mathbf{a}^{(1)}$, and writing

$$\mathbf{a}^{(s+1)} = \mathbf{M}^s\mathbf{a}^{(1)}, \tag{2.6}$$

the first eigenvalue is obtained as the limiting value of the ratio between the absolute values of two successive vectors. If $\mathbf{a}^{(1)} = \mathbf{b}^{(1)}$, the vectors $\mathbf{a}^{(s+1)}$ and $\mathbf{b}^{(s+1)}$ differ only by a scalar factor.

To get the second principal component, the reduced observed values y_{iv}^{II} as given by (1.23) are treated in the same way as the original observed values y_{iv}. The square and product sums are denoted by m_{ij}^{II},

$$m_{ij}^{\mathrm{II}} = \sum_{v=1}^{n} y_{iv}^{\mathrm{II}} y_{jv}^{\mathrm{II}}. \tag{2.7}$$

By introducing expression (1.23) for y_{iv}^{II}, the following relation is obtained:

$$m_{ij}^{\mathrm{II}} = \sum_{v=1}^{n} y_{iv}y_{jv} - b_i \sum_{v=1}^{n} x_v y_{jv} - b_j \sum_{v=1}^{n} x_v y_{iv} + b_i b_j \sum_{v=1}^{n} x_v{}^2. \tag{2.8}$$

The three last terms are equal, apart from the sign, as seen from Eq. (1.16). By introducing λ according to (1.19), and m_{ij} according to (2.1), we get

$$m_{ij}^{\mathrm{II}} = m_{ij} - \lambda b_i b_j. \tag{2.9}$$

Here λ is the largest eigenvalue of the matrix $\mathbf{M}$. This formula shows the equivalence between the methods also for the second principal axis (see Anderson [1], p. 283). Evidently the correspondence extends to the remaining principal axes.

3. A GEOMETRICAL INTERPRETATION OF THE ITERATION

Let $w_1, w_2, \ldots, w_p$ be coordinates in the p-dimensional space. Writing

$$Q = \sum_{i=1}^{p} \sum_{j=1}^{p} m_{ij} w_i w_j, \tag{3.1}$$

we shall consider the so-called moment (hyper-) ellipsoid

$$Q = 1. \tag{3.2}$$

The partial derivative with respect to w_i is

$$\frac{\partial Q}{\partial w_i} = 2 \sum_{j=1}^{p} m_{ij} w_j \qquad (i = 1, 2, \ldots, p). \tag{3.3}$$

These partial derivatives are proportionate to the direction cosines of the normal to the ellipsoid. A comparison with relations (2.2) and (1.22) shows that if the coordinates $w_1, w_2, \ldots, w_p$ are proportionate to the direction cosines in the sth iteration $b_1^{(s)}, b_2^{(s)}, \ldots, b_p^{(s)}$, then the partial derivatives are proportionate to the direction cosines $b_1^{(s+1)}, b_2^{(s+1)}, \ldots, b_p^{(s+1)}$ in iteration number $s+1$. Since the direction cosines of the normal of the ellipsoid are proportionate to the partial derivatives, the iteration method can be described in the following way: If the direction of the sth iteration is represented by a line from the center of the moment ellipsoid, the direction corresponding to iteration $s+1$ is the direction of the normal in the point where the line cuts the moment ellipsoid.

For $p = 2$ an ellipse is obtained. This case is illustrated by Fig. 1. Let O be

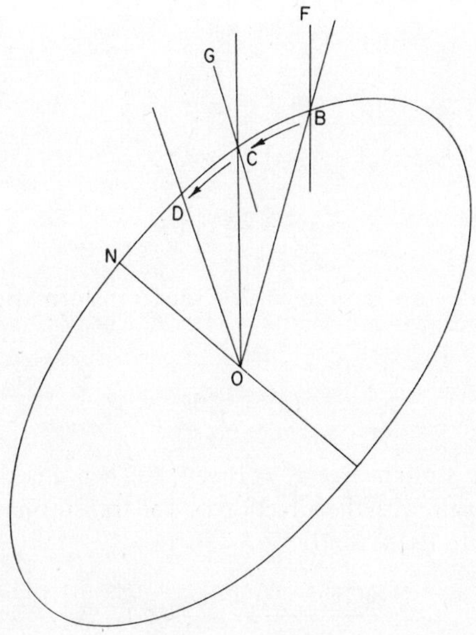

Fig. 1. Geometric interpretation of the iteration in two dimensions.

the center of the ellipse, and the line OB have the direction of the first iteration. The normal BF then has the direction of the second iteration. Draw a line OC parallel to BF. The normal CG then has the direction of the third iteration, which is represented by the ray OD parallel to CG, and so on. In this way the procedure converges to the direction of the small half-axis ON of the ellipse.

4. THE FIX-POINT PROPERTY

Let us first consider the two-dimensional case. If the coordinate system is turned so that the principal axes are taken as coordinate axes, the equation of the moment ellipse can be written

$$\lambda_1 z_1{}^2 + \lambda_2 z_2{}^2 = 1, \tag{4.1}$$

where λ_1 and λ_2 are the eigenvalues. The half-axes of the ellipse are $1/(\lambda_1)^{1/2}$ and $1/(\lambda_2)^{1/2}$. Suppose that $\lambda_1 > \lambda_2$. Let φ be the angle between the first principal axis, in this case the z_1 axis, and a line from the origin to the point (z_1, z_2) on the ellipse, and ψ be the angle between the normal through that point and the principal axis. Then we have

$$\tan \varphi = \frac{z_2}{z_1} \tag{4.2}$$

and

$$\tan \psi = \frac{\lambda_2 z_2}{\lambda_1 z_1}. \tag{4.3}$$

Hence

$$\tan \varphi = \frac{\lambda_2}{\lambda_1} \tan \psi. \tag{4.4}$$

Now we choose $u = \tan \varphi$, and make the transformation $f(u) = \tan \psi$. This gives

$$(u) = \frac{\lambda_2}{\lambda_1} u. \tag{4.5}$$

Let us consider the straight line $z_1 = 1$, say A. Then u is the intercept on A of a ray from the origin with the direction φ. The transformation $f(u)$ evidently maps the line A onto itself. Since

$$\frac{|f(u) - f(v)|}{|u - v|} = \frac{\lambda_2}{\lambda_1} < 1, \tag{4.6}$$

the mapping is contractive. The fix-point condition is thus fulfilled (Kolmogorov and Fomin, [3] p. 43). In the exceptional case, when the procedure is started in the direction of the major axis of the ellipse, the direction of the normal coincides with that of the radius vector. Then $\varphi = \psi = \pi/2$, so that u and $f(u)$ take on infinite values. In passing, we note that the choice of the variable u is not arbitrary, for the angle φ itself the transformation from φ to ψ does not obey a criterion like (4.6) in the whole range $-\pi/2 < \varphi < +\pi/2$. In fact, in the neighborhood of the limits, ψ changes faster than φ.

Proceeding to the case of three dimensions, we have for the moment ellipsoid when referred to its principal axes,

$$\lambda_1 z_1^2 + \lambda_2 z_2^2 + \lambda_3 z_3^2 = 1. \tag{4.7}$$

It is supposed that $\lambda_1 > \lambda_2 \geq \lambda_3$. In a plane A orthogonal to the z axis through the point $z_1 = 1$, we choose the two coordinate axes—say with coordinates u_1 and u_2—parallel to the remaining two principal axes of the ellipsoid. A line through the origin, which cuts the ellipsoidal surface in the point (z_1, z_2, z_3), will cut the plane A in a point with the coordinates

$$u_1 = \frac{z_2}{z_1}, \qquad u_2 = \frac{z_3}{z_1}. \tag{4.8}$$

A line from the origin parallel to the normal N of the ellipsoid in the point (z_1, z_2, z_3) will intersect the plane in the point,

$$f_1(u_1) = \frac{\lambda_2 z_2}{\lambda_1 z_1}, \qquad f_2(u_2) = \frac{\lambda_3 z_3}{\lambda_1 z_1}. \tag{4.9}$$

Hence

$$f_1(u_1) = \frac{\lambda_2}{\lambda_1} u_1, \qquad f_2(u_2) = \frac{\lambda_3}{\lambda_1} u_1. \tag{4.10}$$

The transformation evidently maps the plane A onto itself. Let $\mathbf{u}$ and $\mathbf{v}$ denote vectors with components u_1, u_2, and v_1, v_2 respectively and let $f(\mathbf{u})$ and $f(\mathbf{v})$ be vectors with components $f_1(u_1), f_2(u_2)$, and $f_1(v_1), f_2(v_2)$, respectively. Then we have

$$\frac{|f(\mathbf{u}) - f(\mathbf{v})|}{|\mathbf{u} - \mathbf{v}|}$$

$$= \left[\frac{\lambda_2^2}{\lambda_1^2}(u_1 - v_1)^2 + \frac{\lambda_3^2}{\lambda_1^2}(u_2 - v_2)^2\right]^{1/2} \Big/ [(u_1 - v_1)^2 + (u_2 - v_2)^2]^{1/2}, \tag{4.11}$$

which gives

$$\frac{|f(\mathbf{u}) - f(\mathbf{v})|}{|\mathbf{u} - \mathbf{v}|} \leq \frac{\lambda_2}{\lambda_1} < 1. \tag{4.12}$$

Thus the fix-point criterion is fulfilled for the transformation. In the exceptional case, where the ray from origin is exactly orthogonal to the z_1 axis, $|\mathbf{u}|$ and $|f(\mathbf{u})|$ take on infinite values and the procedure should theoretically lead to the second principal axis, if the ray does not coincide with the third principal axis.[2]

In case $\lambda_1 = \lambda_2 > \lambda_3$, it is convenient to introduce cylindrical coordinates

$$z_1 = r \cos \theta, \qquad z_2 = r \sin \theta, \qquad z_3 = z_3 .$$

Then the equation of the ellipsoid is

$$\lambda_1 r^2 + \lambda_3 z_3{}^2 = 1. \tag{4.13}$$

The line through the origin and the normal N lie in a plane that passes through the axis of symmetry, that is, the z_3 axis. This plane cuts out an ellipse, in which the whole iteration procedure takes place. If the two largest eigenvalues are equal, the whole procedure thus follows the meridian. Hence the longitude θ of the principal axis will retain its starting value during the whole procedure. By comparison with the two-dimensional case, it is seen that in this case the principal axis is orthogonal to the z_3 axis, although it is otherwise undetermined. However, the procedure gives one axis corresponding to the largest eigenvalue. An axis orthogonal to this one, with the same eigenvalue, can then be found by the same procedure as if the eigenvalues were different.

The conclusions made here for the three-dimensional case extend immediately to the case of p dimensions. For the moment ellipsoid as referred to its principal axes we have

$$\sum_{i=1}^{p} \lambda_i z_i{}^2 = 1, \tag{4.14}$$

where $\lambda_1 \geq \lambda_2 \geq \lambda_3 \geq \cdots \geq \lambda_p$ are the eigenvalues. Now let A be the plane $z_1 = 1$ and $u_1, u_2, \ldots, u_{p-1}$ coordinates in that plane measured along axes parallel to the remaining axes of the moment ellipsoid. Then

[2] If the starting direction happens to lie in a principal plane, the iterative procedure should theoretically lead to the principal axis in that plane, which is associated with the largest eigenvalue. In such a case there must be one principal axis, which is orthogonal to that principal plane.

It may further be mentioned that if the starting value happens to coincide with one of the principal axes, the second iteration will reproduce the first one and thereby determine this axis. To test whether we have in actual fact obtained the first principal axis, we run the procedure from a new starting direction. Generally, in the p-dimensional case the worst thing that can happen is that for $p - 2$ such tests need to be performed, the last axis being orthogonal to the others. If we are really interested in all principal axes, the method at the end of Section 1 can conveniently be started from whichever axes have been found first.

$$u_i = \frac{z_{i+1}}{z_1} \qquad (i = 1, 2, \ldots, p-1). \tag{4.15}$$

The corresponding coordinates for a line from the origin parallel to the normal N in the point $(z_1, z_2, \ldots, z_p)$ are

$$f_i(u_i) = \frac{\lambda_{i+1} z_{i+1}}{\lambda_1 z_1} \qquad (i = 1, 2, \ldots, p-1). \tag{4.16}$$

Hence

$$f_i(u_i) = \frac{\lambda_{i+1}}{\lambda_1} u_i. \tag{4.17}$$

Denoting by $\mathbf{u}$ and $\mathbf{v}$ vectors with components u_i and v_i, where $i = 1, 2, \ldots, p-1$ and by $f(\mathbf{u})$ and $f(\mathbf{v})$ the corresponding transformed vectors we have

$$\frac{|f(\mathbf{u}) - f(\mathbf{v})|}{|\mathbf{u} - \mathbf{v}|} = \left[\sum_{i=1}^{p-1} \frac{\lambda_{i+1}^2}{\lambda_1^{\ 2}} (u_i - v_i)^2\right]^{1/2} \Bigg/ \left[\sum_{i=1}^{p-1} (u_i - v_i)^2\right]^{1/2}, \tag{4.18}$$

showing that the fix-point criterion is fulfilled if $\lambda_1 > \lambda_2$:

$$\frac{|f(\mathbf{u}) - f(\mathbf{v})|}{|\mathbf{u} - \mathbf{v}|} \leq \frac{\lambda_2}{\lambda_1} < 1. \tag{4.19}$$

In the exceptional case, where $z_1 = 0$ for the starting direction, $|u|$ and $|f(u)|$ take on infinite values, and the procedure does not give the largest eigenvalue. In the special case where the j largest eigenvalues are equal, but the other eigenvalues are smaller, the following variable is introduced:

$$r^2 = z_1^{\ 2} + z_2^{\ 2} + \cdots + z_j^{\ 2}. \tag{4.20}$$

The equation of the ellipsoid can then be written

$$\lambda_1 r^2 + \sum_{i=j+1}^{p} \lambda_i z_i^{\ 2} = 1. \tag{4.21}$$

This equation has the same form as an ellipsoid in $p - j + 1$ dimensions. From this equation it is seen that the direction of the first principal axis is undetermined within the j-dimensional space spanned by $z_1, z_2, \ldots, z_j$. But when one of these axes has been found, a second axis orthogonal to the first one can be found with the aid of the same procedure, as if the two largest eigenvalues were different. The procedure can be continued in the same way, and gives j axes that correspond to the largest eigenvalue.

If some eigenvalues vanish, we have

$$f_i(u_i) = 0 \qquad \text{for} \quad \lambda_i = 0. \tag{4.22}$$

After the first iteration, the components of u in the direction of zero eigenvalues vanish. If the matrix has the rank $m < p$, after the first iteration the direction cosines define a direction in the m-dimensional subspace, spanned by the nonzero principal axes. We see that the singularity of the matrix creates no difficulty for the method.

As to the case where $m < p$, we further note that the matrix of the product sums m_{ij}^{II}, used to iterate the second principal axis, is always singular.

5. THE FIX-POINT PROPERTY IN THE SAMPLE SPACE

The iteration process considered in the preceding section takes place in the p-dimensional space of the random variables $\eta_1, \eta_2, \ldots, \eta_p$, and gives estimated values of the direction cosines $\beta_1, \beta_2, \ldots, \beta_p$. However, it is possible to use the same procedure in the n-dimensional space, $x_1, x_2, \ldots, x_n$, generated by the first principal component ξ. The product sum of variables pertaining to observations number μ and ν are denoted by $l_{\mu\nu}$,

$$l_{\mu\nu} = \sum_{i=1}^{p} y_{i\mu} y_{i\nu}. \tag{5.1}$$

To obtain $x^{(s+1)}$ directly from $x^{(s)}$, expression (1.22) for $b_i^{(s+1)}$ with $c_i^{(s+1)}$ given by (1.21), is introduced in the formula obtained by writing $s+1$ instead of s in expression (1.20). If the quantities $l_{\mu\nu}$, just defined, and an intermediate quantity, say $t_\nu^{(s+1)}$, are introduced, the result can be expressed in the following way:

$$t_\nu^{(s+1)} = \sum_{\mu=1}^{n} l_{\mu\nu} x_\mu^{(s)} \tag{5.2}$$

and

$$x_\nu^{(s+1)} = t_\nu^{(s+1)} \Bigg/ \left[\sum_{\mu=1}^{n} x_\mu^{(s)} t_\mu^{(s+1)} \right]^{1/2}. \tag{5.3}$$

Let $\mathbf{x}^{(s)}$ and $\mathbf{t}^{(s)}$ denote column vectors of the principal components $x_\nu^{(s)}$ and of the intermediate quantities $t_\nu^{(s)}$, and let $\mathbf{L}$ denote the square matrix of the quantities $l_{\mu\nu}$, where $\mu, \nu = 1, 2, \ldots, n$. The equations can then be written in matrix form as

$$\mathbf{t}^{(s+1)} = \mathbf{L}\mathbf{x}^{(s)}, \tag{5.4}$$

$$\mathbf{x}^{(s+1)} = \frac{\mathbf{t}^{(s+1)}}{[\mathbf{x}'^{(s)}\mathbf{t}^{(s+1)}]^{1/2}}. \tag{5.5}$$

Relation (5.3) being derived in the way indicated, it is seen that the denominator in the right member of this equation equals the denominator of (1.22). Therefore, expression (2.5) for $\lambda^{(s+1)}$ can be written

$$\lambda^{(s+1)} = [\mathbf{x}'^{(s)}\mathbf{t}^{(s+1)}]^{1/2}. \tag{5.6}$$

In the limit this quantity tends to the largest eigenvalue of the matrix **L**.

To find the corresponding procedure for the second-order principal components, the reduced observation y_{iv}^{II} as given by (1.23) is again used, instead of the original observations. Let $l_{\mu\nu}^{\mathrm{II}}$ be the quantity corresponding to $l_{\mu\nu}$ obtained in this way. Then

$$l_{\mu\nu}^{\mathrm{II}} = \sum_{i=1}^{p} y_{i\mu}^{\mathrm{II}} y_{i\nu}^{\mathrm{II}}, \tag{5.7}$$

or, if (1.23) is used,

$$l_{\mu\nu}^{\mathrm{II}} = \sum_{i=1}^{p} y_{i\mu} y_{i\nu} - x_\mu \sum_{i=1}^{p} b_i y_{i\nu} - x_\nu \sum_{i=1}^{p} b_i y_{i\mu} + x_\mu x_\nu \sum_{i=1}^{p} b_i^2 \,. \tag{5.8}$$

If use is made of (1.12) and (1.14) and the notation (5.1) is introduced, the expression is reduced to

$$l_{\mu\nu}^{\mathrm{II}} = l_{\mu\nu} - x_\mu x_\nu \,. \tag{5.9}$$

From these quantities the principal components of the second order can be computed in the same way as before. And the procedure can evidently be continued to principal components of higher orders.

It follows that the matrices **M** and **L** have the same nonvanishing eigenvalues, the direction cosines of the principal axes form eigenvectors of the matrix **M**, and the principal components form eigenvectors of the matrix **L** (cf. Whittle [5]). The equality of the eigenvalues follows also from a general theorem in matrix theory (see, for instance, Mirsky [4]). If **A** and **B** are two matrices, the products **AB** and **BA** have the same nonvanishing eigenvalues, provided that both products exist. In our case we take **A** as the matrix of the observations y_{iv}, and **B** as the transpose of that matrix. Then the matrices **M** and **L** can be interpreted as the products **AB** and **BA**.

The fix-point property in the sample space can now be obtained in the same way as before. Let $\omega_1, \omega_2, \ldots, \omega_n$ be coordinates in the sample space. The generalized ellipsoid

$$\sum_{\mu=1}^{n} \sum_{\nu=1}^{n} l_{\mu\nu} \omega_\mu \omega_\nu = 1 \tag{5.10}$$

is analogous to the moment ellipsoid as given by (3.1) and (3.2). A comparison between the partial derivatives and expression (5.2) shows that if $\omega_1, \omega_2, \ldots, \omega_n$ are proportionate to $x_1^{(s)}, x_2^{(s)}, \ldots, x_n^{(s)}$, then the partial derivatives are proportionate to $t_1^{(s+1)}, t_2^{(s+1)}, \ldots, t_n^{(s+1)}$, and therefore, to $x_1^{(s+1)}, x_2^{(s+1)}, \ldots, x_n^{(s+1)}$. The iteration can therefore be described as the replacement of a vector from the origin directed against a point on the ellipsoid by a vector parallel to the normal in that point.

If the ellipsoid is referred to its principal axes, its equation can be written

$$\sum_{\nu=1}^{n} \lambda_\nu \zeta_\nu^2 = 1, \tag{5.11}$$

where the same nonvanishing eigenvalues occur as in (4.14). Generally, $n > p$, and in this case there are at most p nonvanishing eigenvalues.

If λ_1 is the largest eigenvalue, then the intersection of a line from the origin with the hyperplane $\zeta_1 = 1$ will be considered. Analogous to (4.15) we now take u_ν^* as

$$u_\nu^* = \frac{\zeta_{\nu+1}}{\zeta_1} \qquad (\nu = 1, 2, \ldots, n-1), \tag{5.12}$$

and after the transformation we have

$$f_\nu(u_\nu^*) = \frac{\lambda_{\nu+1}}{\lambda_1} u_\nu^* \qquad (\nu = 1, 2, \ldots, n-1), \tag{5.13}$$

where, for $n > p$, at most p of the values $f_\nu(u_\nu^*)$ are nonvanishing. The components u_ν^*, which correspond to vanishing eigenvalues, are thus eliminated after one iteration.

Let $\mathbf{u}^*$ and $\mathbf{v}^*$ be vectors with components u_ν^* and v_ν^*, where $\nu = 1, 2, \ldots, n-1$ and $f(\mathbf{u}^*)$ and $f(\mathbf{v}^*)$ are the corresponding transformed vectors. Then in the same way as in Section 4 we get

$$\frac{|f(\mathbf{u}^*) - f(\mathbf{v}^*)|}{|\mathbf{u}^* - \mathbf{v}^*|} \leqq \frac{\lambda_2}{\lambda_1} < 1. \tag{5.14}$$

provided that $\lambda_1 > \lambda_2 \geqq \lambda_3 \cdots \geqq \lambda_n$

Thus the fix-point criterion is fulfilled. An exceptional case occurs if $\zeta_1 = 0$ for the starting values. Then $|\mathbf{u}^*|$ and $|f(\mathbf{u}^*)|$ take on infinite values, and the procedure does not give the largest eigenvalue.

The extension to the case, where the first j eigenvalues are equal, can be performed in the same way as in Section 5.

6. A DETAILED COMPARISON BETWEEN THE PROCEDURES

The methods considered not only lead to the same values in the limit, they are also equivalent from iteration to iteration. Suppose that the values $b_1^{(s)}$, $b_2^{(s)}, \ldots, b_p^{(s)}$ have been obtained in the sth approximation. Then the values $x_1^{(s+1)}, x_2^{(s+1)}, \ldots, x_n^{(s+1)}$ can be reached in three ways:

(a) Wold's method has $x_1^{(s)}, x_2^{(s)}, \ldots, x_n^{(s)}$ and $b_1^{(s+1)}, b_2^{(s+1)}, \ldots, b_p^{(s+1)}$ as intermediate results:

$$x_\nu^{(s)} = \sum_{i=1}^{p} b_i^{(s)} y_{i\nu}, \qquad c_i^{(s+1)} = \sum_{\nu=1}^{n} x_\nu^{(s)} y_{i\nu},$$

$$b_i^{(s+1)} = c_i^{(s+1)} \Big/ \left[\sum_{j=1}^{p} (c_j^{(s+1)})^2 \right]^{1/2}, \qquad x_\nu^{(s+1)} = \sum_{i=1}^{p} b_i^{(s+1)} y_{i\nu}.$$

(b) The method of Section 3 uses the matrix **M** and passes directly from the one approximation of the direction cosines to the next one:

$$c_i^{(s+1)} = \sum_{j=1}^{p} m_{ij} b_j^{(s)}, \qquad b_i^{(s+1)} = c_i^{(s+1)} \Big/ \left[\sum_{j=1}^{p} (c_j^{(s+1)})^2 \right]^{1/2},$$

$$x_\nu^{(s+1)} = \sum_{i=1}^{p} b_i^{(s+1)} y_{i\nu}.$$

(c) By iteration in the sample space, dealt with in Section 5, the matrix **L** is used and the iteration procedure concerns the principal components:

$$x_\nu^{(s)} = \sum_{i=1}^{p} b_i^{(s)} y_{i\nu}, \qquad t_\nu^{(s+1)} = \sum_{\mu=1}^{n} l_{\mu\nu} x_\mu^{(s)}, \qquad x_\nu^{(s+1)} = t_\nu^{(s+1)} \Big/ \left[\sum_{\mu=1}^{n} x_\mu^{(s)} t_\mu^{(s+1)} \right]^{1/2}.$$

The demonstration of the fix-point property has been made both for the direction cosines $b_1, b_2, \ldots, b_p$ and the principal components $x_1, x_2, \ldots, x_n$. In both cases, the same geometric interpretation is obtained, and the equivalence has just been shown in detail.

The procedure with the direction cosines utilizes standard methods related to the power method. It follows that even these methods can as well be used for the principal components. The matrix used in the iteration is, however, generally of a higher order, although the nonvanishing eigenvalues are the same in both cases.

7. NOTE ON THE NUMERICAL ACCURACY OF WOLD'S METHOD

Although Wold's method theoretically should lead step by step to the same result as the other methods considered in this paper, it has an advantage in numerical accuracy in the case where the ratio between two successive eigenvalues is large. This fact was found empirically by Dr. Klaus Appel (personal communication). The explanation is the following: Suppose that we have a rounding error in b_i. This rounding error is multiplied by a much larger factor if m_{ij}^{II} is calculated from (2.9) than if m_{ij}^{II} is calculated from (2.7), with y_i^{II} obtained from (1.23). A similar argument holds concerning the effect of rounding errors in the principal components.

Acknowledgment

I wish to thank Professor Herman Wold, who has given me access to his results in advance of publication, for numerous discussions and valuable comments during the course of this investigation.

REFERENCES

1. Anderson, T. W. (1958). *An Introduction to Multivariate Statistical Analysis.* Wiley, New York.
2. Bodewig, E. (1959). *Matrix Calculus.* North-Holland, Amsterdam.
3. Kolmogorov, A. N. and Fomin, S. V. (1957). *Metric and Normed Spaces.* Graylock Press, Rochester, New York.
4. Mirsky, L. (1955). *An Introduction to Linear Algebra.* Clarendon Press, Oxford.
5. Whittle, P. (1953). On principal components and least square methods of factor analysis. *Skand. Aktuarietidskr.* **35** 223.
6. Wold, H. (1966). Nonlinear estimation by iterative least squares procedures. *Festschrift Jerzy Neyman.* Wiley, New York.
7. Wold, H. (1966). On the estimation of principal components by iterative least squares. This volume, pp. 391–420.

Recent Trends in Multivariate Prediction Theory

P. MASANI

DEPARTMENT OF MATHEMATICS
INDIANA UNIVERSITY
BLOOMINGTON, INDIANA

1. INTRODUCTION

From among the many facets of multivariate prediction we shall consider only the theory of linear, least-squares prediction of q-variate, weakly stationary stochastic processes with discrete time. Our purpose is to give a coherent account of the present state of this theory. We shall therefore refer to recent developments not in isolation but within the context of the general theoretical framework. Our emphasis will be on generality and logical order, but the practical side will also be discussed, although somewhat briefly (cf. §§2 and 15). Statistical questions of estimation, etc., will be omitted.

To recall the problem involved in such prediction suppose that $\mathbf{x}$ is a q-dimensional vector quantity associated with some long-enduring mechanism in nature, and that $\mathbf{x}_n$ denotes its value at time $t = n$. Suppose that we have been measuring $\mathbf{x}$ every second from the remote past up to the present moment $t = 0$, and have so obtained a sequence of readings

$$\mathbf{x}_k = \mathbf{a}_k, \qquad k = 0, -1, -2, \dots. \tag{1.1}$$

Is there some way to forecast the future value $\mathbf{x}_\nu$, $\nu \geq 1$, on the basis of the information contained in (1.1)? Without further knowledge of the mechanism, our answer to this question must be in the negative. If, however, we assume that our mechanism is such that the sequence $(\mathbf{x}_k)_{k=-\infty}^{0}$ is part of a time sequence (sample function) of a q-variate stationary stochastic process (S.P.) $(\mathbf{f}_n)_{n=-\infty}^{\infty}$ over a probability space $(\Omega, \mathscr{B}, P)$, so that

$$\mathbf{x}_n = \mathbf{f}_n(\omega_0), \qquad \omega_0 \in \Omega, \quad -\infty < n < \infty \tag{1.2}$$

and that we know the probabilistic structure of this S.P., then the answer is in the affirmative as we proceed to indicate.

Denote the forecast value of $\mathbf{x}_\nu$ by $\hat{\mathbf{x}}_\nu$. As $\hat{\mathbf{x}}_\nu$ is to depend on the past and present values $\mathbf{x}_k$, $k \leq 0$ alone, we must expect that $\hat{\mathbf{x}}_\nu \neq \mathbf{x}_\nu$ except when our mechanism is purely *deterministic*. Such mechanisms are of course very important, but they are only of peripheral interest in the theory of *probabilistic or statistical prediction*, which concerns us here. In this theory the problem is to find the $\hat{\mathbf{x}}_\nu$ which comes closest to $\mathbf{x}_\nu$ under some preassigned statistical error criterion. In least-squares, linear prediction we adopt the root-mean-square (rms) error criterion, and confine attention to $\hat{\mathbf{x}}_\nu$, which are mean limits of linear combinations $\sum_{k=0}^{n} \mathbf{A}_k^{(n)}\mathbf{x}_{-k}$, where $\mathbf{A}_k^{(n)}$ are $q \times q$ matrices.[1] It can be shown that the $\mathbf{A}_k^{(n)}$ are determinable and the problem solvable when the covariance structure of the stationary S.P. $(\mathbf{f}_n)_{-\infty}^{\infty}$ is known.

To state the problem in greater detail, we are given a bisequence $(\mathbf{f}_n)_{n=-\infty}^{\infty}$ of q-variates

$$\mathbf{f}_n = (f_n^{\,1}, \ldots, f_n^{\,q}), \qquad \text{where} \quad f_n^{\,i} \in L_2(\Omega, \mathscr{B}, P), \tag{1.3}$$

such that the $q \times q$ *covariance matrix*

$$[E(f_m^{\,i} \cdot \bar{f}_n^{\,j})] = [\gamma_{m-n}^{(i,j)}] = \mathbf{\Gamma}_{m-n} \tag{1.4}$$

depends only on the difference $m - n$.[2] This is the hypothesis of *weak stationarity*. Now let $\mathscr{M}_0$ be the (closed, linear) subspace of $L_2(\Omega, \mathscr{B}, P)$ spanned by the $f_n^{\,i}$, with $n \leq 0$ and $1 \leq i \leq q$; in symbols,

$$\mathscr{M}_0 = \mathfrak{S}(f_n^{\,i}, \quad n \leq 0, \quad 1 \leq i \leq q). \tag{1.5}$$

Then our problem may be stated as follows:

1.6. Prediction Problem. *Assuming as known the covariance bisequence* $(\mathbf{\Gamma}_k)_{k=-\infty}^{\infty}$ *and given* $\nu \geq 1$, *find variates* $\hat{f}_\nu^{\,1}, \ldots, \hat{f}_\nu^{\,q} \in \mathscr{M}_0$ *such that*

$$E(|f_\nu^{\,i} - \hat{f}_\nu^{\,i}|^2) \leq E(|f_\nu^{\,i} - g|^2), \qquad \textit{for all} \quad g \in \mathscr{M}_0, \quad 1 \leq i \leq q.$$

Also find the prediction-error covariance matrix

$$\mathbf{G}_\nu = [E\{(f_\nu^{\,i} - \hat{f}_\nu^{\,i})(\bar{f}_\nu^{\,j} - \bar{\hat{f}}_\nu^{\,j})\}].$$

Now $L_2(\Omega, \mathscr{B}, P)$ is a Hilbert space with the inner-product $(f, g) = E(f\bar{g})$. Since our problem involves only second-order moments, we can restate it as one for a Hilbert space $\mathscr{H}$, as Kolmogorov first emphasized in 1940; cf. [12]. To get the usual probabilistic version of the theory, we must of course think of this $\mathscr{H}$ as being $L_2(\Omega, \mathscr{B}, P)$. But for a theoretical study it is best to leave $\mathscr{H}$ unspecified. Adopting this point of view, what we have is a bisequence of vectors $(\mathbf{f}_n)_{-\infty}^{\infty}$, such that

$$\mathbf{f}_n = (f_n^{\,1}, \ldots, f_n^{\,q}), \qquad \text{where} \quad f_n^{\,i} \in \mathscr{H};$$

[1] A precise rendition of this statement will follow in a moment.

[2] In calling $\mathbf{\Gamma}_k$ a covariance matrix we are assuming tacitly that each $E(f_n^{\,i}) = 0$. This assumption entails no real loss of generality, since our S.P. is stationary and therefore the vector $E(\mathbf{f}_n)$ is independent of n. Alternatively, we may allow our S.P. $(\mathbf{f}_n)_{n=-\infty}^{\infty}$ to be *non-stationary*, assuming only that (1.4) holds for $\tilde{f}_n^{\,i}$, where $\tilde{f}_n^{\,i} = f_n^{\,i} - E(f_n^{\,i})$.

i.e., each $\mathbf{f}_n$ is in the Cartesian product $\mathscr{H}^q$ of $\mathscr{H}$ with itself q times. For q-variate prediction the structure of this hyperspace $\mathscr{H}^q$ is crucial and must first engage our attention (§2).

2. THE GRAM MATRICIAL STRUCTURE OF $\mathscr{H}^q$

Let $\mathscr{H}$ be any (complex) Hilbert space, $q \geq 1$, and $\mathscr{H}^q$ be the Cartesian product of $\mathscr{H}$ with itself q times, i.e., the set of all vectors $\mathbf{f} = (f^1, \dots, f^q)$ such that each $f^i \in \mathscr{H}$. To make $\mathscr{H}^q$ serviceable in prediction theory, we must endow it with a gram matricial structure, as Doob noted [4, p. 594]. For $\mathbf{f}, \mathbf{g} \in \mathscr{H}^q$, the $q \times q$ matrix

$$(\mathbf{f}, \mathbf{g}) = [(f^i, g^j)] \tag{2.1}$$

is called the *Gramian* of the ordered pair $\mathbf{f}, \mathbf{g}$.[3] It is reasonable to think of it as a *matricial inner product* in view of its properties:[4]

$$(\mathbf{f}, \mathbf{f}) \geq 0; \qquad (\mathbf{f}, \mathbf{f}) = 0 \quad \Rightarrow \quad \mathbf{f} = \mathbf{0}, \tag{2.2}$$

$$\left(\sum_{j \in J} \mathbf{A}_j \mathbf{f}_j, \sum_{k \in K} \mathbf{B}_k \mathbf{g}_k \right) = \sum_{j \in J} \sum_{k \in K} \mathbf{A}_j (\mathbf{f}_j, \mathbf{g}_k) \mathbf{B}_k^*, \tag{2.3}$$

where J and K are finite sets and $\mathbf{A}_j$ and $\mathbf{B}_k$ are $q \times q$ matrices. This suggests defining *orthogonality* in $\mathscr{H}^q$ by the relation

$$\mathbf{f} \perp \mathbf{g} \quad \Leftrightarrow \quad (\mathbf{f}, \mathbf{g}) = \mathbf{0} \qquad (\text{i.e.,} \Leftrightarrow \quad f^i \perp g^j, 1 \leq i, j \leq q). \tag{2.4}$$

It also suggests taking linear combinations of $\mathbf{f}_j \in \mathscr{H}^q$ with $q \times q$ matrix rather than complex coefficients, and calling a subset $\mathscr{M}$ of $\mathscr{H}^q$ a *linear manifold*, if and only if

$$\mathbf{f}, \mathbf{g} \in \mathscr{M} \quad \Rightarrow \quad \text{for all } q \times q \text{ matrices } \mathbf{A}, \mathbf{B}, \ \mathbf{Af} + \mathbf{Bg} \in \mathscr{M}.$$

The appropriate *topology for* $\mathscr{H}^q$ turns out, however, to be the familiar one induced by the (scalar) inner product in $\mathscr{H}^q$:

$$((\mathbf{f}, \mathbf{g})) = \text{trace}(\mathbf{f}, \mathbf{g}) = \sum_{i=1}^{q} f^i \overline{g^j}, \tag{2.5}$$

or rather by the corresponding norm

$$|\mathbf{f}| = ((\mathbf{f}, \mathbf{f}))^{1/2} = \left(\sum_{i=1}^{q} |f^i|^2 \right)^{1/2}. \tag{2.6}$$

[3] Our usage of boldface letters is as follows: $\mathbf{f}$, $\mathbf{g}$, etc., denote members of $\mathscr{H}^q$ and, $\mathscr{M}$, $\mathscr{N}$ denote subsets of $\mathscr{H}^q$. $\mathbf{A}$, $\mathbf{B}$, etc., denote $q \times q$ matrices with complex entries, and $\mathbf{\Phi}$, $\mathbf{\Psi}$, etc., denote $q \times q$ matrix-valued functions.

[4] We write $\mathbf{A} \geq \mathbf{B}$ or $\mathbf{B} \leq \mathbf{A}$ to mean that the matrix $\mathbf{A}$-$\mathbf{B}$ is nonnegative-definite. $\mathbf{A}^*$ denotes the adjoint of $\mathbf{A}$.

It is well known that $\mathscr{H}^q$ *is a Hilbert space under the inner product* (2.5).

We call $\mathscr{M}$ a *subspace* of $\mathscr{H}^q$, if and only if $\mathscr{M}$ is both a linear manifold and a closed set. It is easy to check, cf. [36, I, 5.8], that

$$\mathscr{M} \text{ is a subspace of } \mathscr{H}^q \quad \Leftrightarrow \quad \mathscr{M} = \mathcal{M}^q, \text{ where } \mathcal{M} \text{ is a subspace of } \mathscr{H}. \tag{2.7}$$

With these concepts of orthogonality, distance, and subspace we can extend to $\mathscr{H}^q$ the well-known theory of *orthogonal projections* for Hilbert spaces. Thus we have (cf. [36, I, 5.8; II, 1.17]).

2.8. Lemma. *If* $\mathbf{f} \in \mathscr{H}^q$ *and* $\mathscr{M}$ *is a subspace of* $\mathscr{H}^q$, *then there exists a unique* $\hat{\mathbf{f}} \in \mathscr{H}^q$ *satisfying any one (and therefore both) of the following equivalent conditions*:

(1) $\hat{\mathbf{f}} \in \mathscr{M}$ *and* $\mathbf{f} - \hat{\mathbf{f}} \perp \mathscr{M}$.

(2) $\hat{\mathbf{f}} \in \mathscr{M}$ *and* $(\mathbf{f} - \hat{\mathbf{f}}, \mathbf{f} - \hat{\mathbf{f}}) \leq (\mathbf{f} - \mathbf{g}, \mathbf{f} - \mathbf{g}), \quad \mathbf{g} \in \mathscr{M}$.

Let $\mathscr{M} = \mathcal{M}^q$ [cf. (2.7)]. *Then the* ith *component* $\hat{f}^i$ *of* $\hat{\mathbf{f}}$ *is the (ordinary) orthogonal projection of the* ith *component* f^i *of* $\mathbf{f}$ *on* $\mathcal{M}$.

2.9. Definition. *The* $\hat{\mathbf{f}}$ *mentioned in* (2.8) *is called the* orthogonal projection *of* $\mathbf{f}$ *on* $\mathscr{M}$ *and written* $(\mathbf{f} \,|\, \mathscr{M})$.

We thus obtain a structure for $\mathscr{H}^q$ which differs from but also closely resembles that of a Hilbert space, and which we shall therefore call *Hilbertian.* In terms of this structure we can give a definition of a q-ple, weakly stationary S.P., in which all side issues are purged and the essential idea brought to the forefront; cf. [37, §5]:

2.10. Definition. *A* q*-ple*, weakly stationary S.P. *is a bisequence* $(\mathbf{f}_n)_{n=-\infty}^{\infty}$ *such that each* $\mathbf{f}_n \in \mathscr{H}^q$ *and the Gram matrix*

$$(\mathbf{f}_m, \mathbf{f}_n) = \mathbf{\Gamma}_{m-n}$$

depends only on $m - n$. $(\mathbf{\Gamma}_k)_{k=-\infty}^{\infty}$ *is called the* covariance bisequence *of the S.P.*

Associated with a q-ple weakly stationary S.P. $(\mathbf{f}_n)_{-\infty}^{\infty}$ are the *present and past subspaces* $\mathscr{M}_n$, $\mathcal{M}_n$:[5]

$$\begin{aligned} \mathscr{M}_n &\underset{d}{=} \mathfrak{S}(\mathbf{f}_k, \quad k \leq n) \subseteq \mathscr{H}^q, \\ \mathcal{M}_n &\underset{d}{=} \mathfrak{S}(f_k^i, \quad k \leq n, \quad 1 \leq i \leq q) \subseteq \mathscr{H}, \end{aligned} \tag{2.11}$$

[5] For $\mathscr{A} \subseteq \mathscr{H}^q$, $\mathfrak{S}(\mathscr{A})$ denotes the smallest subspace of $\mathscr{H}^q$ containing $\mathscr{A}$. *N.B.* Linear combinations must be taken with matrix coefficients.

The symbol $\underset{d}{=}$ should be read "equals by definition." We shall often use it to introduce previously undefined expressions.

and the terminal subspaces

$$\mathcal{M}_\infty \underset{d}{=} \mathfrak{S}(\mathbf{f}_k, \quad \text{all } k), \qquad \mathcal{M}_\infty \underset{d}{=} \mathfrak{S}(f_k^i, \text{ all } k, \quad 1 \le i \le q),$$
$$\mathcal{M}_{-\infty} \underset{d}{=} \bigcap_{n=-\infty}^{\infty} \mathcal{M}_n, \qquad \mathcal{M}_{-\infty} \underset{d}{=} \bigcap_{n=-\infty}^{\infty} \mathcal{M}_n. \tag{2.12}$$

We easily find, cf. [36, I, 6.5], that

$$\mathcal{M}_n = \mathcal{M}_n^q, \qquad -\infty \le n \le \infty, \tag{2.13}$$

and obviously

$$\mathcal{M}_{-\infty} \subseteq \mathcal{M}_n \subseteq \mathcal{M}_{n+1} \subseteq \mathcal{M}_\infty. \tag{2.14}$$

In terms of these subspaces we can easily formulate the concept of determinism and tersely restate the prediction problem 1.6:

2.15. Definition. *We call the S.P.* deterministic, nondeterministic, purely nondeterministic, *according as*

$$\mathcal{M}_{-\infty} = \mathcal{M}_\infty, \qquad \mathcal{M}_{-\infty} \subset \mathcal{M}_\infty, \qquad \mathcal{M}_{-\infty} = \{\mathbf{0}\}.$$

2.16. Prediction Problem. *Let* $(\mathbf{f}_n)_{-\infty}^{\infty}$ *be a q-ple, weakly stationary S.P. with covariance bisequence* $(\mathbf{\Gamma}_k)_{-\infty}^{\infty}$ *and let* $v \ge 1$. *Find*

(a) *the matrices* $\mathbf{A}_k^{(n)}$ *such that*

$$\hat{\mathbf{f}}_v \underset{d}{=} (\mathbf{f}_v \mid \mathcal{M}_0) = \lim_{n\to\infty} \sum_{k=0}^{n} \mathbf{A}_k^{(n)} \mathbf{f}_{-k},$$

(b) $$\mathbf{G}_v \underset{d}{=} (\mathbf{f}_v - \hat{\mathbf{f}}_v, \mathbf{f} - \hat{\mathbf{f}}_v).$$

$\mathbf{G}_v$ is called the *prediction error matrix for lag v*. Following Zasuhin [43] we call $\rho = \operatorname{rank} G_1$ the *rank of the S.P.* $(\mathbf{f}_n)_{-\infty}^{\infty}$. Obviously,

$$\textit{the S.P. is deterministic} \quad \Leftrightarrow \quad \rho = 0; \text{ i.e., } \mathbf{G}_1 = \mathbf{0}. \tag{2.17}$$

The deterministic case is only of peripheral interest to us; cf. §1. Of much theoretical interest, although somewhat pathological, are the *nondeterministic cases of degenerate rank* $1 \le \rho < q$. The really interesting case from a practical standpoint is that of *full rank* $\rho = q$, for which $\det \mathbf{G}_1 > 0$. We note that since $\mathbf{G}_v \ge \mathbf{G}_1$ for $v \ge 1$, we have

$$\rho = q \quad \Rightarrow \quad \det \mathbf{G}_v > 0, \qquad v \ge 1. \tag{2.18}$$

3. ELEMENTARY SOLUTION OF THE PREDICTION PROBLEM

Seemingly the easiest way to solve the prediction problem 2.16 is by an extension of the method of undetermined coefficients. This has been explained in [36, II, §2] and it will suffice to indicate only a couple of steps. We may choose the $\mathbf{A}_k^{(n)}$ so that

$$\mathbf{f}_\nu - \sum_{k=0}^{n} \mathbf{A}_k^{(n)}\mathbf{f}_{-k} \perp \mathbf{f}_0, \mathbf{f}_{-1}, \dots, \mathbf{f}_{-n}, \tag{3.1}$$

whence, in block-matrix notation,

$$[\mathbf{A}_0^{(n)}, \dots, \mathbf{A}_n^{(n)}]\begin{bmatrix}\mathbf{\Gamma}_0 & \cdots & \mathbf{\Gamma}_n \\ \vdots & & \\ \mathbf{\Gamma}_{-n} & \cdots & \mathbf{\Gamma}_0\end{bmatrix} = [\mathbf{\Gamma}_\nu, \dots, \mathbf{\Gamma}_{\nu+n}]. \tag{3.2}$$

It may be shown that the second $(n+1)q \times (n+1)q$ matrix on the left is invertible if and only if $\det \mathbf{G}_1 \neq \mathbf{0}$. Thus in the full-rank case $\rho = q$, the coefficients $\mathbf{A}_k^{(n)}$ can be uniquely determined.

This method involves solving a system of linear equations. It would be feasible for so-called *weakly* (or *wide sense*) *N-Markovian processes*, i.e., cf. [4, pp. 90, 506], weakly stationary ones for which

$$\hat{\mathbf{f}}_\nu \underset{d}{=} (\mathbf{f}_\nu \mid \mathfrak{S}(\mathbf{f}_{-k}, k \geq 0)) = (\mathbf{f}_\nu \mid \mathfrak{S}(\mathbf{f}_{-k}, 0 \leq k \leq N)), \qquad \nu \geq 1, \tag{3.3}$$

and where, consequently, for a given $\nu \geq 1$ there is a fixed set of $N+1$ matrices $\mathbf{A}_0, \dots, \mathbf{A}_N$ such that

$$\hat{\mathbf{f}} = \mathbf{A}_0\mathbf{f}_0 + \mathbf{A}_1\mathbf{f}_{-1} + \cdots + \mathbf{A}_N\mathbf{f}_{-N}.$$

One might even be able to shorten the computation by adapting for $q > 1$ the interesting devices suggested by Levinson [15, §3] for $q = 1$. But for other types of processes, as time flows by and our data accumulate, we would like to let the n in (3.1) increase, and thereby utilize our additional data. This would mean solving larger and larger linear systems *de novo*, a procedure of questionable efficiency.

It was Wiener's belief that an efficacious computational procedure would emerge from a deeper analysis of the problem. We now turn to such analysis.

4. THE SHIFT OPERATOR AND WOLD-ZASUHIN DECOMPOSITION

Let $(\mathbf{f}_n)_{-\infty}^{\infty}$ be a q-ple, weakly stationary S.P. Then as Kolmogorov [12] showed, there is a unique unitary operator U on $\mathcal{M}_\infty \subseteq \mathcal{H}$ onto $\mathcal{M}_\infty$ such that[6]

$$U(f_n^i) = f_{n+1}^i, \qquad -\infty < n < \infty, \quad 1 \leq i \leq q. \tag{4.1}$$

U or rather its inflation $\mathbf{U}$, defined by

$$\mathbf{U}(\mathbf{f}) = (Uf^1, \cdots, Uf^q), \qquad \mathbf{f} = (f^i)_{i=1}^q \in \mathcal{H}^q, \tag{4.2}$$

[6] U can, of course, be extended (nonuniquely) to a unitary operator on $\mathcal{H}$ onto $\mathcal{H}$.

is called the *shift operator* of the S.P. Obviously $\mathbf{U}$ is an operator on $\mathscr{M}_\infty$ onto $\mathscr{M}_\infty$ such that

$$\mathbf{U}(\mathbf{f}_n) = \mathbf{f}_{n+1}, \qquad -\infty < n < \infty. \tag{4.3}$$

Now

$$U^*(\mathscr{M}_n) = \mathscr{M}_{n-1} \subseteq \mathscr{M}_n.$$

Hence[7]

$$V \underset{d}{=} \text{Rstr.}_{\mathscr{M}_0} U^* = \textit{an isometry on } \mathscr{M}_0 \textit{ onto } \mathscr{M}_{-1}. \tag{4.4}$$

The theory of this isometry V subsumes the *time-domain analysis* of our S.P., as we shall now indicate.

Since the appearance of von Neumann and Murray's work on operators, it has been known in some implicit form that if V is an isometry on a Hilbert space $\mathscr{H}$ onto $R \subseteq \mathscr{H}$, then

$$\mathscr{H} = \bigcap_{k=0}^{\infty} V^k(\mathscr{H}) + \sum_{k=0}^{\infty} V^k(R^\perp), \qquad V^j(R^\perp) \perp V^k(R^\perp),$$

where the two subspaces on the right side of the equality are themselves orthogonal. But the great importance of this result has emerged only recently; cf. Halmos [6]. As indicated in [22, 2.8] it extends to $\mathscr{H}^q$: if $\mathbf{V}$ is the inflation to $\mathscr{H}^q$ of an isometry on $\mathscr{H}$ and $\mathbf{R} \subseteq \mathscr{H}^q$ is the range of $\mathbf{V}$, then

$$\mathscr{H}^q = \bigcap_{k=0}^{\infty} \mathbf{V}^k(\mathscr{H}^q) + \sum_{k=0}^{\infty} \mathbf{V}^k(\mathbf{R}^\perp), \qquad \mathbf{V}^j(\mathbf{R}^\perp) \perp \mathbf{V}^j(\mathbf{R}^\perp), \tag{4.5}$$

where the subspaces on the right side of the equality are again orthogonal but in the sense of (2.4).

Turning to our S.P., and applying (4.5) with $\mathscr{H} = \mathscr{M}_0$ and V as in (4.4), we get at once

$$\mathscr{M}_0 = \mathscr{M}_{-\infty} + \sum_{k=0}^{\infty} \mathbf{U}^{-k}(\mathscr{M}_{-1}^\perp \cap \mathscr{M}_0).$$

Now, and this is crucial, we can show that for a *nondeterministic S.P.*,

$$\mathscr{M}_{-1}^\perp \cap \mathscr{M}_0 = \mathfrak{S}(\mathbf{g}_0), \qquad \text{where} \quad \mathbf{g}_0 \underset{d}{=} \mathbf{f}_0 - (\mathbf{f}_0 \mid \mathscr{M}_{-1}) \neq \mathbf{0},$$

which means roughly that $\mathbf{R}^\perp = \mathscr{M}_{-1}^\perp \cap \mathscr{M}_0$ is "one-dimensional." Letting $\mathbf{g}_k = \mathbf{U}^k \mathbf{g}_0$, we readily obtain for any n,

$$\mathscr{M}_n = \mathscr{M}_{-\infty} + \sum_{k=0}^{\infty} \mathfrak{S}(\mathbf{g}_{n-k}), \qquad \mathscr{M}_{-\infty} \perp \sum_{k=-\infty}^{\infty} \mathfrak{S}(\mathbf{g}_k). \tag{4.6}$$

This is the *Wold-Zasuhin decomposition* of the subspace $\mathscr{M}_n$.[8]

[7] $\text{Rstr.}_D A$ denotes the restriction of the operator A to the subset D of its domain.

[8] For $q = 1$, it was first proved by Wold [38] in 1938, and extended to continuous time by Karhunen [11] and Hanner [7]. For $q > 1$, it was conjectured by Zasuhin [43], and proved in the full-rank case by Doob [4] and in general by Wiener and the writer [36, I]. The present method of obtaining it is given in [22, §3.1].

In this decomposition the vector

$$\mathbf{g}_n \underset{d}{=} \mathbf{U}^n \mathbf{g}_0, \qquad \text{where} \quad \mathbf{g}_0 \underset{d}{=} \mathbf{f}_0 - (\mathbf{f}_0 \mid \mathscr{M}_{-1}), \tag{4.7}$$

is called the nth *innovation vector* of our S.P., and $(\mathbf{g}_n)_{-\infty}^{\infty}$ is called its *innovation S.P.* Obviously,

$$(\mathbf{g}_m, \mathbf{g}_n) = \delta_{mn} \mathbf{G}, \qquad \text{where} \quad \mathbf{G} \underset{d}{=} (\mathbf{g}_0, \mathbf{g}_0), \tag{4.8}$$

and since $\mathbf{U}\mathbf{g}_0 = \mathbf{f}_1 - (\mathbf{f}_1 \mid \mathscr{M}_0) = \mathbf{f}_1 - \hat{\mathbf{f}}_1$ [cf. (2.16)], we see that

$$\mathbf{G} = \mathbf{G}_1 = \textit{the prediction error matrix for lag } 1. \tag{4.9}$$

It is convenient to "normalize" the innovation vectors. For this we think of the matrix $\mathbf{G}$ as a linear operator on $\mathscr{C}^q$ to $\mathscr{C}^q$, $\mathscr{C}$ being the complex number field. Let the matrix $\mathbf{J}$ represent the projection on $\mathscr{C}^q$ onto the range of $\mathbf{G}$. It is easy to show that *there is a unique $q \times q$ matrix $\mathbf{H}$ such that*

$$\mathbf{H}\mathbf{J}^{\perp} = \mathbf{J}^{\perp} = \mathbf{J}^{\perp}\mathbf{H}, \qquad \mathbf{H}\mathbf{G}^{1/2} = \mathbf{J} = \mathbf{G}^{1/2}\mathbf{H}. \tag{4.10}$$

Indeed,

$$\mathbf{H} = (\mathbf{G}^{1/2} + \mathbf{J}^{\perp})^{-1}, \tag{4.11}$$

which shows that

$$\mathbf{H} \textit{ is invertible, hermitian, and positive-definite.} \tag{4.12}$$

Now let $\mathbf{h}_n = \mathbf{H}\mathbf{g}_n$. Then we find, cf. [22, (3.4) et seq.],

$$\mathbf{g}_n = \mathbf{J}\mathbf{g}_n = \mathbf{G}^{1/2}\mathbf{h}_n, \qquad (\mathbf{h}_m, \mathbf{h}_n) = \delta_{mn}\mathbf{J}, \qquad \mathbf{J}^{\perp}\mathbf{h}_n = \mathbf{0}. \tag{4.13}$$

We call $\mathbf{h}_n$ the nth *normalized innovation vector* of our S.P., and $(\mathbf{h}_n)_{-\infty}^{\infty}$ its *normalized innovation S.P.* In the full-rank case $\rho = q$, we have $\det \mathbf{G} \neq 0$, and so we can define the $\mathbf{h}_n$ by the simple equation $\mathbf{h}_n = (\mathbf{G}^{1/2})^{-1}\mathbf{g}_n$. Since in this case $\mathbf{J} = \mathbf{I}$, we have $(\mathbf{h}_m, \mathbf{h}_n) = \delta_{mn}\mathbf{I}$.

As shown in [22, 3.2, 3.5] the decomposition (4.6) of the subspace $\mathscr{M}_n$ yields a decomposition the process $(\mathbf{f}_n)_{-\infty}^{\infty}$ itself:

$$\mathbf{f}_n = \mathbf{u}_n + \mathbf{v}_n, \qquad \mathbf{u}_m \perp \mathbf{v}_n, \qquad -\infty < m, n < \infty, \tag{4.14}$$

where $(\mathbf{u}_n)_{-\infty}^{\infty}$ is a (purely nondeterministic) one-sided moving average of the normalized innovations and has the same rank as $(\mathbf{f}_n)_{-\infty}^{\infty}$, and $(\mathbf{v}_n)_{-\infty}^{\infty}$ is purely deterministic. More fully,[9]

$$\mathbf{u}_n = \sum_{k=0}^{\infty} \mathbf{A}_k \mathbf{G}^{1/2} \mathbf{h}_{-k}, \qquad \sum_{k=0}^{\infty} |\mathbf{A}_k \mathbf{G}^{1/2}|_E^2 < \infty, \tag{4.15}$$

[9] The Euclidean norm $|\mathbf{A}|_E$ of a matrix $\mathbf{A} = [a_{ij}]$ is defined by

$$|\mathbf{A}|_E^2 = \operatorname{trace} \mathbf{A}\mathbf{A}^* = \sum_{i=1}^{q} \sum_{j=1}^{q} |a_{ij}|^2.$$

where

$$\mathbf{A}_k\mathbf{G}^{1/2} = (\mathbf{f}_0, \mathbf{h}_{-k}), \quad \mathbf{A}_0\mathbf{G}^{1/2} = \mathbf{G}^{1/2}, \quad \mathbf{A}_0\mathbf{g}_0 = \mathbf{g}_0, \quad \mathbf{A}_k\mathbf{G} = (\mathbf{f}_0, \mathbf{g}_{-k}) \tag{4.16}$$

are unique, although the $\mathbf{A}_k$ are not unique. Also,

$$\mathbf{v}_n = (\mathbf{f}_n \mid \mathscr{M}_{-\infty}). \tag{4.17}$$

The relations (4.14) to (4.17) constitute an alternative form of the Wold-Zasuhin decomposition.

It is well known that the conditions (4.14) and

$$\begin{aligned} &(\mathbf{u}_n)_{-\infty}^{\infty} \textit{ is purely nondeterministic,} \\ &(\mathbf{v}_n)_{-\infty}^{\infty} \textit{ is deterministic} \end{aligned} \tag{4.18}$$

do not together characterize the Wold-Zasuhin decomposition. An extra condition is needed, which is usually stated (with an obvious notation) in the form

$$\mathscr{M}_n^{(u)} \subseteq \mathscr{M}_n^{(f)} \quad \textit{for some integer } n.^{10} \tag{4.19}$$

Does (4.19) work with $n = \infty$?[11] Recently Robertson [26, App. B] has shown that the answer is negative for $q > 1$, but that the stronger condition

$$\mathscr{M}_\infty^{(u)} \subseteq \mathscr{M}_\infty^{(f)} \qquad \text{and} \qquad \operatorname{rank}\,(\mathbf{u}_n)_{-\infty}^{\infty} = \operatorname{rank}\,(\mathbf{f}_n)_{-\infty}^{\infty} \tag{4.20}$$

does work for any q; i.e., (4.14), (4.18), and (4.20) together characterize the Wold-Zasuhin decomposition. A recent result of Robertson [27] on the wandering subspaces of unitary operators yields a nice spectral-free proof.

5. SPECTRAL ANALYSIS

The shift operator U of our q-ple weakly stationary S.P. $(\mathbf{f}_n)_{-\infty}^{\infty}$ has a spectral resolution:

$$U = \int_0^{2\pi} e^{-i\theta} E(d\theta), \tag{5.1}$$

where E is a projection-valued measure over $([0, 2\pi], \mathscr{B})$, $\mathscr{B}$ being the family of Borel subsets of $[0, 2\pi]$. By taking the inflation $\mathbf{E}$ of E we associate two new measures with our S.P.:

(a) A *$\mathscr{H}^q$-valued countably additive, orthogonally scattered* (c.a.o.s.) *measure* ξ, defined by

$$\xi(B) \underset{d}{=} \mathbf{E}(B)\mathbf{f}_0, \qquad B \in \mathscr{B}, \tag{5.2}$$

[10] And hence by stationarity for all integers n (and also $n = \infty$).

[11] With $n = \infty$ (4.19) reads: $(\mathbf{u}_n)_{-\infty}^{\infty}$ is subordinate to $(\mathbf{f}_n)_{-\infty}^{\infty}$; cf. §8.

so-called because of its decisive property[12]

$$B, C \in \mathscr{B} \text{ and } B, C \text{ disjoint} \quad \Rightarrow \quad \xi(B) \perp \xi(C).$$

(b) A $q \times q$ *nonnegative hermitian matrix-valued measure* $\mathbf{M}$ defined by

$$\mathbf{M}(B) \underset{d}{=} (\mathbf{E}(B)\mathbf{f}_0, \mathbf{E}(B)\mathbf{f}_0) = (\xi(B), \xi(B)), \qquad B \in \mathscr{B}. \tag{5.3}$$

We then introduce the well-known $q \times q$ *spectral distribution* $\mathbf{F}$ of our S.P. by the definition

$$\mathbf{F}(\theta) \underset{d}{=} 2\pi\, \mathbf{M}(0, \theta], \qquad 0 \leq \theta \leq 2\pi. \tag{5.4}$$

Likewise, one could define the q-ple *process of orthogonal increments* $(\boldsymbol{\eta}_\theta, \theta \in (0, 2\pi])$ associated with our process by

$$\boldsymbol{\eta}_\theta \underset{d}{=} 2\pi\, \xi(0, \theta], \qquad 0 \leq \theta \leq 2\pi.$$

Next, for a complex-valued function ϕ on $[0, 2\pi]$ we define the integrals

$$\int_0^{2\pi} \phi(\theta)\xi(d\theta), \quad \int_0^{2\pi} \phi(\theta)\mathbf{M}(d\theta), \quad \int_0^{2\pi} \phi(\theta)\, d\mathbf{F}(\theta)$$

to be

$$\left(\int_0^{2\pi} \phi(\theta)\xi^i(d\theta)\right)_{i=1}^{q}, \quad \left[\int_0^{2\pi} \phi(\theta)M_{ij}(d\theta)\right], \quad \left[\int_0^{2\pi} \phi(\theta)\, dF_{ij}(\theta)\right].$$

These definitions make sense, since the components ξ^i of ξ are $\mathscr{H}$-valued c.a.o.s. measures for which a theory of integration akin to that given in Doob's book [4, Chap. IX, §2] is available, and the entries M_{ij} and F_{ij} of $\mathbf{M}$ and $\mathbf{F}$ are complex-valued measures, and complex-valued functions of bounded variation. With these definitions we easily get the *spectral representation* of our S.P. and of its covariance (cf. [36, I, 7.1]):

$$\mathbf{f}_n = \int_0^{2\pi} e^{-ni\theta}\mathbf{E}(d\theta)\mathbf{f}_0 = \int_0^{2\pi} e^{-ni\theta}\xi(d\theta), \tag{5.5}$$

$$\boldsymbol{\Gamma}_n = \int_0^{2\pi} e^{-ni\theta}\mathbf{M}(d\theta) = \frac{1}{2\pi}\int_0^{2\pi} e^{-ni\theta}\, d\mathbf{F}(\theta). \tag{5.6}$$

Finally, we define *matricial Riemann-Stieltjes integrals* of the form $\int_0^{2\pi} \boldsymbol{\Phi}(\theta)\, d\mathbf{F}(\theta)\boldsymbol{\Psi}(\theta)$, where $\boldsymbol{\Phi}$ and $\boldsymbol{\Psi}$ are *continuous* matrix-valued functions,

[12] With the probabilistic interpretation of $\mathscr{H}$, viz. $\mathscr{H} = L_2(\Omega, \mathscr{F}, P)$, ξ becomes a *q-variate random measure* over $([0, 2\pi], \mathscr{B})$, but with the nice property that the q-variates corresponding to disjoint Borel sets are uncorrelated.

and $\mathbf{F}$ a matrix-valued function of *bounded variation*, by adopting the classical pattern; cf. [36, I, §4]. From (5.6) we then get

$$\left(\sum_{j\in J}\mathbf{A}_j\mathbf{f}_{-j},\sum_{k\in K}\mathbf{B}_k\mathbf{f}_{-k}\right)=\frac{1}{2\pi}\int_0^{2\pi}\left(\sum_{j\in J}\mathbf{A}_je^{ji\theta}\right)d\mathbf{F}(\theta)\left(\sum_{k\in K}\mathbf{B}_ke^{ki\theta}\right)^*, \tag{5.7}$$

where J and K are finite sets of integers and $\mathbf{A}_j$ and $\mathbf{B}_k$ are $q\times q$ matrices; cf. [36, I, 7.9(a)].

It is natural to ask if the equailty (5.7) continues to hold when limits of linear combinations and of trigonometrical polynomials are taken on the two sides. This raises the preliminary question as to how $\int_0^{2\pi}\mathbf{\Phi}(\theta)\,d\mathbf{F}(\theta)\mathbf{\Psi}(\theta)$ or equivalently $\int_0^{2\pi}\mathbf{\Phi}(\theta)\mathbf{M}(d\theta)\mathbf{\Psi}(\theta)$ is to be defined when $\mathbf{\Phi}$ and $\mathbf{\Psi}$ are any (discontinuous) matrix-valued functions on $[0, 2\pi]$ with Borel measurable entries. We can pose this question for any nonnegative hermitian matrix-valued measure $\mathbf{M}$, not just the one defined in (5.3). The further development of the spectral theory of q-ple processes hinges on the answer (§6).

6. THE SPACE $\mathbf{L}_{2,\mathbf{M}}$ FOR A NONNEGATIVE HERMITIAN MATRIX-VALUED MEASURE

Let $\mathbf{M}$ be any $q\times q$ nonnegative hermitian matrix-valued measure over $([0, 2\pi], \mathscr{B})$ and suppose that we have in some way defined the integrals

$$\int_0^{2\pi}\mathbf{\Phi}(\theta)\mathbf{M}(d\theta)\mathbf{\Psi}(\theta) \tag{$*$}$$

for $q\times q$ matrix-valued functions $\mathbf{\Phi}$ and $\mathbf{\Psi}$ with Borel measurable entries. It would then be natural to define the $\mathbf{L}_2$ class with respect to the measure $\mathbf{M}$ by

$$\mathbf{L}_{2,\mathbf{M}}=\mathbf{L}_2([0, 2\pi], \mathscr{B}, \mathbf{M})\underset{d}{=}\left\{\mathbf{\Phi}\colon \int_0^{2\pi}\mathbf{\Phi}(\theta)\mathbf{M}(d\theta)\mathbf{\Phi}^*(\theta)\quad\text{exists}\right\}. \tag{6.1}$$

Now one of the fundamental properties of the class $L_{2,M}$, when $q=1$, i.e., when Φ and M are complex-valued, is its completeness under the norm

$$|\Phi|_M=\left[\int_0^{2\pi}|\Phi(\theta)|^2M(d\theta)\right]^{1/2}.$$

This is the core of the celebrated Riesz-Fischer theorem. For $q>1$, the corresponding norm would appear to be

$$|\mathbf{\Phi}|_M=\left[\operatorname{trace}\int_0^{2\pi}\mathbf{\Phi}(\theta)\mathbf{M}(d\theta)\mathbf{\Phi}^*(\theta)\right]^{1/2}. \tag{6.2}$$

Our definition of the integral $(*)$ would be useless were the space $\mathbf{L}_{2,\mathbf{M}}$ defined in (6.1) to be incomplete under the norm (6.2). We are thus faced with the following problem:

Problem. *Define the integrals* $(*)$ *in such a way that the space* $\mathbf{L}_{2,\mathbf{M}}$ *defined in* (6.1) *is complete under the norm* (6.2).

This problem was settled independently around 1963 by Rosenberg [32, §3] for rectangular matrices $\mathbf{\Phi}$ and $\mathbf{\Psi}$ and by Rosanov [31, Chapter I, §7] for vectorial $\mathbf{\Phi}$ and $\mathbf{\Psi}$. We shall follow Rosenberg's more inclusive treatment. He observed that a $q \times q$ nonnegative hermitian matrix-valued measure $\mathbf{M}$ is invariably absolutely continuous with respect to the nonnegative real measure trace $\mathbf{M}$. Writing $\tau\mathbf{M}$ for trace $\mathbf{M}$, it follows that each entry of $\mathbf{M}$ has a Radon-Nikodym derivative with respect to $\tau\mathbf{M}$. The $q \times q$ matrix $d\mathbf{M}/d\tau\mathbf{M}$ of these derivatives has nice properties, and this suggests adoption of the definition

$$\int_0^{2\pi} \mathbf{\Phi}(\theta)\mathbf{M}(d\theta)\mathbf{\Psi}(\theta) \underset{d}{=} \int_0^{2\pi} \mathbf{\Phi}(\theta) \frac{d\mathbf{M}}{d\tau\mathbf{M}}(\theta)\, \mathbf{\Psi}(\theta) \cdot \tau\mathbf{M}(d\theta), \tag{6.3}$$

the last integral being defined (earlier) as the matrix of Lebesgue integrals of the entries of $\mathbf{\Phi}(d\mathbf{M}/d\tau\mathbf{M})\mathbf{\Psi}$ with respect to the ordinary measure $\tau\mathbf{M}$. Rosenberg showed that this definition solves the problem. Thus

6.4. Theorem. (Rosenberg-Rosanov). *With the definitions* (6.3) *and* (6.1) *the space* $\mathbf{L}_{2,\mathbf{M}}$ *is complete under the norm* (6.2).[13]

In case the measure $\mathbf{M}$ is absolutely continuous with respect to Lebesgue measure L, it follows at once from simple properties of Radon-Nikodym derivatives that (6.3) is equivalent to the simpler definition

$$\int_0^{2\pi} \mathbf{\Phi}(\theta)\mathbf{M}(d\theta)\mathbf{\Psi}(\theta) \underset{d}{=} \frac{1}{2\pi}\int_0^{2\pi} \mathbf{\Phi}(\theta)\mathbf{F}'(\theta)\mathbf{\Psi}(\theta)\, d\theta, \tag{6.5}$$

where $\mathbf{F}$ is as in (5.4). The work of Rosenberg and Rosanov thus subsumes the partial results obtained previously on the basis of (6.5), e.g., those in [36, II, §4].

Having defined the integrals $(*)$, we can introduce in $\mathbf{L}_{2,\mathbf{M}}$ *matrix- and complex-valued inner products* by the definitions

$$(\mathbf{\Phi}, \mathbf{\Psi})_M \underset{d}{=} \int_0^{2\pi} \mathbf{\Phi}(\theta)\mathbf{M}(d\theta)\mathbf{\Psi}^*(\theta), \qquad \mathbf{\Phi}, \mathbf{\Psi} \in \mathbf{L}_{2,\mathbf{M}}, \tag{6.6}$$

$$((\mathbf{\Phi}, \mathbf{\Psi}))_M \underset{d}{=} \operatorname{trace}(\mathbf{\Phi}, \mathbf{\Psi})_M. \tag{6.7}$$

[13] Actually Rosenberg takes rectangular $\mathbf{\Phi}$ and $\mathbf{\Psi}$ in Definition (6.3), of sizes $p \times q$ and $q \times r$, respectively, and his result [32, §3.9] applies to all the $\mathbf{L}_{2,\mathbf{M}}$ spaces obtained with different choices of p.

The norm introduced in (6.2) can then be written

$$|\mathbf{\Phi}|_M = [((\mathbf{\Phi}, \mathbf{\Phi}))_M]^{1/2}. \tag{6.8}$$

Equations (6.6) to (6.8) are comparable to (2.1), (2.5), and (2.6). The fact that $\mathbf{L}_{2,\mathbf{M}}$ is complete under the norm (6.8) thus shows that $\mathbf{L}_{2,\mathbf{M}}$ is Hilbertian in the sense of §2. Thus *every nonnegative hermitian matrix-valued measure* $\mathbf{M}$ *generates a Hilbertian space* $\mathbf{L}_{2,\mathbf{M}}$.

This result holds in particular for the measure $\mathbf{M}$, defined in (5.3), which is associated with the S.P. $(\mathbf{f}_n)_{-\infty}^{\infty}$. Thus every q-ple, weakly stationary S.P. possesses two Hilbertian spaces $\mathscr{M}_\infty \subseteq \mathscr{H}^q$ and $\mathbf{L}_{2,\mathbf{M}}$. We shall refer to them as the *temporal and spectral spaces* of the S.P. For $q = 1$ we know that they are isomorphic Hilbert spaces under a natural correspondence; cf. [12, (2.7)]. This isomorphism survives when $q > 1$ (§7).

7. ISOMORPHISM BETWEEN THE TEMPORAL AND SPECTRAL SPACES

Let ξ be any $\mathscr{H}^q$-valued, c.a.o.s. measure over $([0, 2\pi], \mathscr{B})$ (cf. §5) and let

$$\mathbf{M}_\xi(B) = (\xi(B), \xi(B)), \qquad B \in \mathscr{B}.$$

Then $\mathbf{M}_\xi$ is clearly a $q \times q$ nonnegative hermitian matrix-valued measure. The crucial fact that the associated space $\mathbf{L}_{2,\mathbf{M}_\xi}$ has a (complete) Hilbertian structure enables us to define integrals of the type $\int_0^{2\pi} \mathbf{\Phi}(\theta)\xi(d\theta)$, where $\mathbf{\Phi} \in \mathbf{L}_{2,\mathbf{M}_\xi}$, by essentially following the procedure adopted for stochastic integration in Doob's book [4, Chap. IX, §2], and to prove the following theorem (for details cf. Rosenberg [32, §4]):

7.1. Theorem. *Let* (i) ξ *be any* $\mathscr{H}^q$*-valued c.a.o.s. measure over* $([0, 2\pi], \mathscr{B})$; (ii) $\mathbf{M}_\xi(B) \underset{d}{=} (\xi(B), \xi(B))$, $B \in \mathscr{B}$; (iii) $\mathscr{S}^{(\xi)} \underset{d}{=} \mathfrak{S}\{\xi(B) \colon B \in \mathscr{B}\} \subseteq \mathscr{H}^q$.[14]

Then (a) $\mathbf{g} \in \mathscr{S}^{(\xi)} \iff \exists \mathbf{\Phi} \in \mathbf{L}_{2,\mathbf{M}_\xi}$ *such that* $\mathbf{g} = \int_0^{2\pi} \mathbf{\Phi}(\theta)\xi(d\theta)$;

(b) *the* $\mathbf{\Phi}$ *in* (a) *is uniquely defined up to a set of zero* $\mathbf{M}_\xi$ *measure*;

(c) *the correspondence* $\mathbf{\Phi} \to \int_0^{2\pi} \mathbf{\Phi}(\theta)\xi(d\theta)$ *is an isomorphism on* $\mathbf{L}_{2,\mathbf{M}}$ *onto the subspace* $\mathscr{S}^{(\xi)}$ *of* $\mathscr{H}^q$; i.e., *it is one-to-one on* $\mathbf{L}_{2,\mathbf{M}_\xi}$ *onto* $\mathscr{S}^{(\xi)}$ *and* [cf. (6.6)],

$$(\mathbf{\Phi}, \mathbf{\Psi})_{M_\xi} = \left(\int_0^{2\pi} \mathbf{\Phi}(\theta)\xi(d\theta), \int_0^{2\pi} \mathbf{\Psi}(\theta)\xi(d\theta)\right), \qquad \mathbf{\Phi}, \mathbf{\Psi} \in \mathbf{L}_{2,\mathbf{M}_\xi}.$$

[14] See footnote 5 for the meaning of the symbol $\mathfrak{S}$.

Each $\mathscr{H}^q$-valued, c.a.o.s. measure thus carries with it two isomorphic Hilbertian spaces $\mathscr{S}^{(\xi)}$ and $\mathbf{L}_{2,\mathbf{M}_\xi}$. This applies in particular to the c.a.o.s. measure, defined in (5.2), which is associated with the S.P. $(\mathbf{f}_n)_{-\infty}^{\infty}$. But now $\xi(B) = \mathbf{E}(B)\mathbf{f}_0$, and so we have

$$\mathscr{S}^{(\xi)} = \mathfrak{S}\{\mathbf{E}(B)\mathbf{f}_0 : B \in \mathscr{B}\} = \mathfrak{S}\{\mathbf{U}^n\mathbf{f}_0 : -\infty < n < \infty\} = \mathscr{M}_\infty . \quad (7.2)$$

Here the first and third equalities are obvious, and the second stems from the basic connection between U and E given in (5.1), as is well known from the theory of cyclic subspaces of Hilbert spaces. We thus get as a corollary of (7.1) the result:

7.3. Theorem. *For a q-ple, weakly stationary S.P.* $(\mathbf{f}_n)_{-\infty}^{\infty}$, *the correspondence*

$$\mathbf{\Phi} \to \int_0^{2\pi} \mathbf{\Phi}(\theta)\mathbf{E}(d\theta)\mathbf{f}_0$$

is an isomorphism on the spectral space $\mathbf{L}_{2,\mathbf{M}}$ *onto the temporal space* $\mathscr{M}_\infty \subseteq \mathscr{H}^q$.

This theorem shows of course that the equality (5.7) holds when limits are taken in the $\mathscr{H}^q$ and $\mathbf{L}_{2,\mathbf{M}}$ topologies on the two sides.

8. CROSS-COVARIANCE AND SPECTRA. SUBORDINATION

To treat simultaneously two or more q-ple, weakly stationary S.P.'s $(\mathbf{f}_n)_{-\infty}^{\infty}$, $(\mathbf{g}_n)_{-\infty}^{\infty}$, ..., it is convenient to use subscripts or superscripts f, g, ... to distinguish their possessions, e.g., to denote their temporal spaces by $\mathscr{M}_\infty^{(f)}$, $\mathscr{M}_\infty^{(g)}$, ... The processes $(\mathbf{f}_n)_{-\infty}^{\infty}$ and $(\mathbf{g}_n)_{-\infty}^{\infty}$ are said to be *stationarily cross-correlated*, if and only if the $q \times q$ Gram matrix

$$(\mathbf{f}_m, \mathbf{g}_n) = \mathbf{\Gamma}_{m-n}^{(f,g)} \quad (8.1)$$

depends on $m - n$ alone. The bisequence $(\mathbf{\Gamma}_k^{(f,g)})_{k=-\infty}^{\infty}$ is then called the *cross-covariance bisequence of* $(\mathbf{f}_n)_{-\infty}^{\infty}$ *with* $(\mathbf{g}_n)_{-\infty}^{\infty}$. Obviously $\mathbf{\Gamma}_k^{(f,f)}$ is the $\mathbf{\Gamma}_k$ introduced in 2.10.

By a slight extension of an argument of Kolmogorov [12, Thm. 1] it follows that if $(\mathbf{f}_n)_{-\infty}^{\infty}$ and $(\mathbf{g}_n)_{-\infty}^{\infty}$ are stationarily cross-correlated, then there is a unique unitary operator U on the subspace clos.$\{\mathscr{M}_\infty^{(f)} + \mathscr{M}_\infty^{(g)}\}$ onto itself such that $Uf_n{}^i = f_{n+1}^i$ and $Ug_n{}^i = g_{n+1}^i$, $1 \leq i \leq q$. In dealing simultaneously with several such processes it is therefore legitimate to start out with a single shift operator U on $\mathscr{H}$ to $\mathscr{H}$:

$$U = \int_0^{2\pi} e^{-i\theta}E(d\theta) \quad (8.2)$$

and to suppose that our S.P.'s are of the form $(\mathbf{U}^n\mathbf{f})_{-\infty}^{\infty}$, $(\mathbf{U}^n\mathbf{g})_{-\infty}^{\infty}$, ..., where $\mathbf{f}, \mathbf{g}, \ldots \in \mathscr{H}^q$, and $\mathbf{U}$ is the inflation of U.

With each ordered pair of $\mathbf{f}, \mathbf{g} \in \mathscr{H}^q$ we associate the $q \times q$ matrix-valued *cross-measure* $\mathbf{M}_{fg}$, no longer hermitian-valued, and the $q \times q$ *cross-spectral distribution* $\mathbf{F}_{fg}$ defined by

$$\mathbf{M}_{fg}(B) \underset{d}{=} (\mathbf{E}(B)\mathbf{f}, \mathbf{E}(B)\mathbf{g},) \qquad B \in \mathscr{B}, \tag{8.3}$$

$$\mathbf{F}_{fg}(\theta) \underset{d}{=} 2\pi\, \mathbf{M}_{fg}(0, \theta], \qquad 0 \le \theta \le 2\pi. \tag{8.4}$$

Obviously,

$$\mathbf{M}_{gf}(B) = \mathbf{M}^*_{fg}(B), \qquad B \in \mathscr{B}$$

and

$$\mathbf{\Gamma}_n^{(f,g)} = \int_0^{2\pi} e^{-ni\theta}\mathbf{M}_{fg}(d\theta) = \frac{1}{2\pi}\int_0^{2\pi} e^{-ni\theta}\, d\mathbf{F}_{fg}(\theta). \tag{8.5}$$

With $\mathbf{g} = \mathbf{f}$, the $\mathbf{M}_{ff}$, $\mathbf{F}_{ff}$, and $\mathbf{\Gamma}_n^{(f,f)}$ we get are of course the $\mathbf{M}$, $\mathbf{F}$, and $\mathbf{\Gamma}_n$ introduced for the S.P. $(\mathbf{f}_n)_{-\infty}^{\infty}$ in (5.3), (5.4), and (5.6).

We can define integrals of the form $\int_0^{2\pi} \mathbf{\Phi}(\theta)\mathbf{M}(d\theta)\mathbf{\Psi}(\theta)$, where $\mathbf{M}$ is *any* (nonhermitian) matrix-valued measure, by a slight extension of (6.3):

$$\int_0^{2\pi} \mathbf{\Phi}(\theta)\mathbf{M}(d\theta)\mathbf{\Psi}(\theta) \underset{d}{=} \int_0^{2\pi} \mathbf{\Phi}(\theta)\frac{d\mathbf{M}}{d\sigma}(\theta)\,\mathbf{\Psi}(\theta)\cdot\sigma(d\theta), \tag{8.6}$$

where σ is not necessarily $\tau\mathbf{M}$ but some nonnegative real measure with respect to which $\mathbf{M}$ is absolutely continuous. We can show that the definition does not depend on the choice of σ. We can then prove the following basic result by using a slightly extended version of the operational calculus:[15]

8.7. Theorem. *Let* (i) $\mathbf{f}, \mathbf{g} \in \mathscr{H}^q$, (ii) $\hat{\mathbf{g}} = (\mathbf{g} \mid \mathscr{M}_\infty^{(f)})$, (iii) $\mathbf{\Phi}_{\hat{g}} \in \mathbf{L}_{2,\mathbf{M}_{ff}}$ *be the isomorph of* $\hat{\mathbf{g}}$, i.e.,

$$\hat{\mathbf{g}} = (\mathbf{g} \mid \mathscr{M}_\infty^{(f)}) = \int_0^{2\pi} \mathbf{\Phi}_{\hat{g}}(\theta)\mathbf{E}(d\theta)\mathbf{f}_0.$$

Then

(a) $$\mathbf{M}_{gf}(B) = \mathbf{M}_{\hat{g}f}(B) = \int_B \mathbf{\Phi}_{\hat{g}}(\theta)\mathbf{M}_{ff}(d\theta), \qquad B \in \mathscr{B}.$$

(b) $$\mathbf{M}_{\hat{g}\hat{g}}(B) = \int_B \mathbf{\Phi}_{\hat{g}}(\theta)\mathbf{M}_{ff}(d\theta)\mathbf{\Phi}_{\hat{g}}{}^*(\theta) = \int_B \mathbf{\Phi}_{\hat{g}}(\theta)\mathbf{M}_{f\hat{g}}(d\theta), \qquad B \in \mathscr{B}.$$

[15] Unfortunately there is no published work which treats the results of this section from our point of view. A treatment from a somewhat different standpoint is available in Rosanov [31, Chapter I, §§7, 8].

Remark. 8.7(a) suggests that $\mathbf{\Phi}_{\hat{g}}$ is in some sense the Radon-Nikodym derivative of $\mathbf{M}_{gf}$ with respect to $\mathbf{M}_{ff}$, and suggests writing

$$\hat{\mathbf{g}} = (\mathbf{g} \mid \mathscr{M}_{\infty}^{(f)}) = \int_0^{2\pi} \frac{d\mathbf{M}_{gf}}{d\mathbf{M}_{ff}}(\theta)\, \mathbf{E}(d\theta)\mathbf{f}. \qquad (*)$$

But whereas for $q = 1$, $(dM_{gf}/dM_{ff})(\theta)$ is a *Besicovitch derivative* [1], i.e. equals

$$\lim_{h \to 0+} \frac{M_{gf}(\theta - h, \theta + h)}{M_{ff}(\theta - h, \theta + h)}, \quad \text{a.e. } (M_{ff});$$

it is not clear if such a limit can be defined for matricial measures, and hence for $q > 1$ little is gained by rewriting 8.7(a) in the form $(*)$.[15′]

Following Kolmogorov [12, §4] we say that the S.P. $(\mathbf{U}^n\mathbf{g})_{-\infty}^{\infty}$ is *subordinate* to the S.P. $(\mathbf{U}^n\mathbf{f})_{-\infty}^{\infty}$, briefly, $\mathbf{g}$ is subordinate to $\mathbf{f}$, if and only if $\mathscr{M}_{\infty}^{g} \subseteq \mathscr{M}_{\infty}^{(f)}$. The last theorem then yields the following extension of Kolmogorov's Theorems 8 and 9 in [12]:

8.8. Corollary. *The following conditions are equivalent:*

(i) $\mathbf{g}$ *is subordinate to* $\mathbf{f}$, i.e., $\mathscr{M}_{\infty}^{(g)} \subseteq \mathscr{M}_{\infty}^{(f)}$.

(ii) $\exists \mathbf{\Phi} \in \mathbf{L}_{2,\mathbf{M}_{ff}}$ *such that* $\mathbf{g} = \int_0^{2\pi} \mathbf{\Phi}(\theta)\mathbf{E}(d\theta)\mathbf{f}$.

(iii) $\exists \mathbf{\Phi} \in \mathbf{L}_{2,\mathbf{M}_{ff}}$ *such that for any* $B \in \mathscr{B}$

$$\mathbf{M}_{gf}(B) = \int_B \mathbf{\Phi}(\theta)\mathbf{M}_{ff}(d\theta), \qquad \mathbf{M}_{gg}(B) = \int_B \mathbf{\Phi}(\theta)\mathbf{M}_{ff}(d\theta)\mathbf{\Phi}^*(\theta).$$

In case $\mathbf{g}$ *is subordinate to* $\mathbf{f}$, *the functions* $\mathbf{\Phi}$ *in* (ii) *and* (iii) *are equal a.e.* $(\mathbf{M}_{ff})$.

The following is M. Rosenberg's unpublished generalization of Kolmogorov's Theorem 10 in [12]:

8.9. Corollary. *Let* $\mathbf{g}$ *be subordinate to* $\mathbf{f}$, *and* $\mathbf{\Phi}$ *be as in* 8.8(ii). *Then* $\mathbf{f}$ *is subordinate to* $\mathbf{g}$ (i.e., $\mathbf{f}$ and $\mathbf{g}$ *are* mutually subordinate), *if and only if*

$$\mathit{rank}\left\{\mathbf{\Phi}(\theta)\, \frac{d\mathbf{M}_{ff}}{d\tau\mathbf{M}_{ff}}(\theta)\, \mathbf{\Phi}^*(\theta)\right\} = \mathit{rank}\, \frac{d\mathbf{M}_{ff}}{d\tau\mathbf{M}_{ff}}(\theta), \quad \text{a.e. } (\tau\mathbf{M}_{ff})$$

Theorem 8.7 has many applications. For instance, we can derive from it the spectral distribution of the projection of a component of a q-ple S.P. on

[15′] *Note added in proof.* Although some recent papers are devoted to the decomposition of vector-valued measures and to building a Radon-Nikodym theory for them (e.g., N. Dinculeneau and C. Foias (1961) *Canad. J. Math.* **13** 529–556; M. M. Rao (1964) *Proc. Nat. Acad. Sci., U.S.A.* **51** 771–774), we know of no attempt to extend the *Besicovitch theory* [1] to *matrix- or operator-valued measures* **M**, **N**. We face at least two difficulties in such an attempt. (i) We get one of *two* possible derivatives, depending on whether we pre- or post-multiply $\mathbf{M}(\theta - h, \theta + h)$ by $\{\mathbf{N}(\theta - h, \theta + h)\}^{-1}$ before taking the limit as $h \to 0+$. (ii) The inverse $\{\mathbf{N}(\theta - h, \theta + h)\}^{-1}$ may not exist.

the orthogonal complement of the space spanned by the rest of its components. First, by taking Besicovitch derivatives [1] of our matricial measures in 8.7 with respect to Lebesgue measure L we can show that[16]

$$(\det F'_{ff})\mathbf{F}'_{\hat{g}\hat{g}} = \mathbf{F}'_{\hat{g}f}(\operatorname{adj} \mathbf{F}'_{ff})\mathbf{F}'_{f\hat{g}}, \quad \text{a.e. } (L), \tag{8.10}$$

whether or not the functions $\mathbf{F}_{ff}$, $\mathbf{F}_{\hat{g}\hat{g}}$, $\mathbf{F}_{f\hat{g}}$ are absolutely continuous on $[0, 2\pi]$. From (8.10) we can in turn deduce the following

8.11. Lemma. *Let* (i) $(\mathbf{f}_n)_{-\infty}^{\infty}$ *be a q-ple, weakly stationary S.P., and* Δ_q *be the determinant of the derivative of its spectral distribution;* (ii) Δ_{q-1} *be defined similarly for the* $(q-1)$*-ple S.P. formed by the first* $q-1$ *components of* $(\mathbf{f}_n)_{-\infty}^{\infty}$; (iii) $\tilde{f}_n^{(q)}$ *be the projection of the last component of* $\mathbf{f}_n$ on $\{\mathfrak{S}(f_m{}^i, -\infty < m < \infty, 1 \le i \le q-1)\}^{\perp}$. *Then the (real-valued) spectral distribution* F_q *of the (1-ple) S.P.* $(\tilde{f}_n^{(q)})_{n=-\infty}^{\infty}$ *satisfies the equation*

$$\Delta_{q-1}(\theta)\cdot F_q{}'(\theta) = \Delta_q(\theta), \quad a.e.\ (Leb.).$$

In case $\Delta_{q-1} > 0$ *a.e. (Leb.), we have of course*

$$F_q{}'(\theta) = \Delta_q(\theta)/\Delta_{q-1}(\theta), \quad a.e.\ (Leb.).$$

This result was obtained by Matveev in 1960 (cf. [23, p. 35, (5)]) in the course of deriving spectral conditions for the determinism of a q-ple S.P.[16′] With $q = 2$, it reappears in 1964 in a paper of Koopmans [13, Theorem 1], many of whose results on *coherence* of processes [13, 14] are deducible from those given above and standard theorems on Besicovitch derivatives [1].

9. SPECTRAL ANALYSIS OF A PURELY NONDETERMINISTIC S.P.

It is easy to show (cf. [36, I, 7.7(a)]), that if $(\mathbf{f}_n)_{-\infty}^{\infty}$ is a *moving average S.P.*, i.e.,

$$f_n = \sum_{k=-\infty}^{\infty} \mathbf{C}_k \mathbf{h}_{n-k}, \qquad (\mathbf{h}_m, \mathbf{h}_n) = \delta_{mn}\mathbf{J}, \qquad \sum_{k=-\infty}^{\infty} |\mathbf{C}_k\mathbf{J}|_E{}^2 < \infty, \tag{9.1}$$

where $\mathbf{J}$ is a projection matrix, then its spectral distribution $\mathbf{F}$ is absolutely continuous and

$$\mathbf{F}'(\theta) = \mathbf{\Psi}(e^{i\theta})\mathbf{\Psi}(e^{i\theta})^*, \quad \text{a.e. (Leb.)}, \qquad \text{where} \quad \mathbf{\Psi}(e^{i\theta}) = \sum_{k=-\infty}^{\infty} \mathbf{C}_k \mathbf{J} e^{ki\theta}. \tag{9.2}$$

[16] adj $\mathbf{A}$ denotes the *adjugate matrix* of $\mathbf{A}$, i.e., the transpose of the matrix formed by the cofactors of $\mathbf{A}$, so that

$$\mathbf{A}\cdot(\operatorname{adj} \mathbf{A}) = (\det \mathbf{A})\mathrm{I} = (\operatorname{adj} \mathbf{A})\cdot\mathbf{A}.$$

[16′] *Note added in proof.* Spectral conditions for determinism which we have not stated in this paper, have also been studied by Jang Se-Pei [10, I, §6; II].

The inequality in (9.1) shows that each entry of $\mathbf{\Psi}$ is in L_2 on the unit circle $C = [|z| = 1]$ of the complex plane, a fact we shall express by writing $\mathbf{\Psi} \in \mathbf{L}_2(C)$.

Now let $(\mathbf{f}_n)_{-\infty}^{\infty}$ be any nondeterministic process. Then, as emphasized in §4, the coefficients $\mathbf{A}_k\mathbf{G}^{1/2}$, which occur in its Wold-Zasuhin decomposition

$$\mathbf{f}_n = \mathbf{u}_n + \mathbf{v}_n = \sum_{k=0}^{\infty} \mathbf{A}_k\mathbf{G}^{1/2}\mathbf{h}_{n-k} + (\mathbf{f}_n \,|\, \mathcal{M}_{-\infty}), \qquad \sum_{k=0}^{\infty} |\mathbf{A}_k\mathbf{G}^{1/2}|_E{}^2 < \infty, \tag{9.3}$$

are uniquely determined by the S.P. This fact and (9.2) suggest associating with our S.P. the function $\mathbf{\Phi}$ defined by

$$\mathbf{\Phi}(e^{i\theta}) \underset{d}{=} \sum_{k=0}^{\infty} \mathbf{A}_k\mathbf{G}^{1/2}e^{ki\theta}. \tag{9.4}$$

We call $\mathbf{\Phi}$ the *generating function* of $(\mathbf{f}_n)_{-\infty}^{\infty}$. It plays a vital role in the theory. The inequality in (9.3) shows that $\mathbf{\Phi} \in \mathbf{L}_2(C)$. But the Fourier series of $\mathbf{\Phi}$ is devoid of negative frequency terms, and actually $\mathbf{\Phi} \in \mathbf{L}_2^{0+}(C)$, where

$$\mathbf{L}_2^{0+}(C) \underset{d}{=} \left\{\mathbf{\Psi}\colon \mathbf{\Psi} \in \mathbf{L}_2(C) \quad \text{and} \quad \int_0^{2\pi} e^{-ki\theta}\mathbf{\Psi}(e^{i\theta})\,d\theta = \mathbf{0} \quad \text{for} \quad k \le 0\right\}. \tag{9.5}$$

From (9.2) we immediately get:

9.6. Theorem. *The purely nondeterministic part* $(\mathbf{u}_n)_{-\infty}^{\infty}$ *in the Wold-Zasuhin decomposition of* $(\mathbf{f}_n)_{-\infty}^{\infty}$ *has an absolutely continuous spectral distribution* $\mathbf{F}_u$ *such that*

$$\mathbf{F}_u'(\theta) = \mathbf{\Phi}(e^{i\theta})\mathbf{\Phi}^*(e^{i\theta}), \quad \textit{a.e. (Leb.)},$$

where $\mathbf{\Phi} \in \mathbf{L}_2^{0+}(C)$ *is the generating function of* $(\mathbf{f}_n)_{-\infty}^{\infty}$, *and* $\mathbf{\Phi}^*(\cdot) \underset{d}{=} \{\mathbf{\Phi}(\cdot)\}^*$.

In case $(\mathbf{f}_n)_{-\infty}^{\infty}$ is itself purely nondeterministic, we have $\mathbf{v}_n = \mathbf{0}$, $\mathbf{u}_n = \mathbf{f}_n$, $\mathbf{F}_u = \mathbf{F}$, and it follows from 9.6 that $\mathbf{F}$ itself is absolutely continuous and $\mathbf{F}' = \mathbf{\Phi}\mathbf{\Phi}^*$ a.e., where $\mathbf{\Phi} \in \mathbf{L}_2^{0+}(C)$. The converse also holds as Rosanov [29] has shown; cf. also [37, 2.3]. We thus get the following spectral characterization of purely nondeterministic S.P.'s:

9.7. Theorem (Rosanov). *A q-ple S.P. is purely nondeterministic, if and only if its spectral distribution* $\mathbf{F}$ *is absolutely continuous and* $\mathbf{F}'$ *admits a factorization*

$$\mathbf{F}'(\theta) = \mathbf{\Psi}(e^{i\theta})\mathbf{\Psi}^*(e^{i\theta}), \quad \textit{a.e. (Leb.)}, \qquad \textit{where } \mathbf{\Psi} \in \mathbf{L}_2^{0+}(C).$$

A function $\mathbf{\Psi}$ in $\mathbf{L}_2^{0+}(C)$ admits a holomorphic extension to the inner disk $D_+ = [|z| < 1]$ and its adjoint $\mathbf{\Psi}^*$ a holomorphic extension to the outer disk $D_- = [1 < |z| \le \infty]$. Theorem 9.7 thus reveals an interesting connection between q-ple prediction and the inner-outer factorization of $q \times q$ matrix-valued functions in $\mathbf{L}_1(C)$.

10. SPECTRAL ANALYSIS OF A FULL-RANK S.P.

Let **F** be the spectral distribution of a q-ple, weakly stationary S.P. $(\mathbf{f}_n)_{-\infty}^{\infty}$, and **G** be its prediction-error matrix for lag 1; cf. (4.8) and (4.9). Then (cf. [36, I, 7.10; or 8, I, Theorem 8]),

$$\det \mathbf{G} = \exp\left\{\frac{1}{2\pi}\int_0^{2\pi} \log \det \mathbf{F}'(\theta)\, d\theta\right\}. \tag{10.1}$$

This fundamental equality, first stated by Whittle [34] in 1953, is a determinental extension of the Szego-Kolmogorov identity [12, (8.44)] for $q = 1$, and shows at once that

$$\rho \underset{d}{=} \text{rank of S.P.} = q \quad \Leftrightarrow \quad \log \det \mathbf{F}(\cdot) \in L_1[0, 2\pi]. \tag{10.2}$$

We thus have a perfect spectral characterization of the full-rank case. A less obvious consequence of (10.1) is the following important result [36, I, 7.11]:

10.3. Theorem. *Let* (i) $(\mathbf{f}_n)_{-\infty}^{\infty}$ *be a q-ple, weakly stationary S.P. of full-rank q*; (ii) $\mathbf{f}_n = \mathbf{u}_n + \mathbf{v}_n$ *be its Wold decomposition* (4.14 et seq.); (iii) $\mathbf{F}$, $\mathbf{F}_u$, $\mathbf{F}_v$ *be the spectral distributions of the processes* $(\mathbf{f}_n)_{-\infty}^{\infty}$, $(\mathbf{u}_n)_{-\infty}^{\infty}$, $(\mathbf{v}_n)_{-\infty}^{\infty}$; (iv) $\mathbf{F}_a$, $\mathbf{F}_b$ *be the absolutely continuous, and nonabsolutely continuous parts of F.*[17] *Then*

$$\mathbf{F}_u = \mathbf{F}_a \qquad \textit{and} \qquad \mathbf{F}_v = \mathbf{F}_b.$$

We may paraphrase this result by saying that *in the full-rank case there is concordance between the Wold-Zasuhin decomposition in the time domain and the Lebesgue-Cramér decomposition in the spectral domain.*

On combining 10.3 and 9.6 we get another important result on full-rank processes. Since $\mathbf{F}_u = \mathbf{F}_a$ and $\mathbf{F}'_b = 0$, we have $\mathbf{F}' = \mathbf{F}'_u$, whence:

10.4. Theorem. *The derivative* $\mathbf{F}'$ *of the spectral distribution of any full-rank S.P. admits the factorization*

$$\mathbf{F}'(\theta) = \mathbf{\Phi}(e^{i\theta})\mathbf{\Phi}^*(e^{i\theta}), \quad \textit{a.e. (Leb.)},$$

where $\mathbf{\Phi} \in \mathbf{L}_2^{0+}(C)$ *is the generating function* [cf. (9.4)].

The results 10.2, 10.3, and 10.4 shed much light on the full-rank case $\rho = q$, and it is natural to ask whether corresponding results are available for $0 \leq \rho < q$. We have three questions:

Q.1. *Given* $0 \leq \rho < q$, *what is the spectral necessary and sufficient condition that a* q-ple *S.P. have the rank* ρ?

[17] That every matricial distribution **F** possesses such parts $\mathbf{F}_a$ and $\mathbf{F}_b$ is a celebrated result of Cramér [3, §4, Theorem 2]. See [19, §1.1] for a formulation of this result, especially suitable for our purposes.

Q.2. For a q-ple S.P. of rank ρ such that $0 \leq \rho < q$, are the Wold-Zasuhin and Lebesgue-Cramér decompositions in concordance? If not, what extra condition would restore this concordance?

Q.3. For a q-ple S.P. of rank ρ such that $0 < \rho < q$, does $\mathbf{F}'$ admit a factorization $\mathbf{F}' = \mathbf{\Psi}\mathbf{\Psi}^*$, a.e. (Leb.), where $\mathbf{\Psi} \in \mathbf{L}_2^{0+}(C)$? If not, what additional condition would ensure such factorization?

Of these the most basic question, Q.1, is still unanswered, despite some important work by Matveev, which we shall discuss in §12. Q.2 and Q.3 have, however, been answered satisfactorily; cf. §§11 and 12.

11. CONCORDANCE OF WOLD-ZASUHIN AND LEBESGUE-CRAMÉR DECOMPOSITIONS FOR DEGENERATE RANKS

In 1959 the writer showed that the answer to the first part of question Q.2 (§10) is in the negative. He gave an example of a 2-ple process of rank 1 for which

$$\{0\} \neq \mathcal{M}_{-\infty} \subset \mathcal{M}_{\infty} \quad \text{and} \quad \mathbf{F} \text{ is absolutely continuous} \qquad (11.1)$$

[19, §3]. For this S.P. concordance between the W.-Z. and L.-C. decompositions fails, since $\mathbf{F}_v \neq 0 = \mathbf{F}_b$; cf. (10.3) et seq.

For 2-ple processes of rank 1, the writer also gave the extra condition needed for concordance, viz. det $\mathbf{F}'(\theta) = 0$, a.e. (Leb.); cf. [19, 4.5]. Now it is easy to show that rank $\mathbf{F}'(\theta) \geq$ rank $\mathbf{F}_u'(\theta) = \rho$, a.e. (Leb.). (Just combine 9.6 with 13.3 below.) Hence for $q = 2$, $\rho = 1$ our result may be written:

$$\text{concordance} \quad \Leftrightarrow \quad \text{rank } \mathbf{F}'(\theta) = 1, \text{ a.e. (Leb.)}.$$

A complete generalization of this result was obtained by Robertson [26, 10.2] in 1963:

11.2. Theorem (Robertson). *For any q-ple, weakly stationary S.P. of (any) rank ρ, there is concordance between the W.-Z. and L.-C. decompositions, if and only if rank $\mathbf{F}'(\theta) = \rho$, a.e. (Leb.), where $\mathbf{F}$ is the spectral distribution of the S.P.*

To prove this theorem Robertson used a result on the ranges of the matrices $\mathbf{F}'(\theta)$, viewed as linear transformations on $\mathscr{C}^q$ to $\mathscr{C}^q$, $\mathscr{C}$ being the complex-number field. This result is itself interesting [26, 9.11]:

11.3. Lemma (Robertson). *Let $(\mathbf{x}_n)_{-\infty}^{\infty}$, $(\mathbf{y}_n)_{-\infty}^{\infty}$, $(\mathbf{z}_n)_{-\infty}^{\infty}$ be q-ple, weakly stationary S.P.'s with the same shift operator, and let*

$$\mathbf{x}_n = \mathbf{y}_n + \mathbf{z}_n$$

$$\mathcal{M}_{\infty}^{(x)} = \mathcal{M}_{\infty}^{(y)} + \mathcal{M}_{\infty}^{(z)}, \qquad \mathcal{M}_{\infty}^{(y)} \perp \mathcal{M}_{\infty}^{(z)}.$$

Then, with an obvious notation,

(a) $\quad$ *Range* $\mathbf{F}_x'(\theta) = $ *range* $\mathbf{F}_y'(\theta) + $ *range* $\mathbf{F}_z'(\theta)$, *a.e.* (*Leb.*).

(b) $\quad$ *Range* $\mathbf{F}_y'(\theta) \cap $ *range* $\mathbf{F}_z'(\theta) = \{0\}$, *a.e.* (*Leb.*).

(c) $\quad$ *Rank* $\mathbf{F}_x'(\theta) = $ *rank* $\mathbf{F}_y'(\theta) + $ *rank* $\mathbf{F}_z'(\theta)$, *a.e.* (*Leb.*).

For processes with absolutely continuous spectral distributions this lemma was proved independently by Jang Ze-Pei [10, I, Theorem 4]. He also obtained a result for such processes [10, I, Eq. (41) et seq.], which may be construed as a reformulation of Theorem 11.2.[17′]

12. DEGENERATE RANK FACTORIZATION

The writer's example mentioned in connection with Q.2 in §11 also shows that the answer to the first part of Q.3 (§10) is in the negative. For this consider the 2-ple process of rank 1 satisfying (11.1). Were $\mathbf{F}' = \mathbf{\Psi\Psi}^*$, a.e. with $\mathbf{\Psi} \in \mathbf{L}_2^{0+}(C)$, then since $\mathbf{F}$ is absolutely continuous, it would follow from Rosanov's Theorem 9.7 that the S.P. is purely nondeterministic, in contradiction to the assertion $\mathscr{M}_{-\infty} \neq \{\mathbf{0}\}$ in (11.1).

As in the case of Q.2, the extra conditions needed to secure a positive answer to Q.3 were first given for the case $q = 2$, this time by Wiener and the writer [37, 4.1] in 1959; and the result was then fully generalized by Matveev [24] in 1960, but for processes with continuous time. Whereas in the full-rank case $\rho = q$, we encounter (holomorphic) functions of the Hardy class H_2 on the Disk D_+, or rather their radial limits in $L_2^{0+}(C)$, for the degenerate rank cases $1 \leq \rho < q$ we encounter quotients of H_∞ functions on D_+, i.e., the (meromorphic) *beschränktartige functions* introduced by R. Nevanlinna to round off the Hardy class theory. (For a brief, relevant account see [37, § 3 and Note on p. 308].) The final result, cf. [24, Theorem 1], is as follows:

12.1. Theorem (Matveev). *Let* $\mathbf{F}$ *be the spectral distribution of a q-ple S.P. Then* $\mathbf{F}'$ *admits a factorization*

$$\mathbf{F}'(\theta) = \mathbf{\Psi}(e^{i\theta})\mathbf{\Psi}^*(e^{i\theta}), \quad a.e.\ (Leb.), \qquad where \quad \mathbf{\Psi} \in \mathbf{L}_2^{0+}(C),$$

if and only if

(1) $$rank\ \mathbf{F}'(\theta) = const.\ \rho, \quad a.e.\ (Leb.)$$

[17′] *Note added in proof.* In the literature there is a tendency to deal only with the absolutely continuous case, and to remark that the results "can be extended without difficulty" to the general case. In view of the known pitfalls in going from $q = 1$ to $q > 1$, the reader is often left wondering as to whether the claimed extensions are in fact easy for $q > 1$, or even possible without qualifications. It is so much clearer to deal explicitly with the general case from the very outset.

(2) *there is a principal* $\rho \times \rho$ *minor*[18] $\mathbf{M} = \mathbf{M}^{i_1,\ldots,i_\rho}_{i_1,\ldots,i_\rho}$ *of* $\mathbf{F}'$ *such that*

$$\log \det \mathbf{M} \in L_1[0, 2\pi],$$

and for each $i \notin \{i_1, \ldots, i_\rho\}$, *and each* $k \in \{1, \ldots, \rho\}$,

$$\frac{\det \mathbf{M}^i_{i_k}(\theta)}{\det \mathbf{M}(\theta)} = \lim_{r \to 1-} \Psi_{i,i_k}(re^{i\theta}), \qquad a.e. \ (Leb.), \qquad \Psi_{i,i_k} \ beschränktartige,$$

where $\mathbf{M}_j{}^i$ *denotes the minor obtained from* $\mathbf{M}$ *by replacing the* jth *row of* $\mathbf{M}$ *by the appropriate entries of the* ith *row of* $\mathbf{F}'$.

Matveev's proof is based on the fact:

$$\mathbf{\Psi} \in \mathbf{L}_2^{0+}(C) \quad \Rightarrow \quad \text{rank } \mathbf{\Psi}(e^{i\theta}) = \text{const., a.e. (Leb.)}, \tag{12.2}$$

which emerges on applying theorems on Hardy class functions to the sums of the determinants of principal $r \times r$ minors of $\mathbf{\Psi}$, $1 \le r \le q$; cf. [16, 2.5]. Matveev showed that if the constant in (12.2) is ρ, then

$$\mathbf{\Psi}(e^{i\theta})\mathbf{\Psi}^*(e^{i\theta}) = \mathbf{X}(e^{i\theta})\mathbf{X}^*(e^{i\theta}),$$

where

$$\mathbf{X} = [\underset{q \times \rho}{\cdots} \mid \underset{q \times q-\rho}{0}] \in \mathbf{L}_2^{0+}(C).$$

The example mentioned above and Theorem 12.1 together answer the question Q.3 completely. Theorem 12.1 also answers completely the following question related to Q.1:

Q.1′. *Given* $0 \le \rho < q$, *what is the spectral necessary and sufficient condition that a* q-ple *S.P. be purely nondeterministic and have rank* ρ?

The answer is immediate from Theorems 9.7 and 10.1 of Rosanov and Matveev:

12.3. Corollary. *A q-ple S.P. is purely nondeterministic and of rank* ρ, *if and only if its spectral distribution* $\mathbf{F}$ *is absolutely continuous and* $\mathbf{F}'$ *satisfies conditions* (1) *and* (2) *of Theorem* 12.1.

Unfortunately, this still leaves us in the dark with regard to Q.1. For instance, the answer:

$\mathbf{F}'$ *satisfies conditions* (1) *and* (2) *of Theorem* 12.1

will not do. Indeed, by Robertson's Theorem 11.2, condition (1) of 12.1 ensures concordance when the rank is ρ, whereas we know that there are processes of rank ρ for which concordance fails. A proper answer to Q.1 would be a major contribution.

[18] $\mathbf{M}^{i_1,\ldots,i_\rho}_{j_1,\ldots,j_\rho}$ denotes the $\rho \times \rho$ minor of $\mathbf{F}'$ made up of the rows $i_1, \ldots, i_\rho$, and the columns $j_1, \ldots, j_\rho$.

13. SPECTRAL AND AUTOREGRESSIVE REPRESENTATIONS FOR THE PREDICTOR OF A PURELY NONDETERMINISTIC S.P.

We shall now turn to prediction proper. Let $(\mathbf{f}_n)_{-\infty}^{\infty}$ be a q-ple, nondeterministic S.P., $\mathbf{h}_n$ be its nth normalized innovation, and $\hat{\mathbf{f}}_\nu = (\mathbf{f}_\nu \mid \mathcal{M}_0)$ be the prediction of $\mathbf{f}_\nu$ with lag $\nu \geq 1$. Since $\mathbf{h}_0, \hat{\mathbf{f}}_\nu \in \mathcal{M}_\infty$, they have, cf. Theorem 7.3, isomorphs $\mathbf{W}, \mathbf{Y}_\nu \in \mathbf{L}_{2,\mathbf{M}}$ such that[19]

$$\mathbf{h}_n = \int_0^{2\pi} e^{-ni\theta}\mathbf{W}(e^{i\theta})\mathbf{E}(d\theta)\mathbf{f}_0, \qquad \hat{\mathbf{f}}_\nu = \int_0^{2\pi} \mathbf{Y}_\nu(e^{i\theta})\mathbf{E}(d\theta)\mathbf{f}_0. \tag{13.1}$$

Our first problem is to find $\mathbf{Y}_\nu$ for a purely nondeterministic S.P. For such a process the Wold-Zasuhin decomposition (4.14) to (4.17) shows that

$$\mathbf{f}_n = \sum_{k=0}^{\infty} \mathbf{A}_k \mathbf{G}^{1/2}\mathbf{h}_{n-k}, \qquad \hat{\mathbf{f}}_\nu = \sum_{k=\nu}^{\infty} \mathbf{A}_k \mathbf{G}^{1/2}\mathbf{h}_{\nu-k}.$$

Letting $n = 0$, taking isomorphs and proceeding heuristically, we get

$$\mathbf{I} = \sum_{k=0}^{\infty} \mathbf{A}_k \mathbf{G}^{1/2} e^{ki\theta}\mathbf{W}(e^{i\theta}) = \mathbf{\Phi}(e^{i\theta})\mathbf{W}(e^{i\theta})$$

$$\mathbf{Y}_\nu(e^{i\theta}) = \sum_{k=\nu}^{\infty} \mathbf{A}_k \mathbf{G}^{1/2} e^{(k-\nu)i\theta}\mathbf{W}(e^{i\theta}) = [e^{-\nu i\theta}\mathbf{\Phi}(e^{i\theta})]_{0+}\mathbf{W}(e^{i\theta}), \tag{13.2}$$

where $\mathbf{\Phi}$ is the generating function of the S.P., and $[\cdots]_{0+}$ denotes the function obtained from $\cdots$ by cutting off the negative frequency terms from its Fourier series. The first equation yields $\mathrm{W}(\cdot) = \{\mathbf{\Phi}(\cdot)\}^{-1}$, which is wrong, since $\mathbf{\Phi}$ need not be invertible. Our heuristic procedure is thus untenable, but it reveals that *the determination of* $\mathbf{Y}_\nu$ *is tied up with the possibility of inverting the generating function* $\mathbf{\Phi}$.

To investigate the invertibility of $\mathbf{\Phi}$, we first note that its degeneracies stem from a constant matrix, as the following *canonical factorization* given in [16, 3.1] and also [22, 3.6] makes clear:

13.3. Theorem. *The generating function* $\mathbf{\Phi}$ *of any q-ple, nondeterministic S.P. is expressible in the form* $\mathbf{\Omega}(\cdot)\mathbf{G}^{1/2}$ *where* $\mathbf{G}$ *is the prediction error matrix with lag* 1, *and* $\mathbf{\Omega} \in \mathbf{L}_2^{0+}(C)$ *is invertible a.e. (Leb.), and*[20] $\mathbf{\Omega}_+(0) = \mathbf{I}$. *In fact,*

$$\mathbf{\Omega}(e^{i\theta}) = \mathbf{J}^\perp + \mathbf{\Phi}(e^{i\theta})\mathbf{H} = \mathbf{I} + \sum_{k=1}^{\infty} \mathbf{A}_k \mathbf{J} e^{ki\theta},$$

where $\mathbf{J}$ *and* $\mathbf{H}$ *are as in* (4.10) *to* (4.12).

[19] For convenience we have transplanted the functions $\mathbf{W}$ and $\mathbf{Y}_\nu$ from $[0, 2\pi]$ to the circle $C = [|z| = 1]$.

[20] $\mathbf{\Psi}_+$ denotes the holomorphic extension to $D_+ = [|z| < 1]$ of a function $\mathbf{\Psi}$ in $\mathbf{L}_2^{0+}(C)$.

Since, $\mathbf{J}$, $\mathbf{H}$, $\mathbf{\Phi}$ are uniquely determined by the S.P., cf. (4.9) *et seq.* and (9.3) *et seq.*, so is $\mathbf{\Omega}$. In fact, as the writer showed in [17, 2.2], its inverse $\mathbf{\Omega}^{-1}(\cdot) \underset{d}{=} \{\Omega(\cdot)\}^{-1}$ is the isomorph in $\mathbf{L}_{2,\mathbf{M}}$ of the nonnormalized innovation $\mathbf{g}_0$ in the purely nondeterministic case; i.e.,

$$\mathbf{g}_n = \int_0^{2\pi} e^{-ni\theta}\mathbf{\Omega}^{-1}(e^{i\theta})\mathbf{E}(d\theta)\mathbf{f}_0, \qquad \mathbf{\Omega}^{-1} \in \mathbf{L}_{2,\mathbf{M}}. \tag{13.4}$$

Since $\mathbf{h}_0 = \mathbf{H}\mathbf{g}_0$, its isomorph $\mathbf{W}$ is of course $\mathbf{H}\mathbf{\Omega}^{-1} = (\mathbf{\Omega}\mathbf{H}^{-1})^{-1}$. From (13.3) it easily follows that $\mathbf{\Omega}\mathbf{H}^{-1} = \mathbf{J}^{\perp} + \mathbf{\Phi}$. Thus, for a purely nondeterministic S.P. we find that

$$\mathbf{W}(e^{i\theta}) = \{\mathbf{J}^{\perp} + \mathbf{\Phi}(e^{i\theta})\}^{-1} \qquad \text{in} \quad \mathbf{L}_{2,\mathbf{M}}. \tag{13.5}$$

For $q = 1$ we know the corresponding result for any (purely or impurely) nondeterministic S.P., viz.

$$W(e^{i\theta}) = \chi_A(\theta)/\Phi(e^{i\theta}) \qquad \text{in} \quad L_{2,M}, \tag{13.6}$$

where A is any subset of $[0, 2\pi]$ such that A and A' are carriers of the (mutually singular) measures $|E(\cdot)u_0|^2$ and $|E(\cdot)v_0|^2$, u_0 and v_0 being as in the Wold decomposition. But for $q > 1$ the difficulties caused by rank deficiencies and the failure of concordance (§11) have so far prevented the discovery of a full-fledged generalization of (13.6).

Inserting the value of $\mathbf{W}$ given by (13.5) into the heuristically obtained equation (13.2), we get

$$\mathbf{Y}_\nu(e^{i\theta}) = [e^{-\nu i\theta}\mathbf{\Phi}(e^{i\theta})]_{0+}\{\mathbf{J}^{\perp} + \mathbf{\Phi}(e^{i\theta})\}^{-1} \qquad \text{in} \quad \mathbf{L}_{2,\mathbf{M}}. \tag{13.7}$$

This equality was proved for purely nondeterministic S.P.'s of full rank q in [36, II, 4.11]; a slight variation of the arguments used therein shows its validity for $1 \le \rho < q$. The equations (13.1), (13.5), and (13.7) thus yield spectral expressions for the predictor and for the innovations of a purely nondeterministic S.P.

We must next investigate the expressibility of the predictor $\hat{\mathbf{f}}_\nu$ directly in terms of the $\mathbf{f}_{-k}$, $k \ge 0$. For this we must appeal to a most basic property of the generating function, established by the writer [19, §2.9], viz. its *optimality*:[21]

13.8. Basic Lemma. (a) *The generating function* $\mathbf{\Phi}$ *of a q-ple, nondeterministic S.P. of any rank* ρ *is an optimal function in* $\mathbf{L}_2^{0+}(C)$; *i.e.,*

(1) $$\mathbf{\Phi}_+(0) \ge \mathbf{0},$$

[21] The word *maximal* is used instead of *optimal* in the English translations of the Russian literature, in which a less explicit but related result appears; cf. [30, Theorem 4]. For $q = 1$, the word *outer* has been used by Beurling [2] and his disciples.

(2) *$\mathbf{\Psi} \in \mathbf{L}_2^{0+}(C)$ and $\mathbf{\Psi\Psi}^* = \mathbf{\Phi\Phi}^*$, a.e. (Leb.) on C*

$$\Rightarrow \quad [\{\mathbf{\Psi}_+(0)\mathbf{\Psi}_+^*(0)\}]^{1/2} \leq \mathbf{\Phi}_+(0).$$

(b) *In case $\rho = q$, we have*

$$\det \mathbf{\Phi}_+(z) = \exp\left\{\frac{1}{2\pi}\int_0^{2\pi} \frac{e^{i\theta}+z}{e^{i\theta}-z} \log \det[\mathbf{F}'(\theta)]^{1/2}\, d\theta\right\}, \qquad |z| < 1.$$

Now let us confine attention to *purely nondeterministic processes of full rank*. By 13.8(b), the holomorphic (matrix-valued) function $\mathbf{\Phi}_+$ on the inner disk D_+ :

$$\mathbf{\Phi}_+(z) = \sum_{k=0}^{\infty} \mathbf{C}_k z^k, \quad z \in D_+, \qquad \text{where } \mathbf{C}_k = \mathbf{A}_k \mathbf{G}^{1/2},$$

is invertible at each $z \in D_+$, and hence

$$\{\mathbf{\Phi}_+(z)\}^{-1} = \sum_{k=0}^{\infty} \mathbf{D}_k z^k, \quad z \in D_+,$$

where the $\mathbf{D}_k$ are matrix coefficients, satisfying

$$\mathbf{C}_0\mathbf{D}_0 = \mathbf{I}, \quad \mathbf{C}_0\mathbf{D}_1 + \mathbf{C}_1\mathbf{D}_0 = \mathbf{0}, \quad \mathbf{C}_0\mathbf{D}_2 + \mathbf{C}_1\mathbf{D}_1 + \mathbf{C}_2\mathbf{D}_0 = \mathbf{0}, \ldots$$

It follows from (13.7) that $\mathbf{Y}_\nu$ has a holomorphic extension $(\mathbf{Y}_\nu)_+$ to D_+ given by

$$(\mathbf{Y}_\nu)_+(z) = \sum_{k=\nu}^{\infty} \mathbf{C}_k z^k \sum_{k=0}^{\infty} \mathbf{D}_k z^k = \sum_{k=0}^{\infty} \mathbf{E}_{\nu k} z^k, \quad z \in D_+,$$

where

$$\mathbf{E}_{\nu k} = \sum_{j=0}^{k} \mathbf{C}_{\nu+j}\mathbf{D}_{k-j}. \tag{13.9}$$

This suggests that in some sense we should have

$$\mathbf{Y}_\nu(e^{i\theta}) \sim \sum_{k=0}^{\infty} \mathbf{E}_{\nu k} e^{ki\theta}.$$

But in general $\mathbf{Y}_\nu \notin \mathbf{L}_1(C)$, and the $\mathbf{E}_{\nu k}$ will not be the ordinary Fourier coefficients of $\mathbf{Y}_\nu$. There will, however, be circumstances under which

$$\sum_{k=0}^{n} \mathbf{E}_{\nu k} e^{ki\theta} \to \mathbf{Y}_\nu(e^{i\theta}) \quad \text{in the } \mathbf{L}_{2,\mathbf{M}} \text{ topology,}^{22} \qquad \text{as } n \to \infty, \tag{13.10}$$

[22] That is, since the spectral distribution **F** is absolutely continuous,

$$\int_0^{2\pi} \left| \left\{ \sum_{k=0}^{n} \mathbf{E}_{\nu k} e^{ki\theta} - \mathbf{Y}_\nu(e^{i\theta}) \right\} [\mathbf{F}'(\theta)]^{1/2} \right|_{\mathbf{E}}^2 d\theta \to 0, \text{ as } n \to \infty.$$

and hence by our Isomorphism Theorem 7.3,

$$\sum_{k=0}^{n} \mathbf{E}_{\nu k}\mathbf{f}_{-k} \to \hat{\mathbf{f}}_\nu \quad \text{in } \mathcal{M}_\infty \qquad \text{as } n \to \infty. \tag{13.11}$$

In short, there are processes for which the coefficients $\mathbf{E}_{\nu k}$ given in (13.9) provide an *autoregressive representation for the predictor*, to wit

$$\hat{\mathbf{f}}_\nu = \sum_{k=0}^{\infty} \mathbf{E}_{\nu k}\mathbf{f}_{-k}. \tag{13.12}$$

For such processes we call $(\mathbf{E}_{\nu k})_{k=0}^{\infty}$ the *time-domain weighting sequence* for the predictor $\hat{\mathbf{f}}_\nu$.

The papers [36, II; 21] are devoted largely to the demarcation of processes for which the equivalent conditions (13.10) to (13.12) prevail. No complete characterization has been obtained so far—only *sufficient conditions*, the best being perhaps the one in [21, 5.2]:

$$\begin{gathered} \mathbf{F} \textit{ is absolutely continuous on } [0, 2\pi], \\ \mathbf{F}' \in \mathbf{L}_\infty[0, 2\pi] \qquad \textit{and} \qquad (\mathbf{F}')^{-1} \in \mathbf{L}_1[0, 2\pi]. \end{gathered} \tag{13.13}$$

Also sufficient, of course, is the stronger *boundedness condition*, of greater practical interest, cf. [36, II, 5.1 and 7.3]:

$$\begin{gathered} \mathbf{F} \textit{ is absolutely continuous on } [0, 2\pi], \\ \lambda\mathbf{I} \le \mathbf{F}'(e^{i\theta}) \le \lambda'\mathbf{I}, \text{ a.e. (Leb.)}, \qquad \text{where } 0 < \lambda < \lambda' < \infty. \end{gathered} \tag{13.14}$$

It is easy to show that the autoregressive relation (13.12) is equivalent to the discrete *matricial Hopf-Wiener equation*:

$$\mathbf{\Gamma}_{n+\nu} = \sum_{k=0}^{\infty} \mathbf{E}_{\nu k}\mathbf{\Gamma}_{n-k}, \qquad n \ge 0. \tag{13.15}$$

The continuous parameter analogues of (13.12) and (13.15) are, for a given real lag $h > 0$,

$$\hat{\mathbf{f}}_h = \int_0^\infty d\mathbf{E}_h(\tau) \cdot \mathbf{f}_{-\tau}, \tag{13.12'}$$

$$\mathbf{\Gamma}(t + h) = \int_0^\infty d\mathbf{E}_h(\tau) \cdot \mathbf{\Gamma}(t - \tau), \qquad t \ge 0, \tag{13.15'}$$

where the weighing $\mathbf{E}_h(\cdot)$ is a $q \times q$ matrix-valued function of bounded variation on $[0, \infty)$. These are the equations with which Wiener began the subject of multivariate prediction [35, Chapter IV]. He showed that in simple cases of practical interest the weighting $\mathbf{E}_h(\cdot)$ can be found by solving the matricial Hopf-Wiener equation (13.15′). We now see that his pioneering work belongs to a rather late chapter of the general theory.

14. DETERMINATION OF THE GENERATING FUNCTION FROM THE SPECTRAL DENSITY

Given the covariance bisequence $(\mathbf{\Gamma}_k)_{-\infty}^{\infty}$ or equivalently the spectral density $\mathbf{F}'$ of a q-ple, purely nondeterministic S.P. of full rank, the determination of its generating function $\mathbf{\Phi}$ is of great importance for prediction. This is because once $\mathbf{\Phi}$ or its Fourier coefficients $\mathbf{C}_k$ are found, we can get $\mathbf{\Phi}^{-1}$ and its Taylor coefficients $\mathbf{D}_k$, and thereafter the crucial function $\mathbf{Y}_\nu$ and its coefficients $\mathbf{E}_{\nu k}$ required to determine the predictor $\hat{\mathbf{f}}_\nu$; cf. (13.7), (13.9), (13.1), and (13.12).

In the case $q = 1$, Φ can be found in principle from the equation

$$\Phi_+(z) = \exp\left\{\frac{1}{2\pi}\int_0^{2\pi} \frac{e^{i\theta}+z}{e^{i\theta}-z} \log[F'(\theta)]^{1/2}\, d\theta\right\}, \qquad |z| < 1, \tag{14.1}$$

and its coefficients C_k found from

$$\sum_{k=0}^{\infty} C_k e^{ki\theta} = \exp\left\{\frac{\alpha_0}{2} + \sum_{1}^{\infty} \alpha_k e^{ki\theta}\right\}, \tag{14.2}$$

where α_k is the kth Fourier coefficient of $\log F'$. These are canonical expressions for optimal Hardy class functions in terms of the norms of their boundary values. But for $q > 1$ analogous expressions are not available, because the exponential law, $\exp(\mathbf{A} + \mathbf{B}) = \exp \mathbf{A} \cdot \exp \mathbf{B}$, fails for matrices. In fact, *no general, closed-form expression for* $\mathbf{\Phi}$ *or for its leading coefficient* $\mathbf{G}^{1/2}$ *in terms of* $\mathbf{F}'$ *is known for the cases* $q \geq 2$. Its discovery would be a major contribution.

Fortunately, we do have an *infinite series* expansion for $\mathbf{\Phi}$ and $\mathbf{G}$ in terms of $\mathbf{F}'$ in case the conditions (13.13) are met, i.e., for the only known case in which the predictor has an autoregressive representation (13.12); cf. [21, 4.7]. Since an explanation of this result and its proof would require a digression, we shall only describe how with its aid the crucial weighting coefficients $\mathbf{E}_{\nu k}$ may be computed from the $\mathbf{\Gamma}_k$. For simplicity we shall assume that our S.P. satisfies the stronger boundedness condition (13.14) rather than (13.13). For details the reader should see the papers [36, II, §6; 21, §§4, 5].

Knowing the covariances $\mathbf{\Gamma}_k$ and the bounds λ and λ' in (13.14), we first obtain the slightly modified coefficients[23]

$$\mathbf{\Gamma}'_0 = \frac{2}{\lambda + \lambda'}\mathbf{\Gamma}_0 - \mathbf{I}, \qquad \mathbf{\Gamma}'_n = \frac{2}{\lambda + \lambda'}\mathbf{\Gamma}_n, \qquad n \neq 0.$$

We then compute $\mathbf{A}_0, \mathbf{A}_1, \mathbf{A}_2, \ldots$, where $\mathbf{A}_0 = \mathbf{I}$, and for $m > 0$,

$$\mathbf{A}_m \underset{d}{=} -\mathbf{\Gamma}'_m + \sum_{n=1}^{\infty} \mathbf{\Gamma}'_n \mathbf{\Gamma}'_{m-n} - \sum_{n=1}^{\infty} \sum_{p=1}^{\infty} \mathbf{\Gamma}'_p \mathbf{\Gamma}'_{n-p} \mathbf{\Gamma}'_{m-n} + \cdots. \tag{14.3}$$

[23] Obviously, Γ'_k is the kth Fourier coefficient of $[2/(\lambda + \lambda')]\mathbf{F}'(\cdot) - \mathbf{I}$.

We next find $\mathbf{B}_0, \mathbf{B}_1, \mathbf{B}_2, \ldots$ from the recurrence relations

$$\mathbf{A}_0\mathbf{B}_0 = \mathbf{I}, \qquad \mathbf{A}_0\mathbf{B}_1 + \mathbf{A}_1\mathbf{B}_0 = \mathbf{0}, \qquad \mathbf{A}_0\mathbf{B}_2 + \mathbf{A}_1\mathbf{B}_1 + \mathbf{A}_2\mathbf{B}_0 = \mathbf{0}, \cdots$$

Since $\mathbf{A}_0 = \mathbf{I}$, this computation does not involve matrix inversion. Finally, for any given $\nu \geq 1$, we compute the coefficients $\mathbf{E}_{\nu 0}, \mathbf{E}_{\nu 1}, \mathbf{E}_{\nu 2}, \ldots$ from

$$\mathbf{E}_{\nu k} = \sum_{j=0}^{k} \mathbf{B}_{\nu+j}\mathbf{A}_{k-j}, \qquad k \geq 0. \tag{14.4}$$

These are the weighting coefficients required in the autoregressive series (13.12) for the predictor $\hat{\mathbf{f}}_\nu$. To complete the solution of the prediction problem 2.16, we must find the prediction error matrix $\mathbf{G}_\nu$ for lag ν. For this, we first compute the crucial matrix $\mathbf{G}$ from

$$\mathbf{G} = \frac{2}{\lambda + \lambda'} \sum_{n=0}^{\infty} \sum_{m=0}^{\infty} \mathbf{A}_m \mathbf{\Gamma}_{n-m} \mathbf{A}_n^*, \tag{14.5}$$

and then $\mathbf{G}_\nu$ from

$$\mathbf{G}_\nu = \sum_{k=0}^{\nu-1} \mathbf{B}_k \mathbf{G} \mathbf{B}_k^*. \tag{14.6}$$

The practical utility of this scheme of computation will be discussed in §15. In it the generating function $\mathbf{\Phi}$ has been by-passed. But if $\mathbf{\Phi}$ is wanted, its Fourier coefficients $\mathbf{C}_k$ can be found from the equations

$$\mathbf{C}_k = \mathbf{B}_k \mathbf{G}^{1/2}. \tag{14.7}$$

15. THE FACTORIZATION OF MATRICIAL RATIONAL SPECTRAL DENSITIES

In most practical problems of prediction the q-ple S.P. $(\mathbf{f}_n)_{-\infty}^{\infty}$ has a spectral density $\mathbf{F}'$ on C,[24] which can be analytically continued to the entire complex plane $\mathscr{C}$ to yield a matrix rational function, i.e., one whose entries are complex-valued rational functions. Such a spectral density is said to be *rational*. Retaining the symbol $\mathbf{F}'$ for the extension to $\mathscr{C}$, we have

$$\mathbf{F}'(z) = \frac{1}{p(z)} \mathbf{P}(z), \qquad z \in \mathscr{C}, \tag{15.1}$$

where $\mathbf{P}$ is a $q \times q$ matrix polynomial and $p(\cdot)$ a complex polynomial. We infer easily that there is an integer r, $1 \leq r \leq q$, such that rank $F'(z) \leq r$, for any z, and rank $\mathbf{F}'(z) = r$, except for a finite number of z. We call *r the rank of* $\mathbf{F}'$.

A basic result, known generally but properly enunciated and proved by

[24] It is now convenient to transplant $\mathbf{F}'$ from $[0, 2\pi]$ to C.

Polyak and Rosanov, cf. [30, Lemma 3; 31, Chapter I, 10.2], is that a (matricial) rational spectral density $\mathbf{F}'$ admits a factorization

$$\mathbf{F}'(e^{i\theta}) = \mathbf{\Psi}(e^{i\theta})\mathbf{\Psi}^*(e^{i\theta}), \qquad 0 \le \theta \le 2\pi, \tag{15.2}$$

where $\mathbf{\Psi} \in \mathbf{L}_2^{0+}(C)$ and $\mathbf{\Psi}$ is rational, i.e., its analytic continuation to $\mathscr{C}$ is rational. It follows from Rosanov's Theorem 9.7 that *a q-ple process with a rational spectral density of rank $r > 0$ is purely nondeterministic and of rank r.* We owe to Rosanov [30, Theorem 7] the proof that *its generating function* $\mathbf{\Phi}$ *itself has a rational extension* $\mathbf{R}$ *to* $\mathscr{C}$, and moreover

$$\operatorname{rank} \mathbf{R}(z) = r, \qquad z \in D_+ .^{25} \tag{15.3}$$

Thus by Theorem 9.6,

$$\mathbf{F}'(z) = \mathbf{R}(z)\mathbf{R}^*(z), \qquad z \in C. \tag{15.4}$$

To carry out the prediction for lag ν for our process when it has full rank q, we must find $\mathbf{R}$ and

$$\mathbf{Y}_\nu(e^{i\theta}) = [e^{-\nu i\theta}\mathbf{R}(e^{i\theta})]_{0+}\{\mathbf{R}(e^{i\theta})\}^{-1}; \tag{15.5}$$

cf. §14 and (13.7). The methods proposed for this fall into two broad categories: algebraic and analytic.

(i) An algebraic method has been proposed by Yaglom [41, §1] for continuous time processes, in which $\mathbf{R}$ is by-passed and $\mathbf{Y}_\nu$ found directly. In the discrete version, it is assumed that rank $\mathbf{F}'(e^{i\theta}) = q$ for *all* θ, so that condition (13.14) is fulfilled. Since the $\mathbf{Y}_\nu$ in (15.5) is rational, Yaglom starts out with a rational function $\mathbf{Y}_\nu$ with undetermined coefficients, and shows that these can be found from the conditions

$\mathbf{Y}_\nu(z)$ *is holomorphic for* $z \in D_+$,

$\{z^{-\nu}\mathbf{I} - \mathbf{Y}_\nu(z)\}\mathbf{F}'(z)$ *is holomorphic for* $z \in D_-$.

The first of these is obvious from (15.5), and the second is just a spectral paraphrasing of the condition $\mathbf{f}_\nu - \hat{\mathbf{f}}_\nu \perp \mathbf{f}_k$, $k \le 0$. Yaglom attacks $\mathbf{Y}_\nu$ row by row, and obtains a system of linear equations for the unknown coefficients of $\mathbf{Y}_\nu$. He also adapts this method to prediction on the basis of a bounded time interval in the past [41, §2].

Youla [42] has given an algebraic technique for carrying out the factorization (15.4) even for $r < q$, again for continuous time, based on the diagonalization of polynomial matrices by elementary transformations; cf. [5, p. 139]. In the discrete case we get from (15.1),

[25] Rosanov's proof can be simplified by appealing to the generalization of the classical canonical factorization of Hardy class functions to matrix-valued functions of the Hardy class H_2 on D_+ given in [18, 20, 22]. This generalization employed prediction theory as well as Potapov's important work [25], and illustrates how the subject has ramified.

$$\mathbf{F}'(z) = \frac{1}{p(z)} \mathbf{C}_1(z) \cdot \mathbf{D}(z) \cdot \mathbf{C}_2(z)$$

where $\mathbf{D}(\cdot)$ is a diagonal matrix polynomial and $\mathbf{C}_1(\cdot)$ and $\mathbf{C}_2(\cdot)$ are matrix polynomials with constant-valued determinants. By exploiting the hitherto unused fact that $\mathbf{F}'$ is a spectral density, Youla shows that the last factorization can be brought into the form (15.4), where $\mathbf{R}$ is a $q \times r$ rational matrix, holomorphic and left-invertible on D_+. (A slight variation of his technique would yield a $q \times q$ rational $\mathbf{R}$ of rank r.) In effect, Youla proves a factorization theorem, but his proof is constructive and provides linear algebraic equations for the determination of $\mathbf{R}$.

Wiener's original approach [35, Chapter IV] may be classified as analytic-cum-algebraic. To solve the Hopf-Wiener equation (13.15′), a Fourier analytic technique is to be used, which leads to the rational factorization problem (15.4). But to solve this problem an algebraic method is proposed; cf. [35, p. 108].

(ii) The only purely analytic method known to us is the one outlined in §14. This will work when $\mathbf{F}'$ satisfies condition (13.13), i.e., for rational $\mathbf{F}'$, only when $\det F'(e^{i\theta}) > 0$ for all θ. This method has been adopted to continuous time processes by Wong and Thomas [39], who also point out some short cuts in case $\mathbf{F}'$ is rational. But their paper contains several obscurities. This question of the extension of the factorization algorithm to continuous time is also the subject of a recent dissertation of Salehi [33]. In many practical situations, we would expect "weak memory," i.e., $\mathbf{\Gamma}_k = 0$ for $|k| > N$. In such cases $\mathbf{F}'$ would be a matrix trigonometrical polynomial (i.e., a rational function with poles only at 0 and ∞). Each series on the right side of (14.3) would then terminate as would the series (14.5), and the method would gain in efficiency.

Which of these methods for finding $\mathbf{R}$ and $\mathbf{Y}_\nu$ is best suited to the modern digital computer? Some interest has been aroused recently in this question because of its bearing on the discrimination of seismic signals due to different types of subterranean disturbances; cf. [28, 40]. A weakness of the analytical technique of §14 is the occurrence of alternating signs in the series (14.3), resulting perhaps in slow convergence. On the other hand, the algebraic techniques that have been proposed involve the solution of large systems of linear equations, and it is not clear to the writer if they are generally more efficient. A comparative study on the computer of the effectiveness of all these methods would be very useful.

Note added in proof. Some preliminary studies by C. Wunsch and R. A. Wiggins at the Massachusetts Institute of Technology on the relative computational merits of the analytic technique of §14 vis à vis E. A. Robinson's extension [28] for $q > 1$ of the least-squares procedure for $q = 1$ due to

N. Levinson [15, §3] suggest that both procedures are feasible, but that the latter converges more rapidly and involves less computing time; cf. R. A. Wiggins (1965) *Sci. Rept.* **9**, *Contract 19(604) 7378*, ARPA, Project Vela-Uniform. The writer, who is grateful to Dr. Wunch and Dr. Wiggins for this information feels, however, that the evidence is not yet conclusive, since a systematic error analysis is lacking.

REFERENCES

1. Besicovich, A. S. (1946). A general form of the covering principle and relative differentiation of additive functions, II. *Proc. Cambridge Philos. Soc.* **42** 1–10.
2. Beurling, A. (1949). On two problems concerning linear transformations in Hilbert space. *Acta Math.* **81** 239–255.
3. Cramér, H. (1940). On the theory of stationary random processes. *Ann. Math.* **41** 215–230.
4. Doob, J. L. (1953). *Stochastic Processes.* Wiley, New York.
5. Gantmacher, F. R. (1959). *Applications of the Theory of Matrices*, Vol. I. Chelsea, New York.
6. Halmos, P.(1961). Shifts of Hilbert spaces. *Crelle's J.* **208** 102–112.
7. Hanner, O. (1950). Deterministic and non-deterministic stationary random processes. *Ark. Mat.* **1** 161–177.
8. Helson, H. and Lowdenslager, D. (1959). Prediction theory and Fourier series in several variables, Part I. *Acta Math.* **99** 165; (1962). Part II. *Acta Math.* **106** 175–213.
9. Helson, H. and Lowdenslager, D. (1961). Vector-valued processes. *Proc. Fourth Berkeley Symp. Math. Statist. Prob.*, 203–212. Univ. California Press, Berkeley, California.
10. Jang Ze-Pei (1963). The prediction theory of multivariate stationary processes, I. *Chinese Math.* **4** 291–322; II. (1964). *Chinese Math.* 471–484.
11. Karhunen, K. (1947). Uber lineare Methoden in der Warhrscheinlickeitsrechnung. *Ann. Acad. Sci. Fenn.* **AI** 37.
12. Kolmogorov, A. N. (1941). Stationary sequences in Hilbert space, *Bull. Math. Univ. Moscow* **2** 1–40. (English transl. by Natasha Artin.)
13. Koopmans, L. H. (1964). On the coefficient of coherence for weakly stationary stochastic processes. *Ann. Math. Statist.* **35** 532–549.
14. Koopmans, L. H. (1964). On the multivariate analysis of weakly stationary stochastic processes. *Ann. Math. Statist.* **35** 1765–1780.
15. Levinson, N. (1947). The Wiener RMS error criterion in filter design and prediction. *J. Math. Phys.* **25** 261–278. (Reprinted as Appendix B in [35].)
16. Masani, P. (1959). Sur la fontion génératrice d'un processus stochastique vectoriel. *C. R. Acad. Sci. Paris* **249** 360–362.
17. Masani, P. (1959). Isomorphie entre les domaines temporel et spectral d'un processus vectoriel, régulier. *C. R. Acad. Sci. Paris* **249** 496–498.
18. Masani, P. (1959). Sur les fontions matricielles de la classe de Hardy H_2. *C. R. Acad. Sci. Paris* **249** 873–875; 906–907.
19. Masani, P. (1959). Cramer's theorem on monotone matrix-valued functions and the Wold decomposition. *Probability and Statistics* (U. Grenander, ed.) 175–189. Wiley, New York.
20. Masani, P. (1960). Une généralisation pour les fonctions matricielles de la classe de Hardy H_2 d'un théorème de Nevanlinna. *C. R. Acad. Sci. Paris* **251** 318–320.

21. MASANI, P. (1960). The prediction theory of multivariate stochastic processes, III. *Acta Math.* **104** 141–162.
22. MASANI, P. (1962). Shift invariant spaces and prediction theory. *Acta Math.* **107** 275–290.
23. MATVEEV, R. F. (1960). On singular multidimensional stationary processes. *Theory Probability Appl.* (*USSR*) *English Transl.* **5** 33–39.
24. MATVEEV, R. F. (1961). On multidimensional regular stationary processes. *Theory Probability Appl.* (*USSR*) *English Transl.* **6** 149–165.
25. POTAPOV, V. P. (1955). The multiplicative structure of J-contractive matrix functions. *Trudy. Moskov. Mat. Obsc.* **4** 125–236 (in Russian); (1960). *Amer. Math. Soc. Transl.* **15** 131–243.
26. ROBERTSON, J. B. (1963). Multivariate continuous parameter weakly stationary stochastic processes. Thesis. Indiana Univ., Bloomington, Indiana.
27. ROBERTSON, J. B. (1965). On wandering subspaces for unitary operators. *Proc. Amer. Math. Soc.* **16** 233–236.
28. ROBINSON, E. A. (1963). Mathematical development of discrete filters for detection of nuclear explosions. *J. Geophys. Res.* **68** 5559–5567.
29. ROSANOV, IU. A. (1958). The spectral theory of multi-dimensional stationary random processes with discrete time. *Uspekhi Mat. Nauk.* **XIII** 93–142 (in Russian).
30. ROSANOV, IU. A. (1960). Spectral properties of multivariate stationary processes and boundary properties of analytic matrices. *Theory Probability Appl.* (*USSR*) *English Transl.* **5** 362–376.
31. ROSANOV, IU. A. (1963). Stationary random processes, Moscow (Russian). (1965). English transl. by M. Ravindranathan, Indian Statistical Institute, Calcutta.
32. ROSENBERG, M. (1964). The square-integrability of matrix-valued functions with respect to a non-negative hermitian measure. *Duke Math. J.* **31** 291–298.
33. SALEHI, H. (1965). The prediction theory of multivariate stochastic processes with continuous time. Thesis. Indiana Univ., Bloomington, Indiana.
34. WHITTLE, P. (1953). The analysis of multiple stationary time series. *J. Roy. Statist. Soc. Ser. B* **15** 125–139.
35. WIENER, N. (1949). Extrapolation, Interpolation and Smoothing of Stationary Time Series with Engineering Applications. Wiley, New York.
36. WIENER, N. and MASANI, P. (1957). The prediction theory of multivariate stochastic processes, Part I. *Acta Math.* **98** 111–150; Part II. *Acta Math.* **99** (1958) 93–137.
37. WIENER, N. and MASANI, P. (1959). On bivariate stationary processes and the factorization of matrix-valued functions. *Theory Probability Appl.* (*USSR*) *English Transl.* **4** 300–308.
38. WOLD, H. (1954). *A study in the analysis of stationary Time Series*, 2nd ed. Almquist and Wiksell, Stockholm.
39. WONG, E. and THOMAS, J. B. (1961). On the multidimensional prediction and filtering problem and the factorization of spectral matrices. *J. Franklin Inst.* **272** 87–99.
40. WUNCH, C. (1965). The multiple spectral factorization method of Wiener and Masani. *IRE Trans. Inform. Theory* **11** 175–182.
41. YAGLOM, A. M. (1960). Effective solutions of linear approximation problems for multivariate stationary processes with a rational spectrum. *Theory Probability Appl.* (*USSR*) *English Transl.* **5** 239–264.
42. YOULA, D. C. (1961). On the factorization of rational matrices. *IRE Trans. Inform. Theory* **7** 172–189.
43. ZASUHIN, V. (1941). On the theory of multidimensional stationary random processes (Russian). *Dokl. Acad. Nauk. USSR* **33** 435–437.

Remarks on Higher Order Spectra[1]

M. ROSENBLATT[2]
MATHEMATICS DEPARTMENT
UNIVERSITY OF CALIFORNIA, SAN DIEGO
LA JOLLA, CALIFORNIA

1. INTRODUCTION

There is an extensive literature on second-order spectra of stationary vector-valued processes and questions relating to their estimation (see [4, 8]). Recently an interest in higher-order spectra of such processes has arisen [1–3, 5, 7–9]. A good deal of this has been due to problems in oceanography [2], where probabilistic models have been used to describe ocean waves and ship motions in seas. The random processes employed in some of these models are non-Gaussian, although they are in a certain sense close to Gaussian processes. The departure from "Gaussian-ness" can be measured in terms of higher-order spectra, and this may in turn be related to a nonlinear aspect of the equations of motion governing the problem.

2. BASIC CONCEPTS

Let $\{x_a(t); a = 1, \ldots, k\}$, $-\infty < t < \infty$, be a column k-vector of real-valued random processes that are jointly strictly stationary with respect to the time variable t. For convenience, assume that all moments of the processes exist and that the processes are continuous in mean. Also let $Ex_a(t) = 0$, $a = 1, \ldots, k$. The assumption of existence of second-order moments alone implies that the process $x(t) = (x_a(t))$ has the Fourier representation

$$\begin{aligned} x(t) &= \int_{-\infty}^{\infty} e^{it\lambda}\, dZ(\lambda) \\ &= \int_0^{\infty} \cos t\lambda\, dZ_1(\lambda) + \int_0^{\infty} \sin t\lambda\, dZ_2(\lambda). \end{aligned} \tag{1}$$

[1] This research was supported in part by the Office of Naval Research.
[2] John Simon Guggenheim Memorial Fellow.

Here $Z(\lambda) = (Z^{(a)}(\lambda))$ is a k-vector-valued process with orthogonal increments such that

$$E\, dZ(\lambda)\, dZ(\mu)' = dF(\lambda)\delta(\lambda - \mu), \tag{2}$$

where δ is the Kronecker delta and F is the second-order spectral distribution function of $x(t)$; that is, $F(\cdot)$ is the positive semi-definite $k \times k$ matrix-valued nondecreasing function of bounded variation such that

$$Ex(t)x(\tau)' = \int_{-\infty}^{\infty} e^{i(t-\tau)\lambda}\, dF(\lambda). \tag{3}$$

Here A' denotes the transpose conjugate of the matrix A. Since the components of $x(t)$ are real-valued, it follows that $dZ(\lambda) = \overline{dZ(-\lambda)}$ and that $dF(\lambda) = \overline{dF(-\lambda)}$. In the real representation (1), $Z_1(\lambda) = (Z_1{}^{(a)}(\lambda))$ and $Z_2(\lambda) = (Z_2{}^{(a)}(\lambda))$ are both k-vector processes of orthogonal increments and real components with the following properties:

$$\begin{aligned} dZ_1(\lambda) &= 2 \operatorname{Re} dZ(\lambda), \\ dZ_2(\lambda) &= -2 \operatorname{Im} dZ(\lambda), \\ E\, dZ_1(\lambda)\, dZ_1(\mu)' &= E\, dZ_2(\lambda)\, dZ_2(\mu)' = 2 \operatorname{Re} dF(\lambda)\delta(\lambda - \mu), \\ E\, dZ_1(\lambda)\, dZ_2(\mu)' &= 2 \operatorname{Im} dF(\lambda)\delta(\lambda - \mu). \end{aligned} \tag{4}$$

The higher-order moments

$$m_{a_1,\ldots,a_j}(t_1, \ldots, t_j) = Ex_{a_1}(t_1) \cdots x_{a_j}(t_j) = \mu_{a_1,\ldots,a_j}(t_2 - t_1, \ldots, t_j - t_1) \tag{5}$$

depend only on the differences $t_2 - t_1, \ldots, t_j - t_1$ because of the stationarity of the process. The moments are the coefficients in the Taylor expansion of the characteristic function

$$\phi(z_1, \ldots, z_k) = E \exp\left\{ i \sum_{s=1}^{k} z_s x_s(t_s) \right\} \tag{6}$$

of the random variables $x_s(t_s)$, $s = 1, \ldots, k$ about $z_1, \ldots, z_k = 0$. It is convenient and appropriate to introduce the semi-invariants or cumulants which are the corresponding coefficients in the Taylor expansion of $\log \phi(z_1, \ldots, z_k)$ about $z_1, \ldots, z_k = 0$. Call the semi-invariants

$$\tilde{S}_{a_1,\ldots,a_j}(t_1, \ldots, t_j) = \sigma_{a_1,\ldots,a_j}(t_2 - t_1, \ldots, t_j - t_1). \tag{7}$$

There are neat and convenient formulas relating the moments to the invariants and vice versa (see [3]). At this point we shall assume that the moments $\mu_{a_1,\ldots,a_j}$ have Fourier-Stieltjes representations in terms of complex-valued measures $M_{a_1,\ldots,a_j}$ of bounded variation

$$\mu_{a_1,\ldots,a_j}(\tau_1, \ldots, \tau_{j-1}) = \int \cdots \int \exp\left(i \sum_{s=1}^{j-1} \tau_s \lambda_s \right) dM_{a_1,\ldots,a_j}(\lambda_1, \ldots, \lambda_{j-1}) \tag{8}$$

In the second-order case, this is a consequence of our assumptions. In the higher-order case it is not. In fact, Sinai has given an example of a bounded strictly stationary process (with therefore all moments finite) for which such a representation in terms of M of bounded variation is not feasible [6]. He has also determined conditions that the spectra M must satisfy in the case of an ergodic process [7]. Nevertheless, the class of processes for which representations of type (8) hold for all moments is quite large and interesting. In particular, it is valid for m-step dependent processes with m finite. The representations (8) are valid for all moments with the functions M of bounded variation if and only if the representations

$$\sigma_{a_1,\dots,a_j}(\tau_1,\dots,\tau_{j-1}) = \int\cdots\int \exp\left(i\sum_{s=1}^{j-1}\tau_s\lambda_s\right) dS_{a_1,\dots,a_j}(\lambda_1,\dots,\lambda_{j-1}) \quad (9)$$

are valid for all semiinvariant functions $\sigma_{a_1,\dots,a_j}$ in terms of spectral functions $S_{a_1,\dots,a_j}$ of bounded variation. Even when the process $x(t)$ is Gaussian, one cannot expect the spectral functions of the moments $\mu_{a_1,\dots,a_j}$ to be absolutely continuous. In the Gaussian case all semi-invariant spectra $S_{a_1,\dots,a_j}$ of order higher than the second vanish, and it is reasonable to assume that the higher-order semi-invariant spectra might be absolutely continuous with

$$dS_{a_1,\dots,a_j}(\lambda_1,\dots,\lambda_{j-1}) = f_{a_1,\dots,a_j}(\lambda_1,\dots,\lambda_{j-1})\, d\lambda_1\cdots d\lambda_{j-1}. \quad (10)$$

We shall assume even more, namely that $\sigma_{a_1,\dots,a_j}(\tau_1,\dots,\tau_{j-1})$ is in L_1 with respect to $\tau_1,\dots,\tau_{j-1}$. Of course, this implies that $f_{a_1,\dots,a_j}$ is continuous in its arguments $\lambda_1,\dots,\lambda_{j-1}$. Such assumptions amount to curious types of mixing conditions on the moments $m_{a_1,\dots,a_j}$.

Note that (1) and (8) imply that

$$\begin{aligned} dM_{a_1,\dots,a_j}&(\lambda_1,\dots,\lambda_{j-1}) \\ &= E\, dZ^{(a_1)}(\lambda)\, dZ^{(a_2)}(\lambda_1)\cdots dZ^{(a_j)}(\lambda_{j-1})\delta(\lambda+\lambda_1+\cdots+\lambda_{j-1}). \end{aligned} \quad (11)$$

Further if we set $\lambda = \lambda_0$, then

$$\begin{aligned} dS_{a_1,\dots,a_j}(\lambda_1,\dots,\lambda_{j-1}) &= dM_{a_1,\dots,a_j}(\lambda_1,\dots,\lambda_{j-1}) \\ &= f_{a_1,\dots,a_j}(\lambda_1,\dots,\lambda_{j-1})\, d\lambda_1\cdots d\lambda_{j-1} \\ &= E\, dZ^{(a_1)}(\lambda_0)\, dZ^{(a_2)}(\lambda_1)\cdots dZ^{(a_j)}(\lambda_{j-1})\delta(\lambda_0+\lambda_1+\cdots+\lambda_{j-1}) \end{aligned} \quad (12)$$

as long as the frequencies $\lambda_0, \lambda_1, \dots, \lambda_{j-1}$ do not also satisfy a restraint of the form

$$\sum_{s\in I}\lambda_s = 0, \quad (13)$$

where I is a proper subset of $\{0, 1, \dots, j-1\}$. Of course, the spectral density $f_{a_1,\dots,a_j}(\lambda_1,\dots,\lambda_{j-1})$ is generally complex-valued and its real and imaginary parts will be referred to as

$$c_{a_1,\dots,a_j}(\lambda_1,\dots,\lambda_{j-1}) \quad \text{and} \quad q_{a_1,\dots,a_j}(\lambda_1,\dots,\lambda_{j-1}). \quad (14)$$

It is clear that

$$
\begin{aligned}
c_{a_1,\ldots,a_j}(\lambda_1, \ldots, \lambda_{j-1}) &= c_{a_1,\ldots,a_j}(-\lambda_1, \ldots, -\lambda_{j-1}),\\
q_{a_1,\ldots,a_j}(\lambda_1, \ldots, \lambda_{j-1}) &= -q_{a_1,\ldots,a_j}(-\lambda_1, \ldots, -\lambda_{j-1}),
\end{aligned} \tag{15}
$$

since the process $x(t)$ has real-valued components. Also,

$$
\begin{aligned}
c_{a_1,\ldots,a_j}(\lambda_1, \ldots, \lambda_{j-1}) = \frac{1}{(2\pi)^{j-1}} \int \cdots \int \cos(\tau_1\lambda_1 + \cdots + \tau_{j-1}\lambda_{j-1})\\
\times \sigma_{a_1,\ldots,a_j}(\tau_1, \ldots, \tau_{j-1})\, d\tau_1 \cdots d\tau_{j-1},
\end{aligned} \tag{16}
$$

$$
\begin{aligned}
q_{a_1,\ldots,a_j}(\lambda_1, \ldots, \lambda_{j-1}) = \frac{1}{(2\pi)^{j-1}} \int \cdots \int \sin(\tau_1\lambda_1 + \cdots + \tau_{j-1}\lambda_{j-1})\\
\times \sigma_{a_1,\ldots,a_j}(\tau_1, \ldots, \tau_{j-1})\, d\tau_1 \cdots d\tau_{j-1}.
\end{aligned} \tag{17}
$$

Equation (12) relates the spectral density $f_{a_1,\ldots,a_j}$ to moments of the complex-valued random spectral functions $dZ_{a_i}(\lambda_{i-1})$. It is clearly of interest to be able to relate the real and imaginary parts of $f_{a_1,\ldots,a_j}$, that is, $c_{a_1,\ldots,a_j}$ and $q_{a_1,\ldots,a_j}$ to the moments of the real-valued random spectral functions $dZ_1^{(a_i)}(\lambda)$ and $dZ_2^{(a_i)}(\lambda)$. Since the relations are somewhat more complicated in the real-valued case than in the complex-valued case, we shall carry out the computations only in a few third-order cases. These computations will indicate how the corresponding relations are obtained for all higher-order moments. Now

$$
\begin{aligned}
E\, dZ_1^{(a_1)}(\lambda_0)\, dZ_1^{(a_2)}(\lambda_1)\, dZ_1^{(a_3)}(\lambda_2)&\\
&= E\, d\{Z^{(a_1)}(\lambda_0) + Z^{(a_1)}(-\lambda_0)\}\, d\{Z^{(a_2)}(\lambda_1) + Z^{(a_2)}(-\lambda_1)\}\\
&\quad \times d\{Z^{(a_3)}(\lambda_2) + Z^{(a_3)}(-\lambda_2)\}\\
&= [f_{a_1,a_2,a_3}(\lambda_1, \lambda_2) + f_{a_1,a_2,a_3}(-\lambda_1, -\lambda_2)]\, d\lambda_1\, d\lambda_2\\
&\quad \times \delta(\lambda_0 - \lambda_1 - \lambda_2)\\
&= 2c_{a_1,a_2,a_3}(\lambda_1, \lambda_2)\, d\lambda_1\, d\lambda_2 \delta(\lambda_0 - \lambda_1 - \lambda_2)\\
E\, dZ_1^{(a_1)}(\lambda_0)\, dZ_1^{(a_2)}(\lambda_1)\, dZ_2^{(a_3)}(\lambda_2)&\\
&= iE\, d\{Z^{(a_1)}(\lambda_0) + Z^{(a_1)}(-\lambda_0)\}\, d\{Z^{(a_2)}(\lambda_1) + Z^{(a_2)}(-\lambda_1\})\\
&\quad \times d\{Z^{(a_3)}(\lambda_2) - Z^{(a_3)}(-\lambda_2)\}\\
&= i[f_{a_1,a_2,a_3}(\lambda_1,\lambda_2) - f_{a_1,a_2,a_3}(-\lambda_1,-\lambda_2)] d\lambda_1 d\lambda_2\\
&\quad \times \delta(\lambda_0 - \lambda_1 - \lambda_2)\\
&= -2q_{a_1,a_2,a_3}(\lambda_1, \lambda_2) d\lambda_1\, d\lambda_2 \delta(\lambda_0 - \lambda_1 - \lambda_2)
\end{aligned} \tag{18}
$$

if $0 < \lambda_1 < \lambda_2 < \lambda_0$. The moment $E\, dZ_{i_1}^{(a_1)}(\lambda_0)\, dZ_{i_2}^{(a_2)}(\lambda_1)\, dZ_{i_3}^{(a_3)}(\lambda_2)$ is a multiple of $c_{a_1,a_2,a_3}(\lambda_1, \lambda_2)\, d\lambda_1\, d\lambda_2 \delta(\lambda_0 - \lambda_1 - \lambda_2)$ if the sum $i_1 + i_2 + i_3$ is odd and is a multiple of $q_{a_1,a_2,a_3}(\lambda_1, \lambda_2)\, d\lambda_1\, d\lambda_2 \times \delta(\lambda_0 - \lambda_1 - \lambda_2)$ if the sum $i_1 + i_2 + i_3$ is even.

3. BISPECTRAL ESTIMATES

We shall just briefly indicate the character of certain results on estimates of third-order spectra. Tukey has called such spectra bispectra, presumably because they are functions of two wave numbers of frequencies. The corresponding results for orders higher than the third would have to be for spectra of semi-invariant functions and would be of a more complicated character. However, there would be substantial parallels to the comments made here and the results cited.

Since the means $Ex_a(t) = 0$, the third-order semi-invariants are the third-order moments. Assume that the process is observed from time zero to time T. Then

$$\mu^{(T)}_{a_1,a_2,a_3}(\tau_1,\tau_2) = \frac{1}{T}\int_{\Delta(\tau_1,\tau_2)} x_{a_1}(\tau)x_{a_2}(\tau+\tau_1)x_{a_3}(\tau+\tau_2)\,d\tau \tag{19}$$

will be a reasonable estimate of $\mu_{a_1,a_2,a_3}(\tau_1, \tau_2)$ at least for moderate values of $|\tau_1|$, $|\tau_2|$ when T is large. Here $\Delta(\tau_1, \tau_2)$ is the interval of values of τ such that τ, $\tau + \tau_1$, $\tau + \tau_2$ all lie in $[0, T]$. Let $w(\tau_1, \tau_2)$ be a real continuous weight function that is zero outside $|\tau_1|, |\tau_2| \leq 1$, with $w(0, 0) = 1$, whose Fourier transform

$$W(\lambda_1, \lambda_2) = \frac{1}{(2\pi)^2}\int\int e^{-i\lambda_1\tau_1 - i\lambda_2\tau_2}w(\tau_1, \tau_2)\,d\tau_1\,d\tau_2 \tag{20}$$

is nonnegative and satisfies the conditions

$$W(\lambda_1, \lambda_2) \leq \frac{K}{1 + (\lambda_1{}^2 + \lambda_2{}^2)^{1/2+\varepsilon}} \tag{21}$$

for some K and $\varepsilon > 0$. Note that

$$W(\lambda_1, \lambda_2) = W(-\lambda_1, -\lambda_2). \tag{22}$$

Now consider a scale factor $B_T \to 0$ as $T \to \infty$ at such a rate that $B_T{}^2T \to \infty$. Then

$$c^{(T)}_{a_1,a_2,a_3}(\lambda_1, \lambda_2) = \frac{1}{(2\pi)^2}\int\int \mu^{(T)}_{a_1,a_2,a_3}(\tau_1, \tau_2)w(B_T\tau_1, B_T\tau_2)\cos(\lambda_1\tau_1 + \lambda_2\tau_2)\,d\tau_1\,d\tau_2, \tag{23}$$

$$q^{(T)}_{a_1',a_2',a_3'}(\lambda_1', \lambda_2') = \frac{1}{(2\pi)^2}\int\int \mu^{(T)}_{a_1',a_2',a_3'}(\tau_1, \tau_2)w(B_T\tau_1, B_T\tau_2)\sin(\lambda_1'\tau_1\ \lambda_2'\tau_2)\,d\tau_1\,d\tau_2 \tag{23'}$$

are reasonable estimates of $c_{a_1,a_2,a_3}(\lambda_1, \lambda_2)$ and $q_{a_1',a_2',a_3'}(\lambda_1, \lambda_2)$. It can readily be shown that they are asymptotically unbiased estimates as $T \to \infty$. Further, the asymptotic behavior of their covariances can be determined as $T \to \infty$.

Now the Fourier transform of $w(B_T\tau_1, B_T\tau_2)$ is

$$B_T^{-2}W(B_T^{-1}\lambda_1, B_T^{-1}\lambda_2), \tag{24}$$

a nonnegative weight function of total mass 1 that concentrates more and more mass in the immediate neighborhood of $(\lambda_1, \lambda_2) = (0, 0)$ as $T \to \infty$. We shall examine the asymptotic behavior of the covariances of (23) and (23′) for $0 < \lambda_1 < \lambda_2$ and $0 < \lambda_1' < \lambda_2'$ as $T \to \infty$. If we write out the full expression for such a covariance, it will consist of weighted sums of products of semi-invariants, where the sum of the orders of the semi-invariants in each such product is 6. Because the weight function (24) acts asymptotically like a delta function at (0, 0), one can show that the products having a factor which is a semi-invariant of order greater than 2 can be neglected. In fact, only one of the terms involving second-order semi-invariants alone, the one pairing a_j with a_j', $j = 1, 2, 3$ will make the main contribution asymptotically. One is led to the following results:

$$\begin{aligned}\lim_{T\to\infty} B_T{}^2T \operatorname{cov}\{c^{(T)}_{a_1,a_2,a_3}(\lambda_1, \lambda_2), c^{(T)}_{a_1',a_2',a_3'}(\lambda_1', \lambda_2')\}& \\ = \lim_{T\to\infty} B_T{}^2T \operatorname{cov}\{q^{(T)}_{a_1,a_2,a_3}(\lambda_1, \lambda_2), q^{(T)}_{a_1',a_2',a_3'}(\lambda_1', \lambda_2')\}& \\ = \pi \operatorname{Re}\{f_{a_1,a_1'}(-\lambda_1 - \lambda_2)f_{a_2,a_2'}(\lambda_1)f_{a_3,a_3'}(\lambda_2)\}& \\ \times \int\int W^2(\lambda_1, \lambda_2)\, d\lambda_1\, d\lambda_2 \delta(\lambda_1 - \lambda_1')\delta(\lambda_2 - \lambda_2')&\end{aligned} \tag{25}$$

$$\begin{aligned}\lim_{T\to\infty} B_T{}^2T \operatorname{cov}\{c^{(T)}_{a_1,a_2,a_3}(\lambda_1, \lambda_2), q^{(T)}_{a_1',a_2',a_3'}(\lambda_1', \lambda_2')\}& \\ = \pi \operatorname{Im}\{f_{a_1,a_1'}(-\lambda_1 - \lambda_2)f_{a_2,a_2'}(\lambda_1)f_{a_3,a_3'}(\lambda_2)\}& \\ \times \int\int W^2(\lambda_1, \lambda_2)\, d\lambda_1\, d\lambda_2 \delta(\lambda_1 - \lambda_1')\delta(\lambda_2 - \lambda_2'),&\end{aligned} \tag{26}$$

where $0 < \lambda_1 < \lambda_2$ and $0 < \lambda_1' < \lambda_2'$. These results are an extension of some of those cited in [4] and [5]. A uniform mixing condition on the processes is enough to ensure asymptotic normality of the estimates [9].

REFERENCES

1. Brillinger, D. (1964). An introduction to polyspectra. Econometric Research Program Research Memorandum No. 67, Princeton Univ.
2. Hasselman, K., Munk, W. and MacDonald, G. (1963). Bispectrum of ocean waves. *Time Series Analysis* (M. Rosenblatt, ed.). 125–139. Wiley, New York.

3. Leonov, V. P. and Shiryaev, A. N. (1959). On a method of calculation of semi-invariants. *Theory Probability Appl.* (*USSR*) (*English Trans.*). 319–329.
4. Rosenblatt, M. (1959). Statistical analysis of stochastic processes with stationary residuals. *Probability and Statistics* (U. Grenander, ed.). 246–275. Wiley, New York.
5. Rosenblatt, M. and Van Ness, J. W. (1965). Estimation of the bispectrum. *Ann. Math. Statist.* **36** 1120–1136.
6. Sinai, Ya. G. (1963). On the properties of spectra of ergodic dynamical systems. *Dokl. Akad. Nauk SSSR* **150** 1235–1237.
7. Sinai, Ya. G. (1963). On higher order spectral measures of ergodic stationary processes. *Theory Probability Appl.* (*USSR*) (*English trans.*) 429–436.
8. Tukey, J. W. (1959). An introduction to the measurement of spectra. *Probability and Statistics* (U. Grenander, ed.). 300–330. Wiley, New York.
9. Van Ness, J. W. (1965). Asymptotic normality of bispectral estimates. Technical Report No. 14, Dept. Statistics. Stanford Univ.

Estimation of Principal Components and Related Models by Iterative Least Squares

HERMAN WOLD
UNIVERSITY INSTITUTE OF STATISTICS
UPPSALA, SWEDEN

SUMMARY

For the estimation of principal components an iterative procedure based on the principle of least squares has recently been reported [19]. Lyttkens in his report to this Symposium [7] developed the rationale of the new technique, and showed the close connection between two approaches in multivariate analysis, (a) principal components [3, 8]; and (b) Young-Whittle's approach in factor analysis [12, 21]. The present paper focuses on the flexibility of the iterative method in adaptations and extensions in various directions. Section 1 deals with factor models with one factor and equal residual variances, and analyzes the component structure in terms of the factor structure. The ensuing relations are exploited in Section 2 to estimate the one-factor model, making use of the least-squares estimate of the first principal component. Section 3 extends the iterative method to a multidimensional approach of principal components, and to hybrid models that involve multiple regression and canonical correlations.

1. COMPONENT STRUCTURE vs. FACTOR STRUCTURE

1.1. Introduction

Sections 1 and 2 of the present paper were planned as a counterpart to [13], a Monte Carlo illustration of Whittle's application of principal-component analysis for the estimation of Young-Whittle's factor model [12], the incentive for a reconsideration being to illustrate the iterative estimation technique recently reported [7, 19]. Specific attention is now paid to similarities and differences between component analysis and factor analysis. Whereas component models and factor models under suitable conditions (equal variances of the factor residuals) have the same numerical values for the parameters β that constitute the loadings in the factor model and the direction cosines in the component model, the two approaches differ when it comes to residuals, factors, and components. The key point is that the *models* differ; hence they call for different estimation techniques. The parting of the ways was not clear to me at the time of the Uppsala Symposium on Psychological Factor Analysis (1953), where [13] was presented and discussed. Therefore, I made it a point to emphasize the differences at issue in the first draft of the present paper as reported and discussed at the Dayton Symposium on Multivariate Analysis. By a suitable transformation, as shown in Section 2, estimates of component structure can be used to obtain estimates of factor structure. In the first draft of the paper, the transformation from component structure to factor structure was carried out in one stroke, by a joint treatment of population properties and sample properties. In the final version, to make for clarity, the transformation is carried out separately for the population and the sample.

The differences between component analysis and factor analysis are by no means a new feature. Specific reference is made to the clarifying paper by Rao [9]. To quote a statement of Rao's that bears upon collective analysis of the variates, principal components aim at reproducing their entire moment matrix, theoretical μ_{ij} or observed m_{ij}, whereas factor analysis only aims at reproducing the nondiagonal elements, $i \neq j$. Thus it is clear from Rao's review that the parting of the ways lies in the model itself, and is not primarily a matter of different estimation techniques, such as maximum likelihood vs. least squares. To some extent the differences between the two types of models have been obscured by other issues, notably collective analysis vs. individual analysis, and the representation of the individual factors or components as parameters vs. random variates.

The approach of the present paper is limited in two respects. One is that the method works only for factor models with equal (or known) residual variances. The other is that the estimation of factor structure provides estimates not of the individual factor values ζ_t but of the conditional expectation of ζ_t for given individual component ξ_t. In practice it is an important problem to estimate the factor structure when the residual variances may be different. For this extension reference is made to the techniques designed by Jöreskog [4; 5; 19, Chap. 8]. It is an interesting question how the estimation of factor structure in Section 2 compares with Jöreskog's and other techniques. This is, however, an order of problems that falls outside the scope of the present paper.

1.2. Principal Components vs. Factor Representation

Throughout the paper we shall be concerned with one and the same set of variates—theoretical,

$$\eta_1, \ldots, \eta_p \tag{1a}$$

or observed in a sample of n observations,

$$y_{i1}, \dots, y_{in}; \qquad i = 1, \dots, p \tag{1b}$$

The number of variates, p, will be kept fixed. We shall consider two theoretical representations,

$$\eta_i = \sum_{a=1}^{k'} \beta_{ia}\xi_a + \varepsilon_i \tag{2}$$

$$= \sum_{a=1}^{k} \beta_{ia}\zeta_a + \delta_i \tag{3}$$

where the parameters β_{ia} are assumed to satisfy conditions

$$\sum_{i=1}^{p} \beta_{ia}^2 = 1 \tag{4a}$$

$$\sum_{i=1}^{p} \beta_{ia}\beta_{ib} = 0; \qquad a \neq b. \tag{4b}$$

Here and in the following, the unspecified integers run as follows:

$$a, b = 1, \dots, k \text{ or } k'; \qquad i, j = 1, \dots, p; \qquad t, u = 1, \dots, n.$$

Model (2) will be specified as a component structure, model (3) as a factor structure. Hence the parameters β_{ia} figure as direction cosines of the principal components ξ_a in model (2), and as loadings of the factors ζ_a in model (3). To bring the similarity between approaches (2) and (3) in relief, we deviate somewhat from current usage, inasmuch as the normalization (4a) is current in component analysis, whereas factor analysis usually adopts the normalization

$$E(\zeta_a{}^2) = 1.$$

Any two components ξ_a and ξ_b are assumed to have zero product moments, just as is customary with factor models,

$$E(\xi_a\xi_b) = 0, \quad E(\zeta_a\zeta_b) = 0; \qquad a \neq b \tag{5}$$

and it is known that this involves no loss of generality (see [12]).

Both representations (2) and (3) will be specified in terms of conditional expectations; thus

$$E(\eta_i \mid \xi_1, \dots, \xi_{k'}) = \sum_{a=1}^{k'} \beta_{ia}\xi_a \tag{6}$$

$$E(\eta_i \mid \zeta_1, \dots, \zeta_k) = \sum_{a=1}^{k} \beta_{ia}\zeta_a . \tag{7}$$

Hence we shall say that the systematic part (6) in relation (2) is a *predictor* of the variate η_i, and similarly for the systematic part (7) of (3); see [18]. Assumption (6) implies

$$E(\varepsilon_i) = 0\,; \qquad E(\xi_a \varepsilon_i) = 0 \tag{8}$$

and similarly for (7),

$$E(\delta_i) = 0\,; \qquad E(\zeta_a \delta_i) = 0\,. \tag{9}$$

In model (2) the components ξ_a are assumed to allow the reverse representation

$$\xi_a = \sum_{i=1}^{p} \beta_{ia} \eta_i\,. \tag{10a}$$

Substituting (10a) to the right in (2), reduction by the use of (4) gives

$$\sum_{i=1}^{p} \beta_{ia} \varepsilon_i = 0\,. \tag{10b}$$

The equivalent relations (10a and b) will be referred to as the *component property* of the model (cf. [7]).

In model (3) the residuals δ_i are assumed to have zero product moments:

$$E(\delta_i \delta_j) = 0 \tag{11}$$

which in conjunction with (9a) implies that the factor residuals are mutually uncorrelated; this will be referred to as the *factor property* of the model.

Comments.[1] (a) Reference is made to the geometric interpretation of the component model (2) in terms of lines and planes of closest fit in the joint distribution of the variates under analysis, theoretical (1a) or observed (1b) [3, 8, 12]. The first component ξ_1 ($a = 1$) has the largest variance and gives the line of closest fit in the sense of least squares. If the joint distribution is nonsingular, the plane of closest fit is orthogonal to the pth component.

The classic estimation method for component structure [3, 8] gives the variances and loadings of the components as eigenvalues and eigenvectors of the product-moment matrix μ, m of the variates under analysis, theoretical

$$\mu = [\mu_{ij}]\,; \qquad \mu_{ij} = E(\eta_i \eta_j) \tag{12a}$$

or observed,

$$m = [m_{ij}]\,; \qquad m_{ij} = \frac{1}{n} \sum_{t=1}^{n} y_{it} y_{jt}\,. \tag{12b}$$

[1] The reader is assumed to have a general orientation about factor and component analysis. The introductory sections of [5] are very instructive for the purpose. For the general background in multivariate analysis, see [1, 6].

(b) Factor models originate from experimental psychology [10, 11]. Distinction is made between *individual* and *collective* analysis; that is, individual representation of the variates η_i as in (2) or (3) vs. models formulated in terms of product moments (12a). Speaking generally, there is no difference in principle between an individual model and the corresponding collective model. Factor models are usually specified in individual terms; factor estimation techniques make use of observed product moments (12b), and the statement of numerical results and verbal conclusions is often oriented toward collective rather than individual aspects. Component models are usually formulated in collective terms. The work of Whittle [12] was pioneering in that it emphasized the equivalence in the component approach between the basic assumptions of collective analysis and individual analysis.

We see that the factor and component properties (10) and (11) are mutually exclusive. This is clearly so, since (10b) implies

$$E\left[\left(\sum_{i=1}^{p} \beta_{ia}\varepsilon_i\right)^2\right] = 0 \tag{13}$$

and this could not be true if the component residuals ε_i and ε_j were to satisfy an assumption of type (11).

Note the difference in current terminology between the numbers k and k' in models (2) and (3). For k-factor models (3) such that all residuals δ_i have the same variance $\sigma^2(\delta_i)$ it has been shown by Whittle [12] that in the corresponding component structure (2), with $k' = p$, there are k components that have larger variance than the remaining $p - k$ ones, all of which have the same variance $\sigma^2(\varepsilon_i)$. In such a case, as shown by Lyttkens [7], the variances of these components are given by

$$E(\xi_a^2) = \sum_i \sum_j \beta_{ia}\beta_{ja}E(\eta_i\eta_j)\,; \qquad a = 1, \ldots, k. \tag{14}$$

(c) In specifying models (2) and (3) in terms of predictors as in (6) and (7), rather than in terms of residual properties (8) or (9) as is customary, the operative use of the models for predictive purposes is emphasized (cf. [15, 17, 18]). For given components ξ_a, the parameters β_{ia} have least-squares properties in model (2), that is, the residuals ε_i have the smallest possible standard deviation, and for given factors ζ_a the same β_{ia}'s have least-squares properties in model (3).

If the probability distribution of the variates η_i is jointly normal, specification (6) is equivalent to (8), and (7) equivalent to (9).

1.3. Young-Whittle's Approach with One Factor and Equal Residual Variances

Following Young [21] and Whittle [12], we shall consider a factor model (3) with equal residual variances. To estimate such a model Whittle applies the

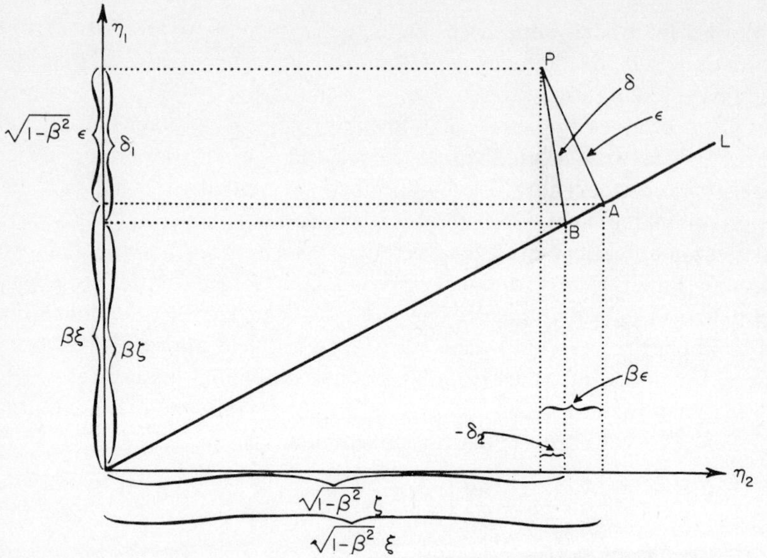

Fig. 1. The dual representation (15) and (16) of two variates η_1 and η_2.

principle of least squares, minimizing the total residual variance. In the case of one factor, as will be briefly reviewed in this section, his estimation procedure gives consistent estimates for the loadings β_i, and a consistent estimate not of the factor ζ but of the first principal component ξ.

The Dual Representation. We form the factor model (3) in the special case of one factor, say ζ,

$$\eta_i = \beta_i \zeta + \delta_i \tag{15a}$$

and assume that all residuals δ_i have the same standard deviation,

$$\sigma(\delta_i) = \text{const.} = \frac{1}{p^{1/2}}\,\sigma(\delta), \tag{15b}$$

where

$$\delta = (\delta_1{}^2 + \cdots + \delta_p{}^2)^{1/2} \tag{15c}$$

is the total residual of the one-factor model.

Further we shall represent the variates η_i in terms of component model (2) with one component ξ and the same parameters β_i,

$$\eta_i = \beta_i \xi + \varepsilon_i. \tag{16a}$$

Here we rewrite the residuals in the normalized form

$$\varepsilon_i = \varphi_i \varepsilon \tag{16b}$$

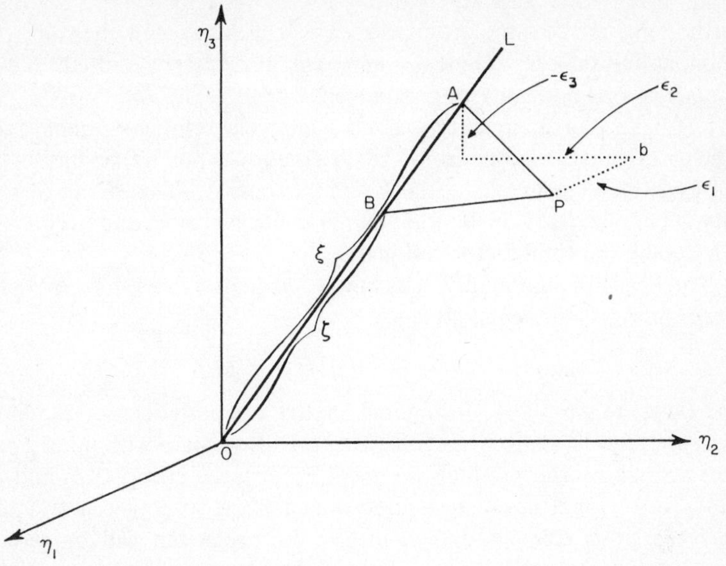

Fig. 2. The dual representation (15) and (16) of three variates η_1, η_2, and η_3.

with

$$\varepsilon = (\varepsilon_1{}^2 + \cdots + \varepsilon_p{}^2)^{1/2}; \qquad \varphi_1{}^2 + \cdots + \varphi_p{}^2 = 1 \tag{16c}$$

where ε is the total residual of the component representation (16a).

The dual representation (15) and (16) of the variates η_i is illustrated in Fig. 1 for $p = 2$ and in Fig. 2 for $p = 3$. The graphs show an arbitrary point $P = (\eta_1, \ldots, \eta_p)$ as generated from model (15) with factor $\zeta(=OB)$ and residuals δ_i. The total factor residual δ is given by the line PB. The projection of P on the line L that extends OB gives the point A and thereby the component $\xi(=OA)$. The line PA gives the total component residual ε, and the projection of PA on the coordinate axes give the component residuals ε_i. We see that the coefficients φ_i may be interpreted as direction cosines of ε. Further we note that the φ_i's for $p > 2$ are random relative to the direction cosines β_i, and have $p - 2$ degrees of freedom.

Orthogonality Properties of Component and Factor Residuals. With reference to Figs. 1 and 2, three different notions of orthogonality are in play. We shall see that component and factor residuals have one mode of orthogonality in common, whereas the two others are characteristic of component and factor residuals, respectively.

(a) Geometric orthogonality, first mode. According to (15a), each factor residual δ_i is measured along the coordinate axis of the corresponding variate η_i. Since the coordinate axes are mutually orthogonal, the residuals δ_i

are orthogonal in the same geometric sense. The situation is the same for the component residuals ε_i. Hence component and factor residuals have this first mode of orthogonality in common.

(b) Geometric orthogonality, second mode. The total component residual ε is the orthogonal distance from the observational point P to the k'-dimensional hyperplane spanned by the k' components ξ_a. This mode of orthogonality is characteristic of the total component residual ε, and accordingly is not shared by the total factor residual δ.

(c) Stochastic orthogonality. The factor residuals δ_i have zero expectation and zero product moments, giving

$$E(\delta_i\delta_j) = E(\delta_i)E(\delta_j) = 0. \tag{17}$$

Hence they are mutually orthogonal in the stochastic sense. Similarly, if we interpret the residuals δ_i as elements in a Hilbert space with inner products (δ_i, δ_j) defined by the product moments $E(\delta_i\delta_j)$, the elements δ_i and δ_j are mutually orthogonal in the terminology of Hilbert-space geometry; that is, if we project one element upon another, the projection will be zero. This mode of orthogonality is characteristic of the factor residuals δ_i; as pointed out in connection with (13), it is not shared by the component residuals ε_i.

Component Structure (16) *Expressed in Terms of One-Factor Structure* (15).

Theorem 1. *For any one-factor Young-Whittle model* (15) *the relations*

$$\xi = \sum_i \beta_i \eta_i \tag{18}$$

$$\varepsilon_i = \eta_i - \beta_i \xi \tag{19}$$

whence

$$\varepsilon = (\varepsilon_1{}^2 + \cdots + \varepsilon_p{}^2)^{1/2}; \qquad \varphi_i = \varepsilon_i/\varepsilon \tag{20}$$

define a component representation (16) *with the following properties*:

$$E(\eta_i{}^2) = \beta_i{}^2 E(\zeta^2) + \frac{1}{p}\sigma^2(\delta) \tag{21}$$

$$= \beta_i{}^2 E(\xi^2) + \sigma^2(\varepsilon_i{}^2) \tag{22}$$

$$E(\xi) = E(\zeta) \tag{23a}$$

$$E(\xi^2) = E(\zeta^2) + \frac{1}{p}\sigma^2(\delta) \tag{23b}$$

$$\sigma(\varepsilon) = \left(\frac{p-1}{p}\right)^{1/2} \sigma(\delta) \tag{24}$$

$$E(\xi\zeta) = E(\zeta^2). \tag{25}$$

Proof. Relations (18) to (20) are immediate implications of (10a) and the normalized expression (16c) for the component residuals ε_i. Relations (21) and (22) follow from definitions (15) and (16) and the general properties (8) and (9).

Substituting (15a) in (18) we obtain

$$\xi = \zeta + \sum_i \beta_i \delta_i \tag{26}$$

which gives (23a). Further, making use of (9) and (15b),

$$E(\xi^2) = E(\zeta^2) + \sigma^2(\delta_i) \qquad E(\xi\zeta) = E(\zeta^2)$$

which verifies (23b) and (25). Finally, summing over i in (21) and (22) and paying regard to (23),

$$\sum_i E(\eta_i{}^2) = E(\zeta^2) + \sigma^2(\delta) = E(\xi^2) + \sigma^2(\varepsilon) \tag{27a}$$

$$= E(\zeta^2) + \frac{1}{p}\,\sigma^2(\delta) + \sigma^2(\varepsilon) \tag{27b}$$

where (27a and b) imply (24). Theorem 1 is proved.

Comment. Writing

$$\xi^* = E(\xi \mid \zeta) \tag{28}$$

we note that (26) gives the conditional expectations

$$\xi^* = \zeta \qquad E[(\xi^*)^2 \mid \zeta] = E(\xi^* \zeta \mid \zeta) = \zeta^2 .$$

This gives the unconditional expectations

$$E(\xi^*) = E(\zeta) \qquad E[(\xi^*)^2] = E(\xi^*\zeta) = E(\zeta^2).$$

1.4. NILES Estimation of Principal Components[2]

We shall consider a $p \times m$ array of observations (1b) which we assume to be a sample of variates (1a) ruled by the dual model (2) and (3). For two models as estimated from the sample we write

$$y_{it} = \sum_{a=1}^{k'} b_{ia} x_{at} + e_{it} \tag{29}$$

$$= \sum_{a=1}^{k} b_{ia} z_{at} + d_{it}. \tag{30}$$

The NILES procedure gives estimates b_{ia}, x_{ia}, e_{it} of parameters, components, and residuals in the component model (2). In Section 2 we shall

[2] NILES = Nonlinear Iterative Least Squares. See [19]; also cf. [16]

adapt the procedure to obtain estimates for the elements z and d of the factor model (3).

NILES estimation of the component model (2) *is an iterative regression procedure that may be summarized as follows.*

(a) The procedure works stepwise, estimating component by component, $a = 1, \dots, k'$. In each step the component $x_{a1}, \dots, x_{an}$ and its direction cosines $b_{1a}, \dots, b_{pa}$ are estimated by the iterative procedure. Thus when the $(a-1)$st component and its cosines have been estimated, the procedure obtains a sequence of iterative estimates of component and cosines in the ath step,

$$x_{at}^{(s)},\ b_{ia}^{(s)}; \qquad s = 1, 2, \dots \tag{31a}$$

giving in the limit

$$x_{at} = \lim x_{at}^{(s)}; \qquad b_{ia} = \lim b_{ia}^{(s)} \qquad (s \to \infty) \tag{31b}$$

as the NILES estimates for the ath component ξ_a and its direction cosines β_{ia} in model (2).

(b) To start the iteration (31) we make $s = 1$, and take for $b_{ia}^{(1)}$ a set of p arbitrary numbers

$$b_{1a}^{(1)}, \dots, b_{pa}^{(1)} \qquad \text{such that} \quad (b_{1a}^{(1)})^2 + \cdots + (b_{pa}^{(1)})^2 = 1. \tag{32}$$

For general s, when the cosines proxy

$$b_{1a}^{(s)}, \dots, b_{pa}^{(s)} \qquad \text{with} \quad (b_{1a}^{(s)})^2 + \cdots + (b_{pa}^{(s)})^2 = 1 \tag{33}$$

has been calculated, the iteration (31) proceeds with the following "criss-cross" regressions:

First, we fix t consecutively $(t = 1, \dots, n)$ and calculate for each t the regression of the tth column y_{it} $(i = 1, \dots, p)$ on the cosines (33). This gives the regression coefficients

$$x_{at}^{(s+1)} = \sum_{i=1}^{p} b_{ia}^{(s)} y_{it}; \qquad t = 1, \dots, n \tag{34}$$

which we take for the $(s+1)$st component proxy.

Second, we fix i consecutively $(i = 1, \dots, p)$ and calculate for each i the regression of the ith row y_{it} $(t = 1, \dots, n)$ on the component proxy (34). This gives regression coefficients

$$B_{ia}^{(s+1)} = \sum_{t=1}^{n} x_{at}^{(s+1)} y_{it} \Big/ \sum_{t=1}^{p} (x_{at}^{(s+1)})^2; \qquad i = 1, \dots, p \tag{35a}$$

which we use as auxiliary entities to calculate the $(s+1)$st cosines proxy,

$$b_{ia}^{(s+1)} = \frac{B_{ia}^{(s+1)}}{\left[\sum_{j=1}^{p} (B_{ja}^{(s+1)})^2\right]^{1/2}}; \qquad i = 1, \dots, p. \tag{35b}$$

In words, we normalize the coefficients B_i to a unit square sum to obtain the cosines b_i.

(c) When the calculations (32) to (35) have given estimates for the first components and their direction cosines, say $a = 1, \dots, h$, the $(h+1)$st round begins by calculating the residuals in the hth step,

$$e_{ith} = y_{it} - \sum_{a=1}^{h} b_{ia} x_{at}; \qquad \begin{cases} i = 1, \dots, p \\ t = 1, \dots, n \end{cases} \tag{36}$$

Taking the residuals thus defined to be our observations y_{it} in the $(h+1)$st step, we apply procedure (2) anew, obtaining

$$e_{ith} = b_{i,h+1} x_{h+1,t} + e_{it,h+1} \qquad y_{it} = \sum_{a=1}^{h+1} b_{ia} x_{at} + e_{it,h+1} \tag{37}$$

Comments. (a) *Convergence.* As shown by Lyttkens [7], the NILES procedure of the previous section converges, giving well-defined estimates b_{ia}, x_{at}, e_{it} for the direction cosines β_{ia}, component sample values ξ_{at}, and residual sample values ε_{it}, and the resulting cosines estimates b_{ia} are equivalent to those given by Hotelling's classic method [3]. In his treatment of the least-squares aspects of principal components, Lyttkens leans heavily on the fundamental work of Whittle [12].

(b) *Consistency.* Least-squares estimates of linear predictors are known to be consistent (that is, a parameter estimate b will tend in probability to the corresponding theoretical parameter β as the sample size is allowed to increase indefinitely) under very general conditions of statistical regularity [14]. The argument extends to NILES estimation of component models (2) as specified in terms of predictors (6). The essential requirement is that as the sample size n increases, each observed moment m_{ij} as defined by (12) tends to the corresponding theoretical moment μ_{ij},

$$\lim_{n\to\infty} \text{prob}\, m_{ij} = \mu_{ij}; \qquad i, j = 1, \dots, p. \tag{38}$$

In different phrasing, condition (38) requires that the sample (1b) under analysis be *ergodic* with respect to the observed product moments m_{ij}.

The key argument in proving the consistency of the NILES estimates (31b) is that in each step of the iterative procedure (34) and (35) every proxy $b_{at}^{(s)}$ is a continuous function of the moments m_{ij}. In conjunction with the ergodicity assumption (38) this implies

$$\lim_{n\to\infty} \text{prob}\, b_{ia} = \beta_{ia} \tag{39}$$

as stated. In view of (34), the component property (10a) carries over to the least-squares estimates b_{ia} and x_{at}, and gives

$$x_{at} = \sum_{i=1}^{p} b_{ia} y_{it} \tag{40}$$

Hence the consistency (39) of the cosine estimates b_{ia} extends to components and residuals, giving

$$\lim_{n\to\infty} \text{prob}\, x_{ia} = \xi_{ia}\,; \qquad \lim_{n\to\infty} \text{prob}\, e_{it} = \varepsilon_{it} \tag{41}$$

Some qualification is needed as to the order of the components and the case of components ξ_a and ξ_b which are equal in mean square, but these exceptional cases can readily be checked and taken into account (see [7]).

2. COMPONENT STRUCTURE AS A BASIS FOR THE ESTIMATION OF ONE-FACTOR STRUCTURE

Considering the one-factor model (15) with equal residual variances, the problem dealt with in this section is to use the structure of the first principal component to assess the factor structure. For the limited purpose of this paper, it suffices to consider the case of one-factor structure, inasmuch as (a) the one-to-one correspondence between factor and largest component in the one-factor structure, (15) and (16), extends to the general case of k-factor models, as we know from the work of Whittle [12] and Lyttkens [7], and (b) the NILES estimates procedure (Section 1.4) gives the components one by one, in the order of the component variance.

The transfer from component to factor structure makes no change in the direction-cosines loading parameters β_i, since these are the same in the component and factor models, (15) and (16). The components and factors differ in the two models, as do the residuals. There is a radical difference here, for the component ξ and the component residuals ε_i can be assessed to be exact linear expressions in the variates η_i, as we know from Theorem 1, whereas the corresponding transfer to factor structure necessarily brings in the unknown factor residuals

$$\delta_i = \eta_i - \beta_i \zeta$$

with the result that the transfer only provides conditional expectations for the factor values ζ.

The population and sampling aspects of the problem will be dealt with separately. As to population properties, we regard the observations (16) under analysis to be generated from the factor model (15) with known theoretical matrix μ_{ij}, unknown loadings β_i, and unknown individual values ζ_t and δ_{it} for the factor and the residuals of the factor structure. We take the loadings β_i to be assessed from the theoretical moments μ_{ij} by Hotelling's classic method. Then relation (10a) provides the corresponding individual values for the first principal component ξ, giving

$$\xi_t = \sum_{i=1}^{p} \beta_i y_{it}\,; \qquad \varepsilon_{it} = y_{it} - \beta_i \xi_t. \tag{42}$$

Writing

$$\zeta_t^* = E(\zeta_t \mid \xi_t) \tag{43a}$$

for the conditional expectations of a factor value ζ_t for known component value ξ_t, and

$$\delta_{it}^* = y_{it} - \beta_i \zeta_t^* \tag{43b}$$

for the corresponding factor residuals, Section 2.1 deals with the assessment of ζ_t^* and δ_t^* in terms of component structure. Furthermore, Section 2.1 is concerned with the collective properties of ζ_t and ζ_t^*, notably the mean square $E(\zeta^2)$.

As to the sampling aspects, we consider representation (29) of the observed sample in terms of the least-squares estimates b_i of the direction cosines of the first principal component and the estimates x_t and e_{it} of the individual values of the component and the component residuals. We take the cosines b_i to be estimated either by Hotelling's classic method or by the NILES procedure (Section 1.4), which in this respect are equivalent. The estimates x_t and e_{it} will be given by

$$x_t = \sum_{i=1}^{p} b_i y_{it}\,; \qquad e_{it} = y_{it} - b_i x_t \tag{44}$$

in accordance with (36) and (40). Writing

$$z_t^*, \quad d_t^*$$

for the sample estimates of the quantities (43a and b), Section 2.2 deals with the correction of the factor-structure estimates for finite-sample bias.

2.1. Population Properties

We shall be concerned with two types of problems:

(a) To estimate collective features of the factor structure in terms of the collective component structure.

(b) To estimate the factor structure when the variates $\eta_1, \ldots, \eta_p$ are known, or, equivalently, when the component ξ is known.

Factor Estimation. The following two simple theorems enter in order under the headings (a) and (b). The first is an immediate implication of relations (23b) and (24).

Theorem 2. *For any one-factor model* (15) *with equal residual variances, the relations*

$$E(\zeta^2) = E(\xi^2) - \frac{1}{p-1} \sum_{i=1}^{p} \sigma^2(\varepsilon_i) \tag{45}$$

gives the factor mean square in terms of the first principal component.

Theorem 3. *A least-squares estimate of the factor ζ for known component ξ is given by*

$$\zeta^* = \lambda\xi \tag{46a}$$

where

$$\lambda = \frac{E(\zeta^2)}{E(\zeta^2) + (1/p)\sigma^2(\delta)} = 1 - \frac{\sigma^2(\varepsilon)}{(p-1)E(\xi^2)}. \tag{46b}$$

Proof. Relation (46a) being in the nature of linear regression, we obtain

$$\lambda = \frac{E(\xi\zeta)}{E(\xi^2)}$$

which by the use of (23) and (25) transforms to (46b).

Comment. The following theorem brings in relief that the unknown factor ζ does not coincide with its estimate ζ^* for known component ξ.

Theorem 4. *The conditional estimate ζ^* is a random variate with the following collective properties:*

$$E(\zeta^*) = \frac{E(\zeta^2)}{E(\zeta^2) + (1/p)\sigma^2(\delta)} E(\zeta) \tag{47}$$

$$E[(\zeta^*)^2] = \frac{E^2(\zeta^2)}{E(\zeta^2) + (1/p)\sigma^2(\delta)} \tag{48}$$

$$E[(\zeta^* - \zeta)^2] = \frac{(1/p)E(\zeta^2)\sigma^2(\delta)}{E(\zeta^2) + (1/p)\sigma^2(\delta)}. \tag{49}$$

Proof. As to (47), relation (46a) implies

$$E(\zeta^* \mid \xi) = \lambda\xi \tag{50}$$

which gives the unconditional expectation

$$E(\zeta^*) = \lambda E(\xi) \tag{51}$$

in accordance with (47). As to (48), we infer from (46a) that

$$E[(\zeta^*)^2] = \lambda^2\xi^2.$$

Hence

$$E[(\zeta^*)^2] = \lambda^2 E[\xi^2]$$

which by use of (23) and (46b) reduces to (48). As to (49), we obtain by the same argument,

$$E(\zeta^*\zeta \mid \xi) = \lambda\xi^2$$

which gives

$$E(\zeta^*\zeta) = \lambda^2 E(\xi^2).$$

Hence

$$E[(\zeta^* - \zeta)^2] = E[(\zeta^*)^2] - 2E(\zeta^*\zeta) + E(\zeta^2)$$
$$= E(\zeta^2) - \frac{E^2(\zeta^2)}{E(\zeta^2) + (1/p)\sigma^2(\delta)}$$

in accordance with (49).

Residual Estimation. The difference between factor values ζ_t and their estimates $\zeta_t{}^*$ carries over to the factor residuals

$$\delta_{it} = y_{it} - \beta_i \zeta_t \tag{52a}$$

and the corresponding conditional residuals

$$\delta_{it}^* = y_{it} - \beta_i \zeta_t^*. \tag{52b}$$

The unknown factor residuals δ_{it} have zero expectation, $E(\delta_{it}) = 0$, as we know from (9a). Expressing their variance in terms of component structure, we obtain by (15) and (24),

$$\sigma^2(\delta_i) = \frac{1}{p}\,\sigma^2(\delta) = \frac{1}{p-1}\,\sigma^2(\varepsilon) = \frac{1}{p-1}\sum_i \sigma^2(\varepsilon_i). \tag{53}$$

The conditional residuals $\delta_i{}^*$ are biased,

$$E(\delta_i{}^*) = \beta_i(1 - \lambda)E(\xi) \tag{54}$$

as readily verified. By deductions similar to the proof of Theorems 3 and 4, their theoretical mean square comes out as

$$E[(\delta_i{}^*)^2] = \beta_i{}^2(1 - \lambda)^2 E(\xi^2) + \sigma^2(\varepsilon_i). \tag{55}$$

2.2. Sample Estimates of One-Factor Structure. Corrections for Finite-Sample Bias

Least-squares estimates of the structure of the first principal component being given by (44), formulas (45) and (53) carry over to yield sample estimates of the one-factor structure. Writing

$$m(x^2) = \frac{1}{n}\sum_{t=1}^{n} x_t{}^2; \qquad m(y_i{}^2) = \frac{1}{n}\sum_{t=1}^{n} y_{it}^2 = m_{ii} \tag{56a}$$

$$s^2(e_i) = \frac{1}{n}\sum_{t=1}^{n} e_{it}^2; \qquad s^2(e) = \sum_{i=1}^{p} s^2(e_i) \tag{56b}$$

for the observed mean squares of the first principal component and of the corresponding residual variances and similarly for the factor structure, we obtain

$$m(z^2) = m(x^2) - \frac{1}{p-1} s^2(e) \tag{57}$$

$$s^2(d_i) = \frac{1}{p} s^2(d) = \frac{1}{p-1} s^2(e) = \frac{1}{p-1} \sum_i s^2(e_i). \tag{58}$$

The corresponding estimates for the individual factor structure are

$$z_t^* = \left[1 - \frac{1}{p-1} \frac{s^2(e)}{m(x^2)}\right] x_t \tag{59}$$

$$d_{it}^* = y_{it} - b_i z_t^*. \tag{60}$$

Formulas (57) and (58) are in the nature of large-sample estimates, with estimation errors that tend to zero as the sample size increases, whereas (59) and (60) are subject to an estimation error that does not vanish in indefinitely large samples. In the following paragraphs we shall adduce three simple corrections for finite-sample bias in the estimation, one for each of the elements β_i, ζ_t, δ_{it} of the one-factor model under consideration.

The limited scope of these subsections must be emphasized. All through we assume that the sample is large relative to the number of variates,

$$p \prec n. \tag{61}$$

The argument is partly heuristic, and the assessment of large-sample standard errors and confidence intervals is not more than mentioned.

The Residual Variance. The one-factor model (15) involves p parameters to be estimated, namely $\beta_1, \dots, \beta_p$, or rather $p-1$ if we take into account the normalization (4a) to a unit square sum. We see that the estimation of the individual factor values ζ_t involves no loss of degrees of freedom, since the estimates are given by (59) on the basis of the observations (1b), formula (44), and the estimated parameters b_i.

The model under estimation involves np residuals, as many as the available observations (1b). By the argument of the previous paragraph the residual variance is estimated on the basis of $np - (p-1)$ degrees of freedom. Hence, letting "est" denote estimates corrected for finite-sample bias,

$$\text{est } \sigma^2(\varepsilon) = \frac{p}{np - p + 1} \sum_i \sum_t e_{it}^2 \tag{62}$$

and in consequence,

$$\text{est } \sigma^2(\delta_i) = \frac{1}{p} \text{ est } \sigma^2(\delta) = \frac{1}{p-1} \text{ est } \sigma^2(\varepsilon)$$

$$= \frac{p}{(p-1)(np-p+1)} \sum_i \sum_t e_{it}^2. \tag{63}$$

We see that the correction needed in the standard deviation $s(d)$ is of relative magnitude const./n,

$$\text{est } \sigma(\delta_i) \sim \left[1 + \frac{p-1}{2np}\right] s(d_i). \tag{64}$$

Factor and Component Corrections. To repeat from Section 1.3, the first component in (16) "explains more" than the factor in (15), or, equivalently, $\sigma(\varepsilon) < \sigma(\delta)$. This feature is somewhat exaggerated in the sample, since $s^2(e)$ comes out on the low side, owing to the loss of degrees of freedom, as we know from Section 2.2. Correcting for this bias, we obtain

$$\begin{aligned} \text{est } E(\xi^2) &= \sum_i m(y_i^2) - \text{est } \sigma^2(\varepsilon) \\ &= \sum_i m(y_i^2) - \frac{p}{np - p + 1} \sum_i \sum_t e_{it}^2. \end{aligned} \tag{65}$$

$$\begin{aligned} \text{est } E(\zeta^2) &= \sum_i m(y_i^2) - \text{est } \sigma^2(\delta) \\ &= \sum_i m(y_i^2) - \frac{p^2}{(np - p + 1)(p-1)} \sum_i \sum_t e_{it}^2. \end{aligned} \tag{66}$$

In formula (59) for the individual factor values, the finite-sample bias affects the negative term under the root sign, and we see that both the numerator and denominator make the term somewhat too small. As a first approximation we obtain

$$\text{est } \zeta_t^* = \left[1 - \frac{1}{p-1} \frac{s^2(e)}{m(x^2)} (1 + \Delta_1)\right] x_t \tag{66a}$$

with

$$\Delta_1 = \frac{p-1}{np} \frac{\sum_i m(y_i^2)}{m(x^2)}. \tag{66b}$$

The Loadings b_i. Here we encounter two sources of finite-sample bias. These will be dealt with separately, and the ensuing corrections are to be applied in conjunction.

One is the counterpart to the bias in the factor z_t. Since the factor estimates z_t come out with a mean square somewhat too large, the negative correction for bias will have to be balanced by a corresponding positive correction in the loadings b_i to maintain the least-squares approximation

$$b_i z_t \sim \beta_i \zeta_t \tag{67}$$

Denoting this partial amendment by $\text{est}^{(1)}$, we obtain

$$\text{est}^{(1)}\,\beta_i = \left[1 + \frac{1}{p-1}\frac{s^2(e)}{m(x^2)}(1+\Delta_1)\right]b_i \tag{68}$$

where Δ_1 is the same quantity as in (66).

The second source of bias in b_i is the normalization (35b) to a unit square sum. Considering h replications of the sample, let $b_i(r)$ denote the direction cosines of the first principal component as estimated from the rth replication, and write

$$\bar{b}_i = \frac{1}{h}\sum_{r=1}^{h} b_i(r)\,; \qquad D(b_i) = \left\{\frac{1}{h}\sum_{r=1}^{h}[b_i(r) - \bar{b}_i]^2\right\}^{1/2} \tag{69}$$

for the mean and standard deviation of b_i as formed on the basis of the h replications. The identity

$$\frac{1}{h}\sum_{r=1}^{h} b_i^2(r) = \bar{b}_i^2 + D^2(b_i)$$

gives

$$\sum_{i=1}^{p}\bar{b}_i^2 + \sum_{i=1}^{p} D^2(b_i) = \frac{1}{h}\sum_{i=1}^{p}\sum_{r=1}^{h} b_i^2(r)$$

$$= \frac{1}{h}\sum_{r=1}^{h}\sum_{i=1}^{p} b_i^2(r) = 1$$

where the last reduction makes use of (38). Hence

$$\sum_{i=1}^{p}\bar{b}_i^2 < 1 = \sum_{i=1}^{p}\beta_i^2$$

which shows that $\bar{b}_i$ and b_i tend to be too small in absolute magnitude. To counteract this bias we assume as a rough approximation that the requisite correction is multiplicative, and independent of i. This gives, indicating the second correction by $\text{est}^{(2)}$,

$$\text{est}^{(2)}\beta_i = b_i(1+\Delta_2) \tag{70a}$$

where

$$\Delta_2 \sim \tfrac{1}{2}\sum_i D^2(b_i) + \tfrac{3}{8}\Big[\sum_i D^2(b_i)^2\Big]. \tag{70b}$$

In fact, taking the average of the corrected loadings over the replications, and forming the square sum of the averages, we obtain

$$\sum_i \bar{b}_i^2(1+\Delta_2)^2 = (1 + 2\Delta_2 + \Delta_2^2)\sum_i \bar{b}_i^2$$

$$= (1 + 2\Delta_2 + \Delta_2^2)\Big[1 - \sum_i D^2(b_i)\Big]$$

$$= 1 + c\,\Delta_2^3 + \cdots \sim \sum_i \beta_i^2 \tag{71}$$

which shows that the correction (70) takes into account first and second powers of $\sum D^2(b_i)$.

Comment. According to (70b) the second correction for the loadings estimates is of the same order of magnitude as the sum of squares of the standard deviations $d(b_i)$ of the loadings estimates. Hence for the correction to work, the sample size n must be so large that this square sum is fairly small.

The assessment of standard deviations $D(b_i)$ falls outside the scope of this paper. In connection with the correction (70) we quote the following large-sample formula,

$$D(b_i) \sim \frac{\sigma(\varepsilon_i)}{[E(\xi^2)]^{1/2}\left[1 - \dfrac{\sigma^2(\varepsilon_i)}{E(\xi^2)(1-\beta_i^2)}\right]} \tag{72}$$

with reference to E. Lyttkens,[3] who has recently obtained the formula by a new argument, under assumptions that involve an extension of related earlier results.

2.3. Illustrations by Monte Carlo Experiments

We shall now in all brevity report some experiments that have been carried out to check and illustrate the NILES procedure (Section 1.4) for the estimation of component structure and its adaptation (Section 2.1) for the estimation of one-factor structure.

In the terminology of experimental psychology, our Monte Carlo experiments simulate the observations of 4 ability tests as applied to 50 persons. This makes 200 observations in each sample. Our experiments involve 100 replications of the sample, once with fixed and once with changing factor values. This makes in all 200 × 200 = 40,000 observations. Further we shall report other similar experiments, once with 25% of the data missing, and once with 50%. All in all, the Monte Carlo study involves 120,000 simulated observations. The numerical work was performed in a pilot round at Battelle Memorial Institute, Columbus, Ohio, and in the production phase at the University of Uppsala, Sweden, using IBM-1620 and CDC 3600 computers.[4]

The One-Factor Structure Taken to Generate the Data of the Experiments

I. *Number of variates in the data set* (1)

$$p = 4 \tag{73}$$

[3] See [19, Chap. 1].

[4] The programs have been written and run by Fil. Kand. S. Wold, Dept. of Chemistry, Univ. of Uppsala, and Fil. Kand. D. Jonsson and Kand. L. Bodin, Dept. of Statistics, Univ. of Uppsala, Sweden.

II. *Model.* The factor model (3) with one factor and equal residual variances,

$$k = 1\,; \qquad \sigma(\delta_i) = \frac{1}{p^{1/2}}\,\sigma(\delta) = \frac{1}{2}\,\sigma(\delta) = \text{const.} \tag{74}$$

III. *Sample size n and number of replications h*

$$n = 50\,; \qquad h = 100. \tag{75}$$

IV. *Loadings*

$$\beta_1 = -\frac{2}{10^{1/2}}; \quad \beta_2 = -\frac{1}{10^{1/2}}; \qquad \beta_3 = \frac{1}{10^{1/2}}; \qquad \beta_4 = \frac{2}{10^{1/2}}. \tag{76}$$

V. *Factor values.* In each sample

$$\zeta_1, \dots, \zeta_{50} \quad \text{are} \quad \text{n.i.d.} \quad (0,1). \tag{77}$$

That is, the individual factor values ζ_t are generated so as to be normally distributed and mutually independent with zero expectation and unit standard deviation.

VI. *Residuals.* In each sample

$$\delta_{i1}, \dots, \delta_{i,50} \quad \text{are} \quad \text{n.i.d.} \quad (0,1). \tag{78}$$

Since $p = 4$, each sample involves 200 independent residuals δ_{it}.

VII. *Replications with fixed vs. changing factor values.* The experiments have been carried through in two versions:

A. Keeping the factor values (77) fixed in the 100 replications.

B. Generating the factor values (77) anew for each replication.

Having now specified the one-factor model (15) that generates the data of our experiments, we note the following properties of the model.

Product moment matrix (12a) of the variates η_i:

$$[\mu_{ij}] = [E(\eta_{it}\eta_{jt})] = \begin{bmatrix} 1.4 & 0.2 & -0.2 & -0.4 \\ 0.2 & 1.1 & -0.1 & -0.2 \\ -0.2 & -0.1 & 1.1 & 0.2 \\ -0.4 & -0.2 & 0.2 & 1.4 \end{bmatrix}$$

in accordance with (76) to (78).

Standard deviation of the total factor residual is

$$\sigma(\delta) = 2\sigma(\delta_i) = 2 \tag{79}$$

in accordance with (73) and (74).

Comments. (a) Small residuals make small differences between the factor and component models, (15) and (16). To bring the differences in relief we have used substantial residuals; specifications (77) and (78) give

$$\sigma(\delta_i) = \sigma(\zeta_t) = [E(\zeta_t{}^2)]^{1/2}$$

which makes larger residuals relative to the factors than is usually met in practice.

(b) Versions A and B of specification VII are analogous to the two standard situations in regression analysis known as fixed vs. random explanatory variates [2]. Just as for many problems in regression analysis, we shall see that in the estimation of component and factor structure the difference between the two versions makes little or no difference in the first approximation.

The Experiments Reinterpreted in Terms of Component Structure. Reinterpreting the data of our experiments as generated by a component model (2) with $k > 1$, Theorem 1 allows us to express the first principal component and its constituent relation (18) in terms of the one-factor structure specified by (73) to (78). The following results are obtained.

(a) *Direction cosines β_i of the first principal component.* Same as the loadings (76). This is in accordance with (18a).

(b) *Individual values for the first component*

$$\xi_t = (1/10^{1/2})(-2y_{1t} - y_{2t} + y_{3t} + 2y_{4t}) \tag{80}$$

in accordance with (18).

(c) *Component residuals*

$$\varepsilon_{1t} = \tfrac{1}{10}(6y_{1t} - 2y_{2t} + 2y_{3t} + 4y_{4t})$$
$$\varepsilon_{2t} = \tfrac{1}{10}(-2y_{1t} + 9y_{2t} + y_{3t} + 2y_{4t})$$
$$\varepsilon_{3t} = \tfrac{1}{10}(2y_{1t} + y_{2t} + 9y_{3t} - 2y_{4t})$$
$$\varepsilon_{4t} = \tfrac{1}{10}(4y_{1t} + 2y_{2t} - 2y_{3t} + 6y_{4t})$$

in accordance with (19).

(d) *Mean square of the first component*

$$E(\xi^2) = 2E(\zeta^2) = 2 \tag{81}$$

in accordance with (23) and (74).

(e) *Residual variances*

$$\sigma^2(\varepsilon_{1t}) = 0.6\,; \qquad \sigma^2(\varepsilon_{2t}) = \sigma^2(\varepsilon_{3t}) = 0.9\,; \qquad \sigma^2(\varepsilon_{3t}) = 0.6 \tag{82}$$

in accordance with (c). Hence the total residual variance

$$\sigma^2(\varepsilon) = 3 \tag{83}$$

in accordance with (20) and (24).

Comments. The features under (a) to (e) suffice to determine the transformation from component to factor structure. The following points provide further details about component vs. factor structure.

(f) *The component property*

$$\beta_1\varepsilon_{1t} + \beta_2\varepsilon_{2t} + \beta_3\varepsilon_{3t} + \beta_4\varepsilon_{4t} = 0 \tag{84}$$

in accordance with (18), and as readily verified from (76) and (c) above.

(g) *The least-squares property* (8)

$$E(\varepsilon_{it}) = E(\xi_t\varepsilon_{it}) = 0 \tag{85}$$

in accordance with (8), and readily verified by the use of (b) and (c). For example, transforming $E(\xi_t\varepsilon_{1t})$ by expressing the expectation in terms of $E(\zeta^2)$ and $E(\delta_i^2)$, the terms that involve $E(\zeta^2)$ cancel out if we make repeated use of the relation $6\beta_1 - 2\beta_2 + 2\beta_3 + 4\beta_4 = 0$, while the terms that involve $E(\delta_i^2)$ cancel out, since $2 \times 6 - 1 \times 2 - 1 \times 2 - 2 \times 4 = 0$.

(h) *The factor property.* Thanks to the specification (78), the factor residuals δ_{it} satisfy the factor property (11). The component residuals ε_{it}, on the other hand, do not possess this property; a case in point is

$$E(\varepsilon_{1t}\varepsilon_{2t}) = -0.2 \neq 0 \tag{86}$$

as is readily verified from (c) above.

Monte Carlo Results. With reference to Table I, we shall now summarize the numerical results of our experiments. The loadings (= direction cosines) β_i being the same for factor and component models, (15) and (16), under analysis, part (1) of the table reports about the estimated loadings. Then in parts (2) and (3) we proceed to the estimates of residuals, components, and factors. Dealing in (2) and (3) with population and sampling aspects of component vs. factor structures, we return finally to the sampling aspects of the estimates b_i reported in part (1). All through we limit the numerical illustrations to collective features of the factor and component structures.

I(1) *The loadings estimates.* For the first of the 100 replications of experiment A the NILES estimates for the four loadings are

$$b_1 = -0.793\,; \quad b_2 = -0.209\,; \quad b_3 = 0.262\,; \quad b_4 = 0.508. \tag{87}$$

The deviations from the theoretical loadings (33) are

$$\Delta_1 = -0.161\,; \quad \Delta_2 = 0.107\,; \quad \Delta_3 = -0.054\,; \quad \Delta_4 = -0.124. \tag{88}$$

Next we turn to averages and standard deviations calculated in accordance with (69). Table I(1) shows the four average estimates

$$\bar{b}_i = \tfrac{1}{100} \sum b_i \tag{89}$$

TABLE I

The One-Factor Model (15) *with* $n = 50, p = 4$

I(1)[a,b]		A			B		
i		β_i	b_i	$D(\bar{b}_i)$	$\bar{b}_i$	$D(b_i)$	(72)
1		−0.632	−0.573	0.182	−0.572	0.174	0.155
2		−0.316	−0.257	0.258	−0.312	0.185	0.187
3		0.316	0.331	0.199	0.304	0.189	0.187
4		0.632	0.555	0.221	0.570	0.239	0.155

I(2)[a,c]	A				B			
Repl.	$m(e^2)$	$m(d^2)$	est $m(\delta^2)$	$m(\delta^2)$	$m(e^2)$	$m(d^2)$	est $m(\delta^2)$	$m(\delta^2)$
1	0.612	0.815	0.828	0.836	0.612	0.815	0.828	0.836
2	0.752	1.003	1.018	1.009	0.654	0.874	0.886	0.923
3	0.617	0.823	0.836	0.814	0.661	0.882	0.895	0.896
4	0.699	0.933	0.947	0.991	0.830	1.107	1.124	1.213
5	0.857	1.143	1.160	1.204	0.721	0.961	0.975	0.980
Aver.	0.714	0.952	0.967	1.003	0.716	0.955	0.969	0.999

I(3)[a,d]	A				B			
Repl.	$m(x^2)$	$m(z^2)$	est $m(\zeta^2)$	$m(\zeta^2)$	$m(x^2)$	$m(z^2)$	est $m(\zeta^2)$	$m(\zeta^2)$
1	1.534	0.719	0.706	0.903	1.534	0.719	0.706	0.903
2	2.020	1.017	1.002	0.903	2.147	1.274	1.261	1.047
3	1.788	0.965	0.952	0.903	1.529	0.647	0.634	0.794
4	2.284	1.352	1.338	0.903	2.480	1.374	1.357	1.130
5	2.181	1.038	1.021	0.903	2.178	1.217	1.202	0.972
Aver.	2.114	1.161	1.147	0.903	2.129	1.147	1.160	1.033

[a] Two Monte Carlo experiments with 100 replications: A, fixed factor values; B, shifting factor values.

[b] Loadings: theoretical, β_i; average of estimates b_i in 100 replications, $\bar{b}_i$. Standard errors of loadings estimates b_i: assessed from 100 replications, $D(b_i)$; theoretical, by (72).

[c] Observed mean squares of total component residuals, $m(e^2)$. Mean squares of total factor residuals: observed, $m(d^2)$; corrected for finite sample bias, est $m(\delta^2)$; actual, $m(\delta^2)$. Items for five replications, and averages for 100 replications.

[d] Observed mean squares of first principal component, $m(x^2)$. Mean squares of factor ζ: observed, $m(z^2)$; corrected for finite-sample bias, est $m(\zeta^2)$; actual, $m(\zeta^2)$. Items for five replications, and averages for 100 replications.

as based on the 100 replications. We see that the averages compare fairly well with the theoretical loadings β_i shown in the second column. In accordance with a previous remark, the results are quite similar for the series A and B of the experiment. On closer comparison with the theoretical loadings β_i, we see that the large loadings b_i and b_4 come out somewhat too small in absolute value. We shall return to this feature later.

Table I(1) further gives the standard errors $D(b_i)$ of the loadings estimates b_i, observed values calculated from

$$D(b_i) = [\tfrac{1}{100} \sum (b_i - \bar{b}_i)^2]^{1/2} \tag{90}$$

and theoretical values given by (72), which covers both cases A and B, and in the present case gives

$$D(b_1) = D(b_4) = (0.024)^{1/2} = 0.155; \qquad D(b_2) = D(b_3) = (0.036)^{1/2} = 0.187$$

The standard errors are about 0.15 to 0.23, well covering the deviations (88) that we have quoted for the first replication under A.

I(2) *Residual variance.* Writing

$$m(\delta^2) = \tfrac{1}{200} \sum_i \sum_t \delta_{it}^2 \tag{91}$$

for the mean square of the 200 residuals generated for each replication of the experiment, Table I(2) gives $m(\delta^2)$ for the first five replications in each version A and B, and its average over all 100 replications. Indicating its variability by the formula

$$\text{Expectation} \pm \text{standard deviation; that is, } E(\delta^2) \pm \frac{\sigma(\delta^2)}{(np)^{1/2}}$$

the specification that δ_{it} is n.i.d. (0.1) gives

$$m(\delta^2) = 1 \pm 0.1; \qquad m(\delta^i) = 1 \pm 0.01 \tag{92}$$

for each replication and, respectively, for the over-all average. As seen from column $m(\delta^2)$ in Table I(2), the factor residuals generated in the experiments are in accordance with this theoretical variability.

Column $m(e^2)$ refers to the total component residuals e_t as obtained by the NILES estimation procedure (Section 1.4). Since $\bar{e}_t = 0$, the mean square $m(e^2)$ can be interpreted as the observed variance $s^2(e)$. Hence $m(e^2) = s^2(e)$ may be interpreted as an estimate of either $\sigma^2(\varepsilon)$ or $m(\varepsilon^2)$. By (24), $\sigma^2(\varepsilon) = (p-1)/p = 0.750$. The observed estimates are in accordance with this theoretical value, as seen from the columns $m(e^2)$ under A and B.

Column $m(d^2)$ refers to the total factor residuals d_t, and is calculated from $ps^2(e)/(p-1)$, in accordance with (58). Just as for the component residuals e_t, we have $m(d^2) = s^2(d)$, and $m(d^2)$ may be interpreted as an estimate either of

$E(\delta^2)(=1)$ or $m(\delta^2)$. The accordance between theoretical and observed values is necessarily the same as for column $m(e^2)$.

I(3) *Component and factor estimates.* Column $m(\zeta^2)$ in Table I(3) gives the mean square

$$m(\zeta^2) = \tfrac{1}{50} \sum_t \zeta_t^2 \tag{93}$$

of the 50 factor values ζ_t generated for the first five replications of experiments A and B, and its average over all 100 replications. Here the variability is twice as large as in (92),

$$m(\zeta^2) = 1 \pm 0.2$$

and the numerical results are seen to be in agreement with this theoretical formula.

Column $m(x^2)$ gives the mean square of the first principal component as assessed by the NILES procedure (Section 1.4). Interpreting $m(x^2)$ as an estimate of $E(\xi^2) = 2$ as given by (81), we see that the observed $m(x^2)$ are in fair agreement with expectation.

Column $m(z^2)$ gives the mean square of the factor ζ as assessed by (57). Interpreting $m(z^2)$ as an estimate either of $m(\zeta^2)$ as defined by (93) or, more crudely, as an estimate of $E(\zeta^2) = 1$, we see that the observed $m(z^2)$ are in fair agreement with the theoretical values.

Finite-sample corrections. The numerical results we have taken up thus far are based on Theorems 1 and 2, and thus refer to the population aspects of the transfer from component structure to factor structure. We shall now turn to the corrections for finite-sample bias as calculated from the formulas given in Section 2.2.

As to the residual variances, we see from (62) and (63) that the corrections in $m(e^2)$ and $m(d^2)$ are given by the multiplicative factor

$$\frac{np}{np - p + 1} = \frac{200}{197} \sim 1.015.$$

Table I(2) gives the corrected estimate for $m(\delta^2)$, denoted by est $m(\delta^2)$. By 1.5% higher than the uncorrected estimate $m(d^2)$, we see that the correction, although quite small, goes in the right direction.

As to the mean squares of factors and components, the finite-sample correction as given by (65) and (66) is 1.5% of the corresponding residual variance. The corrected estimate for the factor mean square $m(\zeta^2)$ is given in Table I(3) under est $m(\delta^2)$. Again we see that the correction is quite small, and that it works in the appropriate direction.

Finally we turn to the two corrections (68) and (70) for the loadings estimates b_i. Both corrections Δ_1 and Δ_2 are positive, and thus have the appropriate sign, as seen from Table I(1). In the present case Δ_1 is quite small, the ensuing correction amounting to about 1% of b_i. The correction by Δ_2 is more important, and if we evaluate $D^2(b_i)$ by the empirical variances reported in Table I(1), we find that it amounts to about 9% of b_i. In all, the two corrections thus increase b_i by 10%. We see from Table I(1) that this correction brings up b_i and $\bar{b}_i$ to the theoretical value β_i.

Standard errors of the loadings estimates. As seen from Table I(1), the standard errors $d(b_i)$ of the loadings estimates are on the whole somewhat larger for case A than for case B. Lyttkens' formula (72) gives more close agreement in case B than in case A, especially so for the standard errors of b_2 and b_3.

Principal-Components Estimation When Some of the Data are Missing. We shall here report an adaptation of the NILES procedure (Section 1.4) to situations when the observational material is incomplete. The device, due to Christoffersson [19, Chap. 4], is to supplement the missing data by dummy observations y_{it}^* such that when the estimation procedure has been applied to the data thus supplemented, the dummy observations y_{it}^* coincide with their principal-components representation

$$y_{it}^* = \sum_a b_{ia} x_{at} \tag{94}$$

or, otherwise expressed, giving zero residuals for the dummy observations. In the case of one component, $k = 1$, the device requires no change in the NILES procedure other than to replace all regressions in (34) and (35a) by weighted regressions, making the weight $w = 1$ for the existing observations, and $w = 0$ for the missing ones. In the case of two or more components, the computational device is somewhat more complicated.

TABLE II[a]

The One-Factor Model with 25% or 50% of the Data Missing

		25% missing				50% missing			
		A		B		A		B	
i	β_i	$\bar{b}_i$	$D(b_i)$	$\bar{b}_i$	$D(b_i)$	$\bar{b}_i$	$D(b_i)$	$\bar{b}_i$	$D(b_i)$
1	−0.632	−0.590	0.151	−0.571	0.182	−0.593	0.189	−0.565	0.182
2	−0.316	−0.294	0.223	−0.297	0.271	−0.314	0.214	−0.312	0.184
3	0.316	0.296	0.209	0.255	0.225	0.247	0.210	0.304	0.190
4	0.632	0.581	0.154	0.569	0.198	0.543	0.261	0.574	0.243

[a] Same model and table code as in Table I.

A Monte Carlo experiment with the dummy device is reported in Table II. The data are generated in the same way as in Table I, except that either one of four or one of two observations is missing. The missing observations are arranged in a systematic pattern; for example, with 25% missing data one observation is excluded for each t, the observation y_{it} with $i \equiv t \pmod 4$.

Comments. (a) Comparing with Table I(1) we see that the omission of as much as 25% or even 50% of the data does not make much difference in the estimation of the loadings. For both versions A and B, the average estimates $\bar{b}_i$ show fair agreement with the theoretical loadings β_i. There is the same tendency as in Table I(1) to a downward bias in the numerical value of the numerically largest loadings b_1 and b_4. What is perhaps more surprising, the observed standard deviations $D(b_i)$ come out with about the same size as in the case of complete observations, Table I(1), maybe with some very slight increase with the percentage of missing data. The requisite modification of the theoretical formula (72) will not be taken up here.

To conclude, our Monte Carlo experiments suggest that the sampling properties of the loadings estimates b_i are influenced primarily by the size of n, not so much by p or by the percentage of missing data for each t.

(b) In applied work there are many situations where principal-components analysis has to cope with incomplete data. For one thing, this is so because there are gaps even in very complete data. Sometimes, and this is of great importance for the scope of the approach, it lies in the very nature of the situation under analysis that the available information is incomplete. A case in point is horse-race data [19]. Letting y_{it} stand for the recorded time from start to goal for horse t in race i, complete data would here mean that all horses under comparison participate in each race; in reality, only some 10 horses are set up at the same start. Another case in point is the incompleteness that occurs in controlled experiments in which for some reason or other the number of replications is limited.

The dummy assumption is just one, and perhaps the simplest, way to handle incomplete data. Speaking generally, approach (94) is *neutral* in the sense that missing data are assumed to occur just by chance, without affinity to any of the components or loadings.

3. EXTENSIONS OF THE PRINCIPAL-COMPONENTS APPROACH

To illustrate the flexibility of the principal-components model (2) and its estimation by the NILES procedure, we shall in all brevity refer to three generalizations of the approach; cf. [19, Chap. 3 and 4].

3.1. Hybrid Model of Principal Components and Canonical Correlation

In the case of one component the model has the form

$$\alpha_1 y_{it} + \alpha_2 u_{it} = \beta_i \xi_t + \varepsilon_{it} \tag{95}$$

with

$$\alpha_1{}^2 + \alpha_2{}^2 = 1\,; \qquad \sum_i \beta_i{}^2 = 1. \tag{96}$$

As in Section 2.3 we consider the application to horse-race data, assume that the primary purpose of the analysis is to assess the racing quality of the horses, and adopt the device to rank them according to their component values ξ_t. In Section 2.3 the ranking exploits the information embodied in the observations y_{it} on racing times; in model (95) the ranking makes joint use of observations on y_{it} and some other variate u_{it}, for example, the saddle weight that horse t carries as a handicap in race i.

A NILES estimation procedure is available for the joint estimation of the parameters $\alpha_1, \alpha_2, \gamma_i$, and ξ_t (see [19, Chap. 3]). The model and the estimation procedure extend (a) to any number of left-hand variates $y, u, \ldots$, and (b) to two or more components ξ_{at} in the right-hand member.

3.2. Hybrid Model of Principal Components and Multiple Regression

The model is formally related to (95):

$$y_{it} = \beta_i \xi_t + \gamma_i u_{it} + \varepsilon_{it} \tag{97}$$

with

$$\sum_i \beta_i{}^2 = 1. \tag{98}$$

Again considering the model as applied to horse-race data, we assume that the purpose of the analysis is now to forecast the racing time y_{it} of horse t in race i, using the horse component ξ_t, the race loading γ_i, and the saddle weight u_{it} as predictive elements.

The NILES procedure for model (95) [Ref. 19, Chap. 3] can readily be adapted for the estimation of model (96). The approach extends (a) to two or more observational variates $u, v, \ldots$ in the right-hand member, and (b) to two or more principal components ξ_{at}.

3.3. Principal Components for a Multidimensional Array of Observations

This generalization is in a direction other than (95) or (96), the model being of the type

$$y_{ijt} = \beta_i \gamma_j \xi_t + \varepsilon_{ijt}$$
$$\sum \beta_i^2 = 1 ; \qquad \sum \gamma_j^2 = 1 \qquad \begin{cases} i = 1, \ldots, p \\ j = 1, \ldots, q \\ t = 1, \ldots, n. \end{cases} \tag{99}$$

The model can be consistently estimated by the following NILES estimation procedure [20].

Initial values $b^{(1)}$ and $g_j^{(1)}$ are chosen arbitrarily, say

$$b_i^{(1)} = u_1 y_{iAB}, \qquad g_j^{(1)} = v_1 y_{CjB}$$

where A, B, and C are fixed subscripts, and the multiplicative factors u_1 and v_1 are determined so as to make

$$\sum (b_i^{(1)})^2 = \sum (g_j^{(1)})^2 = 1.$$

When the proxies $b_i^{(s)}$ and $g_j^{(s)}$ have been calculated, the procedure continues as follows:

$$x_t^{(s+1)} = \sum_i \sum_j b_i^{(s)} g_j^{(s)} y_{ijt} ; \qquad t = 1, \ldots, n$$

$$b_i^{(s+1)} = u_{s+1} \sum_j \sum_t g_j^{(s+1)} x_t^{(s+1)} y_{ijt} \Big/ \sum_j (g_j^{(s+1)})^2 \sum_t (x_t^{(s+1)})^2 ; \qquad i = 1, \ldots, p$$

$$g_j^{(s+1)} = v_{s+1} \sum_i \sum_t b^{(s+1)} x_t^{(s+1)} y_{ijt} \Big/ \sum_i (b_i^{(s+1)})^2 \sum_t (x_t^{(s+1)})^2 ; \qquad j = 1, \ldots, q$$

where the multiplicative factors u_{s+1} and v_{s+1} are to be determined so as to make

$$\sum_i (b_i^{(s+1)})^2 = \sum_j (g_j^{(s+1)})^2 = 1.$$

The procedure gives

$$b_i = \lim b_i^{(s)} ; \quad g_j = \lim g_j^{(s)} ; \quad x_t = \lim x_t^{(s)} \qquad (s \to \infty)$$

as NILES estimates for the parameters β_i, γ_j, and ξ_t.

Acknowledgments

The author is greatly indebted to Professor P. Whittle, University of Manchester, and Professors K. G. Jöreskog and E. Lyttkens, University of Uppsala, for having read and commented upon the paper in draft form.

REFERENCES

1. Anderson, T. W. (1958). *An Introduction to Multivariate Statistical Analysis*. Wiley, New York.
2. Cramér (1945). *Mathematical Methods of Statistics*. Almqvist and Wiksell, Uppsala. (1946), Princeton Univ. Press, Princeton, New Jersey.

3. HOTELLING, H. (1933). Analysis of a complex of variables into principal components. *J. Educational Psychology* **24** 417–441, 498–520.
4. JÖRESKOG, K. G. (1962). On the statistical treatment of residuals in factor analysis. *Psychometrika* **27** 335–354.
5. JÖRESKOG, K. G. (1963). *Statistical Estimation in Factor Analysis.* Almqvist and Wiksell, Uppsala.
6. LAWLEY, D. N. (1963). *Factor Analysis as a Statistical Method.* Butterworth, London.
7. LYTTKENS, E. (1966). On the fix-point property of Wold's iterative estimation method for principal components. Paper in this volume, pp. 335–350.
8. PEARSON, K. (1901). On lines and planes of closest fit to systems of points in space. *Phil. Mag.* **6** 559–572.
9. RAO, C. R. (1955). Estimation and tests of significance in factor analysis. *Psychometrika* **20** 93–111.
10. SPEARMAN, C. (1904). General intelligence, objectively determined and measured. *Amer. J. Psychology* **15** 201–293.
11. THURSTONE, L. L. (1931). Multiple factor analysis. *Psychological Review* **38** 406–427.
12. WHITTLE, P. (1952). On principal components and least square methods of factor analysis. *Skand. Aktuarietidskr.* **36** 223–239.
13. WOLD, H. (1953). A Monte Carlo illustration of principal components analysis. *Uppsala Symposium on Psychological Factor Analysis*, 17–19 *March* 1953. Nordisk Psykologi's Monograph Series, No. 3, pp. 43–64. Munksgaard, Copenhagen.
14. WOLD, H. (1963). On the consistency of least squares regression. *Sankhya* **25A** 211–215.
15. WOLD, H. (1964). Forecasting by the chain principle, *Econometric Model Building. Essays on the Causal Chain Approach*, pp. 5–36. North-Holland, Amsterdam.
16. WOLD, H. (1965). A fix-point theorem with econometric background, I–II. *Ark. Mat.* **6** (11–12) 209–240.
17. WOLD, H. (1965). Toward a verdict on simultaneous equation systems. *Transactions of the Study Week on Econometrics, October* 1963. *Scripta Varia* **28**; I, 115–185. Pontifical Academy of Sciences, Vatican City.
18. WOLD, H. (1966). The approach of model building. Cross-roads of probability theory, statistics, and theory of knowledge. *Transactions des Entretiens de Monaco* 1964. Centre International d'Étude des Problèmes Humains, Monaco.
19. WOLD, H. (1966). Nonlinear estimation by iterative least squares procedures. *Festschrift Jerzy Neyman.* Wiley, New York.
20. WOLD, S. (1965). Principal components analysis of multidimensional arrays of observations. *Seminar communication.* Univ. Institute of Statistics, Uppsala, Sweden.
21. YOUNG, G. (1941). Maximum likelihood estimation and factor analysis. *Psychometrika* **6** 49–53.

PART VII

Ranking and Selection Procedures

An Inverse-Sampling Procedure for Selecting the Most Probable Event in a Multinomial Distribution[1]

THEOPHILOS CACOULLOS[2]
and MILTON SOBEL
DEPARTMENT OF STATISTICS
UNIVERSITY OF MINNESOTA
MINNEAPOLIS, MINNESOTA

1. SUMMARY

The problem of selecting the particular one of k multinomial cells with the highest probability is considered from the ranking theory–indifference zone point of view. The sampling procedure used differs from the fixed-sample-size procedure (FSP) of Bechhofer *et al.* [1] in that observations are taken one at a time, until any one cell has N counts in it. It is shown that for $k = 2$ the same requirement on the probability of a correct selection can be satisfied by the inverse-sampling procedure (ISP) with a smaller expected total number of observations than the fixed sample size of [1], regardless of the true parameter point. A concept of asymptotic proportion saved (APS_2) by the ISP relative to the FSP is defined as an asymptotic limit as the probability requirement gets stricter, i.e., $\theta^* \to 1$ [cf. (3.2) and (7.6)], and it is shown to be positive for any $P^* > \frac{1}{2}$ and any k; analogous comparisons are made for the worst case, i.e., when all the cells have equal probability. The required value of N for this problem is easily obtained from existing tables [4] and relevant results obtained here; a short table of such values is included. The same problem has also been treated by a Wald-type sequential procedure in [2], but comparisons with that procedure have not been made.

[1] This work was supported by the National Science Foundation under Grant GP-3813 and by the United States Air Force Office of Scientific Research, Office of Aerospace Research under Grant AFOSR-885-65.

[2] *Present address:* Department of Industrial Engineering and Operations Research, New York University, New York.

2. INTRODUCTION

This paper was motivated by the Banach[3] match-box problem [5]. In this problem matches are drawn from either of two boxes (of N matches each) with equal probabilities until one box is found to be empty; the problem deals with the distribution of the number R remaining in the other box at stopping time; here R takes on integer values from 0 to N, inclusive. A closely related problem is to stop sampling when the last match is drawn out from either box, so that R only takes on values from 1 to N, inclusive. This paper deals mostly with generalizations and applications of the latter variation, which appears to have more application than the original variation of the problem.

Although the problem deals with the removal of matches from the boxes, we could equally well consider the same problem with matches being put into the boxes. Then we continue until either box has N matches in it and consider the distribution of the number X of matches in the other box at stopping time. Clearly the two problems are equivalent, with X corresponding to $N - R$. This latter aspect shows that the problem is one of inverse sampling from a Bernoulli or, more generally for $k \geq 2$, from a multinomial distribution.

The problem of deciding which cell has the highest probability is considered here with this inverse-sampling procedure (ISP). The corresponding problem with a fixed-sample-size procedure (FSP) was considered by Bechhofer *et al.* [1]. The two procedures are comparable, since they satisfy the same requirement on the probability of a correct selection, and the so-called least-favorable configuration in the parameter space is the same for both procedures.

Let n_0 denote the fixed sample size needed for the FSP and let $E(T \mid \text{LF})$ denote the expected total number of observations T required by the ISP in the least-favorable (LF) configuration (defined in Section 4). The main results of this paper deal with a comparison of n_0 and $E(T \mid \text{LF})$; for $k = 2$ we can make exact comparisons, and for $k \geq 3$ we make comparisons based on asymptotic normal approximations. In [1] the normal approximation to n_0 is carried out after the arcsin–square root transformation is applied to the chance variables; a corresponding (but not the same) transformation is used in this paper to give a better normal approximation. Comparisons of n_0 and $E\{T \mid \text{W}\}$, i.e., the expected value of T in the equal parameter, i.e., worst (W), configuration, are also made in this paper.

The value of N needed to make the ISP explicit and to satisfy the probability requirement turns out to be easily obtainable from an existing table in [6]; a short table of N values is included here to make this paper self-contained.

[3] This refers to Stefan Banach, "whose matches, even behind barbed wires, lighted the torch for new areas of research."

A basic tool used several times in this paper is an identity [see (4.2)] connecting a negative multinomial sum and a Dirichlet integral; this identity is proved in [10].

The application of inverse sampling to a different problem dealing with the multinomial distribution (with asymptotic considerations similar to those in Theorem 5.2) was recently considered by Kudo and Yao [8].

3. FORMULATION OF THE PROBLEM

Observations are taken one at a time from a multinomial distribution with k cells, $C_1, C_2, \dots, C_k$ with probabilities $p_1, p_2, \dots, p_k$ respectively such that $\sum_1^k p_i = 1$. The ordered values of these cell probabilities are denoted by

$$p_{[1]} \leq p_{[2]} \leq \cdots \leq p_{[k]}, \tag{3.1}$$

and we let $C_{(i)}$ denote the cell associated with $p_{[i]}$ ($i = 1, 2, \dots, k$). The problem (or goal) is to select the cell $C_{(k)}$, which we shall sometimes refer to as the "best" cell. The probability requirement to be satisfied is expressed in terms of the ratio $\theta_{k,k-1} = \theta$ (say) of $p_{[k]}$ to $p_{[k-1]}$ and two preassigned constants, P^* and θ^*, such that $1/k < P^* < 1$ and $\theta^* > 1$. For any $\theta > 1$, we define a correct selection (CS) in the obvious way, as the selection of the cell $C_{(k)}$; for $\theta = 1$ we would define it as the selection of any cell $C_{(i)}$ with $p_{[i]} = p_{[k]}$, but we shall not need the definition for $\theta = 1$. The experimenter would like to have a procedure R for selecting the best cell which satisfies the probability requirement

$$P\{\text{CS} \mid R\} \geq P^* \qquad \text{for} \quad \theta \geq \theta^*. \tag{3.2}$$

Let $R_0 = R_0\ (k, \theta^*, P^*)$ denote the fixed sample procedure (FSP) of [1] that satisfies (3.2) and let $R_1 = R_1\ (k, \theta^*, P^*)$ denote the following inverse-sampling procedure (ISP) that satisfies (3.2). Let $E_i = E_i^{(N)}$ denote the event that we observe N observations from cell C_i before observing N observations from any other cell ($i = 1, 2, \dots, k$); the integer $N = N(k, P^*, \theta^*)$ is chosen in advance of experimentation in such a way that (3.2) is satisfied.

Inverse-Sampling Procedure (R_1). Continue sampling until one of the events E_i occurs and then select the cell C_i as being the best cell.

Fixed-Sample Procedure (R_0). Sample n_0 observations and select the cell with the largest cell frequency as the best cell; if two or more cells are tied with the same largest cell frequency, then one is selected by randomization.

4. THE $P\{\text{CS} \mid R_1\}$ AND THE DETERMINATION OF N

Let $E_{(j)} = E_{(j)}^{(N)}$ denote the event that the cell $C_{(j)}$ associated with $p_{[j]}$ is emptied first ($j = 1, 2, \dots, k$) and let $X_{(i)}$ denote the number of observations taken from $C_{(i)}$, $i \neq j$, at the time $E_{(j)}$ occurs, so that $0 \leq X_{(i)} \leq N-1$ for each $i \neq j$. [In the dual model of taking out items (without replacement) from k cells all containing N items at the outset, we use $Z_{(i)}$ to denote the number remaining in cell $C_{(i)}$ for $i \neq j$ when $E_{(j)}$ occurs; then $Z_{(i)} = N - X_{(i)}$ and $1 \leq Z_{(i)} \leq N$.] The probability of a correct selection is easily seen to be

$$P\{\text{CS} \mid R_1\} = P\{E_{(k)}\} = p_{[k]}^N \sum_{x_1=0}^{N-1} \cdots \sum_{x_m=0}^{N-1} \frac{\Gamma(N+x_0)}{\Gamma(N)} \prod_{i=1}^{m} \frac{p_{[i]}^{x_i}}{x_i!}, \tag{4.1}$$

where $m = k-1$ and $x_0 = x_1 + x_2 + \cdots + x_m$. The multiple sum in (4.1) can be written as a Dirichlet integral using Theorem 2.4 of [10]: if $s_1, s_2, \ldots, s_m$ are positive integers, $s > 0$, $\pi_i \geq 0$, $i = 1, 2, \ldots, m$, and $\pi_0 = \pi_1 + \pi_2 + \cdots + \pi_m < 1$; then

$$(1-\pi_0)^s \sum_{x_1=0}^{s_1-1} \cdots \sum_{x_m=0}^{s_m-1} \frac{\Gamma(s+x_0)}{\Gamma(s)} \prod_{i=1}^{m} \frac{\pi_i^{x_i}}{x_i!}$$

$$= \frac{\Gamma(s+s_0)}{\Gamma(s)\prod_{i=1}^{m}\Gamma(s_i)} \int_{\pi_1^*} \cdots \int_{\pi_m^*} \frac{\prod_{i=1}^{m}[y_i^{s_i-1}\,dy_i]}{(1+y_0)^{s+s_0}}, \tag{4.2}$$

where $y_0 = y_1 + y_2 + \cdots + y_m$, $s_0 = s_1 + s_2 + \cdots + s_m$, $\pi_i^* = \pi_i/(1-\pi_0)$, $i = 1, 2, \ldots, m$, and x_0 is as defined above. Since $p_{[k]} > 0$, we obtain from (4.1) and (4.2),

$$P\{\text{CS} \mid R_1\} = \frac{\Gamma(kN)}{[\Gamma(N)]^k} \int_{\theta_1^{-1}}^{\infty} \cdots \int_{\theta_m^{-1}}^{\infty} \frac{\prod_{i=1}^{m}[y_i^{N-1}\,dy_i]}{(1+y_0)^{kN}}, \tag{4.3}$$

where $\theta_i = p_{[k]}/p_{[i]}$ $(i = 1, 2, \ldots, m)$ (and $\theta = \theta_{k-1}$).

[It should be noted that the probability $P\{C_{(i)} \mid R_1\}$ that the cell $C_{(i)}$ associated with $p_{[i]}$ empties first is given by the same integral as in (4.3) except that the lower limits are replaced by $\theta_{i,j}^{-1}$ $(j = 1, 2, \ldots, i-1, i+1, \ldots, k)$, where $\theta_{ij} = p_{[i]}/p_{[j]}$.]

Clearly the $P\{\text{CS} \mid R_1\}$ is minimized if the lower limits of integration in (4.3) are maximized or the θ_i are minimized subject to the condition $\theta_i \geq \theta^*$ [cf. (3.2)]. Hence to obtain the minimum we need only set $\theta_i = \theta^*$ $(i = 1, 2, \ldots, m)$; i.e., the least-favorable configuration (LFC), where the $P\{\text{CS} \mid R_1\}$ attains its minimum subject to the condition $\theta \geq \theta^*$, is given by

$$p_{[1]} = p_{[2]} = \cdots = p_{[m]} = \frac{1}{\theta^* + m} = q \quad \text{(say)},$$

$$p_{[k]} = \frac{\theta^*}{\theta^* + m} = p \quad \text{(say)}, \qquad p + mq = 1. \tag{4.4}$$

We remark that the same configuration (4.4) is least favorable for the FSP in [1]; the proof in that case is more difficult and is given in a separate paper

[7]. This makes the FSP and the ISP directly comparable and comparisons are made in Section 7. The above discussion proves

Theorem 4.1. *The value of N required to satisfy* (3.2) *is the smallest integer equal to or greater than the solution* $n = n(k, \theta^*, P^*)$ *of the equation*

$$\frac{\Gamma(kn)}{[\Gamma(n)]^k} \int_{1/\theta^*}^{\infty} \cdots \int_{1/\theta^*}^{\infty} \frac{\prod_{i=1}^{m} [y_i^{n-1}\, dy_i]}{(1 + y_0)^{kn}} = P^*. \tag{4.5}$$

Using already existing tables [6] of $1/\theta^*$ values satisfying (4.5) for selected values of k, P^*, and n, it is easy to find the required N values for selected values of k, P^*, and θ^* (see Table I; our symbols $k = m + 1$, N, P^*, and θ^* correspond to $k = p + 1$, $\nu/2$, P^*, and $1/c$, respectively, in [6]).

The tables in [6] are limited to $N \leq 25$ and apply only for $P^* = .75$, .90, .95, and .99; the tables in [3], where the same integral arises, are also of limited usefulness, since they give P values for specified N values instead of the reverse. It is therefore desirable to develop an asymptotic expansion for the left side of (4.5) and an asymptotic solution of (4.5) for n. We shall also need asymptotic expressions for $E(T \mid \mathrm{LF})$ and $E(T \mid \mathrm{W})$ for the ISP to make comparisons with the value of n_0 needed by the FSP, since the exact expressions for $k > 2$ are involved. Finally, these results may have some interest per se.

For the special case $k = 2$, the right side of (4.3) can be written exactly as an incomplete beta function by applying the transformation $1 + y_1 = u^{-1}$; we obtain

$$P\{\mathrm{CS} \mid R_1\} = \frac{\Gamma(2N)}{[\Gamma(N)]^2} \int_0^p u^{N-1}(1 - u)^{N-1}\, du = I_p(N, N), \tag{4.6}$$

where $p = \theta/(1 + \theta)$. This result will be especially useful in making comparisons in Section 7 with the result for the FSP in [1].

5. ASYMPTOTIC THEORY

Consider the random vector $Y = (Y_1, Y_2, \ldots, Y_m)$ with the Dirichlet density

$$f(y_1, \ldots, y_m) = \frac{\Gamma(s + s_0)}{\Gamma(s)\prod_{i=1}^{m}\Gamma(s_i)} \frac{\prod_{i=1}^{m} y_i^{s_i - 1}}{(1 + y_0)^{s + s_0}} \qquad y_i \geq 0 \quad (i = 1, 2, \ldots, m), \tag{5.1}$$

where s and the s_i are any positive numbers and $s_0 = s_1 + s_2 + \cdots + s_m$. The means of the Y_i for $s > 1$ and the covariances of the Y_i for $s > 2$ exist and are easily computed. If s and the $s_i (i = 1, 2, \ldots, m) \to \infty$ in such a way that $s/N \to 1$ and

$$\frac{s_i}{s} \to \lambda_i \qquad (i = 1, 2, \ldots, m), \tag{5.2}$$

TABLE I

N Values Needed to Satisfy (4.5) *for the* ISP[a]

θ^* \ m	1	2	3	4	5	6	7	8	9
					$P^* = .75$				
1.2	29^{-1}	63	87	104	119	130	140	149	157
1.4	9^{-0}	19^{-0}	27^{-0}	32	36	40	43	46	48
1.6	5	10	14	17	19	21	23	24^{-0}	26^{-0}
1.8	3	7	10	11	13	14	15	16	17
2.0	3	5	7	9	10	11	11	12	13
2.2	2	4	6	7	8	8	9	10	10
2.4	2	4	5	6	7	7	8	8	8
2.6	2	3	4	5	6	6	7	7	7
2.8	2	3	4	4	5	5	6	6	6
3.0	1	3	3	4	5	5	5	6	6
					$P^* = .90$				
1.2	100	151	182	205	223	238	250	261	270
1.4	30	45	55	62	67	71	75	78	81
1.6	16	24^{-0}	29	32	35	38	40	41	43
1.8	10	16	19	21	23	25	26	27	28^{-0}
2.0	8	12	14	16	17	18	19	20	21
2.2	6	9	11	12	13	14	15	16	16
2.4	5	8	9	10	11	12	12	13	13
2.6	4	7	8	9	10	10	11	11	12
2.8	4	6	7	8	8	9	9	10	10
3.0	4	5	6	7	8	8	8	9	9
					$P^* = .95$				
1.2	163	222	257	283	302	318	332	344	354
1.4	49	66	77	84	90	95	99	103	106
1.6	25	34	40	44	47	50	52	54	56
1.8	17	22^{-0}	26^{-0}	29	31	33	34	35	37
2.0	12	16	19^{-0}	21^{-0}	23^{-0}	24^{-0}	25^{-0}	26^{-0}	26^{+1}
2.2	10	13	15	17	18	19	19	20	21
2.4	8	11	12	14	15	15	16	17	17
2.6	7	9	11	12	12	13	14	14	15
2.8	6	8	9	10	11	11	12	12	13
3.0	5	7	8	9	10	10	11	11	11

TABLE 1—*continued*

θ^* \ m	1	2	3	4	5	6	7	8	9
					$P^* = .99$				
1.2	326	395	435	464	486	505	520	533	545
1.4	96	117	129	138	144	150	154	158	162
1.6	51	60	67	71	75	78	80	82	84
1.8	33	39	43	46	49	51	52	54	50
2.0	24	28^{-0}	32	34	36	37	38	39	40
2.2	19	22^{-0}	25^{-0}	26^{+1}	28	29	30	31	32
2.4	15	18^{-0}	20^{-0}	22^{-0}	23^{-0}	24^{-0}	24^{+1}	25^{+1}	25^{+1}
2.6	13	16	17	18	19	20	21	21	22
2.8	11	14	15	16	17	17	18	18	19
3.0	10	12	13	14	15	15	16	16	17

[a] All entries above the heavy line are based on the asymptotic normal approximation (5.14); those below the heavy line are exact values taken from Table III of [6]. The "exponents" in certain boundary cells are the differences between the asymptotic (A) and the exact (E) values of N, i.e., $A - E$, and give some indication of their agreement.

where the λ_i are positive, finite limits, then

$$E(Y_i) = \frac{s_i}{s-1} \sim \lambda_i \qquad (i = 1, 2, \ldots, m),$$

$$\operatorname{Var}(Y_i) = \frac{s_i(s_i + s - 1)}{(s-1)^2(s-2)} \sim \frac{\lambda_i(1+\lambda_i)}{N} \qquad (i = 1, 2, \ldots, m), \tag{5.3}$$

$$\rho(Y_i, Y_j) = \left[\frac{s_i s_j}{(s_i + s - 1)(s_j + s - 1)}\right]^{1/2} \sim \left[\frac{\lambda_i \lambda_j}{(1+\lambda_i)(1+\lambda_j)}\right]^{1/2} \qquad (j \neq i).$$

It is clear from the left side of (4.5) that our main interest is in the case $\lambda_i = 1$ $(i = 1, 2, \ldots, m)$, in which case the common mean, variance, and correlation in (5.3) are asymptotically 1, $2/N$, and $\frac{1}{2}$, respectively.

Theorem 5.1. *If the limits λ_i in* (5.2) *are positive and finite, then the asymptotic distribution of the variables*

$$X_i = \left[\frac{N}{\lambda_i(1+\lambda_i)}\right]^{1/2}(Y_i - \lambda_i) \qquad (i = 1, 2, \ldots, m) \tag{5.4}$$

is a joint normal distribution with zero means, unit variances, and an $m \times m$ correlation matrix $\Lambda = \{\rho_{ij}\}$ with $\rho_{ij} = \rho(Y_i, Y_j)$ given by (5.3). *In particular, for $\lambda_i = 1$ $(i = 1, 2, \ldots, m)$ we obtain*

$$f(x_1, \ldots, x_m) = \frac{\exp\{-[m \sum_1^m x_i^2 - 2 \sum_{i<j} x_i x_j]/(m+1)\}}{\pi^{m/2}(m+1)^{1/2}}. \tag{5.5}$$

Proof. Using Stirling's well-known approximation to $\Gamma(\cdot)$ throughout (5.1) and some elementary limiting arguments, we obtain Theorem 5.1 by a direct limiting process; the details are omitted.

Corollary 5.1. *If $\lambda_i = \lambda > 0$ $(i = 1, 2, \ldots, m)$ and $\lambda\theta^* \neq 1$, then*

$$N \sim \frac{(\theta^*)^2 \lambda(1+\lambda)}{(\lambda\theta^* - 1)^2} H_m^2\left(P^*, \frac{\lambda}{1+\lambda}\right), \tag{5.6}$$

where $H = H_m(P^*, \rho)$ is given in terms of the standard univariate normal density $f(x)$ and the corresponding c.d.f. $F(x)$, as the solution of

$$\int_{-\infty}^{\infty} F^m\left(\frac{x(\rho^{1/2} + H)}{(1-\rho)^{1/2}}\right) f(x)\, dx = P^*. \tag{5.7}$$

Proof. If N is large, then, by Theorem 5.1, N satisfies

$$P\left\{X_i \geq -\frac{N^{1/2}(\lambda\theta^* - 1)}{\theta^*[\lambda(1+\lambda)]^{1/2}} \quad (i = 1, 2, \ldots, m)\right\} = P^*, \tag{5.8}$$

where the X_i are standard normal chance variables with common correlation $\rho = \lambda/(1+\lambda) > 0$. It is clear that for $\rho > 0$ we can set

$$X_i = (1-\rho)^{1/2} Y_i + \rho^{1/2} Y_0 \qquad (i = 1, 2, \ldots, m), \tag{5.9}$$

where the Y_i and Y_0 are all independent, standard normal chance variables. Hence (5.8) can be written in the form (5.7) with $\rho = \lambda/(1+\lambda)$ and

$$H = H_m\left(P^*, \frac{\lambda}{1+\lambda}\right) = \frac{N^{1/2}(\lambda\theta^* - 1)}{\theta^*[\lambda(1+\lambda)]^{1/2}}. \tag{5.10}$$

Solving (5.10) for N gives the result (5.6), which completes the proof.

It was found that a better normal approximation could be had if we first transform the Dirichlet variable by a logarithmic transformation; this would be the appropriate transformation for stabilizing the variance if a common scale parameter were present. A similar transformation was used in [3] and [6]. (All logs in this paper are taken to the natural base e.)

Corollary 5.2. *If the limits λ_i in (5.2) are positive and finite, then the asymptotic $(N \to \infty)$ distribution of the chance variables*

$$W_i = \left(\frac{N\lambda_i}{1+\lambda_i}\right)^{1/2} \log(Y_i/\lambda_i) \qquad (i = 1, 2, \ldots, m) \tag{5.11}$$

is a joint normal distribution with zero means, unit variances, and the same $m \times m$ correlation matrix Λ as given by (5.3).

Proof. The proof follows from straightforward asymptotic methods using Theorem 5.1 and the facts that asymptotically

$$E(\log Y_i) \sim \log E(Y_i) \sim \log \lambda_i \qquad (i = 1, 2, \ldots, m),$$

$$\operatorname{Var}(\log Y_i) \sim \frac{1}{\lambda_i^2} \operatorname{Var}(Y_i) \sim \frac{1 + \lambda_i}{N\lambda_i} \qquad (i = 1, 2, \ldots, m), \tag{5.12}$$

$$\rho(\log Y_i, \log Y_j) \sim \rho(Y_i, Y_j) \sim \left[\frac{\lambda_i \lambda_j}{(1 + \lambda_i)(1 + \lambda_j)}\right]^{1/2} \qquad (j \neq i).$$

From Corollary 5.2 we now obtain, as in (5.6),

Corollary 5.3. *If* $\lambda_i = \lambda > 0$ $(i = 1, 2, \ldots, m)$, *and* $\lambda\theta^* \neq 1$, *then*

$$N \sim \frac{1 + \lambda}{\lambda(\log \lambda\theta^*)^2} H_m^2\left(P^*, \frac{\lambda}{1 + \lambda}\right), \tag{5.13}$$

where $H = H_m(P^*, \rho)$ *is given by* (5.7).

Tables of H values have been obtained by several authors (see e.g. [9]) and are available in the literature. For the case $\lambda = 1$ of special interest here, it has been found by empirical comparisons with the exact solutions in [6] that the addition of $\log m$, i.e.,

$$N \sim \frac{2}{(\log \theta^*)^2} H_m^2(P^*, \tfrac{1}{2}) + \log m, \tag{5.14}$$

appears to give a uniform improvement to (5.13) with $\lambda = 1$; some numerical results based on this correction term are given above the heavy lines in Table I.

The following asymptotic results describe the basic structure of the inverse-sampling procedure for large values of N. They deal with the asymptotic $(N \to \infty)$ distributions of the number of observations $X_{(i)}$ taken from the cell $C_{(i)}$ associated with the cell probability $p_{[i]}$ when event $E_{(j)}$ occurs $(j \neq i)$ [or equivalently with the number of remaining items $Z_{(i)} = N - X_{(i)}$ in the dual model when $E_{(j)}$ occurs $(j \neq i)$]. We obtain two different types of results, both of interest, according to whether $p_{[k-1]} < p_{[k]}$ or $p_{[1]} = \cdots = p_{[k]} = 1/k$; the other cases are considered in Addendum C. For convenience, let $\eta_i = \theta_i^{-1} = p_{[i]}/p_{[k]}$ $(i = 1, 2, \ldots, m)$; we define standardized variables X_i^* and analogous nonnegative variables Z_i^* by

$$X_i^* = (X_{(i)} - N\eta_i)/[N\eta_i(1 + \eta_i)]^{1/2} \qquad (i = 1, 2, \ldots, m). \tag{5.15}$$

$$Z_i^* = Z_{(i)}/[N\eta_i(1 + \eta_i)]^{1/2} \qquad (i = 1, 2, \ldots, m). \tag{5.16}$$

Theorem 5.2. (a) *For* $\eta_m < 1$, *the asymptotic* $(N \to \infty)$ *joint density of the* X_i^* *is the same joint normal density as in Theorem* 5.1, *with* λ_i *replaced by*

η_i $(i = 1, 2, \dots, m)$. *In particular, if* $\eta_i = \eta < 1$ $(i = 1, 2, \dots, m)$, *then the asymptotic* $(N \to \infty)$ *joint density of the* X_i^* *is*

$$\frac{1}{(1+m\eta)^{1/2}}\left(\frac{1+\eta}{2\pi}\right)^{m/2}$$

$$\times \exp\left\{-\frac{(1+\eta)}{2(1+m\eta)}\left[(1+(m-1)\eta)\sum_{i=1}^{m} x_i^2 - 2\eta\sum_{i<j} x_i x_j\right]\right\}. \quad (5.17)$$

(b) *For* $\eta_i = 1$ $(i = 1, 2, \dots, m)$ *the conditional asymptotic* $(N \to \infty)$ *joint density of the*

$$Z_i^* = \frac{Z_{(i)}}{(2N)^{1/2}} = \frac{N - X_{(i)}}{(2N)^{1/2}} = -X_i^* \qquad (i = 1, 2, \dots, m), \quad (5.18)$$

given that cell $C_{(k)}$ *empties first, is the restricted joint normal density*

$$g(z_1, \dots, z_m) = \left(\frac{k}{\pi^m}\right)^{1/2} \exp\left\{-\left[m\sum_{i=1}^{m} z_i^2 - 2\sum_{i<j} z_i z_j\right]\Big/ k\right\}, \quad (5.19)$$

where $z_i > 0$ $(i = 1, 2, \dots, m)$; *with the appropriate relabeling of the z's, the same result holds if any other cell empties first.*

Proof. Setting $x_0' = x_i(\delta_1)^{1/2} + \cdots + x_m(\delta_m)^{1/2}$ where $\delta_i = \eta_i(1 + \eta_i)$ $(i = 1, 2, \dots, m)$ and $\eta_0 = \eta_1 + \eta_2 + \cdots + \eta_m = (1 - p_{[k]})/p_{[k]}$ we easily obtain [cf. (4.1)]

$$P\{X_i^* = x_i \qquad (i = 1, 2, \dots, m)\}$$

$$= \frac{\Gamma(N + x_0' N^{1/2} + \eta_0 N)}{\Gamma(N)} p_{[k]}^N \prod_{i=1}^{m}\left[\frac{p_{[i]}^{x_i(N\delta_i)^{1/2} + N\eta_i}}{\Gamma(x_i(N\delta_i)^{1/2} + N\eta_i + 1)}\right]. \quad (5.20)$$

Since each X_i^* takes steps of size $(N\delta_i)^{-1/2}$, we need to adjoin the factor $(N^m \Pi_1^m \delta_i)^{1/2}$ on the right side of (5.20) in passing over to the limiting continuous density. Using Stirling's formula for $\Gamma(\cdot)$ throughout (5.20) and passing to the limit (with the above factor adjoined) gives the first result of Theorem 5.2. The proof of (5.19) is quite similar, except that we multiply the final result by k to make it a probability density.

Remark. The vector $(X_{(i)}^*, X_{(2)}^*, \dots, X_{(m)}^*)$ is asymptotically a *bona fide* random vector when $\eta_m < 1$, since $P\{E_{(k)}\} \to 1$ as $N \to \infty$; i.e., $P\{X_{(k)} = N\} \to 1$ as $N \to \infty$. We also remark that the Z_i^* in (5.18) are interchangeable, and equicorrelated, and that the corresponding unrestricted chance variables Z_i'(say) with $-\infty < Z_i' < \infty$ $(i = 1, 2, \dots, m)$, whose density is $1/k$ times the density in (5.19), are standardized normal chance variables with common correlation $\rho = \frac{1}{2}$.

Corollary 5.4. *If* $\theta_i = \theta = p/q > 1$ $(i = 1, 2, \ldots, m)$, *where* p *and* q *are defined in* (4.4), *then* X_i^* *in* (5.15) *are jointly normal with mean* 0, *variance* 1, *and common correlation*

$$\rho = \frac{q}{p+q} = \frac{1}{1+\theta} < \frac{1}{2} \tag{5.21}$$

Another type of result follows from the fact that the conditional c.d.f. of $X_0 = X_{(1)} + X_{(2)} + \cdots + X_{(m)}$, given that cell $C_{(k)}$ empties first, can be written

$$P\{X_0 \le x\} = \sum_{x_0=0}^{x} \frac{\Gamma(N+x_0)}{\Gamma(N)x_0!} p_{[k]}^N (1-p_{[k]})^{x_0} \sum \frac{x_0!}{\prod_1^m x_i!} \prod_{j=1}^{m} \left[\frac{p_{[j]}}{1-p_{[k]}}\right]^{x_j}, \tag{5.22}$$

where the multinomial sum is over m-vectors $(x_1, x_2, \ldots, x_m)$ with $x_1 + x_2 + \cdots + x_m = x_0$ and $0 \le x_i \le N-1$ $(i = 1, 2, \ldots, m)$. If we disregard the latter restriction or if $x \le N-1$, then the multinomial sum in (5.22) is unity, and we obtain

$$P\{X_0 \le x\} = p_{[k]}^N \sum_{i=0}^{x} \frac{\Gamma(N+i)}{\Gamma(N)i!} (1-p_{[k]})^i = I_{p_{[k]}}(N, x+1) \tag{5.23}$$

(cf. (2.24) and (2.3) in [10]).

A lower bound to $E_k(X_0) = E(X_0 \mid C_{(k)}$ empties first) is easily seen to be

$$E_k(X_0) \ge E_k(X_0|X_0 \le N-1) = \frac{p_{[k]}^N}{I_{p_{[k]}}(N,N)} \sum_{i=0}^{N-1} \frac{i\Gamma(N+i)}{\Gamma(N)i!} (1-p_{[k]})^i$$

$$= \frac{N(1-p_{[k]})}{p_{[k]}} \frac{I_{p_{[k]}}(N+1, N-1)}{I_{p_{[k]}}(N,N)} = \frac{N(1-p_{[k]})}{p_{[k]}} \left[1 - \frac{b_{2N-1}(N; p_{[k]})}{I_{p_{[k]}}(N,N)}\right] \tag{5.24}$$

where $b_n(x;p)$ is the binomial probability $\binom{n}{x} p^x(1-p)^{n-x}$. For $p_{[k]} = 1/k$,

$$Nm\left[1 - \frac{b_{2N-1}(N; 1/k)}{I_{1/k}(N,N)}\right] \le E_k(X_0|W) \le m(N-1); \tag{5.25}$$

by symmetry, the same result (5.25) holds whichever cell empties first, and hence it also holds unconditionally. Note that for the left side of (5.25) we get equality for $k = 2$ and agreement with (6.29); for $k > 2$ strict inequality holds.

6. EXACT AND ASYMPTOTIC EVALUATION OF $E(T)$

To assess the cost of using the ISP and to make comparisons with other procedures, e.g., the FSP, it is necessary to evaluate $E(T \mid R_1)$; we obtain asymptotic as well as exact results, since in certain cases the exact results are too involved to compute.

We define a generalized least favorable (GLF) configuration to be one with

$$p_{[1]} = p_{[2]} = \cdots = p_{[m]} = q(\text{say}) \quad \text{and} \quad p_{[k]} = p(\text{say}). \tag{6.1}$$

We are interested in $E(T \mid \text{GLF})$ and, in particular, $E(T \mid \text{LF})$ and $E(T \mid \text{W})$ for procedure R_1. First we shall give an upper bound for $E(T \mid \text{GLF})$ based on a simple probability argument. Then we shall develop exact formulas for $E(T \mid \text{GLF})$ and asymptotic ($\theta^* \to 1$) approximations based on these exact results. It will be seen that the leading term in the asymptotic approximations is in agreement with the upper bound.

Upper Bound for $E(T)$

An upper bound to $E(T \mid \text{GLF})$ for any number of cells k can be obtained by using a negative binomial probability argument. We assume $q < p$ and write

$$E(T \mid \text{GLF}) = P^* E(T \mid \text{GLF}), \text{CS}) + (1 - P^*) E(T \mid \text{GLF}, \text{IS}) \tag{6.2}$$

where IS denotes an incorrect selection. Consider the first conditional expectation on the right side of (6.2) and let an observation from the cell $C_{(k)}$ be called a success and an observation from any other cell a failure. Then the expected number of observations required to obtain the first success is well known to be $1/p$; hence we obtain N/p for N successes. This argument disregards the restriction we need, that the number of failures from any one cell should be at most N. It is, therefore, clear that the resulting value will necessarily be an upper bound. A similar argument holds for the second conditional expectation in (6.2) and we thus obtain

$$E(T \mid \text{GLF}) < P^* \left(\frac{N}{p}\right) + (1 - P^*) \left(\frac{N}{q}\right). \tag{6.3}$$

Under the GLF configuration we have $q \le 1/k$ and hence $N/q \ge kN > kN - m = \max T$, where the maximum is over all possible configurations. Hence

$$E(T \mid \text{GLF}) < P^* \left(\frac{N}{p}\right) + (1 - P^*)(kN - m), \tag{6.4}$$

which for the LF configuration becomes

$$E(T \mid \text{LF}) < P^* N \left(\frac{m + \delta^*}{\delta^*}\right) + (1 - P^*)[kN - m]. \tag{6.5}$$

This upper bound will be used to make comparisons with the FSP in Section 7. The coefficient of P^* in (6.5) can also be regarded as a useful (i.e., quickly computable) rough approximation to $E(T|\text{LF})$ for large N, since (for large N and fixed θ^*) P^* will be close to 1 and the restrictions, which were omitted to obtain (6.5), have a negligible effect on the result; more precise asymptotic results for $E(T \mid \text{LF})$ are obtained below.

An inequality on $E(T)$ for the W configuration can be obtained by adding N to each of the three members of (5.25); this gives

$$N\left[k - \frac{mb_{2N-1}(N, 1/k)}{I_{1/k}(N, N)}\right] \leq E(T \mid \text{W}) \leq kN - m. \tag{6.6}$$

Exact Evaluation of $E(T)$

Clearly we have for any configuration,

$$E(T) = N + \sum_{i=1}^{k} P(E_{(i)})\left[\sum_{j \neq i} E(X_{(j)} \mid E_{(i)})\right]. \tag{6.7}$$

For the GLF configuration, using symmetry, we obtain from (6.7),

$$\begin{aligned} E\,(T \mid \text{GLF}) &= N + P(E_{(k)})(k-1)E(X_{(1)} \mid E_{(k)}) \\ &\quad + (k-1)\left[\frac{1 - P(E_{(k)})}{k-1}\right]\left[E(X_{(k)} \mid E_{(1)}) + (k-2)E(X_{(2)} \mid E_{(1)})\right] \\ &= N + (k-1)[\mu_{1,k} + \mu_{k,1} + (k-2)\mu_{2,1}], \end{aligned} \tag{6.8}$$

where for $i \neq j$,

$$\mu_{i,j} = P(E_{(j)})E(X_{(i)} \mid E_{(j)}) = \sum_{x=0}^{N-1} xP(X_{(i)} = x, E_{(j)})$$

$$= \begin{cases} p^N \sum \dfrac{x_1\Gamma(N + x_0)}{\Gamma(N)\prod_{\alpha=1}^{m} x_\alpha!}\, q^{x_0} & \text{for } j = k,\ i \neq k, \\ q^N \sum \dfrac{x_1\Gamma(N + x_0)}{\Gamma(N)\prod_{\alpha=1}^{m} x_\alpha!}\, p^{x_1} q^{x_0 - x_1} & \text{for } i = k,\ j \neq k, \\ q^N \sum \dfrac{x_2\Gamma(N + x_0)}{\Gamma(N)\prod_{\alpha=1}^{m} x_\alpha!}\, p^{x_1} q^{x_0 - x_1} & \text{for } i \neq k,\ j \neq k \text{ (needed only for } k \geq 3), \end{cases} \tag{6.9}$$

$x_0 = x_1 + x_2 + \cdots + x_m$ throughout, and each summation is over all ordered m-tuples $(x_1, x_2, \ldots, x_m)$ with $0 \leq x_i \leq N - 1$ $(i = 1, 2, \ldots, m)$. For the LF configuration we merely set $p = \theta^*/(m + \theta^*)$ and $q = 1/(m + \theta^*)$; in the W configuration we set $p = q = 1/k$ and obtain

$$E(T \mid \text{W}) = N + (k-1)E(X_{(2)} \mid E_{(1)}) = N + (k-1)k\mu, \tag{6.10}$$

where

$$\mu = \sum_{x=0}^{N-1} xP(X_{(2)} = x, E_{(1)}) = \sum \frac{x_2 \Gamma(N + x_0)}{\Gamma(N)\prod_{i=1}^{m} x_i!} \left(\frac{1}{k}\right)^{N+x_0}, \tag{6.11}$$

the summation being over the same range, as in (6.9). Using the above result (4.2) taken from [10], the above sums in (6.9) and (6.11) can be written in the form of Dirichlet integrals, and those that do not have equal exponents and equal lower limits of integration can be "symmetrized" by using appropriate identities and integration by parts. We state the result first in terms of the Dirichlet integral:

$$D_m(M, N_1, \ldots, N_m; a_1, a_2, \ldots, a_m)$$
$$= \frac{\Gamma(M + N_0)}{\Gamma(M)\prod_{x=1}^{m}\Gamma(N_i)} \int_{a_1}^{\infty} \cdots \int_{a_m}^{\infty} \frac{\prod_{i=1}^{m}[y_i^{N_i-1}\, dy_i]}{(1 + y_0)^{M+N_0}} \qquad \begin{array}{l}(M, N_i > 0),\\ (i = 1, 2, \ldots, m),\end{array} \tag{6.12}$$

where $y_0 = y_1 + y_2 + \cdots + y_m$ and $N_0 = N_1 + N_2 + \cdots + N_m$, and finally in terms of "semisymmetric" Dirichlet integrals with $N_1 = \cdots = N_m = N$ (say) or "completely symmetric" Dirichlet integrals with $M = N_1 = \cdots = N_m = N$ (say). We shall write $D_m(M, N_1, \ldots, N_m; a)$ if $a_1 = a_2 = \cdots a_m = a$ and if, in addition, we have $N_1 = N_2 = \cdots = N_m = N$, then we write $D_m(M, N; a)$; by definition $D_0(N; a) \equiv 1$, and it is easily checked that $D_1(M, N; a) = I_c(M, N)$, where $c = (1 + a)^{-1}$. For convenience let $q_1 = q/(p + q)$.

Theorem 6.1. *For the* GLF *configuration with* $q \le p$,

$$E(T \mid \text{GLF})$$
$$= \frac{N}{q}\left[1 - \left(\frac{p-q}{p}\right) D_m(N, N; q/p) - \frac{1}{2p} b_{2N}(N; q_1) D_{m-1}(2N, N; q_1)\right]. \tag{6.13}$$

[*Remark*: Note that $q < p$ and $q = p$ are both included in (6.13). Special results for the LF configuration and for $k = 2$ are given at the end of the proof of Theorem 6.1. Another expression for $E(T \mid \text{LF})$ in terms of the derivative of $D_m(N, N; q/p)$ is given in (B.7) of the Addenda.]

For the proof of Theorem 6.1 we require the following two lemmas. The first lemma is a generalization of the well-known result $1 - I_c(M, N) = I_{1-c}(N, M)$ for the incomplete beta function, which is obtained by setting $m = 1$ in (6.14).

Lemma 6.1. *For any* $c \ge 0$, *any* $M \ge 1$, *and any* $N_i \ge 1$ $(i = 1, 2, \ldots, m)$,

$$mD_m(M, N_1, \ldots, N_m; c, 1, \ldots, 1) = 1 - D_m(N_1, M, N_2, \ldots, N_m; 1/c). \tag{6.14}$$

More generally, if c in the left member of (6.14) *is associated with the integral of* x_i, *which has the exponent* $N_i - 1$, *then an analogous result holds with* N_i

as the first argument and M as the $(i+1)$*st argument in the expression corresponding to the right side of* (6.14).

Proof. Starting with the right side of (6.14), the region of integration is such that at least one $y_i < 1/c$. This integral, by a symmetry argument, is easily seen to be m times the integral with y_m as the smallest y_i; i.e.,

$$1 - D_m(M, N_1, \ldots, N_m; 1/c) = \frac{m\Gamma(M+N_0)}{\Gamma(M)\prod_{i=1}^{m}\Gamma(N_i)} \int_0^{1/c}\int_{y_m}^{\infty}\cdots\int_{y_m}^{\infty} \frac{\prod_{i=1}^{m}[y_i^{N_i-1}\,dy_i]}{(1+y_0)^{M+N_0}}. \quad (6.15)$$

If we now let $x_i = y_i/y_m$ $(i = 1, 2, \ldots, m-1)$ and $x_m = 1/y_m$, then the Jacobian is $(1/x_m)^{m+1}$, and the result (6.14) follows immediately after simplification.

Lemma 6.2. *If* $N_1 = N_2 = \cdots = N_m = N$ *(say) and* $M > 1$, *then*

$$D_m(M, N; a) = D_m(M-1, N; a) - \frac{Nm}{M+N-1}\, b_{M+N-1}(N; \bar{c}) D_{m-1}(M+N-1, N; \bar{c}), \quad (6.16)$$

where $\bar{c} = a/(1+a) = 1-c$.

Proof. Starting with the left member of (6.16), we insert $(1+y_0) - y_0$ in the integrand and separate into two terms. Using symmetry on the 2^d integral, we obtain

$$D_m(M, N; a) = \left(\frac{M+mN-1}{M-1}\right) D_m(M-1, N; a) - \frac{Nm}{M-1} D_m(M-1, N+1, N, \ldots, N; a). \quad (6.17)$$

Integrating the last member of (6.17) by parts with respect to y_1 and collecting like terms gives the required result (6.16).

Proof of Theorem 6.1. We shall evaluate each of the $\mu_{i,j}$ in the last expression of (6.8). From (4.2) and (6.12),

$$\mu_{1,k} = \frac{Nq}{p} D_m(N+1, N-1, N, \ldots, N; q/p), \quad (6.18)$$

$$\mu_{k,1} = \frac{Np}{q} D_m(N+1, N-1, N, \ldots, N; p/q, 1, \ldots, 1), \quad (6.19)$$

$$\mu_{2,1} = ND_m(N+1, N-1, N, \ldots, N; 1, \ldots, 1, p/q). \quad (6.20)$$

Integrating by parts with respect to y_1 in (6.18) gives

$$\mu_{1,k} = \frac{Nq}{p} D_m(N+1, N; q/p) - \frac{N}{2} b_{2N}(N; q_1)D_{m-1}(2N, N; q_1). \tag{6.21}$$

Using Lemma 6.2 to replace D_m above we obtain

$$\mu_{1,k} = \frac{Nq}{p} D_m(N, N; q/p) - \frac{N}{2p} b_{2N}(N; q_1)D_{m-1}(2N, N; q_1). \tag{6.22}$$

For (6.19) we first apply Lemma 6.1 with $c = p/q$, $N_1 = N - 1$, $N_2 = N_3 = \cdots = N_m = N$ and $M = N + 1$ and obtain

$$\mu_{k,1} = \frac{Np}{mq}[1 - D_m(N - 1, N + 1, N, \ldots, N; q/p)] \tag{6.23}$$

First integrating by parts with respect to y_1 and then using Lemma 6.2 gives

$$\mu_{k,1} = \frac{Np}{mq}[1 - D_m(N, N; q/p)] - \frac{N(kN-1)}{m(2N-1)} b_{2N-1}(N - 1; q_1)D_{m-1}(2N - 1, N; q_1). \tag{6.24}$$

Applying Lemma 6.1 to (6.20) gives

$$\mu_{2,1} = \frac{N}{m}[1 - D_m(N, N - 1, N, \ldots, N, N + 1; q/p)]. \tag{6.25}$$

Integrating by parts (twice) with respect to y_1 and y_m gives

$$\mu_{2,1} = \frac{N}{m}[1 - D_m(N, N; q/p) - \tfrac{1}{2}b_{2N}(N; q_1)D_{m-1}(2N, N; q_1)] + \frac{N^2}{m} b_{2N-1}(N - 1; q_1) \times \left[\frac{D_m(2N - 1, N; q_1)}{2N - 1} + b_{3N-1}(N; q_2)\frac{D_{m-2}(3N - 1, N; q_2)}{3N - 1}\right], \tag{6.26}$$

where $q_2 = q/(1 + q)$. If we now use Lemma 6.2 with $M = 2N$ and $a_1 = q_2$ to replace the last term in (6.26), then

$$\mu_{2,1} = \frac{N}{m}[1 - D_m(N, N; q/p)] + \frac{N}{m(m-1)} b_{2N-1}(N - 1, q_1) \times \left[\frac{kN - 1}{2N - 1} D_{m-1}(2N - 1, N; q_1) - \left(\frac{1}{p + q}\right) D_{m-1}(2N, N; q_1\right]. \tag{6.27}$$

Substituting (6.22), (6.24), and (6.27) in (6.8) finally gives the desired result (6.13); this proves Theorem 6.1.

For the special case $k = 2$, we obtain a simpler result for $E(T \mid \text{GLF})$ with $q \leq p$ in terms of the incomplete beta function; i.e., for $N > 1$,

$$E(T \mid \text{GLF}) = N\left[1 + \frac{q}{p} I_p(N+1, N-1) + \frac{p}{q} I_q(N+1, N-1)\right], \quad (6.28)$$

and for $p = q$ we have $p = q = \frac{1}{2}$, and this reduces to

$$E(T \mid \text{W}) = N[1 + 2I_{1/2}(N+1, N-1)] = 2N\left[1 - \binom{2N}{N}\left(\frac{1}{2}\right)^{2N}\right]. \quad (6.29)$$

Clearly if $N = 1$, then $T = 1$, and, of course, $E(T) = 1$. It is easily verified that these results are in agreement with (6.13).

Remark. For the more general ISP problem with $N_i \geq 1$ and $p_i > 0$ associated with cell C_i ($i = 1, 2, \ldots, k$) (cf. Sections 2 and 3), it should be noted that we can still write $E(T)$ in terms of D_m integrals; in fact, the result by (4.2) is easily seen to be

$$E(T) = \sum_{j=1}^{k} N_j D_m\left(N_j, N_1, \ldots, N_k; \frac{p_1}{p_j}, \ldots, \frac{p_k}{p_j}\right)$$
$$+ \sum_{j=1}^{k} \sum_{\substack{i=1 \\ i \neq j}}^{k} \frac{N_j p_i}{p_j} D_m\left(N_j + 1, N_1, \ldots, N_i - 1, \ldots, N_k; \frac{p_1}{p_j}, \ldots, \frac{p_k}{p_j}\right), \quad (6.30)$$

where it is to be understood that, for each j, N_j is only the first argument of D_m and the lower limit of integration p_j/p_j is omitted. This can be further simplified using a generalization of Lemma 6.2, but Lemma 6.1 is not available for unequal p's and the resulting D_m's are not simple; we omit these results, as they are not used here.

Corollary 6.1. *In addition to the exact* $E(T \mid \text{W})$ *obtained by setting all the* p*'s equal and to the exact* $E(T \mid \text{LF})$ *obtained by using* (4.4), *we also have the approximation* ($\approx$)

$$E(T \mid \text{LF}) \approx \frac{N}{\theta^*}(m + \theta^*)^2$$
$$\times \left\{\frac{P^* + \theta^*(1 - P^*)}{m + \theta^*} - \frac{1}{2} b_{2N}(N; q_1^*) D_{m-1}(2N, N; q_1^*)\right\}, \quad (6.31)$$

where $q_1^* = 1/(1 + \theta^*)$.

Proof. By the definition of N in (4.5) we can replace the first D_m expression by P^* and (6.31) readily follows; the approximation is due only to the discreteness of N.

The following recursion formula is a corollary of Lemmas 6.1 and 6.2; it is useful for computing $D_m(M, N; a)$ for small values of m, especially when M is not too large.

Corollary 6.2. *For $M \geq 1$, $N \geq 1$, and $m \geq 1$,*

$$D_m(M, N; a) = 1 - Nm \sum_{j=0}^{M-1} \frac{b_{N+j}(N; \bar{c})}{N+j} D_{m-1}(N+j, N; \bar{c})$$

$$= 1 - m\bar{c}(1-\bar{c}) \sum_{j=0}^{M-1} b_{N-1+j}(N-1, \bar{c}) D_{m-1}(N+j, N; \bar{c}). \quad (6.32)$$

In particular, for $m = 2$ this gives

$$D_2(M, N; a) = 1 - 2\bar{c}(1-\bar{c}) \sum_{j=0}^{M-1} b_{N-1+j}(N-1; \bar{c}) I_d(N+j, N), \quad (6.33)$$

where $\bar{c} = a/(1+a)$ and $d = 1(1+\bar{c})$.

Proof. Iterating Lemma 6.1 on the argument M gives

$$D_m(M, N; a) = D_m(1, N; a)$$

$$- Nm \sum_{j=1}^{M-1} \frac{b_{M+N-j}(N; \bar{c})}{M+N-j} D_{m-1}(M+N-j, N; \bar{c}). \quad (6.34)$$

From Lemma 6.2 with $N_1 = 1$ and $M = N_2 = \cdots = N_m = N$, we obtain after integration,

$$D_m(1, N; a) = 1 - m\bar{c}^N D_{m-1}(N, N; \bar{c}), \quad (6.35)$$

and substituting this in (6.34) gives the desired result (6.32).

Asymptotic Results for $E(T)$

The results of Corollary 5.2, Stirling's approximation to the Γ function, and some lemmas below will be combined to give an asymptotic expression for $E(T \mid \text{GLF})$ which requires that N be large and that $p > q$. In a subsequent corollary we replace N in this expression as a function of θ^* (for fixed P^*) using (5.14), and, staying in the LF configuration, we then let $\theta^* \to 1$ (which implies that $N \to \infty$) and obtain an asymptotic approximation for $E(T \mid \text{LF})$. Later we also obtain asymptotic ($N \to \infty$) results for $E(T \mid \text{W})$.

Theorem 6.2. *For the* GLF *configuration with $q < p$ and N large,*

$$E(T \mid \text{GLF}) \sim \frac{N}{q}\left\{1 - \left(\frac{p-q}{p}\right) \int_{-\infty}^{\infty} F^m\left(x + N^{1/2}\log\frac{p}{q}\right) f(x)\,dx\right.$$

$$- \frac{1}{2p(N\pi)^{1/2}} \left[\frac{4pq}{(p+q)^2}\right]^N$$

$$\left.\times \int_{-\infty}^{\infty} F^{m-1}\left(\frac{x + N^{1/2}\log[(p+q)/2q]}{2^{1/2}}\right) f(x)\,dx\right\}. \quad (6.36)$$

Proof. By Corollary 5.2 with $\lambda_i = \lambda = \lim(N/M)$ as $N \to \infty$ $(i = 1, 2, \ldots, m)$ and by an argument similar to the one used for Corollary 5.1 we obtain for $q < p$

$$D_m(M, N; a) \sim \int_{-\infty}^{\infty} F^m\left(x\lambda^{1/2} + (N\lambda)^{1/2} \log\frac{\lambda}{a}\right) f(x)\, dx. \qquad (6.37)$$

Applying this in (6.13) for D_m and D_{m-1} and using Stirling's approximation to $\Gamma(\cdot)$ in the binomial factor, gives the desired result (6.36).

Corollary 6.3. *For the* LF *configuration with N large*

$$E(T \mid \text{LF}) \sim N\left(\frac{m+\theta^*}{\theta^*}\right)[P^* + \theta^*(1 - P^*)]$$
$$- \left(\frac{N}{\pi}\right)^{1/2} \frac{(m+\theta^*)^2}{2\theta^*}\left[\frac{4\theta^*}{(1+\theta^*)^2}\right]^N$$
$$\times \int_{-\infty}^{\infty} F^{m-1}\left(\frac{x + N^{1/2}\log[(1+\theta^*)/2]}{2^{1/2}}\right) f(x)\, dx. \qquad (6.38)$$

Proof. This follows from (6.36), (5.7), and (5.13) with $\lambda = 1$.

We shall use the symbol $E_0(T \mid \text{LF})$ to denote the asymptotic value of $E(T \mid \text{LF})$ as $\theta^* \to 1$, after using (5.14) to replace N; let $H = H_m(P^*, \frac{1}{2})$ be defined by (5.7).

As $\theta^* \to 1$ (for fixed P^*) in the LF configuration, it follows from (5.14) that $N \to \infty$ and expanding (6.38) in increasing powers of $\theta^* - 1$ gives

$$E_0(T \mid \text{LF}) = \frac{2H^2}{(\log \delta^*)^2}[k + (\delta^* - 1)(1 - kP^*)]$$
$$- \frac{k^2 H f(H)}{\log \delta^*} \int_{-\infty}^{\infty} F^{m-1}\left(\frac{x2^{1/2} + H}{2}\right) f(x)\, dx + \mathcal{O}\left(\frac{1}{\log \delta^*}\right)$$
$$= \frac{2kH^2}{(\delta^* - 1)^2} + \frac{H}{\delta^* - 1}\left\{2H[1 + k(1 - P^*)]\right.$$
$$\left. - k^2 f(H) \int_{-\infty}^{\infty} F^{m-1}\left(\frac{x\,2^{1/2} + \mathrm{H}}{2}\right) f(x)\, dx\right\} + \mathcal{O}\left(\frac{1}{\delta^* - 1}\right). \qquad (6.39)$$

Thus for θ^* sufficiently close to 1 we have

$$E_0(T \mid \text{LF}) \leq \frac{2kH^2}{(\theta^* - 1)^2} + \frac{2H^2}{\theta^* - 1}[1 + k(1 - P^*)]. \qquad (6.40)$$

It is interesting to compare (6.40) with the corresponding result obtained from the upper bound (6.5); expanding the latter about $\theta^* = 1$ gives, for θ^* in some interval of the form $(1, 1 + \varepsilon)$, as an upper bound for $E_0(T \mid \text{LF})$,

$$\frac{2kH^2}{(\theta^* - 1)^2} + \frac{2H^2}{\theta^* - 1}[P^* + k(1 - P^*)] + \mathcal{O}(1); \tag{6.41}$$

this is a slightly better upper bound than (6.40) in this interval. We shall therefore use (6.41) in making comparisons with the FSP in Section 7.

For the W configuration (i.e., with equal parameters) we use (6.13) with $q = p$ and $N \to \infty$ to obtain an asymptotic expression for $E(T \mid \mathrm{W})$. This is the direct approach involving the limit [of the exact expression for $E(T \mid \mathrm{W})$] as $N \to \infty$ and is somewhat different from that obtained by finding $E(T \mid \mathrm{W})$ for the limiting distribution, i.e., for the "restricted normal" distribution. The former, i.e., the limit of the exact $E(T \mid \mathrm{W})$, is the more appropriate value for our needs, and it is also numerically more meaningful; the latter is given for purposes of comparison. More specifically, these two asymptotic results agree on the "leading term," kN, but give different results for the "$N^{1/2}$ term"; this exhibits the fact that in general the limit of the exact expectation need not be the same as the expectation under the limiting distribution.

Corollary 6.4. *For the* W *configuration,*

$$E(T|\mathrm{W}) \sim kN\left[1 - \frac{k}{2(N\pi)^{1/2}} \int_{-\infty}^{\infty} F^{m-1}\left(\frac{x}{2^{1/2}}\right) f(x)\, dx\right]. \tag{6.42}$$

Proof. Clearly we can disregard the middle term in (6.13), and using Stirling's approximation for $\Gamma(\cdot)$ we obtain $(N\pi)^{-1/2}$ for the binomial factor. For the last factor, we consider upper and lower bounds by writing

$$D_{m-1}(2N, N; q_1 e^{\varepsilon/N}) \leqq D_{m-1}(2N, N; q_1) \leqq D_{m-1}(2N, N; q_1 e^{-\varepsilon/N}) \tag{6.43}$$

for a fixed $\varepsilon > 0$. Since $D_{m-1}(2N, N; q_1)$ must lie between these for every N, it is easy to see using Corollary 5.2 and continuity with respect to ε in (6.43) that $D_{m-1}(2N, N; q_1)$ approaches the orthant probability

$$D_{m-1}(2N, N; q_1) \sim \int_{-\infty}^{\infty} F^{m-1}\left(\frac{x}{2^{1/2}}\right) f(x)\, dx, \tag{6.44}$$

which completes the proof of (6.42). The computations of numerical values for $E(T \mid \mathrm{W})$ in Table II are based on (6.42); the values of the right side of (6.44) are tabulated in [12] with the notation $\overline{V}_{m-1,m-1}(3) = \bar{u}_{m-1}(3)$.

For purposes of comparison we now give (see Addendum D for proof) formulas for $E(T \mid \mathrm{W})$ and $\sigma^2(T|\mathrm{W})$ computed under the limiting "restricted normal" distribution (cf. Theorem 5.2); they are

$$E(T \mid \mathrm{W}) \sim k[N - N^{1/2} E(V_k^*)], \tag{6.45}$$

$$\sigma^2(T \mid \mathrm{W}) \sim kN[k\sigma^2(V_k^*) - 1], \tag{6.46}$$

Exact and Asymptotic $E(T)$ Values for the ISP *and Comparisons with n_0 Values for the* FSP (the number of cells is $k = m + 1$)[a]

θ^*	N, $E(T)$, and n_0 values		$P^* = .75$ $m = 1$	$P^* = .75$ $m = 2$	$P^* = .75$ $m = 3$	$P^* = .90$ $m = 1$	$P^* = .90$ $m = 2$	$P^* = .90$ $m = 3$
1.2	N		29	(63)	(87)	100	(151)	(182)
	$E(T \mid \text{LF})$	Exact	50.97	168.23	—	181.99	403.59	—
		Asympt.	(51.01)	(169.89)	(309.84)	(182.04)	(405.29)	(642.04)
	$E(T \mid \text{W})$	Exact	51.95	179.15	—[b]	188.73	437.62	—
		Asympt.	(51.92)	(178.92)	(335.20)	(188.72)	(437.45)	(709.48)
	n_0		57	(180)	(327)	199[c]	(437)	(694)
1.6	N		5	10	14	16	24	29
	$E(T \mid \text{LF})$	Exact	7.30	22.86	45.88	25.51	54.71	86.54
		Asympt.	(7.32)	(24.45)	(42.71)	(25.57)	(56.73)	(85.67)
	$E(T \mid \text{W})$	Exact	7.54	26.17	47.17	27.52	65.95	102.64
		Asympt.	(7.48)	(25.99)	(50.86)	(27.49)	(65.78)	(109.08)
	n_0		9	26	(46)	31	(64)	(98)
2.0	N		3	5	7	8	12	14
	$E(T \mid \text{LF})$	Exact	3.96	10.40	18.93	11.68	25.65	36.40
		Asympt.	(4.08)	(11.02)	(19.63)	(11.80)	(25.76)	(36.78)
	$E(T \mid \text{W})$	Exact	4.13	12.37	21.87	12.86	31.78	47.17
		Asympt.	(4.05)	(12.16)	(24.37)	(12.81)	(31.60)	(50.86)
	n_0		5	12	20	15	28	(56)
3.0	N		1	3	3	4	5	6
	$E(T \mid \text{LF})$	Exact	1	6.19	7.28	5.16	8.94	13.20
		Asympt.	(0.87)	(6.20)	(7.50)	(5.45)	(9.92)	(13.33)
	$E(T \mid \text{W})$	Exact	1	7.02	8.04	5.81	12.37	17.72
		Asympt.	(0.87)	(6.80)	(9.62)	(5.74)	(12.16)	(20.64)
	n_0		1	5	8	7	11	16

[a] The six entries in each cell are based on (4.5) or (5.14), (6.13) or (6.31), (6.38), (6.13), (6.42), and [1] or (7.9), respectively. All entries in parentheses are asymptotic; all entries without parentheses are based on exact formulas (and hence are exact if the corresponding integer N is exact), except that $E(T/\text{LF})$ for $m = 2$, 3 is based on the approximation (6.31). The second decimal of the $E(T)$ entries may be off (computationally) by one unit in some cases.

[b] A dash means no value computed. [c] This entry is based on (7.4); the result obtained by using the asymptotic formula in [1] is (198).

where V_k^* is the maximum of k independent standard normal chance variables.

7. COMPARISON OF ISP AND FSP

In this section the ISP will be compared with the FSP which selects the cell with the highest observed frequency as the best cell and uses randomization when ties occur. A separate comparison will be made for $k = 2$ and for $k > 2$, since the results for $k = 2$ form one of the motivating factors for writing this paper. One of the difficulties of making "small sample" comparisons of the ISP and FSP is that the tables in [1] give the values of the $P(\text{CS})$ for fixed $n_0 = 1(1)30$ instead of giving the values of n for fixed P^*; this makes them quite inadequate for any triple (k, θ^*, P^*) that requires $n > 30$. There is a large sample approximation given but no table gives explicit n_0 values based on the normal approximation. Special values were extracted from the tables in [1] and numerical comparisons are made in Table II for these selected values. Asymptotic $(\theta^* \to 1)$ comparisons for $k \geq 2$ given below indicate that the ISP is more efficient than the FSP for any $P^* \geq \frac{1}{2}$; for $k = 2$ we can state a stronger result, i.e., that the random variable T is at most equal to n_0 with probability 1.

Binomial Case ($k = 2$)

The $P(\text{CS} \mid R_1)$ for the ISP with $k = 2$ is given in (4.6). For the FSP, which we denote by R_0, the corresponding $P(\text{CS} \mid R_0)$ for $k = 2$ can also easily be written as an incomplete beta function, and we obtain for odd n,

$$P(\text{CS}|R_0) = \sum_{i=(n+1)/2}^{n} \binom{n}{i} p^i q^{n-i} = I_p\left(\frac{n+1}{2}, \frac{n+1}{2}\right), \tag{7.1}$$

and for even n,

$$P(\text{CS}|R_0) = \frac{1}{2}\binom{n}{n/2} p^{n/2} q^{n/2} + \sum_{i=(n/2)+1}^{n} \binom{n}{i} p^i q^{n-i}$$

$$= \frac{1}{2}\left[I_p\left(\frac{n}{2}, \frac{n}{2}+1\right) + I_p\left(\frac{n}{2}+1, \frac{n}{2}\right)\right] = I_p\left(\frac{n}{2}, \frac{n}{2}\right), \tag{7.2}$$

where $p \geq \frac{1}{2}$ and the last equality of (7.2) is straightforward. It follows from (7.1) and (7.2) that we get the same probability for any odd n and the even integer $n + 1$, and this is evident in the tables for $k = 2$ in [1]; hence we can restrict our attention to odd-integer solutions.

It follows that the value of n required by the FSP for $k = 2$ is the smallest odd integer $n_0 \geq x$, where x is the solution of

$$I_{\theta^*/(1+\theta^*)}\left(\frac{x+1}{2}, \frac{x+1}{2}\right) = P^*. \tag{7.3}$$

Comparing (7.7) with the corresponding probability requirement based on (4.6) with the same θ^* and P^*, we get the remarkable result that

$$n_0 = 2N - 1 = \max(T) > E(T), \tag{7.4}$$

where the last inequality holds for any configuration of the parameters.

Remark. For the special case $k = 2$, the FSP can be curtailed, i.e., instead of stopping after taking all n_0 observations we can stop when either cell has more than $n_0/2$ observations in it, inasmuch as the decision is then determined. Since n_0 is odd (see proof above), the curtailed FSP stops as soon as either cell has $(n_0 + 1)/2 = N$ observations in it, and hence the curtailed FSP and the ISP are equivalent[4] for $k = 2$. This yields an alternative proof of (7.4). It should be noted however that for $k > 2$, the curtailed FSP is in general no longer equivalent to the ISP (cf. Table II).

We define a procedure R to be "LF-more efficient relative to (θ^*, P^*)" than R' if they satisfy the same probability requirement and the $E(T \mid R) \leq E(T \mid R')$ in the LF configuration. If the inequality holds for all configurations for a fixed pair (θ^*, P^*), then we say that R is everywhere-more-efficient than R' relative to (θ^*, P^*); if this property holds for all pairs (θ^*, P^*), then we say that R is uniformly everywhere-more-efficient than R'.

Since (7.4) holds for any configuration, it follows *a fortiori* that we have proved

Theorem 7.1. *For* $k = 2$, *the* ISP *is uniformly everywhere-more-efficient than the* FSP.

Moreover, for $k = 2$, we can assert the stronger result that with probability 1, the random variable T associated with the ISP is at most equal to the value of n_0 required by the FSP for the same probability requirement; it should be pointed out that this stronger result does not hold for $k > 2$.

Multinomial Case ($k > 2$)

As already mentioned, exact "small sample" comparisons are difficult to make for $k > 2$, and it is necessary to make "asymptotic" comparisons. Our principal results deal with the LF and W configurations with P^* fixed and $\theta^* \to 1$. In accord with the definition of "LF-more-efficient" above, we now

[4] Pointed out by Professor T. W. Anderson of Columbia University, New York.

define for fixed P^* the first-order asymptotic ($\theta^* \to 1$) proportion saved for any procedure R relative to R' as

$$\mathrm{APS}_1(R, R'; P^*) = \lim_{\theta^* \to 1} \left[\frac{E(T \mid \mathrm{R}', \mathrm{LF})}{E(T \mid R, \mathrm{LF})} - 1 \right]; \tag{7.5}$$

if this is positive we say that R is asymptotically first-order more-efficient than R'. Of course, $E(T \mid \mathrm{LF}) = n_0$ for the FSP; we shall take R_0 for the procedure R' and R_1 for R in (7.5). If the limit in (7.5) is zero, then we say that R and R' are asymptotically first-order equivalent; in this case we define the second-order asymptotic proportion saved for R relative to R' as

$$\mathrm{APS}_2(R, R'; P^*) = \lim_{\theta^* \to 1} \frac{1}{\theta^* - 1} \left[\frac{E(T \mid R', \mathrm{LF})}{E(T \mid R, \mathrm{LF})} - 1 \right]. \tag{7.6}$$

If this quantity is positive and the APS_1 is zero, then we say that R is asymptotically second-order more-efficient than R'.

Theorem 7.2. *For $k \geq 2$ and all P^*,*

$$\mathrm{APS}_1(R_1, R_0; P^*) = 0, \tag{7.7}$$

$$\mathrm{APS}_2(R_1, R_0; P^*) \geq \frac{k+2}{2[k - (k-1)P^*]} - 1, \tag{7.8}$$

which is positive for all $P^* \geq \frac{1}{2}$; in particular, for $k = 2$ and 3, it is positive for all nontrivial P^* values, i.e., for all $P^* > 1/k$.

Proof. It is clear that for fixed P^* as $\theta^* \to 1$, $N \to \infty$. For R_1 we shall use the results of (6.39) and (6.41), but first we need analogous results for the $n_0 \equiv E(T \mid R_0)$ of the FSP.

Using the arcsin–square root transformation and the subsequent normal approximation for the FSP given in [1], we have asymptotically ($\theta^* \to 1$), using the notation in [1],

$$n_0 \sim \frac{b_1}{a_1^{\,2}} \frac{\Lambda^2}{2} = \frac{b_1}{a_1^{\,2}} H_m^{\,2}(P^*, \tfrac{1}{2}), \tag{7.9}$$

where we have set $\rho = \frac{1}{2}$ since $\rho \to \frac{1}{2}$ as $\theta^* \to 1$, and where $a_1 = 2[\arcsin p^{1/2} - \arcsin q^{1/2}]$,

$$b_1 = 2 + 2\left[\frac{p}{m(1-q)}\right]^{1/2}, \tag{7.10}$$

and p and q are in the LF configuration (4.4). Expanding the right side of (7.9) in increasing powers of $\theta^* - 1$, we obtain

$$n_0 \sim \frac{2kH_m^{\,2}(P^*, \frac{1}{2})}{(\theta^* - 1)^2} + \frac{(k+2)H_m^{\,2}(P^*, \frac{1}{2})}{\theta^* - 1} + \mathcal{O}(1). \tag{7.11}$$

Using the first terms of (6.39) and (7.11), we obtain (7.7). To get a lower bound for $\text{APS}_2(R_1, R_0; P^*)$ we use the upper bound given by (6.41) and (7.11) to obtain the right member of (7.8); the latter is positive whenever

$$P^* > \frac{1}{2}\left(\frac{k-2}{k-1}\right) \tag{7.12}$$

and, *a fortiori*, whenever $P^* > \frac{1}{2}$. Since the right side of (7.12) is $\leq 1/k$ for $k = 2$ and 3, the rest of the assertion in Theorem 7.2 follows.

It is also of interest to see whether the stronger result, that $E(T \mid \text{W}) \leq n_0$, is true for any values of $k > 2$; we have already seen that this holds for $k = 2$. For this purpose we expand (6.42) in increasing powers of $\theta^* - 1$ after substituting for N from (5.14) and compare term by term with the expansion in (7.11); the values of the integral in (6.42) are taken from [12]. We find that for θ^* sufficiently close to 1 (and hence N large),

$$\begin{aligned} E(T \mid \text{W}) &< n_0 \qquad \text{for} \quad k \leq 3, \\ E(T \mid \text{W}) &> n_0 \qquad \text{for} \quad k > 3, \end{aligned} \tag{7.13}$$

The numerical results of Table II are consistent with (7.13).

ADDENDA

A. Remarks on the Variance of T

It is interesting to note that by applying (4.2) we can obtain an exact expression for ET^2, and hence for $\sigma^2(T)$, in terms of D_m integrals defined in (6.12). This initial expression can then be symmetrized by using Lemmas 6.1 and 6.2, but the final expression appears to be tediously long and is omitted. The intermediate result with a common lower limit of integration q/p for each D_m is

$$\begin{aligned} &E(T^2 \mid \text{GLF}) \\ &\quad = (2N+1)E(T \mid \text{GLF}) + N(N+1) \\ &\qquad \times \left\{-1 + \frac{mq^2}{p^2}[D_m(N+2, N-2, N, \ldots, N; q/p)\right. \\ &\qquad + (m-1)D_m(N+2, N-1, N-1, N, \ldots, N; q/p)] \\ &\qquad + \left(\frac{p}{q}\right)^2 [1 - D_m(N-2, N+2, N, \ldots, N; q/p)] \\ &\qquad + (m-1)[1 - D_m(N, N-2, N+2, N, \ldots, N; q/p)] \\ &\qquad + 2(m-1)\frac{p}{q}[1 - D_m(N-1, N+2, N-1, N, \ldots, N; q/p)] \\ &\qquad \left. + (m-1)(m-2)[1 - D_m(N, N-1, N-1, N+2, N, \ldots, N; q/p)]\right\}. \end{aligned} \tag{A.1}$$

Using the symmetrized form of (A.1) and the result for $E(T \mid \mathrm{GLF})$ in (6.13) to compute $\sigma^2(T)$, it was found that the sum of the terms, say $T_1(N)$, involving N^2 (after much calculation!) reduced to

$$T_1(N) = N^2(p-q)^2 D_m(N, N; q/p)[1 - D_m(N, N; q/p)]/p^2q^2. \tag{A.2}$$

It should be noted that $D_m(N, N; q/p) \to 1$ as $N \to \infty$ (or $P^* \to 1$) and $N^2[1 - D_m(N, N; q/p)] \to 0$, since $1 - D_m(N, N; q/p) \sim 1 - P^*$, and it can be shown using (5.14) and the definition of $H_m(P^*, \frac{1}{2})$ in (5.7) that $N \sim -4 \log(1 - P^*)$. It is conjectured that a similar result holds for the terms involving $N^{3/2}$ and that the leading "nonzero" term in the asymptotic expression for $\sigma^2(T)$ is the same as that obtained from Theorem 5.2(a), namely, for $q < p$,

$$\sigma^2(T) \sim Nmq/p^2. \tag{A.3}$$

It should also be noted that $T_1(N) \equiv 0$ for $q = p$. It is conjectured that a similar result holds for the terms involving $N^{3/2}$ and that the leading "nonzero" term for $\sigma^2(T)$ when $q = p$ is asymptotically equivalent to that given in (6.46).

B. A Property of $D_m(M, N; a)$

For convenience we denote $D_m(M, N; a)$ by $f(M, a)$ and we use $M^{(r)}$ to denote the product of the r factors $M(M+1)\cdots(M+r-1)$. Differentiating the expression (6.12) for $D_m(M, N; a)$ with respect to a and letting $D = \partial/\partial a$ denote the partial derivative with respect to a, we obtain

$$aDf(M, a) = M[f(M+1, a) - f(M, a)] = M\,\Delta f(M, a), \tag{B.1}$$

where Δ denotes the usual finite-difference operator.

We now prove the more general

Theorem B. *For any M, N, a and any r ($r = 0, 1, \dots$),*

$$M^{(r)}\,\Delta^r f(M, a) = a^r D^r f(M, a). \tag{B.2}$$

Proof. The proof is by induction, and we have already shown it to be true for $r = 1$. Assuming it is true for $r = k$, we have by applying the operator $M\,\Delta$ to the left side of (B.2) for $r = k$,

$$\begin{aligned} M\,\Delta\{M^{(k)}\,\Delta^k f(M, a)\} &\\ &= M[(M+1)^{(k)}\,\Delta^{k+1} f(M, a) + k(M+1)^{(k-1)}\,\Delta^k f(M, a)] \\ &= M^{(k+1)}\,\Delta^{k+1} f(M, a) + kM^{(k)}\,\Delta^k f(M, a). \end{aligned} \tag{B.3}$$

Now, using the induction hypothesis and the fact that Δ and D operate on different arguments and hence commute, we have from (B.3),

$$M^{(k+1)}\,\Delta^{k+1}f(M,a) + k\theta^k D^k f(M,a)$$
$$= M\,\Delta\{a^k D^k f(M,a)\} = a^k D^k\{M\,\Delta f(M,a)\} = a^k D^k\{aDf(M,a)\}$$
$$= a^k[aD^{k+1}f(M,a) + kD^k f(M,a)] = a^{k+1}D^{k+1}f(M,a) + ka^k D^k f(M,a), \tag{B.4}$$

from which (B.2) follows.

As a corollary we note that if we let $f^{(r)}(M, a)$ denote the left (or right) side of (B.2), then

$$M\,\Delta f^{(r)}(M,a) = aDf^{(r)}(M,a) \qquad (r = 0, 1, \ldots). \tag{B.5}$$

We remark that by using Lemma 6.2 or by taking the derivative of $D_m(M, N, a)$ directly that

$$\frac{\partial}{\partial a} D_m(M,N,a) = -\frac{mNM}{a(M+N)}\, b_{M+N}\left(N; \frac{a}{1+a}\right) D_{m-1}\left(M+N, N, \frac{a}{1+a}\right), \tag{B.6}$$

and hence the expression for $E(T\,|\,\text{GLF})$ in Theorem 6.1 can also be written

$$E(T\,|\,\text{GLF}) = \frac{N}{q}\left[1 - \frac{p-q}{p} D_m(N, N; q/p)\right] + \frac{1}{mp^2}\frac{\partial}{\partial a} D_m(N, N; q/p). \tag{B.7}$$

C. An Extension of Theorem 5.2

Here we consider the joint asymptotic distribution of the $X_{(i)}$ and the $Z_{(i)}$ (defined in Section 5) under a more general configuration in the parameter space; this results in a generalization of Theorem 5.2.

Theorem C. *Suppose*

$$p_{[s]} < p_{[s+1]} = \cdots = p_{[k]} = p, \quad \text{say},$$

and let

$$\eta_i = \frac{p_{[i]}}{p} \qquad (i = 1, \ldots, s).$$

Define

$$X_i^{**} = (X_{(i)} - N\eta_i)/N^{1/2} \qquad (i = 1, \ldots, s), \tag{C.1}$$

$$Z_j^{**} = Z_{(s+j)}/N^{1/2} \qquad (j = 1, \ldots, t, \quad t = k - s - 1 = m - s). \tag{C.2}$$

Then the conditional asymptotic ($N \to \infty$) *joint density of the* X_i^{**} *and the* Z_j^{**}, *given that cell* $C_{(k)}$ *empties first, is the restricted joint normal m-dimensional density*

$$h(x_1, \ldots, x_s, z_1, \ldots, z_t) = \frac{(t+1)p^{(s+1)/2}}{(2\pi)^{m/2}\prod_{i=1}^{s} p_i^{1/2}} \exp\left\{-\frac{p}{2}\left[\sum_{i=1}^{s}\left(\frac{1-p_{[i]}}{p_{[i]}}\right)x_i^2 \right.\right.$$
$$\left.\left. + \frac{1-p}{p}\sum_{j=1}^{t} z_j^2 - 2\left(\sum_{i<i'} x_i x_{i'} + \sum_{j<j'} z_j z_{j'} - \sum_{i=1}^{s}\sum_{j=1}^{t} x_i z_j\right)\right]\right\}, \tag{C.3}$$

where $-\infty < x_i < \infty$, $i = 1, \ldots, s$, $z_j > 0$, $j = 1, \ldots, t$.

Proof. Setting $x_0 = \sum_{i=1}^{s} x_i$, $z_0 = \sum_{j=1}^{t} z_j$, $\eta_0 = \sum_{i=1}^{s} \eta_i = (1/p) - t - 1$ we have, as in Theorem 5.2,

$$P[X_1^{**} = x_1, \ldots, X_s^{**} = x_s, Z_1^{**} = z_1, \ldots, Z_t^{**} = z_t]$$

$$= \frac{\Gamma[(\eta_0 + t + 1)N + (x_0 - z_0)N^{1/2}]}{\Gamma(N)} \frac{p_{[k]}^{(t+1)N - z_0 N^{1/2}}}{\prod_{j=1}^{t} \Gamma(N - N^{1/2} z_j + 1)}$$

$$\times \prod_{i=1}^{s} \frac{p_{[i]}^{N\eta_i + x_i N^{1/2}}}{\Gamma(N\eta_i + x_i N^{1/2} + 1)} \qquad \text{(C.4)}$$

Since each X_i^{**} and each Z_j^{**} takes steps of size $N^{-1/2}$, the factor $N^{m/2}$ must be adjoined on the right side of (C.4) in passing over to the limiting continuous density. The proof now proceeds as in Theorem 5.2. The limiting expression thus obtained is multiplied by $t + 1$, since the probability that any of the cells $C_{(\gamma)}$, $\gamma = s + 1, \ldots, k$, empties first is the same, $(t + 1)^{-1}$. Thus, with appropriate relabeling of the z's, the same result holds if any other cell $C_{(\gamma)}$ empties first. Note that the probability that cell $C_{(i)}$ $(i = 1, \ldots, s)$ empties first tends to zero as $N \to \infty$.

Remarks. The unrestricted chance variables Z_j'' with $-\infty < Z_j'' < \infty$ $(j = 1, \ldots, t)$ corresponding to the $Z_j^{**} > 0$, in conjunction with the X_i^{**}, $i = 1, \ldots, s$, define an m-dimensional normal distribution, whose density is $(t + 1)^{-1}$ times the density in (C.3); its covariances $(\sigma_{\alpha\beta})$ and correlations $(\rho_{\alpha\beta})$ are easily found to be (for $i, i' = 1, 2, \ldots, s$; $\gamma, \gamma' = s + 1, \ldots, m$)

$$\begin{aligned} &\sigma_{ii} = \eta_i(1 + \eta_i), \\ &\sigma_{ii'} = \eta_i \eta_{i'} \qquad \rho_{ii'} = (\eta_i \eta_{i'})^{1/2} / [(1 + \eta_1)(1 + \eta_{i'})]^{1/2}, \\ &\sigma_{\gamma\gamma} = 2 \\ &\sigma_{\gamma\gamma'} = 1 \qquad \rho_{\gamma\gamma'} = \tfrac{1}{2}, \\ &\sigma_{i\gamma} = -\eta_i \qquad \rho_{i\gamma} = -(\eta_i)^{1/2} / [2(1 + \eta_i)]^{1/2}, \end{aligned} \qquad \text{(C.5)}$$

[cf. the remark and corollary following Theorem 5.2; $t = 0$ gives Theorem 5.2(a) and $s = 0$ gives Theorem 5.2(b)]. It should be noted that the marginal distributions of the X_i^{**} as obtained from (C.3) are not normal.

D. Moments and Marginals of Equicorrelated Orthant-Restricted Normal Variables

In Section 6 it was stated that we could also get approximations to the mean and variance of T by finding the mean, variance, and covariances of the restricted normal chance variables Z_i^* in Theorem 5.2 together with the relation

$$T = kN - (2N)^{1/2} \sum_{i=1}^{m} Z_i^*. \tag{D.1}$$

We introduce a little extra generality by assuming that the Z_i^* have common correlation $\rho \geq 0$, instead of $\rho = \frac{1}{2}$; some remarks about $\rho < 0$ will be made later. It was found that the moments of Z_1^* (or Z^*, say) could be expressed as linear combinations of the moments of a random variable V_k having the density

$$g_k(x) = Cf(x)F^m(\rho_0 x) \qquad (-\infty < x < \infty), \tag{D.2}$$

where $\rho_0 = [\rho/(1-\rho)]^{1/2} \geq 0$ if $\rho \geq 0$ and C^{-1} denotes the orthant probability, which makes $g_k(x)$ a density. If $\rho = \frac{1}{2}$, then $\rho_0 = 1$, $C = k$ [see (D.7)] and (D.2) is the density of the maximum of k standardized, independent normal chance variables, which is well tabulated, e.g., in [12]; for the case $\rho = \frac{1}{2}$ we shall write V_k^* instead of V_k. The main purpose of this addendum is to develop these moment formulas. (The joint distribution of the Z_i^* can be regarded as a generalized chi distribution, since it reduces to a product of chi densities for $\rho = 0$, but it should be noted that for $\rho \neq 0$ the marginals are not chi distributions.)

Let $H_n(x)$ denote the nth Hermite polynomial given by

$$H_n(x) = n! \sum_{i=0}^{[n/2]} \frac{(-1)^i x^{n-2i}}{2^i i!(n-2i)!} \equiv \sum_{j=0}^{n} a_{n,j} x^j \quad \text{(say)}, \tag{D.3}$$

and let $H_n^*(x)$ denote the "inverse" polynomial obtained from (D.3) by changing the sign of every term in the middle expression of (D.3) to plus. To justify the term *inverse* we note that

$$x^n = n! \sum_{i=0}^{[n/2]} \frac{H_{n-2i}(x)}{2^i i!(n-2i)!} \equiv \sum_{j=0}^{n} b_{n,j} H_j(x) \quad \text{(say)} \tag{D.4}$$

and that the infinite matrices $A = \{a_{n,j}\}$ and $B = \{b_{n,j}\}$ ($n = 0, 1, \dots; j = 0, 1, \dots$) are indeed inverse to each other since $A \cdot B = I = \{\delta_{n,j}\}$, where $\delta_{n,j} = 1$ if $n = j$ and $= 0$ if $n \neq j$.

For $\rho \geq 0$ the joint c.d.f. of any subset of the Z_i^* ($i = 1, 2, \dots, m$) (say, $Z_1^*, \dots, Z_a^*$) can be written in terms of independent, standard normal chance variables [for $z_i \geq 0$ ($i = 1, 2, \dots, a$) and $z_{a+1} = z_{a+2} = \cdots = z_m = \infty$] as

$$\frac{P\{0 < (1-\rho)^{1/2} X_i - \rho^{1/2} X_0 < z_i \quad (i = 1, 2, \dots, m)\}}{P\{0 < (1-\rho)^{1/2} X_i - \rho^{1/2} X_0 \quad (i = 1, 2, \dots, m)\}}$$

$$= C \int_{-\infty}^{\infty} f(x)[1 - F(\rho_0 x)]^{m-a} \prod_{i=1}^{a} \left[F\left(\frac{x\rho^{1/2} + z_i}{(1-\rho)^{1/2}} \right) - F(x\rho_0) \right] dx. \tag{D.5}$$

The corresponding joint density of $Y_i = Z_i^*/(1-\rho)^{1/2}$ $(i = 1, 2, \ldots, a)$ can be written

$$g_a(\mathbf{y}) = C \int_{-\infty}^{\infty} f(x) F^{m-a}(\rho_0 x) \prod_{i=1}^{a} f(\rho_0 x - y_i)\, dx \tag{D.6}$$

for any $\mathbf{y} = (y_1, y_2, \ldots, y_a)$ with all components nonnegative, and $g_a(\mathbf{y}) = 0$ otherwise.

Theorem D. *For $\rho \geq 0$ and any integers $r \geq 0$, $s \geq 0$,*

$$\begin{aligned} E\{Y_1{}^r Y_2{}^s\} = & \sum_{i=0}^{[(r-1)/2]} \sum_{j=0}^{[(s-1)/2]} \frac{g(r,i)g(s,j)}{m(m-1)} E\{(\rho_0 V_k)^{r+s-2i-2j-4}[(1+\rho_0{}^2)V_k{}^4 \\ & + (1 - [2+\rho_0{}^2][r+s-2i-2j-1])V_k{}^2 \\ & + (r+s-2i-2j-2)(r+s-2i-2j-3)]\} \\ & + \sum_{i=0}^{[r/2]} \sum_{j=0}^{[(s-1)/2]} \frac{r!g(s,j)}{i!2^i(r-2i)!m} E\{(\rho_0 V_k)^{r+s-2i-2j-2} \\ & \times [V_k{}^2 - (r+s-2i-2j-)1]\} \\ & + \sum_{i=0}^{[(r-1)/2]} \sum_{j=0}^{[s/2]} \frac{g(r,i)s!}{j!2^j(s-2j)!m} E\{(\rho_0 V_k)^{r+s-2i-2j-2} \\ & \times [V_k{}^2 - (r+s-2i-2j-1)]\} + E\{H_r{}^*(\rho_0 V_k) H_s{}^*(\rho_0 V_k)\}, \end{aligned} \tag{D.7}$$

where $[x]$ denotes the largest integer $\leq x$, sums from 0 to $[-\frac{1}{2}]$ are replaced by zero, and

$$g(x, y) = \frac{\Gamma(x-y)}{\Gamma(x-2y)} 2^{x-y} I_{1/2}(x-y, y+1). \tag{D.8}$$

Proof. The proof will be outlined and the details will be omitted. From (D.6) we have

$$\begin{aligned} E\{Y_1{}^r Y_2{}^s\} &= C \int_0^{\infty} \int_0^{\infty} \int_{-\infty}^{\infty} y_1^r y_2^s f(x) F^{m-2}(\rho_0 x) f(\rho_0 x - y_1) f(\rho_0 x - y_2)\, dx\, dy_1 dy_2 \\ &= C \int_{-\infty}^{\infty} \int_{-\infty}^{\rho_0 x} \int_{-\infty}^{\rho_0 x} (\rho_0 x - t_1)^r (\rho_0 x - t_2)^s F^{m-2} \\ &\qquad \times (\rho_0 x) f(x) f(t_1) f(t_2)\, dt_1\, dt_2\, dx. \end{aligned} \tag{D.9}$$

Expanding both binomials and then using (D.4) to expand the powers of t_1 and t_2 that arise, we then separate the terms containing $H_0(t_1)$ or $H_0(t_2)$ or both and integerate with respect to t_1 and t_2. To simplify the resulting expressions, we use the fact that for integer values of $c \geq 0$,

$$\sum_{j=0}^{d}(-1)^j\binom{d}{j}\frac{\Gamma(aj+b)}{\Gamma(aj+b+c+1)}$$

$$=\begin{cases}\dfrac{d!\Gamma(b/2)}{2\Gamma[(b/2)+d+1]} & \text{for} \quad a=2,\ c=0,\\[2ex] \dfrac{(d+c)!2^{d+2c+2}}{(d+2c+1)!}I_{1/2}(d+c+1,c+1) & \text{for} \quad a=b=\tfrac{1}{2}.\end{cases} \tag{D.10}$$

The proof of Eq. (D.10) can be easily obtained by writing the left member as an integral and inverting the order of integration; the details are omitted.

Using (D.3) and (D.10) in the expanded form of (D.9) gives

$$\begin{aligned}E\{Y_1{}^rY_2{}^s\} = &\sum_{i=0}^{[(r-1)/2]}\sum_{j=0}^{[(s-1)/2]} g(r,i)g(s,j)\\ &\times C\int_{-\infty}^{\infty}(\rho_0x)^{Q-2}f(x)f^2(\rho_0x)F^{m-2}(\rho_0x)\,dx\\ &-\sum_{i=0}^{[r/2]}\sum_{j=0}^{[(s-1)/2]}\frac{r!g(s,j)}{i!2^i(r-2i)!}\\ &\times C\int_{-\infty}^{\infty}(\rho_0x)^{Q-1}f(x)f(\rho_0x)F^{m-1}(\rho_0x)\,dx\\ &-\sum_{i=0}^{[(r-1)/2]}\sum_{j=0}^{[s/2]}\frac{g(r,i)s!}{j!2^j(s-2j)!}\\ &\times C\int_{-\infty}^{\infty}(\rho_0x)^{Q-1}f(x)f(\rho_0x)F^{m-1}(\rho_0x)\,dx\\ &+\sum_{i=0}^{[r/2]}\sum_{j=0}^{[s/2]}\frac{r!s!}{i!2^i(r-2i)!j!2^j(s-sj)!}C\int_{-\infty}^{\infty}(\rho_0x)^Qf(x)F^m(\rho_0x)\,dx,\end{aligned} \tag{D.11}$$

where $Q=r+s-2(i+j)$ and $g(x,y)$ is defined in (D.6). Then (D.7) follows easily.

Some special results for $\rho=\frac{1}{2}$ (or $\rho_0=1$) and $(r,s)=(1,0)$, $(2,0)$, and $(1,1)$ give

$$E(Z^*\mid\rho=\tfrac{1}{2})=\frac{k}{m2^{1/2}}E(V_k{}^*), \tag{D.12}$$

$$\sigma^2(Z^*\mid\rho=\tfrac{1}{2})=\frac{k}{2m}\left\{\sigma^2(V_k{}^*)-\frac{1}{m}[E(V_k{}^*)]^2+\frac{m-1}{k}\right\}, \tag{D.13}$$

$$\sigma(Z_1{}^*\ Z_2{}^*\mid\rho=\tfrac{1}{2})=\frac{k}{2(m-1)}\left\{\sigma^2(V_k{}^*)+\frac{1}{m^2}[E(V_k{}^*)]^2-\frac{2}{k}\right\}. \tag{D.14}$$

From (D.1), using these results, we easily obtain the results (6.45) and (6.46).

It will be shown that Theorem D also holds for negative ρ [i.e., for $-1/(m-1) < \rho < 0$]; for this purpose an extension of the result of Owen and Steck [11] is needed. Let $\mathbf{q} = (q_1, q_2, \ldots, q_m)$ and let $\mathbf{t} = (t_1, t_2, \ldots, t_m)$; let $F_m(\mathbf{q}, \mathbf{t} \mid \rho) = P\{q_i < X_i < t_i \ (i = 1, 2, \ldots, m) \mid \rho\}$, where the X_i's are standard normal with common correlation ρ. Then for any $\rho > -1/(m-1)$ and $q_i \le t_i \ (i = 1, 2, \ldots, m)$,

$$F_m(\mathbf{q}, \mathbf{t} \mid \rho) = \int_{-\infty}^{\infty} f(x) \prod_{i=1}^{m} \left[F\left(\frac{t_i + x\rho^{1/2}}{(1-\rho)^{1/2}}\right) - F\left(\frac{q_i + x\rho^{1/2}}{(1-\rho)^{1/2}}\right) \right] dx. \tag{D.15}$$

This result is proved in [11] for $t_1 = t_2 = \cdots = t_m$ and $q_i = \infty \ (i = 1, 2, \ldots, m)$, and the same proof holds for unequal t values. The extension to finite q_i values is also straightforward, and the proof is omitted.

It follows from (D.15) that for $t_i \ge 0 \ (i = 1, 2, \ldots, a)$ and $t_{a+1} = t_{a+2} = \cdots t_m = \infty$ and any $\rho > -1/(m-1)$ we have, corresponding to (D.5),

$$P\{0 < X_i < t_i \ (i = 1, 2, \ldots, m \mid \rho\} / P\{0 < X_i \ (i = 1, 2, \ldots, m) \mid \rho\}$$

$$= C \int_{-\infty}^{\infty} f(x)[1 - F(\rho_0 x)]^{m-a} \prod_{i=1}^{a} \left[F\left(\frac{x\rho^{1/2} + t_i}{(1-\rho)^{1/2}}\right) - F(\rho_0 x) \right] dx. \tag{D.16}$$

Since $F(z)$ and $f(z)$ are analytic functions of the complex variable z, and since $f(z) = f(-z)$ and $1 - F(-z) = F(z)$, etc., all the operations of Theorem D can again be carried out. In particular, the inversion of the order of integration in (D.9) gives for both t_1 and t_2 the integration from $-\infty + \rho_0 x$ along the horizontal line to $0 + \rho_0 x$ for negative ρ values and any real x.

For example, we now have from Theorem D and the above that for $(r, s) = (1, 0)$ and any $\rho > -1/(m-1)$,

$$E\{Z^*\} = \left(\frac{1 + (m-1)\rho}{m\rho^{1/2}}\right) C \int_{-\infty}^{\infty} x F^m(\rho_0 x) f(x)\, dx$$

$$= \left(\frac{1 + (m-1)\rho}{(2\pi)^{1/2}}\right) C \int_{-\infty}^{\infty} F^{m-1}(x\rho^{1/2}) f(x)\, dx, \tag{D.17}$$

where for $\rho < 0$ and $z = u + iv$ we can (for convenience) take $F(z)$ to be the integral of $f(z)$ from $-\infty + iv$ along a horizontal line to $u + iv$. No calculations based on these formulas for $\rho < 0$ have been attempted.

Acknowledgment

The authors wish to thank Professor R. E. Bechhofer of Cornell University for his comments, and also Satindar Kumar, Mahamunulu Desu, and George G. Woodworth for their help with the computation of Table II.

REFERENCES

1. BECHHOFER, R. E., ELMAGHRABY, S. and MORSE, N. (1959). A single-sample multiple-decision procedure for selecting the multinomial event which has the highest probability. *Ann. Math. Statist.* **30** 102–119.
2. BECHHOFER, R. E., KIEFER, J. and SOBEL, M. (to appear). *Sequential Identification and Ranking Procedures.* Statist. Res. Monog. Ser., Inst. Math. Statist. and Univ. Chicago Press, Chicago.
3. BECHHOFER, R. E. and SOBEL, M. (1954). A single-sample multiple decision procedure for ranking variances of normal populations. *Ann. Math. Statist.* **25** 273–289.
4. CRAMÉR, H. (1946). *Methods of Mathematical Statistics.* Princeton Univ. Press, Princeton, New Jersey.
5. FELLER, W. (1957). *An Introduction to Probability Theory and Its Applications.* Wiley, New York.
6. GUPTA, S. and SOBEL, M. (1962). On the smallest of several correlated *F*-statistics *Biometrika* **49** 509–523.
7. KESTEN, H. and MORSE, N. (1959). A property of the multinomial distribution. *Ann. Math. Statist.* **30** 120–127.
8. KUDO, A. and YAO, J. (1964). Some considerations on the multiple inverse sampling method. *Bull. Math. Statist.* **11** 63–77.
9. MILTON, R. (1963). Tables of the equally correlated multivariate normal probability integral. Tech. Rep. 27. Dept. Statistics, Univ. Minnesota, Minneapolis, Minnesota.
10. OLKIN, I. and SOBEL, M. (1965). Integral expressions for tail probabilities of the multinomial and negative multinomial distribution. *Biometrika* **52** 167–179.
11. OWEN, D. and STECK, G. P. (1962). A note on the equicorrelated multivariate normal distribution. *Biometrika* **49** 269–271.
12. RUBEN, H. (1954). On the moments of order statistics in normal samples. *Biometrika* **41** 200–227.

On Some Selection and Ranking Procedures for Multivariate Normal Populations Using Distance Functions[1]

SHANTI S. GUPTA

DEPARTMENT OF STATISTICS
PURDUE UNIVERSITY
LAFAYETTE, INDIANA

1. INTRODUCTION AND SUMMARY

An important class of problems is concerned with the selection and ranking of k populations. For most univariate problems the selection and ranking has been defined in terms of location or scale parameters (see [6, 8–14, 18, 20, 22, 23]). In problems dealing with multivariate populations, one is usually interested in the ranking and selection problems in terms of suitably defined functions of the several parameters. These functions are usually some scalar quantities. For example, for k multivariate normal populations with mean vectors $\boldsymbol{\mu}_i'(i = 1, 2, \ldots, k)$ each of which has p components, a function that naturally arises and is of interest is the Mahalanobis distance function $\lambda_i = \boldsymbol{\mu}_i'\Sigma^{-1}\boldsymbol{\mu}_i$, where Σ is the common covariance matrix of the k populations. Thus the ranking of multivariate populations in terms of λ_i reduces to the ranking with respect to parameters of noncentrality of noncentral chi-square populations each with p degrees of freedom.

In this paper we are primarily concerned with the selection problem for the $k(k \geq 2)$ noncentral chi-square populations. We are interested in selecting populations with large values of the parameters λ_i, selecting as far as possible the best ones. The procedure to be defined is such that the probability is at least equal to a given number $P^*(1/k < P^* < 1)$ that the population with the largest value of the parameter is included in the selected subset. The size of the subset is an integer-valued random variable which takes values $1, 2, \ldots, k$. We are clearly interested in procedures which select a nonempty subset which

[1] This research was supported in part by Contract AF 33(657)11737 with the Aerospace Research Laboratories. Reproduction in whole or in part permitted for any purpose of the United States Government.

is small and yet large enough to guarantee the basic probability requirement and which have some desirable properties. In the above formulation, the loss connected with the selection and nonselection of the population with the largest value of the parameter, i.e., the best population, is 0 or 1 and the risk is bounded above: we guarantee that the least upper bound of this risk be $\leq (1 - P^*)$.

It should be pointed out that this *selecting a subset* formulation is different from the *indifference zone* approach, where the selection is in terms of a subset of fixed size, which is usually 1. In the latter formulation, the width (ratio) of an indifference zone in the parameter space is specified, the number of observations needed is tabulated, and the final decision is the selection of a single population which is asserted to be the best one. Contributions to selection and ranking problems using this approach are presented in [3–5, 7]. The present formulation is more flexible in that a decision can be made on any given number of observations with the assertion that a certain subset contains the best population, the size of the subset depending upon the observed results.

A formal statement of the problem is given in Section 2. Section 3 deals with a result relevant to ranking and selection in terms of any general parameters (not necessarily scale or location). The procedure for the noncentral χ^2 populations is given in Section 4, and its application to the ranking of multivariate populations is presented. An approximation to the probability of a correct selection and its infimum is given which enables us to compute constants (approximate) to carry out the procedure.

Sections 5 and 7 deal with the distribution function, and the moments of the ratio of the maximum of several correlated statistics each of which has a noncentral χ^2 in the numerator and a noncentral χ^2 in the denominator. An exact evaluation of the probability of the correct selection and its infimum is accomplished in Section 6, and it is shown that for this case the infimum of this probability is attained at $\lambda_1 = \lambda_2 = 0$.

2. STATEMENT OF THE PROBLEM

Suppose each of the k populations $\pi_1, \pi_2, \ldots, \pi_k$ has an observable random variable $Y_i (i = 1, 2, \ldots, k)$ whose density function is a noncentral χ^2 given by

$$f_{\lambda_i}(x) = \frac{e^{-x/2} \exp(-\lambda_i/2)}{2^{p/2}} \sum_{j=0}^{\infty} \frac{\lambda_i^{\,j} x^{(p/2)+j-1}}{j! 2^{2j} \Gamma[(p/2)+j]}, \qquad (x \geq 0), \tag{2.1}$$

where $\lambda_i (\geq 0)$ is the noncentrality parameter and p is the degree of freedom. Let the ranked λ's be denoted by

$$\lambda_{[1]} \leq \lambda_{[2]} \leq \cdots \leq \lambda_{[k]},$$

and it is assumed that there is no *a priori* information available about the correct pairing of the ordered $\lambda_{[j]}$ and the k given populations.

Any population associated with $\lambda_{[k]}$ will be called the best population. A correct selection is defined as the selection of any subset of the k populations which includes the best population. Our problem is to define a selection procedure which selects a small, nonempty subset of the k populations and guarantees that the best population has been included with probability at least P^*, P^* being a specified number between $1/k$ and 1. Mathematically, if CS stands for a correct selection, then our goal is to define a decision rule R such that

$$\inf_{\Omega} P\{\text{CS} \mid R\} = P^* \tag{2.2}$$

where $\Omega = \{\boldsymbol{\lambda} = (\lambda_1, \ldots, \lambda_k) : \lambda_i \geq 0\}$. In the limiting case where all λ's are equal (we need to consider such cases for evaluating the infimum of the probability of a correct selection), the definition of a correct selection is modified to mean the selection of a "tagged" population.

The above formulation uses a zero–one loss function, i.e.,

$$\begin{aligned} L(S_j, \lambda) &= 0 \qquad \text{if } \pi_{[k]} \text{ with } \lambda_{[k]} \in S_j, \text{ the selected subset,} \\ &= 1 \qquad \text{if } \pi_{[k]} \notin S_j. \end{aligned} \tag{2.3}$$

Thus

$$\text{risk} = E_{\lambda} L(S_j, \boldsymbol{\lambda}) = 1 - P\{\text{CS} \mid R\}. \tag{2.4}$$

Hence, the above formulation requires that we find a procedure with risk $\leq 1 - P^*$.

However, the problem could be considered within the framework of more general loss functions. Multiple-decision problems for the subset selection and with a more general loss function of the type

$$L(S_j, \boldsymbol{\lambda}) = \sum_{q \in S_j} \alpha_{jq}(\lambda_{[k]} - \lambda_q), \quad \alpha_{jq} \geq 0 \tag{2.5}$$

have been considered recently by Deely [6].

We give the procedure in Section 4. From the results at the end of Section 3, it follows that the procedures in Section 4 follow the property of monotonicity, namely, that the probability of selecting a population with a larger value of λ is at least as large as the probability of selecting a population with a smaller value of λ. An approximation to the procedure is given which also can be used to provide simultaneous upper (lower) confidence bounds on certain ratios of the linear functions of the parameters. An important application of this problem is to the ranking and selections of multivariate populations in terms of the Mahalanobis distance from the origin.

3. A CLASS OF SELECTION AND RANKING PROCEDURES

Let π_j be the population with density $f_{\lambda_j}(x)$, $j = 1, 2, \ldots, k$. Let

$$\lambda_{[1]} \leq \lambda_{[2]} \cdots \leq \lambda_{[k]} \tag{3.1}$$

be the ordered λ_i's. It should be noted that the λ_i's in this section have a different meaning than that in Section 2 and the rest of this paper. It is not known what the correct pairing of the ordered and unordered λ's is. Let $\mathbf{x}' = (x_1, x_2, \ldots, x_k)$ be an observation of $\mathbf{X}' = (X_1, X_2, \ldots, X_k)$ whose components are independent random variables, $f_\lambda(x_j)$ being the density of X_j. Based on the observation vector $\mathbf{x}'$ we are interested in selecting a subset such that the probability is at least P^* that the best, i.e., the population with the largest $\lambda_{[k]}$, is included in the subset. Let $h_b(x)$, $b \in [0, \infty)$, (or $b \in [1, \infty)$), be a class of functions such that for every x,

(a) $h_b(x) > x$,

(b) $h_0(x) = x$ (or $h_1(x) = x$),

(c) $\lim_{b\to\infty} h_b(x) = \infty$,

(d) $h_b(x)$ is continuous and monotone-increasing in b. Then the class $\mathscr{C}$ of procedures R_{h_b} is defined as follows:

R_{h_b}: Select π_i iff

$$h_b(x_i) \geq x_{\max}. \tag{3.2}$$

The above procedure selects a nonempty set of random size in view of (a). The justification for conditions (b), (c), and (d) will be provided later. It is clear that the probability of a correct selection (correct selection $\leftrightarrow$ selection of any subset which includes the best) for this procedure can be evaluated as follows. Assume that the random variable $X_{(j)}$ is associated with the population with $\lambda_{[j]}$. The $X_{(j)}$ is, of course, unknown.

$$\begin{aligned} P\{\text{CS} \mid R_{h_b}\} &= P\{h_b(X_{(k)}) \geq X_{(j)},\quad j = 1, 2, \ldots, k-1\} \\ &= \int \left[\prod_{j=1}^{k-1} F_{\lambda_{[j]}}(h_b(x))\right] f_{\lambda_{[k]}}(x)\, dx. \end{aligned} \tag{3.3}$$

Assume now that $F_\lambda(x)$ is stochastically increasing in λ, i.e., $F_{\lambda_2}(x) \leq F_{\lambda_1}(x)$ for all $\lambda_2 > \lambda_1$; then

$$\inf_{\Omega} P\{\text{CS} \mid R_{h_b}\} = \inf_{\lambda} \int F_\lambda^{k-1}(h_b(x)) f_\lambda(x)\, dx, \tag{3.4}$$

where Ω is the space of $\boldsymbol{\lambda}' = (\lambda_1, \ldots, \lambda_k)$.

Now we discuss the infimum over λ of

$$\int F_\lambda^{k-1}(h_b(x)) f_\lambda(x)\, dx.$$

First we prove a lemma.

Lemma. *The symbol X is a random variable with density $f_\lambda(x)$ and the cumulative distribution function (c.d.f.) $F_\lambda(x)$. Let $h_b(x)$, defined above, be a class of functions and suppose there exists a density $f(x)$ with c.d.f. $F(x)$ such that*

$$h_b(g_\lambda(x)) \geq g_\lambda(h_b(x)) \qquad \text{for all } \lambda \text{ and all } x, \tag{3.5}$$

where $g_\lambda(x)$ is defined by

$$F_\lambda(g_\lambda(x)) = F(x) \qquad \text{for all } x. \tag{3.6}$$

Then for any $t > 0$,

$$\int [F_\lambda(h_b(x))]^t f_\lambda(x)\, dx \geq \int [F(h_b(x))]^t f(x)\, dx,$$

where the integral extends over the whole range of values of x.

Proof. Let

$$\psi(\lambda, b) = \int F_\lambda^t(h_b(x)) f_\lambda(x)\, dx = \int F_\lambda^t(h_b(g_\lambda(z)) f_\lambda(g_\lambda(zg))_\lambda'(z)\, dz. \tag{3.7}$$

From (3.6) it follows that

$$f_\lambda(g_\lambda(x)) g_\lambda'(x) = f(x). \tag{3.8}$$

Thus

$$\psi(\lambda, b) = \int F_\lambda^t(h_b(g_\lambda(z)) f(z)\, dz. \tag{3.9}$$

Now using (3.5) and (3.6),

$$\psi(\lambda, b) \geq \int F^t(h_b(x)) f(x)\, dx. \tag{3.10}$$

Application of the lemma in (3.4) allows us to write

$$\inf_{\Omega} P\{\text{CS} \mid R_{h_b}\} \geq \int F^{k-1}(h_b(y)) f(y)\, dy. \tag{3.11}$$

From (3.11) we see that for the procedure R_{h_b} to guarantee the probability of a correct selection to be at least equal to P^* for all points in Ω, $h_b(y)$ may be chosen so as to make

$$\int F^{k-1}(h_b(y)) f(y)\, dy = P^*. \tag{3.12}$$

It should be noted that conditions (b), (c), and (d) ensure that the probability of a correct selection will always be $\geq 1/k$ and that this probability $\to 1$ as $b \to \infty$.

Remark. Equation (3.5) is a sufficient condition and gives an actual infimum if equality holds.

Examples of $h_b(x)$ Satisfying the Lemma

A. If λ is a location (translation) or a scale parameter in $f_\lambda(x)$, then

$$(1) \int_{-\infty}^{g_\lambda(x)} f_\lambda(\xi)\,d\xi = \int_{-\infty}^{g_\lambda(x)} f(\xi-\lambda)\,d\xi = \int_{-\infty}^{g_\lambda(x-\lambda)} f(\xi)\,d\xi = \int_{-\infty}^{x} f(\xi)\,d\xi$$

$$\text{or} \quad g_\lambda(x-\lambda) = x,$$

$$(2) \frac{1}{\lambda}\int_0^{g_\lambda(x)} f\left(\frac{\xi}{\lambda}\right)d\xi = \int_0^{g_\lambda(x/\lambda)} f(t)\,dt = \int_0^x f(\xi)\,d\xi \quad \text{or} \quad g_\lambda\left(\frac{x}{\lambda}\right) = x.$$

Hence

(1) If $h_b(x) = x + b$, then $h_b(g_\lambda(x)) = h_b(x+\lambda) = x + \lambda + b = g_\lambda(h_b(x))$ for all λ and all x.

(2) If $h_b(x) = xb$, $h_b(g_\lambda(x)) = h_b(x\lambda) = x\lambda b = g_\lambda(h_b(x))$, for all λ and all x.

Thus, from the lemma, it follows that

$$\inf_{\Omega} P\{\text{CS} \mid R_{h_b}\} = \int F^{k-1}(h_b(x))f(x)\,dx. \tag{3.13}$$

Note here that $f(x)$ is the density corresponding to $\lambda = 0$ (central) for the location-parameter case and it is the density corresponding to $\lambda = 1$ for the scale-parameter case.

B. For the problem of selection and ranking of the noncentral χ^2 parameters, the function $h_c(x) = x/c$, $0 < c$. Let $\chi_\alpha'^2$ and $\chi_\alpha{}^2$ be

$$\int_0^{\chi_\alpha'^2} f_\lambda(x)\,dx = 1 - \alpha = \int_0^{\chi_\alpha^2} f(x)\,dx, \tag{3.14}$$

where $f_\lambda(x)$ and $f(x)$ are, respectively, the densities of the noncentral and central chi-square r.v. with p degrees of freedom, λ being the noncentral parameter. It is known that for large p,

$$g_\lambda(x) = \chi_\alpha'^2 \approx \frac{p+2\lambda}{p+\lambda}\chi_\alpha{}^2 = \frac{p+2\lambda}{p+\lambda}x \qquad \text{all } \lambda \text{ and all } x, \tag{3.15}$$

$$h_c(g_\lambda(x)) \approx \frac{(p+2\lambda)x}{(p+\lambda)c} = g_\lambda(h_c(x)) \qquad \text{all } \lambda \text{ and all } x. \tag{3.16}$$

Thus the lemma may be applied to show that if the approximation is sufficiently good, the infimum of the probability of a correct selection in using the above rule occurs when $\lambda = 0$ in (3.4).

Monotonicity Property of the Procedure R_{h_b}

We shall now show that the procedure R_{h_b} satisfies the following property. If $\lambda_i \geq \lambda_j$, then

$$P\{\text{selecting the population with parameter } \lambda_i\} \geq P\{\text{selecting the population with parameter } \lambda_j\}, \tag{3.17}$$

provided the function $h_b(x)$ is a nondecreasing function of x.

Without loss of generality we may assume $\lambda_1 \geq \lambda_2$. Then

$$P\{\text{select } \Pi_1\} = \int \left[\prod_{j=3}^{k} F_{\lambda_j}(h_b(y))\right] F_{\lambda_2}(h_b(y)) f_{\lambda_1}(y)\, dy$$
$$\geq \int \left\{\left[\prod_{j=3}^{k} F_{\lambda_j}(h_b(y))\right] F_{\lambda_2'}(h_b(y))\right\} f_{\lambda_1}(y)\, dy, \tag{3.18}$$

for any $\lambda_2' > \lambda_2$, since F is stochastically increasing.

Since the function within the braces on the right side of the inequality is a nondecreasing function of $h_b(x)$ and hence a nondecreasing function of x by our assumption, it follows from a result in Lehmann [17, Lemma 2, p. 74] that the integral is nondecreasing in λ_1. Hence

$$P\{\text{select } \Pi_1\} \geq \int \left\{\left[\prod_{j=3}^{k} F_{\lambda_j}(h_b(y))\right] F_{\lambda_2'}(h_b(y))\right\} f_{\lambda_2}(y)\, dy$$
$$\geq P\{\text{select } \Pi_2\} \quad \text{by choosing } \lambda_2' = \lambda_1. \tag{3.19}$$

4. PROCEDURE R AND THE PROBABILITY OF A CORRECT SELECTION

Let Y_i be a noncentral χ^2 random variable with p degrees of freedom and noncentrality parameter λ_i.

Let n independent observations $y_1, y_2, \ldots, y_n$ on Y_i be given and let $\bar{y}_i$ be the arithmetic mean of the y_i's. Then the selection procedure for parameters λ_i is as follows.

Procedure R: Select the population π_i iff

$$\bar{y}_i \geq c\bar{y}_{\max}, \tag{4.1}$$

where $\bar{y}_{\max} = \max\{\bar{y}_j, j = 1, 2, \ldots, k\}$ and where $c = c(k, p, n, P^*)$ is a predetermined number between 0 and 1 which is such that the procedure R satisfies the basic P^* probability requirement.

Such a number c clearly exists, since by taking $c = 0$, we select all the populations and guarantee the probability P^* condition to be unity.

Expression for the Probability of a Correct Selection

Let $\bar{y}_{(j)}$ (unknown) be the observed value of $\bar{y}_i$ which is associated with $\lambda_{[j]}$ $(j = 1, 2, \ldots, k)$, where $\lambda_{[1]} \le \lambda_{[2]} \le \cdots \le \lambda_{[k]}$ are the ordered values of the vector $\boldsymbol{\lambda}' = (\lambda_1, \lambda_2, \ldots, \lambda_k)$. Then

$$P\{\mathrm{CS} \mid R\} = P\{\bar{y}_{(k)} \ge c\bar{y}_{\max}\} = P\{\bar{y}_{(k)} \ge c\bar{y}_{(j)},\quad j = 1, 2, \ldots, k-1\}$$

$$= \int_0^\infty \left[\prod_{j=1}^{k-1} F_{\lambda'_{[j]}}\left(\frac{x}{c}\right)\right] f_{\lambda'_{[k]}}(x)\, dx \tag{4.2}$$

where $F_{\lambda'}(\cdot)$ and $f_{\lambda'}(\cdot)$ refer to the cumulative distribution function and the density of the noncentral χ^2 distribution with parameter $\lambda' = n\lambda$ and degrees of freedom $p' = np$.

Infimum of $P\{\mathrm{CS} \mid R\}$

The number c in our procedure R is defined such that

$$\inf_{\Omega} P\{\mathrm{CS} \mid R\} = P^*,$$

where Ω is the space of all possible configurations of all λ,

$$\inf_{\Omega} P\{\mathrm{CS}|R\} = \inf_{\Omega} \int_0^\infty \left[\prod_{j=1}^{k-1} F_{\lambda'_{[j]}}\left(\frac{x}{c}\right)\right] f_{\lambda'_{[k]}}(x)\, dx. \tag{4.2$'$}$$

It is known that the distribution of a noncentral χ^2 random variable has the property TP_2, i.e., total positivity of order 2 which is equivalent to the property of monotone likelihood ratio. From the TP_2 or MLR property, it follows that the distribution of Y is stochastically increasing, i.e., $F_{\lambda'}(y)$, the c.d.f., is a nonincreasing function of λ' for all y. It follows that

$$\int_0^\infty \left[\prod_{j=1}^{k-1} F_{\lambda'_{[j]}}\left(\frac{x}{c}\right)\right] f_{\lambda'_{[k]}}(x)\, dx \ge \int_0^\infty F_{\lambda'_{[k]}}^{k-1}\left(\frac{x}{c}\right) f_{\lambda'_{[k]}}(x)\, dx, \tag{4.3}$$

and thus

$$\inf_{\Omega} P\{\mathrm{CS} \mid R\} = \inf_{\lambda \ge 0} \int_0^\infty F_{\lambda'}^{k-1}\left(\frac{x}{c}\right) f_{\lambda'}(x)\, dx. \tag{4.4}$$

It will be shown later that for the case $k = 2$, the infimum takes place at $\lambda' = 0$. In this case the exact values of c are obtained by

$$\int_0^\infty G_{m'}\left(\frac{x}{c}\right) g_{m'}(x)\, dx = P^*, \tag{4.5}$$

TABLE I

Probability That the Ratio fo Two Independent Noncentral χ^2 Variates, Each with p Degrees of Freedom and Noncentrality Parameter λ, Does Not Exceed $1/c$

λ \ c	.05	.10	.15	.20	.25	.30	.35	.40	.45	.50	.55	.60	.65	.70	.75	.80	.85	.90	.95	1.00
									$(p=2)$											
0	.952	.909	.870	.833	.800	.769	.741	.714	.690	.667	.645	.625	.606	.588	.571	.556	.541	.526	.513	.500
.2	.953	.909	.870	.834	.800	.770	.741	.715	.690	.667	.645	.625	.606	.588	.572	.556	.541	.526	.513	.500
.4	.953	.910	.871	.835	.802	.771	.742	.716	.691	.668	.646	.626	.607	.589	.572	.556	.541	.527	.513	.500
.6	.954	.912	.873	.837	.804	.773	.744	.718	.693	.669	.648	.627	.608	.590	.573	.557	.541	.527	.513	.500
.8	.955	.913	.875	.839	.806	.775	.746	.720	.695	.671	.649	.629	.609	.591	.574	.557	.542	.527	.513	.500
1.0	.956	.915	.877	.842	.809	.778	.749	.722	.697	.673	.651	.630	.611	.592	.575	.558	.542	.528	.513	.500
2.0	.963	.927	.892	.859	.826	.795	.766	.738	.712	.687	.664	.641	.620	.600	.581	.563	.546	.530	.515	.500
5.0	.983	.962	.937	.909	.881	.851	.821	.791	.762	.733	.705	.678	.652	.627	.604	.581	.559	.538	.519	.500
									$(p=4)$											
0	.993	.977	.953	.926	.896	.865	.833	.802	.771	.741	.712	.684	.657	.631	.606	.583	.561	.539	.519	.500
.2	.993	.977	.953	.926	.896	.865	.833	.802	.771	.741	.712	.684	.657	.631	.606	.583	.561	.539	.519	.500
.4	.993	.977	.954	.926	.897	.865	.834	.802	.771	.741	.712	.684	.657	.631	.607	.583	.561	.540	.519	.500
.6	.994	.977	.954	.927	.897	.866	.835	.803	.772	.742	.713	.685	.658	.632	.607	.584	.561	.540	.519	.500
.8	.994	.977	.955	.928	.898	.867	.836	.804	.773	.743	.714	.685	.658	.632	.608	.584	.561	.540	.519	.500
1.0	.994	.978	.955	.928	.899	.868	.837	.805	.774	.744	.715	.686	.659	.633	.608	.584	.562	.540	.520	.500
2.0	.995	.980	.959	.934	.906	.876	.844	.813	.782	.751	.721	.692	.664	.638	.612	.587	.564	.542	.520	.500
5.0	.997	.988	.973	.954	.930	.903	.874	.843	.811	.780	.748	.716	.686	.656	.627	.599	.573	.547	.523	.500
									$(p=6)$											
0	.999	.993	.982	.965	.942	.916	.886	.855	.823	.790	.757	.725	.693	.662	.632	.603	.576	.549	.524	.500
.2	.999	.993	.982	.965	.942	.916	.887	.855	.823	.790	.757	.725	.693	.662	.632	.603	.576	.549	.524	.500
.4	.999	.994	.982	.965	.942	.916	.887	.856	.823	.790	.758	.725	.693	.662	.632	.603	.576	.549	.524	.500
.6	.999	.994	.982	.965	.943	.916	.887	.856	.824	.791	.758	.725	.694	.663	.633	.604	.576	.549	.524	.500
.8	.999	.994	.982	.965	.943	.917	.888	.857	.824	.791	.758	.726	.694	.663	.633	.604	.576	.550	.524	.500
1.0	.999	.994	.982	.965	.943	.917	.888	.857	.825	.792	.759	.726	.694	.663	.633	.604	.576	.550	.524	.500
2.0	.999	.994	.984	.968	.946	.921	.892	.862	.829	.796	.763	.730	.698	.666	.636	.606	.578	.551	.525	.500
5.0	.999	.996	.989	.976	.958	.936	.910	.880	.849	.816	.782	.747	.713	.680	.647	.615	.585	.555	.527	.500

TABLE II

Values of c Based on an Approximation[a]

p \ k	2		3	4	5	6	7	8	9	10
				($P^* = .75$)						
5	.529	(.529)[b]	.397	.345	.316	.296	.282	.270	.262	.254
6	.562	(.561)	.433	.381	.350	.330	.316	.304	.295	.287
7	.589	(.588)	.462	.410	.380	.359	.344	.332	.323	.315
8	.610	(.610)	.486	.435	.405	.384	.369	.357	.347	.339
9	.629	(.629)	.508	.457	.427	.406	.391	.379	.369	.361
10	.645	(.645)	.526	.476	.446	.425	.410	.398	.388	.380
15	.701	(.699)	.594	.546	.517	.497	.482	.471	.461	.453
20	.737	(.736)	.637	.592	.565	.546	.531	.520	.510	.502
25	.761		.668	.626	.600	.581	.567	.556	.547	.539
30	.780	(.780)	.692	.652	.627	.609	.596	.585	.576	.569
35	.795		.711	.673	.649	.632	.619	.608	.600	.592
40	.807	(.807)	.727	.690	.667	.650	.638	.628	.619	.612
45	.817		.741	.705	.682	.666	.654	.644	.636	.629
50	.825	(.825)	.752	.717	.696	.680	.668	.659	.651	.644
				($P^* = .90$)						
5	.289	(.290)	.224	.198	.182	.172	.168	.158	.153	.149
6	.327	(.327)	.260	.232	.215	.203	.195	.188	.183	.178
7	.359	(.360)	.290	.261	.243	.231	.222	.215	.209	.204
8	.386	(.386)	.317	.286	.268	.255	.246	.239	.233	.228
9	.410	(.410)	.340	.309	.290	.277	.268	.260	.254	.248
10	.430	(.430)	.361	.330	.310	.297	.287	.280	.273	.268
15	.507	(.508)	.439	.407	.388	.374	.364	.355	.348	.343
20	.558	(.558)	.492	.461	.441	.428	.417	.409	.402	.396
25	.594		.531	.501	.482	.468	.458	.449	.443	.437
30	.623	(.622)	.561	.532	.514	.500	.490	482	.475	.469
35	.645		.586	.558	.540	.527	.517	.509	.502	.496
40	.664	(.664)	.607	.579	.562	.549	.539	.531	.525	.519
45	.680		.625	.598	.581	.568	.559	.551	.544	.539
50	.694	(.694)	.640	.614	.597	.585	.576	.568	.562	.556
				($P^* = .95$)						
5	.195	(.198)	.154	.136	.125	.118	.113	.109	.105	.102
6	.232	(.233)	.186	.167	.155	.147	.141	.136	.132	.129
7	.263	(.264)	.215	.194	.182	.173	.166	.161	.157	.153
8	.290	(.291)	.241	.219	.205	.196	.189	.183	.179	.175
9	.314	(.314)	.263	.241	.227	.217	.210	.204	.199	.195
10	.335	(.336)	.284	.261	.246	.236	.229	.223	.218	.213
15	.416	(.417)	.363	.339	.323	.312	.304	.297	.292	.287
20	.471	(.471)	.419	.394	.378	.367	.358	.352	.346	.341
25	.511		.461	.436	.420	.409	.401	.394	.388	.383
30	.543	(.543)	.494	.470	.454	.443	.434	.427	.422	.417
35	.569		.521	.497	.482	.471	.462	.456	.450	.445
40	.591	(.591)	.544	.520	.506	.495	.486	.480	.474	.469
45	.609		.563	.540	.526	.515	.507	.500	.495	.490
50	.625	(.625)	.580	.558	.544	.533	.525	.518	.513	.508

TABLE II—*Continued*

p \ k	2		3	4	5	6	7	8	9	10
					($P^* = .99$)					
5	.085	(.091)	.067	.059	.054	.051	.048	.047	.045	.044
6	.113	(.118)	.092	.082	.077	.072	.069	.067	.065	.063
7	.139	(.143)	.115	.104	.098	.093	.089	.087	.084	.082
8	.162	(.166)	.137	.125	.118	.112	.108	.105	.103	.101
9	.184	(.187)	.157	.144	.136	.130	.126	.123	.120	.117
10	.204	(.206)	.175	.162	.153	.147	.143	.139	.136	.133
15	.282	(.284)	.251	.235	.225	.218	.213	.208	.204	.202
20	.340	(.340)	.306	.290	.279	.272	.266	.261	.257	.254
25	.383		.350	.333	.322	.314	.308	.303	.299	.295
30	.419	(.419)	.385	.368	.357	.349	.343	.338	.334	.330
35	.448		.415	.398	.387	.379	.372	.367	.363	.359
40	.473	(.473)	.440	.423	.412	.404	.398	.393	.388	.385
45	.494		.462	.445	.434	.426	.420	.415	.410	.407
50	.513	(.513)	.481	.464	.454	.446	.440	.434	.430	.426

[a] For given k, p, and P^*, the table gives values of c which satisfy the equation

$$\int_{-\infty}^{\infty} \Phi^{k-1}\left(c^{-1/3}x + \frac{(c^{-1/3}-1)(9p-2)}{3(2p)^{1/2}}\right)\phi(x)\,dx = P^*,$$

where $\Phi(\cdot)$ and $\phi(\cdot)$ refer to the c.d.f. and the density function of the standard normal distribution, respectively.

[b] The values inside the parentheses in the column for $k = 2$ are the exact values.

where $G_{m'}(\cdot)$ and $g_{m'}(\cdot)$ refer to the c.d.f. and the density of a standard gamma chance variable with $g_{m'}(x) = e^{-x}x^{m'-1}/\Gamma(m')$ and $m' = p'/2$. It has been shown elsewhere (Gupta [9]) that for the problem of ranking and selection of the scale parameters of gamma populations, (4.5) provides the solution in c. The values of the constants c for this case have been tabulated in the above paper and also in a paper by Armitage and Krishnaiah [2].

Normal Approximation

Now we shall write p for p' and λ for λ'. Define $a = p + \lambda$, $b = \lambda/(p + \lambda)$; then it is known that $(\bar{y}/a)^{1/3}$ is approximately normally distributed with mean $d = 1 - [2(1 + b)/9a]$ and variance $2(1 + b)/9a$. Using this fact, (4.4) can be approximated by

$$\inf_{\lambda \geq 0} P\{\mathrm{CS} \mid R\} = \inf_{\lambda \geq 0} \int_{-\infty}^{\infty} \Phi^{k-1}\left[c^{-1/3}x - \frac{d(1-c^{-1/3})}{(1-d)^{1/2}}\right]\phi(x)\,dx \tag{4.6}$$

where $\Phi(\cdot)$ and $\phi(\cdot)$ are the cumulative distribution function and the density of a standard normal variable.

Since $0 < d < 1$, $1 - c^{-1/3} < 0$, the integral on the right side of (4.6) is a monotone-increasing function of d. Since the derivative of d with respect to λ is positive, it follows that the integral on the right side has its minimum value at $\lambda = 0$. Hence the approximate c is determined by

$$\int_{-\infty}^{\infty} \Phi^{k-1}\left[c^{-1/3}x + \frac{(c^{-1/3}-1)(9p-2)}{3(2p)^{1/2}}\right]\phi(x)\,dx = P^*. \tag{4.7}$$

The above integral equation has been solved for c for selected values of p, k, and P^*, and these approximate values appear in Table II. A comparison with the exact values for $k = 2$, indicates good accuracy for this approximation.

The approximation based on the Wilson-Hilferty cube-root transformation used above has been discussed along with other approximations by Abdel-Aty [1]. In this paper the tabulated values indicate that the approximation is good. Other approximations for the distribution of noncentral χ^2 have been discussed by Patnaik [19], Johnson [15], and Roy and Mohamad [21].

Procedure for Selecting the Subset to Contain the Multivariate Population with the Largest Value of the Mahalanobis Distance from the Origin

Let $\pi_i : N(\boldsymbol{\mu}_i, \Sigma)$, $i = 1, 2, \ldots, k$, be p-variate normal populations with mean vectors $\boldsymbol{\mu}_i$, respectively, and with a common known positive-definite matrix Σ. Let $\lambda_i = \boldsymbol{\mu}_i'\Sigma^{-1}\boldsymbol{\mu}_i$ denote the Mahalanobis distance function for the population π_i from the origin.

We take a sample of n independent observations from each of the k populations. Let $\mathbf{x}_{ij}$ denote the jth observation of the p-dimensional random vector on the ith population; then for each $j = 1, 2, \ldots, n$, we compute

$$y_{ij} = \mathbf{x}_{ij}'\Sigma^{-1}\mathbf{x}_{ij}, \qquad (i = 1, 2, \ldots, k;\ \ j = 1, 2, \ldots, n). \tag{4.8}$$

Since the $y_{ij}(j=1, 2, \ldots, n)$ correspond to the n independent observations on a noncentral χ^2 for each i, and since $Y_i = \sum_{j=1}^{n} Y_{ij}$ is distributed as a noncentral χ^2 with noncentrality parameter $\lambda_i' = n\lambda_i = n\boldsymbol{\mu}_i'\Sigma^{-1}\boldsymbol{\mu}_i$ and degrees of freedom $p' = np$, it follows that the selection rule for the population with the largest value of the Mahalanobis distance function is:

Rule R: Select the population π_i if

$$\sum_{j=1}^{n} y_{ij} \geq c \max_i \left\{\sum_{j=1}^{n} y_{ij}:\ \ i = 1, 2, \ldots, k\right\}, \tag{4.9}$$

where the values of c are given in Table II. It should be pointed out that the appropriate value of c for the above procedure is obtained by using $p' = np$ as the number for the d.f. p in the table. It will be noted that for a fixed p as n

increases, the tabulated values of c (for fixed k and P^*) increase, which would be expected.

Another procedure for this problem is as follows: Compute

$$z_i = \bar{\mathbf{x}}_i' \Sigma^{-1} \bar{\mathbf{x}}_i \tag{4.10}$$

where $\bar{\mathbf{x}}_i' = (\bar{x}_{i1}, \bar{x}_{i2}, \ldots, \bar{x}_{ip})$ is the sample mean vector based on n observations. Then the procedure is: Select π_i iff

$$z_i \geq z_{\max} - d, \tag{4.11}$$

where $d = d(k, p, n, P^*)$ is given by

$$\inf_{\lambda' \geq 0} \int_0^\infty F_{\lambda'}^{k-1}(x + d) f_{\lambda'}(x)\, dx = P^*, \tag{4.12}$$

where F and f refer to the noncentral χ^2 with p d.f. and noncentral parameter $\lambda' = n\lambda$. Properties and relative performance of this procedure are being developed at this time and will be published later.

Simultaneous Approximate Confidence Bounds on the $(k - 1)$ Ratios $(p + \lambda_j)/(p + \lambda_i)$, $j \neq i$, for a Fixed i

We have shown earlier in this section that for any $i = 1, 2, \ldots, k$, we have

$$P^* = \int_{-\infty}^{\infty} \Phi^{k-1}\left(c^{-1/3}x + \frac{(c^{-1/3} - 1)(9p - 2)}{3(2p)^{1/2}}\right) \phi(x)\, dx$$

$$\approx \inf_{\lambda \geq 0} P\left\{\max_j \left(\frac{y_j}{p + \lambda}\right)^{1/3} \leq c\left(\frac{y_i}{p + \lambda}\right)^{1/3}\right\}$$

$$= \inf_{\Omega} P\left\{\max_j \left(\frac{y_j}{p + \lambda_j}\right)^{1/3} \leq c\left(\frac{y_i}{p + \lambda_i}\right)^{1/3}\right\}$$

$$= \inf_{\Omega} P\left\{\frac{p + \lambda_j}{p + \lambda_i} \geq \frac{1}{c^3}\frac{y_j}{y_i}, \quad j = 1, 2, \ldots, k, \quad j \neq i\right\}. \tag{4.13}$$

Thus

$$P\left\{\frac{p + \lambda_j}{p + \lambda_i} \geq \frac{1}{c^3}\frac{y_j}{y_i}, \quad j = 1, 2, \ldots, k, \quad j \neq i\right\} \approx P^* \tag{4.14}$$

provides simultaneous (approximate) lower $100P^*$ percent confidence bounds on the desired ratios.

Selection of the Subset with Respect to the Minimum Value of the Parameter

If we are interested in selecting a subset to contain the population with the smallest value of λ_i, the procedure R' is as follows:

R': Select π_i iff

$$\bar{y}_i \leq b\bar{y}_{\min} \tag{4.15}$$

where $b = b(k, p, n, P^*)$ is a number greater than one which is such that R' satisfies the basic probability requirement. As before, it can be shown that the values of the constants b are obtained from

$$\inf_{\lambda \geq 0} \int_0^\infty \left[1 - F_\lambda\left(\frac{x}{b}\right)\right]^{k-1} f_\lambda(x)\, dx = P^*. \tag{4.16}$$

In the special case $k = 2$ it follows from the derivations [in particular (6.10)] of Section 6 that the function

$$I_1(\lambda) = \int_0^\infty \left(1 - F_\lambda\left(\frac{x}{b}\right)\right) f_\lambda(x)\, dx \qquad (b > 1) \tag{4.17}$$

is a monotone-increasing function of $\lambda(\lambda \geq 0)$, its minimum being at zero. Again from arguments similar to those given earlier, it follows that the approximate value of b in (4.16) is obtained by setting $\lambda = 0$, and solving

$$\int_{-\infty}^\infty \left[1 - \Phi\left(xb^{-1/3} + \frac{(b^{-1/3} - 1)(9p - 2)}{3(2p)^{1/2}}\right)\right]^{k-1} \phi(x)\, dx = P^*. \tag{4.18}$$

Tables of necessary constants b for the central case ($\lambda = 0$) are available in [14] and [16].

5. DISTRIBUTION OF AN ASSOCIATED STATISTIC

Consider the statistic

$$Z = \max_{j=1,\dots,t} (Y_j/Y) = Y_{\max}/Y, \tag{5.1}$$

where $Y_1, Y_2, \dots, Y_t$ and Y are independent noncentral χ^2 random variables each with p degrees of freedom and noncentrality parameter λ.

Now,

$$P(Z \leq b) = \int_0^\infty F_\lambda^{\,t}(by)\, f_\lambda(y)\, dy = I_\lambda(b, t), \tag{5.2}$$

where F_λ and f_λ refer to the cumulative distribution function and the density function of the noncentral χ^2 random variable with p degrees of freedom and noncentrality parameter $= \lambda(\lambda \geq 0)$.

Bounds on $I_\lambda(b, t)$

If we keep λ fixed, then

$$\frac{1}{t+1} \leq I_\lambda(b, t) \leq 1$$

$$I_\lambda(b, t-1) \geq I_\lambda(b, t)$$

$$I_\lambda(b, t) \geq I_\lambda^{\,t}(b, 1) \tag{5.3}$$

[Equation (5.3) follows from Jensen's inequality, since $F_\lambda^{\,t}(bx)$ is convex for $t > 1$.]

$$I_\lambda(b, t) \geq I_\lambda(b, 1) + 1 - t \tag{5.4}$$

$$e^{-\lambda} \sum_{0}^{\infty} a_l \lambda^l \leq I_\lambda(b, 1) \leq e^{-\lambda} \sum_{0}^{\infty} a_l \lambda^l + R(n), \tag{5.5}$$

where n is any positive integer and p = even integer = $2m$, say, and $R(n)$ and a_l are defined as follows:

$$R(n) = e^{-\lambda/2} \sum_{j=0}^{\infty} \frac{(\lambda/2)^j}{j!} \left[1 - \sum_{\alpha=0}^{m+n-1} \frac{b^\alpha}{\alpha!(1+b)^{\alpha+m+j}} \frac{\Gamma(\alpha+m+j)}{\Gamma(m+j)}\right],$$

$$a_l = \begin{cases} \dfrac{1}{2^l(l!)} \displaystyle\sum_{r=0}^{l} \binom{l}{r} \left[1 - \sum_{\alpha=0}^{m+l-r-1} \frac{b^\alpha \Gamma(m+\alpha+r)}{r!(1+b)^{\alpha+m+r}\Gamma(m+r)}\right], & (l \leq n-1) \\ \dfrac{1}{2^l(l!)} \displaystyle\sum_{r=0}^{l} \binom{l}{r} \left[1 - \sum_{\alpha=0}^{m+r-1} \frac{b^\alpha \Gamma(\alpha+m+r)}{\alpha!(1+b)^{\alpha+m+l-r}\Gamma(m+r)}\right], & (l > n-1). \end{cases} \tag{5.6}$$

It should be pointed out that for $p = 2m$ (a positive even integer), say,

$$I_\lambda(b, 1) = e^{-\lambda} \sum_{0}^{\infty} a_l \lambda^l, \tag{5.7}$$

where a_l is given by the first (top) part of (5.6) for all l.

6. THE INFIMUM OF THE PROBABILITY OF A CORRECT SELECTION FOR THE CASE $k = 2$

We have already seen that the probability of correct selection is minimized on the hyperplane $\lambda_1 = \lambda_2 = \cdots = \lambda_k = \lambda$. Now we would like to find out for what value of $\lambda \geq 0$ the infimum of the probability of correct selection takes place. Let us define, for any positive numbers n_1 and n_2 and any $c (0 < c < 1)$,

$$I(n_1, n_2, c) = \int_0^\infty G_{n_1}\left(\frac{t}{c}\right) g_{n_2}(t)\, dt \tag{6.1}$$

where $g_n(x) = d/dx\, G_n(x) = e^{-x} x^{n-1}/\Gamma(n)$. First we give two lemmas.

Lemma 1.

$$I(n_1, n_2, c) = I(n_1 - r - 1, n_2, c) - \frac{c^{n_2}}{\Gamma(n_2)(1+c)^{n_1+n_2-1}} \sum_{j=0}^{r} \frac{\Gamma(n_1+n_2-j-1)}{\Gamma(n_1-j)} (1+c)^j. \tag{6.2}$$

Proof. The proof of the lemma follows by observing that

$$G_{n_1}(t) = G_{n_1-r-1}(t) - \sum_{j=0}^{r} g_{n_1-j}(t), \qquad (r < n_1) \tag{6.3}$$

and that

$$\int_0^\infty g_{n_2}(t) g_{n_1-j}\left(\frac{t}{c}\right) dt = \frac{c^{n_2}}{(1+c)^{n_1+n_2-j-1}} \frac{\Gamma(n_1+n_2-j-1)}{\Gamma(n_2)\Gamma(n_1-j)}. \tag{6.4}$$

Lemma 2.

$$I(n_1, n_2, c) = I(n_1, n_2 - r - 1, c) + \frac{c^{n_2-1}}{\Gamma(n_1)(1+c)^{n_1+n_2-1}} \sum_{j=0}^{r} \frac{\Gamma(n_1+n_2+j-1)(1+c)^j}{\Gamma(n_2-j)c^j}. \tag{6.5}$$

The proof of lemma 2 is simple and is omitted.

For any $p = 2m$ (m is not necessarily an integer), and any $x > 0$, the c.d.f. and the density of the random variable X which is noncentral χ^2 with parameter λ and degrees of freedom p, are given by

$$F_\lambda\left(\frac{x}{c}\right) = e^{-\lambda/2} \sum_{j=0}^{\infty} \frac{\lambda^j}{j!2^j} G_{m+j}\left(\frac{x}{2c}\right) \qquad (c > 0), \tag{6.5'}$$

$$f_\lambda(x) = e^{-\lambda/2} \sum_{j=0}^{\infty} \frac{\lambda^j}{j!2^{j+1}} g_{m+j}\left(\frac{x}{2}\right). \tag{6.6}$$

From (6.5′) and (6.6), we obtain, after term-by-term integration,

$$I_\lambda = \int_0^\infty F_\lambda\left(\frac{x}{c}\right) f_\lambda(x)\, dx = e^{-\lambda} \sum_{\alpha=0}^{\infty} \lambda^\alpha \frac{1}{\alpha!2^\alpha} \sum_{r=0}^{\alpha} \binom{\alpha}{r} \int_0^\infty G_{m+\alpha-r}\left(\frac{t}{c}\right) g_{m+r}(t)\, dt$$

$$= e^{-\lambda} \sum_0^\infty a_\alpha \lambda^\alpha \tag{6.7}$$

where a_α is defined by

$$\alpha!2^\alpha a_\alpha = \sum_{r=0}^{\alpha} \binom{\alpha}{r} I(m+\alpha-r, m+r, c). \tag{6.8}$$

Using Lemma 1 and the fact that

$$\binom{\alpha+1}{r} = \binom{\alpha}{r} + \binom{\alpha}{r-1},$$

we obtain, after some simplification,

$$(\alpha+1)!2^{\alpha+1} a_{\alpha+1} = \alpha!2^\alpha a_\alpha - \frac{c^m}{(1+c)^{2m+\alpha}} \sum_{r=0}^{\alpha} \binom{\alpha}{r} \frac{c^r}{m+\alpha-r} \times \frac{\Gamma(2m+\alpha)}{\Gamma(m+\alpha-r)\Gamma(m+r)} + \sum_{r=0}^{\alpha} \binom{\alpha}{r} I(m+\alpha-r, m+r+1, c). \tag{6.9}$$

Using Lemma 2 in the last term in (6.9), we obtain, after some algebraic simplification,

$$(\alpha + 1)a_{\alpha+1} - a_\alpha = \frac{c^m\Gamma(2m+\alpha)}{\alpha!2^{\alpha+1}(1+c)^{2m+\alpha}} \sum_{r=0}^{[(\alpha-1)/2]} \binom{\alpha}{r}$$

$$\times \frac{(\alpha - 2r)c^r}{\Gamma(m+r+1)\Gamma(m+\alpha-r+1)}(1 - c^{\alpha-2r})$$

$$> 0 \qquad \text{since } \alpha - 2r > 0,\ 0 < c < 1. \tag{6.10}$$

Thus $a_1 = a_0$, $2a_1 - a_0 > 0$. Now,

$$\frac{dI_\lambda}{d\lambda} = e^{-\lambda} \sum_0^\infty [(\alpha+1)a_{\alpha+1} - a_\alpha]\alpha. \tag{6.11}$$

From (6.10) and (6.11) it follows that the derivative is positive for all values of λ except at $\lambda = 0$, where it equals zero. Thus we have the following theorem.

Theorem.[2] *For $k = 2$, the infimum of the probability of a correct selection occurs at $\lambda = 0$ and*

$$\inf_\Omega P\{\text{CS} \mid R\} = \inf_{\lambda \geq 0} \int_0^\infty F_\lambda\left(\frac{x}{c}\right) f_\lambda(x)\,dx = \int_0^\infty G_m\left(\frac{x}{c}\right) g_m(x)\,dx$$

Remark 1. In the derivation of the above theorem, it is seen that for any c, $0 < c < 1$, the function $I_\lambda(1/c, 1)$ is a monotone-increasing function of λ, its minimum being at $\lambda = 0$.

7. MOMENTS OF THE STATISTIC Z

Since the random variables $Y_{\max}$ and Y are independent,

$$E(Z^r) = E(Y_{\max}^r / Y^r)$$

$$= E(Y^{-r})E(Y_{\max}^r) \qquad \text{provided } EY^{-r} \text{ exists.} \tag{7.1}$$

Thus the evaluation of the moments of Z depends upon the negative moments of Y as in (7.2) and the moments of the largest of t independent noncentral χ^2.

$$E(Y^{-r}) = e^{-\lambda/2} \sum_{j=0}^\infty \frac{\lambda^j}{j!} \frac{1}{2^{j+r}} \frac{\Gamma(m+j-r)}{\Gamma(m+j)} \qquad \text{provided } r < m = \frac{p}{2}, \tag{7.2}$$

$$E(Y_{\max}^r) = t \int_0^\infty y^r F_\lambda^{t-1}(y) f_\lambda(y)\,dy. \tag{7.3}$$

[2] More recently this theorem has been shown to hold also for $k > 2$ by Gupta and Studden.

Special Cases

Now we discuss the evaluation of (7.3) for some cases. For $t = 1$, (7.3) reduces to the moment μ_r' of the noncentral χ^2, which can be obtained in terms of κ_r, the cumulants of the noncentral χ^2, which are

$$\kappa_r = 2^{r-1}(r-1)!(p + r\lambda). \tag{7.4}$$

Case $t = 2$. Following the methods used in Section 5 we obtain

$$E(Y^r_{\max}) = 2e^{-\lambda} \sum_{\alpha=0}^{\infty} \lambda^\alpha A_\alpha, \tag{7.5}$$

where

$$A_\alpha = \sum_{j=0}^{\alpha} \binom{\alpha}{j} \frac{2^{r-\alpha}\Gamma(m+j+r)}{\alpha!\Gamma(m+j)} \int_0^\infty G_{m+\alpha-j}(t) g_{m+j+r}(t)\, dt. \tag{7.6}$$

Now using the notation of Section 6 we can write

$$A_\alpha = \sum_{j=0}^{\alpha} \binom{\alpha}{j} \frac{2^{r-\alpha}\Gamma(m+j+r)}{\alpha!\Gamma(m+j)} I(m+\alpha-j, m+j+r, 1), \tag{7.7}$$

in which the result of Lemma 1 in Section 6 can be used to express $I(m+\alpha-j, m+j+r, 1)$ explicitly as

$$I(m+\alpha-j, m+j+r, 1) = 1 - \frac{1}{2^{m+j+r}} - \frac{1}{2^{2m+\alpha+r-1}\Gamma(m+j+r)}$$

$$\times \left[\sum_{h=0}^{m+\alpha-j-2} \frac{2^h\Gamma(2m+\alpha+r-1-h)}{\Gamma(m+\alpha-j-h)} \right], \quad \text{if } m \text{ is a positive integer.} \tag{7.8}$$

For $t > 2$, the computation of the moments of $Y_{\max}$ will follow from an extension of Lemma 1. However, the computations become very tedious.

ACKNOWLEDGMENTS

The author is very thankful to his colleague, Professor William J. Studden, for several very helpful suggestions and discussions. Thanks are also due to Dr. John J. Deely for assistance during the writing of this paper. Mrs. L. Lui of the Statistical Laboratory, Purdue University, carried out the computations of tables, and her help is gratefully acknowledged.

REFERENCES

1. ABDEL-ATY, S. H. (1954). Approximate formulae for the percentage points and the probability integral of the non-central χ^2 distribution. *Biometrika* **41** 538–540.
2. ARMITAGE, J. V. and KRISHNAIAH, P. R. (1964). Tables for the studentized largest chi-square distribution and their applications. ARL 64-188. Aerospace Research Laboratories, Wright-Patterson Air Force Base, Dayton, Ohio.

3. Bechhofer, R. E. (1954). A single-sample multiple decision procedure for ranking means of normal populations with known variances. *Ann. Math. Statist.* **25** 16–29.
4. Bechhofer, R. E. and Sobel, M. (1954). A single sample decision procedure for ranking variances of normal populations. *Ann. Math. Statist.* **25** 273–289.
5. Bechhofer, R. E., Dunnett, C. W. and Sobel, M. (1954). A two-sample multiple decision procedure for ranking means of normal populations with a common unknown variance. *Biometrika* **41** 170–176.
6. Deely, J. J. (1965). Multiple decision procedures from an empirical Bayes approach. Ph.D. thesis. Purdue Univ., Lafayette, Indiana.
7. Dunnett, C. W. (1960). On selecting the largest of k normal population means. *J. Roy. Statist. Soc. Ser. B* **22** 1–40.
8. Gupta, S. S. (1956). On a decision rule for a problem in ranking means. Mimeo. Series 150. Institute of Statistics, Univ. North Carolina, Chapel Hill, North Carolina.
9. Gupta, S. S. (1963). On a selection and ranking procedure for gamma populations. *Ann. Inst. Statist. Math.* **14** 199–216.
10. Gupta, S. S. (1965). On some multiple decision (selection and ranking) rules. *Technometrics* **7** 225–245.
11. Gupta, S. S. and Sobel, M. (1958). On selecting a subset which contains all populations better than a standard. *Ann. Math. Statist.* **29** 235–244.
12. Gupta, S. S. and Sobel, M. (1960). Selecting a subset containing the best of several binomial populations. *Contributions to Probability and Statistics*, Ch. XX. Stanford Univ. Press, Stanford, California.
13. Gupta, S. S. and Sobel, M. (1962) On selecting a subset containing the population with the smallest variance. *Biometrika* **49** 495–507.
14. Gupta, S. S. and Sobel, M. (1962) On the smallest of several correlated F statistics. *Biometrika* **49** 509–523.
15. Johnson, N. L. (1959). On an extension of the connection between Poisson and χ^2 distributions. *Biometrika* **46** 352–363.
16. Krishnaiah, P. R. and Armitage, J. V. (1964). Distribution of the studentized smallest chi-square, with tables and applications. ARL 64–218. Aerospace Research Laboratories, Wright-Patterson Air Force Base, Dayton, Ohio.
17. Lehmann, E. L. (1959). *Testing Statistical Hypotheses.* Wiley, New York.
18. Lehmann, E. L. (1961). Some model I problems of selection. *Ann. Math. Statist.* **32** 990–1012.
19. Patnaik, P. B. (1949). The non-central χ^2 and F-distribution and their applications. *Biometrika* **36** 202–232.
20. Paulson, E. (1949). A multiple decision procedure for certain problems in analysis of variance. *Ann. Math. Statist.* **20** 95–98.
21. Roy, J. and Mohamad, J. (1964). An approximation to the non-central chi-square distribution. *Sankhyā Ser. A* **26** 81–100.
22. Seal, K. C. (1955). On a class of decision procedures for ranking means of normal populations. *Ann. Math. Statist.* **26** 387–398.
23. Seal, K. C. (1958). On ranking parameters of scale in type III populations. *J. Amer. Statist. Assoc.* **53** 164–175.

Some Procedures for Selection of Multivariate Normal Populations Better Than a Control

P. R. KRISHNAIAH

AEROSPACE RESEARCH LABORATORIES
WRIGHT-PATTERSON AIR FORCE BASE, OHIO

M. HASEEB RIZVI[1]

DEPARTMENT OF MATHEMATICS
OHIO STATE UNIVERSITY
COLUMBUS, OHIO

1. INTRODUCTION AND SUMMARY

In many practical situations one is interested in selecting populations better than a control population. Paulson [12], Dunnett [3], and Gupta and Sobel [6] have treated the problem for various specific univariate populations. They require the procedures to satisfy different types of specifications. Lehmann [11] defines a number of optimum properties of selection procedures, and for some of these characterizes the optimal procedure in the univariate case. He also treats the applications to distributions with monotone likelihood ratio when the parameter of the standard population is known. Recently Krishnaiah [9] has considered the problem of selecting multivariate normal populations better than a control on the basis of the linear combinations of the elements of covariance matrices. In the present paper, selection procedures are proposed when comparisons are made on the basis of the linear combinations of the elements of the mean vectors of multivariate normal populations.

Given a set of $k \geq 1$ multivariate normal populations π_i with mean vectors $\boldsymbol{\mu}_i$ and covariance matrices Σ_i, we wish to select a subset of them which are better than a control. In Section 3 π_i is said to be *positive* (*or good*) if $\theta_{ic} \geq \theta_{0c} + \Delta_c$ for $c = 1, \ldots, r$ and *negative* (*or bad*) if $\theta_{ic} \leq \theta_{0c}$ for $c = 1, \ldots, r$, where $\theta_{ic} = \mathbf{a}_c'\boldsymbol{\mu}_i$, $\theta_{0c} = \mathbf{a}_c'\boldsymbol{\mu}_0$ and $\boldsymbol{\mu}_0$ is the mean vector of a control multivariate normal population π_0 with covariance matrix Σ_0, and $\Delta_1, \ldots, \Delta_r$ are given positive constants. In Section 4, π_i is defined to be positive if

[1] This author's work was supported in part by the National Science Foundation under Grant GP-3813 at the University of Minnesota, Minneapolis, Minnesota.

$(\theta_{ic} - \theta_{0c})^2 \geq \Delta_{1c}$ for $c = 1, \ldots, r$ and negative if $(\theta_{ic} - \theta_{0c})^2 < \Delta_{2c}$ for $c = 1, \ldots, r$, where $\Delta_{1c} \geq \Delta_{2c} > 0$ and Δ_{1c} and Δ_{2c} are specified. In Section 5, π_i is said to be positive if $|\theta_{ic}| \geq |\theta_{0c}|$ for $c = 1, \ldots, r$ and negative if $|\theta_{ic}| < |\theta_{0c}|$ for $c = 1, \ldots, r$. In Section 6, for given $\Delta_1 \geq \Delta_2 > 0$, π_i is said to be positive if $(\mathbf{a}'\boldsymbol{\mu}_i - \mathbf{a}'\boldsymbol{\mu}_0)^2 \geq \Delta_1$ for all $\mathbf{a} \neq 0$ and negative if $(\mathbf{a}'\boldsymbol{\mu}_i - \mathbf{a}'\boldsymbol{\mu}_0)^2 < \Delta_2$ for all $\mathbf{a} \neq 0$. Finally, in Section 7, π_i is defined to be positive if $\boldsymbol{\mu}_i' \Sigma_i^{-1} \boldsymbol{\mu}_i \geq \boldsymbol{\mu}_0' \Sigma_0^{-1} \boldsymbol{\mu}_0$ and negative if $\boldsymbol{\mu}_i' \Sigma_i^{-1} \boldsymbol{\mu}_i < \boldsymbol{\mu}_0' \Sigma_0^{-1} \boldsymbol{\mu}_0$. The selection procedures considered are of the form that they select π_i when $T_{ic} \geq d$ for $c = 1, \ldots, r$, where T_{ic} is a suitable function of the sufficient statistics from π_i and π_0 and d is a constant determined by requiring the procedure to satisfy a certain specification.

2. NOTATIONS AND PRELIMINARIES

The transpose of a matrix A is denoted by A', whereas its inverse (if the matrix is square and nonsingular) is denoted by A^{-1}. Also, $\mathbf{v} : p \times 1$ denotes a column vector of p elements. In addition, we shall abbreviate the cumulative distribution function and the probability density function by cdf and pdf, respectively.

As in [11] we shall define *true positives* as the positive populations that are included in the subset selected by a selection procedure δ and *false positives* as those populations included in the subset by the procedure δ which are actually negative. Let $P(\omega, \delta)$ denote the probability of including all positive populations, $S(\omega, \delta)$ the expected proportion of true positives, and $R(\omega, \delta)$ the expected proportion of false positives in the selected subset; ω and δ will be used as generic notations for a point in the space of parameters involved and the selection procedure applied, respectively. It is to be understood here that $P(\omega, \delta)$ and $S(\omega, \delta)$ are defined only for the set of those parameters for which at least one of the populations is positive. It is desirable for a selection procedure δ to have $P(\omega, \delta)$ and $S(\omega, \delta)$ as large and $R(\omega, \delta)$ as small as possible. Specifically, we shall consider the problem of determining a procedure (that is, a constant d involving δ) subject to

$$\inf_{\omega} P(\omega, \delta) \geq P^* \tag{2.1}$$

or

$$\inf_{\omega} S(\omega, \delta) \geq p^* \tag{2.2}$$

where P^* and p^* are given constants, and shall desire to have $R(\omega, \delta)$ as small as possible and will consequently derive $\sup_{\omega} R(\omega, \delta)$ as a measure of performance of δ with respect to false positives. Equivalently, one can consider the dual problem, where d is determined subject to

$$\sup_{\omega} R(\omega, \delta) \leq q^* \tag{2.3}$$

where q^* is a given constant, and $\inf_\omega P(\omega, \delta)$ or $\inf_\omega S(\omega, \delta)$ is derived as a measure of performance of δ with respect to true positives. Here we note that selection procedures based on (2.1), (2.2), or (2.3) were considered in the literature for some problems different from those considered in the present paper.

Each of the following sections treats a different problem for which we define positive and negative populations, propose selection procedure δ explicitly, and obtain expressions for $\inf_\omega P(\omega, \delta)$, $\inf_\omega S(\omega, \delta)$, and $\sup_\omega R(\omega, \delta)$. We shall only consider the case when the mean vector $\boldsymbol{\mu}_0$ of the control population is unknown; the case of known $\boldsymbol{\mu}_0$ will follow by simple modification of our discussion.

Let a sample of size n_m be taken from each π_m $(m = 0, 1, \ldots, k)$, and let $\bar{\mathbf{x}}_m$ denote the sample mean vector from π_m. Also, let $\boldsymbol{\mu}_i$ and Σ_i, respectively, denote the population mean vector and covariance matrix of ith population. In each problem we shall use k_1 and k_2 to denote the unknown number of positive and negative populations, respectively; the cases where both or any one of k_1 and k_2 are specified introduce only trivial modifications, which we shall omit. Let the jth positive population have the mean vector $\boldsymbol{\mu}_{(j)}$, the covariance matrix $\Sigma_{(j)}$, the sample mean vector $\bar{\mathbf{x}}_{(j)}$, and the associated sample size $n_{(j)}$ for $j = 1, 2, \ldots, k_1$. Similarly let the jth negative population have the mean vector $\boldsymbol{\mu}^*_{(j)}$, the covariance matrix $\Sigma^*_{(j)}$, the sample mean vector $\bar{\mathbf{x}}^*_{(j)}$, and the associated sample size $n^*_{(j)}$ for $j = 1, 2, \ldots, k_2$. Also, let

$$N = \sum_{i=0}^{k} n_i, \qquad (N - k - 1)S = \sum_{i=0}^{k} (n_i - 1)S_i$$

where $(n_i - 1)S_i/n_i$ is the maximum likelihood estimate of Σ_i.

3. SELECTION BASED ON LINEAR COMBINATIONS OF THE ELEMENTS OF MEAN VECTOR—ONE-SIDED CASE

Let $\theta_{mc} = \mathbf{a}_c'\boldsymbol{\mu}_m$, $(c = 1, \ldots, r;\ m = 0, 1, \ldots, k)$, where $\mathbf{a}_1, \ldots, \mathbf{a}_r$ are specified vectors whose elements can be considered as economic weights assigned to the elements of the mean vectors. The ith population π_i is said to be positive if

$$\theta_{ic} \geq \theta_{0c} + \Delta_c \qquad c = 1, \ldots, r, \tag{3.1}$$

negative if

$$\theta_{ic} \leq \theta_{0c} \qquad c = 1, \ldots, r, \tag{3.2}$$

where Δ_c are given positive constants. Note that, in particular, when $r = p$ and $\mathbf{a}_\alpha$ is the vector with αth element equal to unity and all other elements equal to zero, then π_i is said to be positive if, for $\alpha = 1, 2, \ldots, p$, the αth element of its mean vector exceeds the corresponding element of the mean vector of the control population by a quantity at least equal to Δ_α.

For the case of known Σ_m $(m = 0, 1, \ldots, k)$, consider the following selection procedure δ. Retain π_i in the selected subset if and only if

$$\mathbf{a}_c'(\bar{\mathbf{x}}_i - \bar{\mathbf{x}}_0)/[\mathbf{a}_c'(n_i^{-1}\Sigma_i + n_0^{-1}\Sigma_0)\mathbf{a}_c]^{1/2} \geq d \qquad c = 1, \ldots, r. \tag{3.3}$$

For this selection procedure δ and the parameter point ω, we can write

$$P(\omega, \delta) = P\{\mathbf{a}_c'(\bar{\mathbf{x}}_{(j)} - \bar{\mathbf{x}}_0)/[\mathbf{a}_c'(n_{(j)}^{-1}\Sigma_{(j)} + n_0^{-1}\Sigma_0)\mathbf{a}_c]^{1/2} \geq d,\ c = 1, \ldots, r; \quad j = 1, \ldots, k_1\}. \tag{3.4}$$

Writing

$$y_{(j)c} = \mathbf{a}_c'(\bar{\mathbf{x}}_{(j)} - \boldsymbol{\mu}_{(j)}),\ y_{0c} = \mathbf{a}_c'(\bar{\mathbf{x}}_0 - \boldsymbol{\mu}_0),\ y_{ic} = \mathbf{a}_c'(\bar{\mathbf{x}}_i - \boldsymbol{\mu}_i),$$

$$d_{(j)c} = d[\mathbf{a}_c'(n_{(j)}^{-1}\Sigma_{(j)} + n_0^{-1}\Sigma_0)\mathbf{a}_c]^{1/2}, \text{ and } d_{ic} = d[\mathbf{a}_c'(n_i^{-1}\Sigma_i + n_0^{-1}\Sigma_0)\mathbf{a}_c]^{1/2},$$

we have

$$\begin{aligned}\inf_{\omega} P(\omega, \delta) &= P\{y_{(j)c} \geq d_{(j)c} + y_{0c} - \Delta_c,\ c = 1, \ldots, r; j = 1, \ldots, k_1\} \\ &\geq P\{y_{ic} \geq d_{ic} + y_{0c} - \Delta_c,\ c = 1, \ldots, r;\ i = 1, \ldots, k\} \\ &= \int_{-\infty}^{\infty} \cdots \int_{-\infty}^{\infty} \left[\prod_{i=1}^{k} \int_{d_{i1}+y_{01}-\Delta_1}^{\infty} \cdots \int_{d_{ir}+y_{0r}-\Delta_r}^{\infty} f(y_{i1}, \ldots, y_{ir}) \prod_{c=1}^{r} dy_{ic}\right] \\ &\qquad \times f(y_{01}, \ldots, y_{0r}) \prod_{c=1}^{r} dy_{0c}\end{aligned} \tag{3.5}$$

where $f(y_{m1}, \ldots, y_{mr})$ is the r-variate normal pdf with mean vector $\mathbf{0}$ and covariance matrix $n_m^{-1}A'\,\Sigma_m A$ with $A = (\mathbf{a}_1, \ldots, \mathbf{a}_r)$; $m = 0, 1, \ldots, k$. Now the constant d of the procedure δ can be evaluated by equating the last expression in (3.5) to P^* and solving for d. In general, expressions like the last one in (3.5) are quite involved and difficult to evaluate; this is related to the difficulty of evaluating a multivariate normal probability integral in all its generality. However, for simple situations, where covariance matrices have certain nice structures, some techniques for evaluating the multivariate normal integrals are available in the literature; see, for instance, the survey article by Gupta [4].

We shall now discuss how one can use (2.2) or (2.3) instead of (2.1) to determine the value of d. We know that

$$S(\omega, \delta) = k_1^{-1} \sum_{j=1}^{k_1} P\{\mathbf{a}_c'(\bar{\mathbf{x}}_{(j)} - \bar{\mathbf{x}}_0)/[\mathbf{a}_c'(n_{(j)}^{-1}\Sigma_{(j)} + n_0^{-1}\Sigma_0)a_c]^{1/2} \geq d; \quad c = 1, 2, \ldots, r\}. \tag{3.6}$$

So, when the quantities Σ_m/n_m $(m = 0, 1, \ldots, k)$ are all equal, we have

$$\inf_{\omega} S(\omega, \delta) = \int_{-\infty}^{\infty} \cdots \int_{-\infty}^{\infty} \left[\int_{d_{11}+y_{01}-\Delta_1}^{\infty} \cdots \int_{d_{1r}+y_{0r}-\Delta_r}^{\infty} f(y_{11}, \ldots, y_{1r}) \prod_{c=1}^{r} dy_{1c}\right] \times f(y_{01}, \ldots, y_{0r}) \prod_{c=1}^{r} dy_{0c}. \tag{3.7}$$

We can solve for d by equating the right side of (3.7) to p^* if we wish to use criterion (2.2) instead of (2.1). Similarly, we know that

$$\sup_{\omega} R(\omega, \delta) = \int_{-\infty}^{\infty} \cdots \int_{-\infty}^{\infty} \int_{d_{11}+y_{01}}^{\infty} \cdots \int_{d_{1r}+y_{0r}}^{\infty} f(y_{11}, \ldots, y_{1r}) \prod_{c=1}^{r} dy_{1c}$$

$$\times f(y_{01}, \ldots, y_{0r}) \prod_{c=1}^{r} dy_{0c} \quad (3.8)$$

when the quantities Σ_m/n_m $(m = 0, 1, \ldots, k)$ are all equal. We can evaluate d by equating the right side of (3.8) to q^* if we wish to use the criterion (2.3) instead of (2.1).

Next, let us assume that the covariance matrices of all populations are equal to Σ, which is unknown. Then, we retain π_i in the selected subset iff

$$\mathbf{a}_c'(\bar{\mathbf{x}}_i - \bar{\mathbf{x}}_0) \Big/ \left\{\mathbf{a}_c' S \mathbf{a}_c\left(\frac{1}{n_i} + \frac{1}{n_0}\right)\right\}^{1/2} \geq d \qquad c = 1, 2, \ldots, r \qquad (3.9)$$

where d is chosen satisfying the criterion (2.1). But

$$P(\omega, \delta) = P(E_1 \cdots E_r)$$

where

$$E_c : (\mathbf{a}_c'\bar{\mathbf{x}}_{(i)} - \mathbf{a}_c'\bar{\mathbf{x}}_0) \Big/ \left\{\mathbf{a}_c' S \mathbf{a}_c\left(\frac{1}{n_{(i)}} + \frac{1}{n_0}\right)\right\}^{1/2} \geq d \qquad i = 1, 2, \ldots, k_1.$$

Using Bonferroni's inequality, we know that

$$P(E_1 \cdots E_r) \geq 1 - \sum_{c=1}^{r} P(E_c^*)$$

where E_c^* is the complement of E_c. Also

$$\sup_{\omega} P(E_c^*) \leq P_0$$

where

$$P_0 = 1 - \int_0^{\infty} h(w)\left[\int_{d_1^*}^{\infty} \cdots \int_{d_k^*}^{\infty} f(y_1, \ldots, y_k) \prod_{i=1}^{k} dy_i\right] dw,$$

$$d_i^* = \frac{wd}{(N-k-1)^{1/2}} \qquad \text{for} \quad i = 1, 2, \ldots, k,$$

$h(w)$ is the density function of the chi distribution with $(N - k - 1)$ degrees of freedom and $f(y_1, \ldots, y_k)$ is the frequency function of the multivariate normal with zero mean vector and with $\Omega = (\omega_{il})$ as the covariance matrix, where

$$\omega_{il} = \begin{cases} 1 & i = l \\ \dfrac{(n_i n_l)^{1/2}}{[(n_i + n_0)(n_l + n_0)]^{1/2}} & i \neq l. \end{cases}$$

Hence

$$\inf_{\omega} P(\omega, \delta) \geq 1 - rP_0. \tag{3.10}$$

So, we can equate the right side of (3.10) to P^* and solve for d.

We shall now consider how criterion (2.2) can be used to solve for d. When the sample sizes are equal to n, we can show that

$$\inf_{\omega} S(\omega, d) \geq 1 - rP(t \leq d) \tag{3.11}$$

where t is distributed as central t distribution with $(N - k - 1)$ degrees of freedom. So, we can equate the right side of (3.11) to p^* and solve for d. The derivation of any meaningful upper bound on $\sup_\omega R(\omega, \delta)$ is complicated and hence is not dealt with here.

4. SELECTION BASED ON LINEAR COMBINATIONS OF THE ELEMENTS OF MEAN VECTOR—TWO-SIDED CASE

Let us define that π_i is positive if

$$(\mathbf{a}_c'\boldsymbol{\mu}_i - \mathbf{a}_c'\boldsymbol{\mu}_0)^2 \geq \Delta_{1c} \qquad c = 1, 2, \ldots, r \tag{4.1}$$

and negative if

$$(\mathbf{a}_c'\boldsymbol{\mu}_i - \mathbf{a}_c'\boldsymbol{\mu}_0)^2 \leq \Delta_{2c} \qquad c = 1, 2, \ldots, r \tag{4.2}$$

where Δ_{1c} and Δ_{2c} are known positive constants and $\Delta_{1c} \geq \Delta_{2c}$.

Let us first assume that the covariance matrices are unequal but known. Then we retain π_i in the selected subset if and only if (for $c = 1, 2, \ldots, r$)

$$(\mathbf{a}_c'\bar{\mathbf{x}}_i - \mathbf{a}_c'\bar{\mathbf{x}}_0)^2/[\mathbf{a}_c'(n_i^{-1}\Sigma_i + n_0^{-1}\Sigma_0)\mathbf{a}_c] \geq d \tag{4.3}$$

where d is chosen satisfying (2.1), (2.2), or (2.3). But, using Bonferroni's inequality, we obtain

$$P(\omega, \delta) \geq 1 - \sum_{i=1}^{k_1} \sum_{j=1}^{r} P[w_{ij} \leq d]$$

where

$$w_{ij} = \frac{(\mathbf{a}_j'\bar{\mathbf{x}}_{(i)} - \mathbf{a}_j'\bar{\mathbf{x}}_0)^2}{[\mathbf{a}_j'\{n_{(i)}^{-1}\Sigma_{(i)} + n_0^{-1}\Sigma\}\mathbf{a}_j]}.$$

But w_{ij} is distributed as a noncentral χ^2 with one degree of freedom and with $(\mathbf{a}_j'\boldsymbol{\mu}_{(i)} - \mathbf{a}_j'\boldsymbol{\mu}_0)^2$ as the noncentrality parameter. Also, the cdf of the noncentral χ^2 is a monotonic decreasing function of the noncentrality parameter. So,

$$\inf_{\omega} P(\omega, \delta) \geq 1 - k_1 \sum_{c=1}^{r} P[\chi_c^2 \leq d] \geq 1 - k \sum_{c=1}^{r} P[\chi_c^2 \leq d] \tag{4.4}$$

where χ_c^2 is the noncentral χ^2 variate with one degree of freedom and with noncentrality parameter Δ_{1c}. Similarly, we can show that

$$\inf_{\omega} S(\omega, \delta) \geq 1 - \sum_{c=1}^{r} P[\chi_c^2 \leq d]. \tag{4.5}$$

Now, let us assume that the covariance matrices are equal to Σ, which is unknown. The selection procedure δ in this case is given below.

Retain π_i in the selected subset if

$$(\mathbf{a}_c'\bar{\mathbf{x}}_i - \mathbf{a}_c'\bar{\mathbf{x}}_0)^2 \Big/ \left\{\mathbf{a}_c' S \mathbf{a}_c \left(\frac{1}{n_i} + \frac{1}{n_0}\right)\right\} \geq d \qquad c = 1, 2, \ldots, r \tag{4.6}$$

where d is chosen satisfying (2.1), (2.2), or (2.3). We can show that

$$\inf_{\omega} P(\omega, \delta) \geq 1 - k \sum_{c=1}^{r} P[F_c \leq d] \tag{4.7}$$

$$\inf_{\omega} S(\omega, \delta) \geq 1 - \sum_{c=1}^{r} P[F_c \leq d] \tag{4.8}$$

where F_c has noncentral F distribution with $(1, N-k-1)$ degrees of freedom and Δ_{1c} as the noncentrality parameter. It is complicated to derive meaningful upper bounds on $\sup_{\omega} R(\omega, \delta)$ in both of the cases discussed above.

5. SELECTION BASED ON ABSOLUTE VALUES OF THE LINEAR COMBINATIONS OF ELEMENTS OF MEAN VECTOR

Let us define that π_i is positive if

$$|\mathbf{a}_c'\boldsymbol{\mu}_i| \geq |\mathbf{a}_c'\boldsymbol{\mu}_0| \qquad c = 1, 2, \ldots, r \tag{5.1}$$

and negative if

$$|\mathbf{a}_c'\boldsymbol{\mu}_i| < |\mathbf{a}_c'\boldsymbol{\mu}_0| \qquad c = 1, 2, \ldots, r. \tag{5.2}$$

We shall first assume that the covariance matrices of populations are equal to Σ, which is known. Also, the sample sizes are equal to n. Then we include π_i in the selected subset if

$$w_i \geq w_0 + d \qquad c = 1, 2, \ldots, r \tag{5.3}$$

where

$$w_i = n^{1/2}|\mathbf{a}_c'\bar{\mathbf{x}}_i|/[\mathbf{a}_c'\Sigma\mathbf{a}_c]^{1/2} \qquad i = 0, 1, \ldots, k$$

and d is chosen satisfying (2.1), (2.2), or (2.3). We need the following lemma in the sequel.

Lemma 1. *Let $z_0, z_1, \ldots, z_k$ be independently distributed normal variates with means $\theta_0, \theta_1, \ldots, \theta_k$ and unit variances. Then if $|\theta_i| \geq \theta_0$ $(i = 1, \ldots, k)$*

$$Pr[|z_i| \geq |z_0| + d;\, i = 1, 2, \ldots, k] \geq Pr[|z_i^*| \geq |z_0^*| + d;\, i = 1, 2, \ldots, k] \tag{5.4}$$

where $z_0^*, z_1^*, \ldots, z_k^*$ are independently distributed normal variates with zero means and unit variances, and $d \geq 0$.

Proof. Let $\lambda_i = |\theta_i|$ for $i = 0, 1, \ldots, k$. Also, let F and f denote the cdf and pdf of standard normal, respectively. Since the cdf of $|z_i|$ is nonincreasing in λ_i, we know that

$$Pr[|z_i| \geq |z_0| + d;\, i = 1, 2, \ldots, k] \geq I(\lambda_0) \tag{5.5}$$

where

$$I(\lambda_0) = \int_0^\infty [F(-u - d + \lambda_0) + F(-u - d - \lambda_0)]^k \{f(u - \lambda_0) + f(u + \lambda_0)\}\, du. \tag{5.5a}$$

Differentiating both sides with respect to λ_0 we get, after simplification,

$$\frac{dI}{d\lambda_0} = 2k \int_0^\infty [F(-u - d + \lambda_0) + F(-u - d - \lambda_0)]^{k-1} \times [f(+u + d - \lambda_0) f(u + \lambda_0) - f(u + d + \lambda_0) f(u - \lambda_0)]\, du. \tag{5.6}$$

But

$$f(u + d - \lambda_0) f(u + \lambda_0) \geq f(u + d + \lambda_0) f(u - \lambda_0)$$

since the normal pdf $f(\cdot)$ possesses monotone likelihood ratio property. So

$$\frac{dI}{d\lambda_0} \geq 0 \qquad \text{and} \qquad I(\lambda_0) \geq I(0).$$

Hence (5.4) holds good.

Now, using Bonferroni's inequality and Lemma 1, we can show that

$$\inf_\omega P(\omega, \delta) \geq 1 - r(1 - P_1) \tag{5.7}$$

where

$$P_1 = \int_0^\infty g(v_0) \left[\int_{d+v_0}^\infty g(v)\, dv \right]^k dv_0$$

and $g(v_0)$ and $g(v)$ are frequency functions of the central chi distribution with one degree of freedom. We can also show that

$$\inf_{\omega} S(\omega, \delta) \geq 1 - r(1 - P_2) \tag{5.8}$$

where

$$P_2 = \int_0^{\infty} g(v_0)\left[\int_{d+v_0}^{\infty} g(v)\, dv\right] dv_0 .$$

6. SELECTION BASED ON DISTANCES OF POPULATIONS FROM CONTROL POPULATION

For given $\Delta_1 \geq \Delta_2 > 0$, ith population π_i is said to be positive if

$$(\mathbf{a}'\boldsymbol{\mu}_i - \mathbf{a}'\boldsymbol{\mu}_0)^2 \geq \Delta_1 \qquad \text{for all} \quad \mathbf{a} \neq 0, \tag{6.1}$$

negative if

$$(\mathbf{a}'\boldsymbol{\mu}_i - \mathbf{a}'\boldsymbol{\mu}_0)^2 \leq \Delta_2 \qquad \text{for all} \quad \mathbf{a} \neq 0. \tag{6.2}$$

When $\Sigma_m (m = 0, 1, \ldots, k)$ are known, consider the selection procedure δ that selects π_i if and only if

$$\bigcap_{\mathbf{a} \neq \mathbf{0}} \{(\mathbf{a}'\bar{\mathbf{x}}_i - \mathbf{a}'\bar{\mathbf{x}}_0)^2/[\mathbf{a}'(n_i^{-1}\Sigma_i + n_0^{-1}\Sigma_0)\mathbf{a}]\} \geq d \tag{6.3}$$

or, equivalently, if and only if

$$u_i = (\bar{\mathbf{x}}_i - \bar{\mathbf{x}}_0)'[n_i^{-1}\Sigma_i + n_0^{-1}\Sigma_0]^{-1}(\bar{\mathbf{x}}_i - \bar{\mathbf{x}}_0) \geq d. \tag{6.4}$$

Then

$$P(\omega, \delta) \geq 1 - \sum_{j=1}^{k_1} Pr\{u_{(j)} \leq d\}, \tag{6.5}$$

$$S(\omega, \delta) = k_1^{-1} \sum_{j=1}^{k_1} Pr\{u_{(j)} \geq d\}, \tag{6.6}$$

$$R(\omega, \delta) = k_2^{-1} \sum_{j=1}^{k_2} Pr\{u_{(j)}^* \geq d\}, \tag{6.7}$$

where

$$u_{(j)}^* = (\bar{\mathbf{x}}_{(j)}^* - \bar{\mathbf{x}}_0)'[n_{(j)}^{*-1}\Sigma_{(j)}^* + n_0^{-1}\Sigma_0^{-1}](\bar{\mathbf{x}}_{(j)}^* - \bar{\mathbf{x}}_0),$$

$$u_{(j)} = (\bar{\mathbf{x}}_{(j)} - \bar{\mathbf{x}}_0)'[n_{(j)}^{-1}\Sigma_{(j)} + n_0^{-1}\Sigma_0^{-1}]^{-1}(\bar{\mathbf{x}}_{(j)} - \bar{\mathbf{x}}_0).$$

Note that $u_{(j)}$ is a noncentral χ^2 variable with p degrees of freedom and noncentrality parameter $\theta_{(j)} = (\boldsymbol{\mu}_{(j)} - \boldsymbol{\mu}_0)'[n_{(j)}^{-1}\,\Sigma_{(j)} + n_0^{-1}\Sigma_0]^{-1}(\boldsymbol{\mu}_{(j)} - \boldsymbol{\mu}_0)$ and that its cdf $G_p(u_{(j)}, \theta_{(j)})$ is a nonincreasing function of $\theta_{(j)}$ for all $u_{(j)}$. Also, we observe that

$$\begin{aligned}\theta_i &= (\boldsymbol{\mu}_i - \boldsymbol{\mu}_0)'[n_i^{-1}\Sigma_i + n_0^{-1}\Sigma_0]^{-1}(\boldsymbol{\mu}_i - \boldsymbol{\mu}_0)\\ &= \max_{\mathbf{a}\neq\mathbf{0}} \{(\mathbf{a}'\boldsymbol{\mu}_i - \mathbf{a}'\boldsymbol{\mu}_0)^2/[\mathbf{a}'(n_i^{-1}\Sigma_i + n_0^{-1}\Sigma_0)\mathbf{a}]\}\\ &\geq \min_{\mathbf{a}\neq\mathbf{0}} \{(\mathbf{a}'\boldsymbol{\mu}_i - \mathbf{a}'\boldsymbol{\mu}_0)^2\}/C_{iL} \end{aligned}\tag{6.8}$$

where C_{iL} denotes the largest characteristic root of $n_i^{-1}\Sigma_i + n_0^{-1}\Sigma_0$. Therefore, we have

$$\inf_{\omega} P(\omega, \delta) \geq 1 - \sum_{i=1}^{k} G_p(d, C_{iL}^{-1}\Delta_1)\tag{6.9}$$

Furthermore, when $n_m^{-1}\Sigma_m$ $(m = 0, 1, \ldots, k)$ are all equal,

$$\inf_{\omega} P(\omega, \delta) \geq 1 - kG_p(d, C_{1L}^{-1}\Delta_1),\tag{6.10}$$

$$\inf_{\omega} S(\omega, \delta) \geq 1 - G_p(d, C_{1L}^{-1}\Delta_1),\tag{6.11}$$

$$\sup_{\omega} R(\omega, \delta) \leq 1 - G_p(d, C_{1s}^{-1}\Delta_2),\tag{6.12}$$

where C_{is} denotes the smallest characteristic root of $n_i^{-1}\Sigma_i + n_0^{-1}\Sigma_0$. The right members of (6.10), (6.11), and (6.12) are immediately evaluated with the help of noncentral χ^2 tables.

For the case when $\Sigma_m = \Sigma$ for $m = 0, 1, \ldots, k$ and Σ is unknown, but its largest and smallest characteristic roots are known, we replace (6.4) by

$$(\bar{\mathbf{x}}_i - \bar{\mathbf{x}}_0)'\left\{S\left(\frac{1}{n_i} + \frac{1}{n_0}\right)\right\}^{-1}(\bar{\mathbf{x}}_i - \bar{\mathbf{x}}_0) \geq d.\tag{6.13}$$

Now let

$$v_{(j)} = \frac{(N-k-p)}{p(N-k-1)}(\bar{\mathbf{x}}_{(j)} - \bar{\mathbf{x}}_0)'\left[S\left(\frac{1}{n_{(j)}} + \frac{1}{n_0}\right)\right]^{-1}(\bar{\mathbf{x}}_{(j)} - \bar{\mathbf{x}}_0).$$

Then $v_{(j)}$ is a noncentral F variate with p and $N - k - p$ degrees of freedom and noncentrality parameter

$$\theta_{(j)} = (\boldsymbol{\mu}_{(j)} - \boldsymbol{\mu}_0)'\left\{\Sigma\left(\frac{1}{n_j} + \frac{1}{n_0}\right)\right\}^{-1}(\boldsymbol{\mu}_{(j)} - \boldsymbol{\mu}_0)$$

and that its cdf $H_{p,N-k-p}(v_{(j)}, \theta_{(j)})$ is a nonincreasing function of $\theta_{(j)}$ for all $v_{(j)}$. Thus if $n_m = n$ for $m = 0, 1, \ldots, k$, we again obtain inequalities (6.10), (6.11), and (6.12), where $G_p(d, \cdot)$ is now replaced by $H_{p,N-k-p}([(N - k - p)/$

$p(N-k-1)]d, \cdot)$. Again, noncentral F tables can be used to evaluate these quantities.

When the covariance matrices of all populations are equal to Σ, we can define that the population π_i is positive if (for $\Delta_1^* \geq \Delta_2^* > 0$)

$$(\boldsymbol{\mu}_i - \boldsymbol{\mu}_0)'\Sigma^{-1}(\boldsymbol{\mu}_i - \boldsymbol{\mu}_0) \geq \Delta_1{}^* \tag{6.14}$$

and negative if

$$(\boldsymbol{\mu}_i - \boldsymbol{\mu}_0)'\Sigma^{-1}(\boldsymbol{\mu}_i - \boldsymbol{\mu}_0) \leq \Delta_2{}^*. \tag{6.15}$$

The motivation behind using the above definition is the fact that the left side of (6.14) can be viewed as a meaningful measure of distance between π_i and π_0. In this case, if the sample sizes are equal to n and Σ is known, we retain π_i in the selected subset if and only if

$$u_i = n(\bar{\mathbf{x}}_i - \bar{\mathbf{x}}_0)'\,\Sigma^{-1}(\bar{\mathbf{x}}_i - \bar{\mathbf{x}}_0) \geq d \tag{6.16}$$

where d is chosen satisfying (2.1), (2.2), or (2.3). We can show that

$$\inf_{\omega} P(\omega, \delta) \geq 1 - kG_p(d, \Delta_1{}^*n), \tag{6.17}$$

$$\inf_{\omega} S(\omega, \delta) = 1 - G_p(d, \Delta_1{}^*n), \tag{6.18}$$

$$\sup_{\omega} R(\omega, \delta) = 1 - G_p(d, \Delta_2{}^*n). \tag{6.19}$$

When the sample sizes are equal and Σ is unknown, the selection procedure δ is the same as (6.16) if we replace Σ with S. In this case, we can show that the bounds $\inf_\omega P(\omega, \delta)$, $\inf S(\omega, \delta)$, and $\sup R(\omega, \delta)$ are obtained from (6.17), (6.18), and (6.19), respectively, if we replace $G_p(d, \cdot)$ with $H_{p,N-k-p}$ $([(N-k-p)/p(N-k-1)]d, \cdot)$.

7. SELECTION BASED ON DISTANCES OF POPULATIONS FROM A MULTIVARIATE NORMAL POPULATION WITH ZERO MEAN VECTOR

Let the covariance matrices of all populations be equal to Σ. Then, we can interpret $\boldsymbol{\mu}_i'\,\Sigma\boldsymbol{\mu}_i$ $(i = 0, 1, \ldots, k)$ as a measure of distance of π_i from a multivariate normal population with zero mean vector and with Σ as the covariance matrix. So we can define that π_i is positive if

$$\boldsymbol{\mu}_i'\Sigma^{-1}\boldsymbol{\mu}_i \geq \boldsymbol{\mu}_0'\Sigma^{-1}\boldsymbol{\mu}_0 \tag{7.1}$$

and negative if

$$\boldsymbol{\mu}_i'\Sigma^{-1}\boldsymbol{\mu}_i < \boldsymbol{\mu}_0'\Sigma^{-1}\boldsymbol{\mu}_0. \tag{7.2}$$

Let us assume that $\boldsymbol{\mu}_0' \Sigma^{-1} \boldsymbol{\mu}_0 < \tau$, where τ is known. Also, let $n_m = n$ for $m = 0, 1, \ldots, k$.

When Σ is known, consider the procedure δ that selects π_i if and only if

$$\bar{\mathbf{x}}_i' \Sigma^{-1} \bar{\mathbf{x}}_i \geq d \bar{\mathbf{x}}_0 \Sigma^{-1} \bar{\mathbf{x}}_0 \tag{7.3}$$

where $d > 1$ is a constant to be determined. Then

$$\inf_{\omega} P(\omega, \delta) \geq \inf_{\theta_0} \int_0^\infty [1 - G_p(ud, n\theta_0)]^k g_p(u, n\theta_0)\, du, \tag{7.4}$$

$$\inf_{\omega} S(\omega, \delta) \geq \inf_{\theta_0} \int_0^\infty [1 - G_p(ud, n\theta_0)] g_p(u, n\theta_0)\, du, \tag{7.5}$$

$$\sup_{\omega} R(\omega, \delta) \leq \sup_{\theta_0} \int_0^\infty [1 - G_p(ud, n\theta_0)] g_p(u, n\theta_0)\, du, \tag{7.6}$$

where $G_p(u, n\theta_0)$ and $g_p(u, n\theta_0)$ are the cdf and pdf, respectively, of a noncentral χ^2 variate with p degrees of freedom and noncentrality parameter $n\theta_0 = n\boldsymbol{\mu}_0 \Sigma_0^{-1} \boldsymbol{\mu}_0$. Letting $\theta = n\theta_0$, we propose to minimize

$$I(\theta) = \int_0^\infty [1 - G_p(ud, \theta)]^k g_p(u, \theta)\, du. \tag{7.7}$$

Using the relations (see Alam and Rizvi [1])

$$2 \frac{\partial}{\partial \theta} g_p(u, \theta) = g_{p+2}(u, \theta) - g_p(u, \theta), \tag{7.8}$$

$$2 \frac{\partial}{\partial \theta} G_p(u, \theta) = G_{p+2}(u, \theta) - G_p(u, \theta) = -2 g_{p+2}(u, \theta), \tag{7.9}$$

we obtain

$$\begin{aligned} \frac{dI(\theta)}{d\theta} &= k \int_0^\infty [1 - G_p(ud, \theta)]^{k-1} g_{p+2}(ud, \theta) g_p(u, \theta)\, du \\ &\quad + \tfrac{1}{2} \int_0^\infty [1 - G_p(ud, \theta)]^k [g_{p+2}(u, \theta) - g_p(u, \theta)]\, du \end{aligned} \tag{7.10}$$

and integrating the second term by parts, (7.10) becomes

$$\begin{aligned} \frac{dI(\theta)}{d\theta} &= k \int_0^\infty [1 - G_p(ud, \theta)]^{k-1} \\ &\quad \times \{g_{p+2}(ud, \theta) g_p(u, \theta) - g_{p+2}(u, \theta) g_p(ud, \theta) d\}\, du. \end{aligned} \tag{7.11}$$

By Lemma 2 the quantity inside the braces in (7.11) is negative and, consequently, $dI(\theta)/d\theta \leq 0$. Therefore, we have

$$\inf_{\omega} P(\omega, \delta) > \int_0^\infty [1 - G_p(ud, n\tau)]^k g_p(u, n\tau)\, du, \tag{7.12}$$

$$\inf_{\omega} S(\omega, \delta) > 1 - \int_0^\infty G_p(ud, n\tau) g_p(u, n\tau)\, du, \tag{7.13}$$

and

$$\sup_{\omega} R(\omega, \delta) = 1 - \int_0^\infty G_p(ud) g_p(u)\, du, \tag{7.14}$$

where $g_p(u) = g_p(u, 0)$ is the pdf of a central χ^2 variate with p degrees of freedom.

When Σ_m $(m = 0, 1, \ldots, k)$ are equal to Σ which is unknown and all sample sizes are equal to n, we replace (7.3) by

$$\bar{\mathbf{x}}_i' S_i^{-1} \bar{\mathbf{x}}_i \geq d \bar{\mathbf{x}}_0' S_0^{-1} \bar{\mathbf{x}}_0. \tag{7.15}$$

Let

$$v_m = n \bar{\mathbf{x}}'_m S_m^{-1} \bar{\mathbf{x}}_m/(n-1), \qquad q = (n-p).$$

Then it is known that the distribution of qv_m/p is the noncentral F with p and q degrees of freedom and noncentrality parameter $n\theta_m = n\mu'_m \Sigma_m^{-1} \mu_m$. Let the cdf and pdf of v_m be denoted by $H_{p,q}(v_m, n\theta_m)$ and $h_{p,q}(v_m, n\theta_m)$ respectively. Now, the whole of the above discussion follows through; this is so because for

$$h_{p,q}(v, \theta) = \frac{e^{-\theta/2}}{\Gamma(q/2)} \sum_{r=0}^\infty \frac{\theta^r}{2^r r!} \frac{v^{(p/2)+r-1} \Gamma[(p/2)+(q/2)+r]}{(1+v)^{r+[(p+q)/2]} \Gamma[(p/2)+r]} \qquad v > 0 \tag{7.16}$$

and $H_{p,q}(v, \theta) = \int_0^v h_{p,q}(x, \theta)\, dx$, we have the relations

$$2 \frac{\partial}{\partial \theta} h_{p,q}(v, \theta) = h_{p+2,q}(v, \theta) - h_{p,q}(v, \theta), \tag{7.17}$$

$$\begin{aligned} 2 \frac{\partial}{\partial \theta} H_{p,q}(v, \theta) &= H_{p+2,q}(v, \theta) - H_{p,q}(v, \theta) \\ &= -\frac{e^{-\theta/2}}{\Gamma(q/2)} \sum_{r=0}^\infty \frac{\theta^r}{2^r r!} \\ &\qquad \times \int_0^v \frac{x^{(p/2)+r} \Gamma[(p/2)+(q/2)+r+1]}{(1+x)^{(p/2)+(q/2)+r+1} \Gamma[(p/2)+r+1]}\, dx \\ &= -\frac{2}{q-2} h_{p+2,q-2}(v, \theta). \qquad q > 2 \end{aligned} \tag{7.18}$$

These relations appear in a similar context in Alam and Rizvi [1]. Finally, for the procedure δ described by (7.15), we again obtain (7.12), (7.13), and (7.14) with $G_p(\cdot)$, $g_p(\cdot, \cdot)$, and $G_p(\cdot, \cdot)$, respectively, replaced by $H_{p,q}(\cdot)$, $h_{p,q}(\cdot, \cdot)$, and $H_{p,q}(\cdot, \cdot)$, where $H_{p,q}(\cdot) = H_{p,q}(\cdot, 0)$. For the common unknown Σ, one may use the pooled matrix S of within group mean sum of squares and cross products to estimate Σ and describe δ; the distribution problem in this situation seems to be involved, and we do not treat this.

The following lemma has been cited above (for proof see Lehmann [10], p. 313).

Lemma 2. *Let* $h(z) = (\sum_{i=0}^{\infty} b_i z^i)/(\sum_{i=0}^{\infty} a_i z^i)$, *where the constants* a_i *and* b_i *are nonnegative and* $\Sigma\, a_i z^i$ *and* $\Sigma\, b_i z^i$ *converge for all* $z > 0$. *If the sequence* $\{b_i/a_i\}$ *is monotone, then* $h(z)$ *is a monotone function of* z *in the same direction.*

8. CONCLUDING REMARKS

We have intended to point out the scope of selection procedures in the multivariate case. The treatment of this paper is not claimed to be all-embracing; the aspects of certain optimal properties of the proposed procedures and the tabulation of certain exact and asymptotic results are not considered here. Also, we have occasionally resorted to using inequalities, not necessarily very sharp. The discussions of this paper can be easily modified when the definitions of positive and negative populations are interchanged.

REFERENCES

1. Alam, K. and Rizvi, M. H. (1965). Selection from multivariate normal populations. Tech. Rept. 65–1. Statist. Lab., Dept. Math., Ohio State University, Columbus, Ohio.
2. Armitage, J. V. and Krishnaiah, P. R. (1964). Tables for the studentized largest chi-square distribution and their applications. ARL 64–188. Aerospace Res. Labs., Wright-Patterson Air Force Base, Ohio.
3. Dunnett, C. W. (1965). A multiple comparison procedure for comparing several treatments with a control. *J. Amer. Statist. Assoc.* **50** 1091–1121.
4. Gupta, S. S. (1963). Probability integrals of multivariate normal and multivariate *t*. *Ann. Math. Statist.* **34** 792–828.
5. Gupta, S. S. (1963). On selection and ranking procedures for gamma populations. *Ann. Inst. Statist. Math.* **14** 199–216.
6. Gupta, S. S. and Sobel, M. (1958). On selecting a subset which contains all populations better than a standard. *Ann. Math. Statist.* **29** 235–244.
7. Gupta, S. S. and Sobel, M. (1962). On the smallest of several correlated *F* statistics. *Biometrika* **49** 509–523.
8. Krishnaiah, P. R. and Armitage, J. V. (1964). Distribution of the studentized smallest chi-square, with tables and applications. ARL 64–218. Aerospace Res. Labs., Wright-Patterson Air Force Base, Ohio.
9. Krishnaiah, P. R. (1965). Selection procedures based on covariance matrices of multivariate normal populations (unpublished manuscript).
10. Lehmann, E. L. (1959). *Testing Statistical Hypotheses*. Wiley, New York.
11. Lehmann, E. L. (1961). Some model I problems of selection. *Ann. Math. Statist.* **32** 990–1012.
12. Paulson, E. (1952). On the comparison of several experimental categories with a control. *Ann. Math. Statist.* **23** 239–246.

PART VIII

Applications

Clustering Procedures[1]

J. J. FORTIER
S.M.A., INC.
MONTREAL, QUEBEC, CANADA

H. SOLOMON
DEPARTMENT OF STATISTICS
STANFORD UNIVERSITY
STANFORD, CALIFORNIA

INTRODUCTION AND SUMMARY

It is often useful to group individuals, or test items, or tests, or any set of elements, in accordance with the value obtained for a measure of resemblance or a measure of proximity. This measure is a function of the outcomes for a set of variables and provides a unique mapping for each set of responses into one of several classes. The responses can be unidimensional or multidimensional. This type of problem arises in many ways and is a familiar one in science whenever an operational summarization of data is attempted to assign individuals to groups.

Educators, psychologists, and others have a pragmatic interest in these grouping procedures, and in a global sense the difficulties encountered are referred to as the clustering problem. An intuitive criterion for assessing clustering procedures is one which operates such that the groups or the clusters which are formed are homogeneous "within" a cluster (elements in a cluster are similar) and heterogeneous "between" clusters (elements from different clusters are not alike). Naturally the groups which are produced by a clustering criterion should always be examined for substantive meaning. The difficulties stressed in analyses heretofore have related to (1) the establishment of measures of homogeneity and heterogeneity and (2) the construction of clustering procedures which minimize the relative frequencies of the two types of misclassification that are possible. Still another difficulty which usually follows some success in these two problems is the management of the excessive enumeration which occurs in many studies.

[1] Prepared under Contract 2-10-065 with the U.S. Office of Education.

Therefore, an assessment of a proposed clustering procedure requires first an evaluation of two measures of error: (1) the error incurred by grouping dissimilar elements in the same cluster; and (2) the error incurred by *not* grouping similar elements in the same cluster. Measurement of these errors leads to the examination of appropriate loss functions for a given structure of clusters. These loss functions should give a value to any pair of variables whether clustered or not, so that a resultant value obtained by summing over all such pairs is the quantity by which we may judge simultaneously the worth of both the number of clusters produced and their configuration.

The new clustering criterion developed in this paper satisfies this type of risk function and provides a method for the construction of clusters and the subsequent evaluation of the cluster configuration. This method can lead swiftly to almost insurmountable computing problems even when large-scale electronic digital computers are available. Approximations are required to make an analysis somewhat manageable. Probability sampling provides one approach which reduces the computing load and will yield results which are capable of quantitative assessment. Simple random sampling is discussed and explored in this paper. Other forms of probability sampling may be more appropriate, and they require further study.

1. THE *B* CLUSTERING FUNCTION: AN UNSUCCESSFUL ATTEMPT

In what follows we use the correlation coefficient ρ as a measure of distance between two variables. By an orthogonal linear transformation the variables can be located on the unit sphere in a space of orthogonal factors obtained through the principal-components method; then ρ is a monotonic function of the cartesian distance and, like distance, ρ is invariant under any orthogonal linear transformation. Actually any measure of distance could be used for the clustering index we now discuss.

The ratio of the average ρ (assume all ρ's are positive) for pairs belonging to the same cluster to the average ρ for pairs *not* belonging to the same cluster seems, at first, a reasonable function to maximize. It is a version of the value developed by Holzinger [2], who considered it as a coefficient of "belongingness" and labeled it B. It is similar to the index employed by Tryon [4], as an index for grouping variables. We observe here that in the "belongingness" procedure the structure (number and configuration) of clusters is given in advance and the criterion is applied as a checking or inspection device. In this way the clusters are initiated directly by some substantive arguments and then modified afterward by inspection of the B values.

Theoretically speaking, we have a finite problem at hand for which there exists a solution: (1) Prepare a list of all possible partitions of a set of n

points; (2) for each partition (set of clusters) calculate the B function; and (3) choose the clustering configuration which corresponds to the optimal (large) B value. However, matters can get out of hand rather quickly, for the amount of computation becomes inordinately large even when n is moderate in size.

Some previous work in item selection by Fortier [1] employed data from an article by Kahl and Davis [3] to demonstrate some results. The extensive computational analysis applied previously to their basic data can be used to good advantage if we permit their work to serve as an illustrative example again. The Kahl and Davis data is based on 19 variables which we shall now subject to cluster analysis. Suppose, for example, that we are interested in the number of partitions of those 19 variables in, say, 8 clusters and that for each such partition we shall compute our version of the B value. We might then do the same for all possible clusters obtained by dividing up the 19 variables. That is, we might do all this if it is feasible, and thus an analysis of the combinatorial situation is required. The development which follows leads to the recursive formula:

$$P(n, m) = \left(m^n - \sum_{i=1}^{m-1} m_{(m-i)} P(n, i)\right) \Big/ m!$$

where m is the number of clusters $m \geq 2$; n is the number of variables in the set, $n \geq m$; $P(n,m)$ is the number of distinct partitions containing exactly m clusters; and $m_{(m-i)} = m(m-1)(m-2)\cdots(m-i+1)$.

To prove this, one can view the clusters as m boxes indexed from 1 to m in which the n variables are to be distributed. If none of the boxes is empty, the number of ways one can distribute the n variables corresponds to the number of partitions of the first n integers into m categories except for the $m!$ permutations of the indexes. However, from the m^n ways of distributing the variables one must subtract the number of situations where there are exactly $(m - i)$ empty boxes whenever there are $i < m$ clusters. To do this recall that a distribution with i nonempty boxes is a partition with i clusters except for the permutation of the indexes. Since there are $\binom{m}{i}$ ways of choosing the nonempty boxes, one must also multiply $P(n, i)$ by that number. So there are $\binom{m}{i} i! P(n, i)$ partitions, or $m_{(m-i)} P(n, i)$ partitions, containing $(m - i)$ empty boxes. If we sum over i from 1 to $(m - 1)$ and subtract from m^n, we have the number of partitions with m nonempty boxes. Dividing finally by $m!$ to allow for permutation of the indexes we arrive at the formula for $P(n, m)$.

To help answer the type of question raised in the previous paragraphs, a table of the formula was computed for values of n and m. This appears as Table I. The entry in each cell, $P_{n,m}$, is a Stirling number of the second kind

TABLE I

Number of Distinct Partitions of n Variables Containing Exactly m Clusters: $P_{n,m} = mP_{n-1,m} + P_{n-1,m-1}$

m \ n	3	4	5	6	7	8	9	10	11	12	13	14	…	19[a]
2	3	7	15	31	63	127	255	511	1023	2047	4095	8191		262143
3		6	25	90	301	966	3025	9330	28501	86526	261625	788970		19344810×10^1
4			10	65	350	1701	7770	34105	145750	611501	2532530	10391745		11259666×10^3
5				15	140	1050	6951	42525	246730	1379400	7508501	40075035		14758928×10^4
6					21	266	2646	22827	179487	1323652	9321312	63436373		69308159×10^4
7						28	462	5880	63987	627396	5715424	49329280		14929248×10^5
8							36	750	11880	159027	1899612	20912320		17097507×10^5
9								45	1155	22275	359502	5135130		11446150×10^5
10									55	1705	39325	752757		47729690×10^4
11										66	2431	66066		12941322×10^4
12											78	3367		23466998×10^3
13												91		28924104×10^2
14														24358702×10^1
15														13916309
16														526029
17														13270
18														171

[a] Approximate values.

and obeys the recursion formula

$$P_{n,m} = mP_{n-1,m} + P_{n-1,m-1}.$$

This permits easy construction of the table. Actually there are 1,709, 751, 003, 480 distinct partitions of 19 variables in 8 clusters—the table gives 1,709,750,700,000 as an approximation. To examine them all is out of the question, even with the present state of computer technology. Thus the following strategy based on unrestricted random sampling was employed. It was developed originally for an item-selection problem and is discussed in [1].

From the laws of simple random sampling we can compute how many cluster selections are to be attempted and enumerated before one attains a probability α of having captured one of the selections which rank among the best. The number of selections desired is thus a function of a predetermined β, the proportion of all the selections which can be labeled "best" or acceptable in some sense. In our present setting all "B" values larger than a preassigned constant determine those clusterings which are considered good, and these together are a fraction β of the total number of possible clusterings. From this point on, "B" represents our version of Holzinger's B. This function of α and β, say, $s(\alpha, \beta)$, is the number of samplings required and is given by

$$s(\alpha, \beta) = \left[\frac{\log \alpha}{\log(1-\beta)}\right],$$

where the brackets denote the smallest integer greater than or equal to the value enclosed. This result assumes sampling with replacement which is adequate for any practical situation. A table of $s(\alpha, \beta)$ appears in [1] for values of α, β ranging from .0001 to .20 and is reproduced here as Table II.

Using a computer, 10,000 clusterings were obtained by unrestricted random sampling for each fixed m, and to each clustering a computed "B" value was attached. This was done for values of $m = 2, \ldots, 18$ (170,000 clusterings in all). The results were disappointing and so will not be discussed here. Indeed the clustering for the data in Kahl and Davis [3] using Tryon's method, which constructs clusters sequentially and yielded 8 clusters, has a B value superior to that B value for our best sample clustering for $m = 8$. In Tryon's method clusters are formed on the basis of average distance between all points in a cluster.

This fact seems to indicate that simple random sampling is not effective when the distribution of the index is very skewed and favorable values of the index are in the tail. For example if $\alpha = .05$, then the number of partition samples required jumps quickly from 299 to 3026 to 32,526 as β goes from .01 to .001 to .0001. To get some idea of the actual frequency distribution of maximum values of B, an empirical distribution for $m = 10$ was obtained as follows. The 10,000 sample partitions were viewed now as 100 random

TABLE II

$s = s(\alpha, \beta)$ *for Certain Values of* α *and* β

β \ α	.20	.10	.05	.01	.001	.0001
.20	8	11	14	21	31	42
.10	16	22	29	44	66	88
.05	32	45	59	90	135	180
.01	161	230	299	459	689	918
.001	1,626	2,326	3,026	4,652	6,977	9,303
.0001	17,475	25,000	32,526	50,000	75,000	100,000

repetitions each producing 100 partitions of 19 variables in 10 clusters. For each partition, a "B" was computed and the maximum of the 100 values so obtained was recorded. Since there are 100 repetitions, we get 100 such maximum B values. These are given in histogram form in Fig. 1 and indicate an

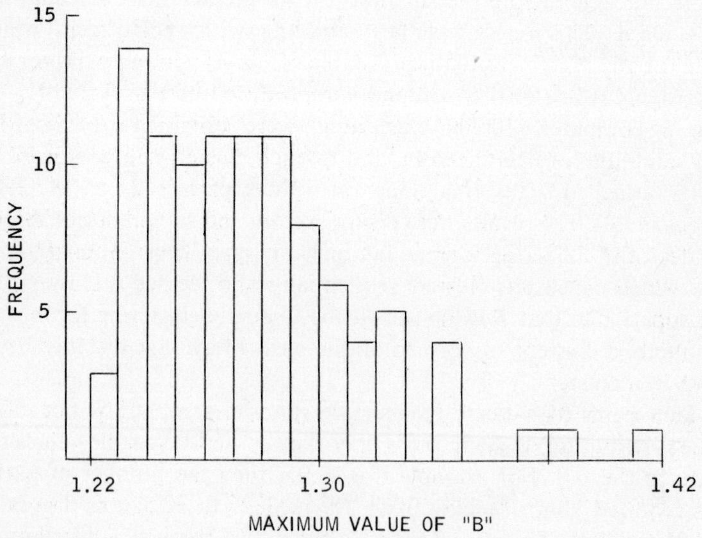

Fig. 1. Frequency distribution of maximum B values for 100 sets of 100 selections for $m = 10$ (distribution of 100 maximum values).

exponential-type distribution. This is not unusual for ratio-type variables and for extreme value variables. Thus we may very well be in a situation where for reasonable values of α, β and for unrestricted random sampling there is a horde of either *poor* or *not good* solutions and a minute number of *good* solutions; and extensive sampling, and thus high cost or terrible tedium, represents the only way out. Modifications of the sampling strategy may improve the situation and these should be studied.

2. A CLUSTERING FUNCTION WHICH IS DEFINED FOR EACH PAIR OF VARIABLES

The previous discussion indicates that we should look for some new clustering indexes if we wish to examine a cluster structure globally (nonsequentially). It would be nice if this new index is more indicative in advance as to whether a certain pair of variables should be assigned to the same cluster or not. Our previous methodology did not employ prior knowledge, it was based on *a posteriori* information arrived at by sampling techniques or complete enumeration. We would like a procedure which could lead to an amenable solution by eliminating in advance most of the "poor" solutions. We would also like to give a cumulative form to the clustering function which is defined for each pair, so that the distribution of the clustering index can be approximated, possibly by a Gaussian distribution if one of the central limit theorems applies. This would mitigate the kind of problem we encountered previously if sampling is required, since it would permit a value for β from Gaussian tables for any value of the clustering index which is labeled "good."

First we suggest that two variables should be clustered if ρ^2 is greater than a preassigned constant, say ρ^{*2}. In the contrary case they should not be in the same cluster. The gain (positive or negative) incurred by taking any action a could be expressed by $G_{ij}(a)$. Suppose we let $\rho^{*2} = .50$ for purposes of exposition. In actual practice, $\rho \geq .7$ signifies a close relationship. Then we may write

$$G_{ij}(a) = (\rho_{ij}^2 - .5) \cdot g(a),$$

where

$$g(a) = \begin{cases} +1 & \text{if the } i\text{th and } j\text{th variable are put in the same cluster} \\ -1 & \text{otherwise.} \end{cases}$$

Summing over all pairs we obtain a value, call it C, for any clustering:

$$C(A) = \sum_{i<j} G_{ij}(a_{ij}),$$

where a_{ij} is the specific action taken for the pair (i, j) and A is the matrix of those a_{ij}'s. We observe that some a_{ij}'s depend on others. For instance if the pair (2, 3) is in the same cluster and this is so for the pair (3, 4) then the pair (2, 4) is also in the same cluster.

Let us now consider the critical values

$$D_{ij} \equiv (\rho_{ij}^2 - .5).$$

The matrix D consists of a number of positive values. For example, the Kahl and Davis correlation matrix (19 × 19) leads to a D matrix with 16 positive values. This demonstrates in this case that from one to 16 clusters may be possible, since a cluster formed only by pairs having negative D_{ij} values should not be considered, for it reduces the gain function (increases the loss function). There may be less than 16 clusters, as we shall see subsequently, even if one chooses to include all 16 pairs. A closer examination of the problem shows that

$$C(A) = 2 \sum_{(i,j \in S)} D_{ij} - \sum_{i<j} D_{ij},$$

where S is the set of pairs of variables that belong to the same cluster. Thus the critical quantity is

$$C^* \equiv \sum_{(i,j \in S)} D_{ij}.$$

This is so because $\sum_{i<j} D_{ij}$ is a constant, for it is the sum of the elements of the lower half of the D matrix and each element is fixed when ρ_{ij} and ρ^* are given.

Thus we would like C^* to be as large as possible, and we hope to achieve this maximum value by a prudent selection of positive D_{ij}'s. Indeed if we group only pairs with negative D_{ij}'s, one can do better by not clustering at all. Therefore any reasonable clustering demands at least one pair with positive D_{ij} in the same cluster. We must remember that the selection of other pairs to be grouped in the same cluster leads implicitly to other D_{ij}'s, which must be included in the calculation of C^*. Of course we would like many positive D_{ij}'s after the first positive D_{ij}, but each addition introduces other D_{ij}'s, some of which may be negative, and the total effect may outweigh what is ostensibly a gain. As a matter of fact, the choice of D_{ij}'s determines the configuration of the clusters. For example, the choice of D_{12}, D_{23}, D_{45} provides the clusters:

Cluster 1	Cluster 2
Variable 1	Variable 4
Variable 2	Variable 5
Variable 3	

In this case variables 1 and 2 are in a cluster, variables 2 and 3 are in a cluster, and thus variables 1, 2, and 3 are together in the same cluster. Variables 4 and 5 are grouped in one independent cluster and the other variables are left alone. It is to be noted here that D_{13} is introduced implicitly in the sum C^*. In general, the choice of say p of the D_{ij}'s leads to $m \leq p$ clusters and to $q \geq p$ elements in the sum C^*. If $m < p$, then $q > p$, since at least two pairs (three or more variables) are grouped together, introducing one or more new D_{ij} values.

In mathematical terms one must maximize C^*, but choosing the appropriate partition of the n variables into m clusters still requires inspection in addition to algebra. In the Kahl and Davis matrix, for instance, one has to choose p pairs out of 16 pairs, decide which D_{ij}'s are also implicitly chosen through the p pairs selected for examination, and then sum these together with the p D_{ij}'s already chosen. This process is repeated for another set of p pairs. There are, of course $\binom{16}{p}$ possible combinations, and these represent a heavy work load for all values of p from 2 to 15, even when using a large and fast computer. This was done for all the combinations associated with each value of p for the Kahl-Davis data, and the maximum C^* was obtained for each p.

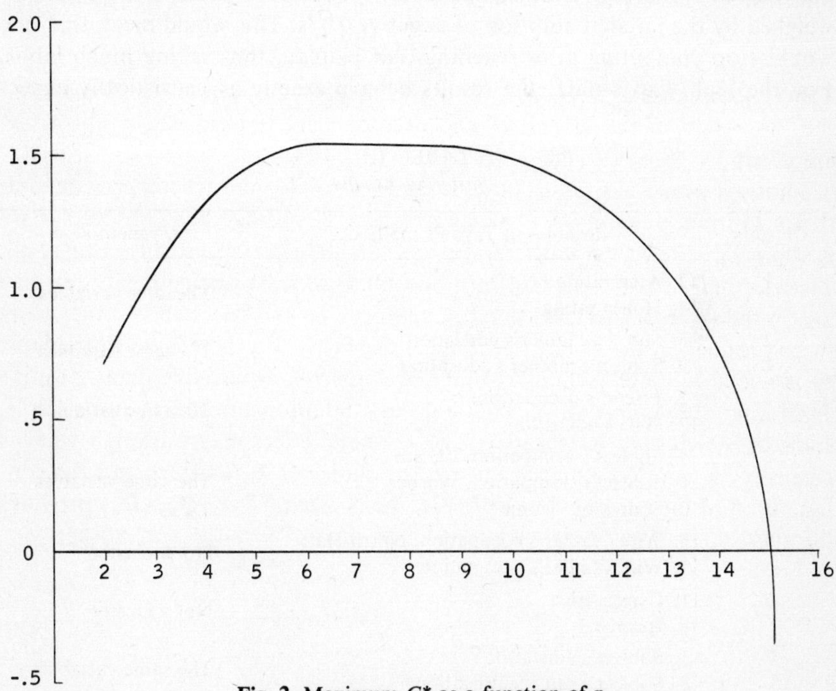

Fig. 2. Maximum C^* as a function of p.

These results are graphed in Fig. 2. This demonstrates that the optimal value of p is 6 or 7, which in this case leads to five clusters ($m = 5$).

If all the ρ's were equal, the criterion would lead to one obvious solution: If $\rho^2 > .5$, group all the variables in one cluster, since all the D_{ij}'s are positive; otherwise do not cluster at all, since the D_{ij}'s are all negative. This "all or none" behavior does not depend on the constant .5 and is valid for any preassigned value for ρ. As a matter of fact, if the distance between any pair of variables is constant, there is no difference in choosing one configuration over another, since it is impossible to decide to which cluster one should assign a variable.

A program has been developed in Fortran language to handle the procedure described above, and this was applied to the Kahl-Davis data. Naturally the type of computer available will determine both the size of the correlation matrix and the values of p that can be analyzed. This program involves tricky manipulations to account for all the pairs that are implicitly selected through other pairs. However, a saving of effort was anticipated in future attempts by the hope that, in this completely worked out example, the maximum C^* for each value of p would increase for a while, then reach a plateau and decrease sharply, because the addition of more positive D_{ij}'s is outweighed by the implicit addition of negative D_{ij}'s. This would mean that one would stop computing after reaching that plateau, thus saving much labor. For the Kahl-Davis data, the results behave exactly as heuristically expec-

TABLE III

Clustering Results

Clusters[a]	Variables in Tryon's method	C^* method
1	12. Area rating 14. House rating	The same variables
2	15. Subject's father's education 9. Subject's mother's education	The same variables
3	2. Friend's occupation 17. Wife's education	The same variables
4	4. Subject's occupation, Census 1. Subject's occupation, Warner 10. Source of income	The same variables
5	16. Wife's father's occupation, North-Hatt 17. Wife's father's occupation	Not a cluster
6	11. Census tract 18. Income	Not a cluster
7	3. Subject's education 8. Subject's self identification	The same variables
8	19. Subject's father's occupation, North-Hatt 13. Subject's father's occupation, Census	Not a cluster

[a] The clusters are ordered by decreasing values of Tryon's index.

ted. The optimal value of p shown in Fig. 2 is 6 or 7, and leads essentially to the clustering obtained by Kahl and Davis using Tryon's method.

Table III demonstrates the clustering results using the C^* method and Tryon's method on the Kahl-Davis data.

We observe a striking resemblance between the two results, although they were arrived at by completely different methods. We could probably arrive at almost the same result by inspection. But this is not the point, since our purpose is an objective method which is amenable to analysis and does not exhaust the capacity of digital computers.

However, there is a perplexing difference in the results obtained by each of the two methods. In the C^* result, some clusters are conspicuously absent. Being less homogeneous they may have been eliminated through the choice of $\rho^{*2} = .50$. But the 7th cluster is present and this suggests that changing the value of ρ^* may never produce the same clustering by the two methods. One possible explanation is that Tryon's is a sequential method and the other method (C^*) is a global procedure. However, this one difference does not detract from a most extraordinary similarity of clustering results which also have substantive meaning.

The distribution of C^* is important, since knowledge of it permits the estimation of β and consequently the selection of an appropriate sample size when total enumeration is out of the question. Figure 3 gives a distribution for the C^* values obtained in the case where $p = 4$. It is roughly normal, and this indicates the feasibility of sampling. For example, one can estimate the mean and variance of the distribution of C^* on the basis of some selections

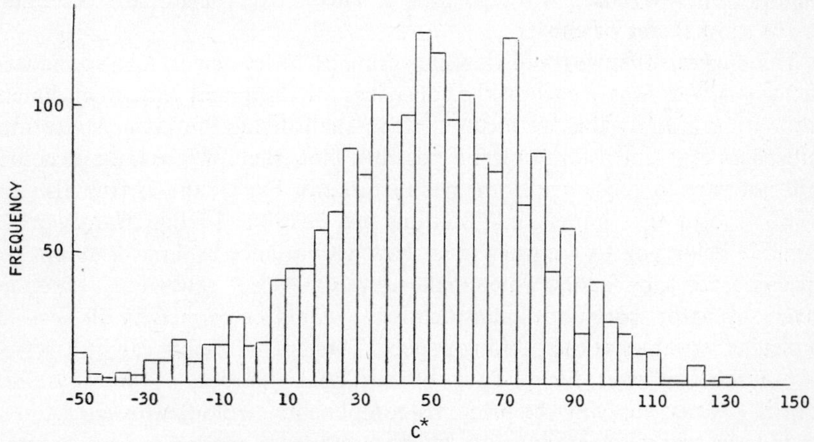

Fig. 3. Frequency distribution of C^* for $p = 4$.

and then proceed to fix a level for the β value under the assumption of normality. With this knowledge, or an assumption of it beforehand, the clustering could have been achieved more cheaply. It would be good to get the empirical distribution of C^* for other situations, and when p takes on values other than 4 in this case to see if the normal distribution assumption is realistic over a wider class.

Whether this assumption holds or not, a most reasonable approach seems to be the following. Considering the shape of the curve of maximum C^* as a function of p (Fig. 2), which has a sharp increase then a wide plateau followed by a sharp decrease, it should be easy to obtain a good estimate of the optimal value(s) of p: Simply take a limited sample for each value of p. On the basis of the estimated C^* curve, determine an optimal p. Then proceed to extensive sampling for just that optimal value of p to determine the approximate optimal clustering, both for number of clusters and configuration.

3. A GENERALIZATION OF THE C^* CRITERION

In many studies concerned with factorial analysis the problem is not only one of reducing the space generated by the variables under study into a factor space of fewer dimensions, but also that of assigning subsets of variables to subspaces of this factor space. At least this has been attempted by several contributors to the field, for example through various rotational methods to achieve simple structure.

In a manner similar to those methods, the C^* method can be viewed as an attempt to reduce the space of factors to subspaces of one dimension (i.e., our clusters). Indeed if two variables are heavily "loaded" in the same unique factor, their correlation will tend to ± 1. This is true for all pairs belonging to the same factor or cluster.

This suggests that we try to view clustering in the framework of a specialized factor structure where each of the subspaces are disjointed and are of dimensionality $k \geq 1$. By this we mean that we shall divide the factor space into subspaces of k dimensions or less if possible. Note that for $k = 1$, the structure will not vary in substance from that pictured in Fig. 4; this is true also for $k = 3$, except that more configurations are possible. In that framework a variable belonging to a cluster must have its variance explained, except for specific factors, by factors which make up the cluster. A general loss function, given subfactor spaces of dimensionality k, would be defined by all $(k + 1)$-tuplets of variables of the subfactor space. The dimensionality can be assessed in a number of ways, for instance, by extracting the roots of the covariance matrix (that is, applying the principal-components method). However, this is an indirect way of clustering, and we have proposed more direct procedures, which unfortunately depend on the structure (which is usually not known in the first place).

One can repeat the same process within each cluster and obtain subclusters.

Each time the method applied would be similar to the C^* method except that there is more computation involved (k-tuplets instead of pairs; $D_{(r,p,t,\ldots)}$ values instead of D_{ij} values; implicit formation of many more combinations). But this seems theoretically feasible, especially through the use of sampling methods.

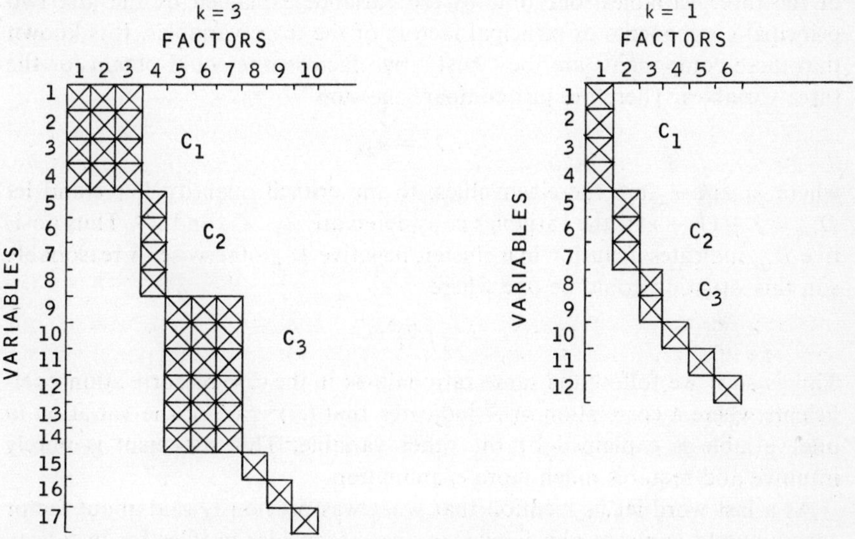

Fig. 4. Disjointed factor spaces $k = 3$ and $k = 1$.

Let us illustrate the method in the case of $k = 2$; that is, the factor space is composed of several completely disjointed two-factor subspaces. This is a situation where triplets of variables exhaust the information available except for specific factors. This means the basic data is now composed of a three-dimensional array of values $\{D_{ijk}\}$. These values are the differences between a preassigned constant and a measure of the predictability of any variable in the triplet by the other two variables. The values D_{ijk} are positive if we group the triplet of variables in one cluster and negative otherwise. This predictability would be perfect if each variable is a linear function of only two factors, or in other words if they are part of a subspace generated by only two factors. In this case, D_{ijk} assumes its maximum positive value. This can be seen by applying an inverse transformation to any two variables of the triplet to generate the two factors and therefore the third variable. On the other hand there exists a subspace generated by two factors (first two principal components) that would explain at least the sum of the variances, call it V, of the two variables in the triplet, each having a variance greater than that of the third variable, whose variance we label v. Therefore the only meaningful subspace which serves as a basis is one constituted by these factors. Should the clustering index attain values which would explain $V+\varepsilon(\varepsilon \geq 0)$ of the total variance which is $V+v$, clustering of the three variables is indicated. Otherwise, clustering is not indicated.

By computing the sum of the first two eigenvalues of the covariance matrix of the three variables, one obtains the variance explained by the first two principal components or principal factors of the three variables. It is known that these components are the "best" two factors one could obtain for the three variables. Therefore just compare the sum

$$\lambda = \lambda_1 + \lambda_2,$$

where λ_1 and λ_2 are the eigenvalues, to the critical quantity $V+\varepsilon$ and let $D_{ijk} = \lambda - (V+\varepsilon)$ if the variables considered are X_i, X_j, and X_k. Thus positive D_{ijk} indicates inclusion in a cluster, negative D_{ijk} otherwise. A reasonable ε in this situation could be one where

$$\varepsilon = (.7)^3 v.$$

This is so if we follow the same rationale as in the case of correlation coefficients where a correlation of .7 indicates that $(.7)^2 \cong .5$ of the variation in one variable is explained by the other variable. This statement is purely intuitive and requires much more examination.

As a last word let us mention that what was previously said about factor spaces would apply to any Euclidean space (consider profiles for instance). There a "vector" would be included in a subspace if it belongs to it or is "almost attainable" in some sense from the basis of that subspace.

REFERENCES

1. Fortier, J. J. (1962). Contributions to item selection. Tech. Rep. 2. Laboratory for Quantitative Research in Education, Stanford Univ., Stanford, California.
2. Holzinger, K. J. and Harman, H. H. (1941). *Factor Analysis.* Chicago Press, Chicago, Illinois.
3. Kahl, J. A. and Davis, J. A. (1955). A comparison of indexes of socio-economic status. *Amer. Sociological Rev.* **20** 317–325.
4. Tryon, R. C. (1939). *Cluster Analysis.* Edward Bros., Ann Arbor, Michigan.

Sequential Multivariate Procedures for Means with Quality Control Applications

J. EDWARD JACKSON
EASTMAN KODAK COMPANY
ROCHESTER, NEW YORK

RALPH A. BRADLEY
DEPARTMENT OF STATISTICS
FLORIDA STATE UNIVERSITY
TALLAHASSEE, FLORIDA

1. INTRODUCTION

The development of the methods given below was motivated largely by a problem which occurred about seven years ago in the field of ballistic-missile testing. By this time some of the smaller missiles, such as the Honest John and the Nike-Ajax, had become operational and were being manufactured in production lots. The final quality-control testing was in the form of static firings, data being collected on measures of thrust, chamber pressure, and action time (length of time required to burn all the propellant). These tests were very expensive and suggested sequential sampling as a method of reducing testing cost. However, the test measurements were trivariate in nature, so that the establishment of separate sequential plans for each test might lead to conflicting results. This would suggest then a *sequential multivariate* procedure for testing means. The procedure developed consisted of a sequential χ^2 test for the case where the covariance matrix of the test variables was known or assumed known and a sequential T^2 test for the case where this matrix had to be estimated from a sample. These procedures were extended to the generalized $\chi_0{}^2$ statistics, so that it was possible to test not only for shifts in level from lot to lot but also to test the within-lot variability. This paper will review the progress of these techniques to date and propose a new method of specifying alternative hypotheses with particular reference to a class of quality-control problems.

2. SEQUENTIAL MULTIVARIATE PROCEDURES FOR TESTING MEANS

In a p-variate situation, the null hypothesis under consideration is

$$H_0: \quad \boldsymbol{\mu} = \boldsymbol{\mu}_0 \qquad (\text{or} \quad \boldsymbol{\mu} - \boldsymbol{\mu}_0 = \boldsymbol{\delta}_0),$$

where $\boldsymbol{\mu}_0$ is a p-element vector of hypothetical means and $\boldsymbol{\mu}$ is the corresponding vector of population means. The usual sequential procedures require a similarly specific alternative hypothesis, but in the multivariate case an alternative such as

$$H_1: \quad \boldsymbol{\mu} = \boldsymbol{\mu}_1$$

would be too restrictive to be of much use. The alternative to be used in this case is not a single point in p space but an infinite collection of points presumably in the form of an ellipsoid. To do this, both hypotheses must be restated in terms of quadratic forms:

$$\begin{aligned} H_0&: \quad (\boldsymbol{\mu} - \boldsymbol{\mu}_0)\,\boldsymbol{\Sigma}^{-1}(\boldsymbol{\mu} - \boldsymbol{\mu}_0)' = \lambda_0{}^2, \\ H_1&: \quad (\boldsymbol{\mu} - \boldsymbol{\mu}_0)\,\boldsymbol{\Sigma}^{-1}(\boldsymbol{\mu} - \boldsymbol{\mu}_0)' = \lambda_1{}^2(\lambda_1{}^2 > \lambda_0{}^2), \end{aligned} \tag{2.1}$$

where $\boldsymbol{\Sigma}$ is the true or assumed covariance matrix of the p variables. If the original null hypothesis was $H_0 : \boldsymbol{\mu} = \boldsymbol{\mu}_0$, then $\lambda_0{}^2 = 0$. The result is that both hypotheses have been reduced to expressions involving only a scalar quantity λ^2, which simplifies things considerably. The effect on the sequential procedure is something else again. Wald's sequential probability ratio test (S.P.R.T.) is of the form

$$\frac{p_{1n}}{p_{0n}} = \frac{f(x_1, \theta_1) \cdots f(x_n, \theta_1)}{f(x_1, \theta_0) \cdots f(x_n, \theta_0)},$$

where the hypotheses are $H_0 : \theta = \theta_0$ and $H_1 : \theta = \theta_1$; $f(x, \theta_i)$ is the distribution of x under H_i, and $x_1, x_2, \ldots, x_n$ represents successive independent observations on x. If after n observations,

$$\frac{p_{1n}}{p_0} < \frac{\beta}{1 - \alpha},$$

where α and β are the customary type I and type II errors associated with H_0 and H_1, the null hypothesis is accepted. If

$$\frac{p_{1n}}{p_{0n}} > \frac{1 - \beta}{\alpha},$$

the alternative hypothesis is accepted. If the ratio lies between these two quantities, the $(n + 1)$st observation is obtained and the procedure repeated. However, when composite hypotheses of the form (2.1) are being tested, the procedure above cannot be used. Wald [20] proposed a *method of weight functions* for handling composite hypotheses, but as it is a cumbersome method and does not guarantee optimum weights, it has not been widely used. The method most popularly used today is the *method of frequency functions.*

This latter method appears to have been first proposed by Goldberg, as reported by Wallis [21] and by Nandi [17]. The method consists of replacing $f(x, \theta)$ by the distribution of the test statistic used so that the "observations" are now successive values of this test statistic and, in fact, the ratio involves only the latest value of the statistic. Barnard [4], Cox [5], and Hall *et al.* [7] have established conditions under which the distribution of a test statistic may be used in a S.P.R.T. and still guarantee, approximately, the risks α and β. If these conditions are fulfilled in the case under discussion, the S.P.R.T. may be written

$$\frac{p_{1n}}{p_{0n}} = \frac{g_n(t_n, \lambda_1^2)}{g_n(t_n, \lambda_0^2)},$$

where $g_n(t_n, \lambda_i^2)$ is the distribution of the test statistic based on n observations under H_i.

The choice of test statistic will depend on the knowledge about $\mathbf{\Sigma}$, the population covariance matrix. If $\mathbf{\Sigma}$ is known or assumed, the statistic is

$$\chi_n^2 = n(\bar{\mathbf{x}} - \boldsymbol{\mu}_0)\mathbf{\Sigma}^{-1}(\bar{\mathbf{x}} - \boldsymbol{\mu}_0)', \tag{2.2}$$

where $\bar{\mathbf{x}}$ is a vector of sample means, estimators of $\boldsymbol{\mu}$, based on n observations. The S.P.R.T. becomes the sequential χ^2 test involving the ratio of two noncentral χ^2 distributions:

$$\frac{p_{1n}}{p_{0n}} = \exp\left[\frac{-n}{2}(\lambda_1^2 - \lambda_0^2)\right] {}_0F_1(p/2; n\lambda_1^2\chi_n^2/4)/{}_0F_1(p/2; n\lambda_0^2\chi_n^2/4), \tag{2.3}$$

where ${}_0F_1(c; x)$ is the generalized hypergeometric function

$${}_0F_1(c; x) = 1 + \frac{x}{c} + \frac{x^2}{c(c+1)2!} + \frac{x^3}{c(c+1)(c+2)3!} + \cdots$$

which has been tabulated by Jackson [12].

If the population covariance matrix $\mathbf{\Sigma}$ is not known, its estimate $\mathbf{S}$ must be obtained from the sample of n observations and χ_n^2 must be replaced by

$$T_n^2 = n(\bar{\mathbf{x}} - \boldsymbol{\mu}_0)\mathbf{S}^{-1}(\bar{\mathbf{x}} - \boldsymbol{\mu}_0)'. \tag{2.4}$$

The result is the sequential T^2 test involving the noncentral T^2 distribution

$$\frac{p_{1n}}{p_{0n}} = \exp\left[\frac{-n}{2}(\lambda_1^2 - \lambda_0^2)\right] \frac{{}_1F_1[n/2, p/2; n\lambda_1^2T_n^2/2(n-1+T_n^2)]}{{}_1F_1[n/2, p/2; n\lambda_0^2T_n^2/2(n-1+T_n^2)]}, \tag{2.5}$$

where ${}_1F_1(a, c; x)$ is another generalized hypergeometric function,

$${}_1F_1(a, c; x) = 1 + \frac{ax}{c} + \frac{a(a+1)x^2}{c(c+1)2!} + \frac{a(a+1)(a+2)x^3}{c(c+1)(c+2)3!} + \cdots,$$

generally known as the *confluent hypergeometric function* [19]. Jackson and Bradley [14] give termination proof for both procedures and show that the requirements of Cox's theorem are fulfilled, so the risks of accepting H_0 and H_1 are approximately α and β, respectively. A more recent and somewhat simpler proof using the invariance principle was given by Hall *et al.* [7].

Not much theory is available either for operating characteristic functions or ASN (average sample number) functions when applied to composite hypotheses. A very crude approximation to the ASN function, known as Bhate's conjecture, reported by Ray [18], can be used to obtain estimates of the ASN when H_0 or H_1 are true. These approximations for the sequential χ^2 and T^2 tests were given by Jackson and Bradley [14]. A Monte Carlo study of these two tests by Appleby and Freund [1] showed that the agreement between the conjectured and Monte Carlo ASN's is quite good, differences generally being less than 10% of conjectured values, and that these differences decreased with increased p and λ^2. These results are similar to those obtained in some univariate studies [3, 18]. This same study showed that the actual risks appeared to be less than the stated α and β, results similar to earlier univariate studies [2, 3, 8], and that these risks became smaller as p increased.

From a practical standpoint, both of these procedures involve a fair amount of computation, since each involves the evaluation of two hypergeometric series (only one if $\lambda_0^2 = 0$), and in addition the covariance matrix must be inverted each time for the sequential T^2 test. The inversion procedure could possibly be speeded up for large matrices by using the inverse for the nth stage as the first approximation for the $(n+1)$st stage using Hotelling's iterative technique [9]. The series evaluation may, in some cases, be eliminated by the use of tables by Freund and Jackson [6], which for $\alpha = \beta = .05$ and $.01$, $\lambda_0^2 = 0$, and for selected values of λ_1^2, give the boundaries of the sequential test in terms of χ^2 or T^2 directly. If these particular choices of α, β, p, λ_0^2, and λ_1^2 do not apply to a particular problem, the limits could easily be produced on a computer.

As for the matrix-inversion problem, if the testing involved is expensive, as it was in the missile program, the cost involved in time and money for inverting a matrix is negligible by comparison; on the other hand, if one is working with a high-volume, low-cost product, sequential sampling by groups [14] should be considered. However, most quality-control applications assume some prior knowledge of the covariance matrix, so the χ^2 test may be used and no inversion is required after the procedure is set up.

3. TWO-SAMPLE CASES

The sequential techniques discussed can also be used for two-sample tests with paired observation vectors. Let the first population have mean vector $\boldsymbol{\mu}^{(1)}$ and dispersion matrix $\boldsymbol{\Sigma}_{11}$, the second $\boldsymbol{\mu}^{(2)}$ and $\boldsymbol{\Sigma}_{22}$. Suppose further that the cross-covariance matrix is $\boldsymbol{\Sigma}_{12}$. Let $\boldsymbol{\mu} = \boldsymbol{\mu}^{(1)} - \boldsymbol{\mu}^{(2)}$ and $\mathbf{x}_i = \mathbf{x}_i^{(1)} - \mathbf{x}_i^{(2)}$, $i = 1, \ldots, n$, where $\mathbf{x}_i^{(1)}$ and $\mathbf{x}_i^{(2)}$ are, respectively, the ith observation vectors for populations 1 and 2. The dispersion matrix of $\mathbf{x}$ is $\boldsymbol{\Sigma}_{11} + \boldsymbol{\Sigma}_{22} - \boldsymbol{\Sigma}_{12} - \boldsymbol{\Sigma}_{12}'$. Now when $\boldsymbol{\Sigma}_{11}$, $\boldsymbol{\Sigma}_{22}$, and $\boldsymbol{\Sigma}_{12}$ are known, the two-sample problem is reduced to an application of the sequential χ^2 test.

When the variance-covariance matrices are not known and must be estimated, the situation is even simpler. Again let $\boldsymbol{\mu} = \boldsymbol{\mu}^{(1)} - \boldsymbol{\mu}^{(2)}$ and use variates $\mathbf{x} = \mathbf{x}^{(1)} - \mathbf{x}^{(2)}$. $\boldsymbol{\Sigma}_{11} + \boldsymbol{\Sigma}_{22} - \boldsymbol{\Sigma}_{12} - \boldsymbol{\Sigma}_{12}'$ is estimated directly from the observation vectors $\mathbf{x}_i = \mathbf{x}_i^{(1)} - \mathbf{x}_i^{(2)}$, $i = 1, \ldots, n$, and this problem is reduced to that handled by the sequential T^2 test.

4. GENERALIZED χ^2 STATISTICS

In the notation of Hotelling's generalized T^2 statistics [10], the statistics discussed would be denoted by $\chi_M{}^2$ and $T_M{}^2$ and represent the generalized distance of the sample mean from the hypothetical mean. For quality-control operations, in particular, a procedure for simultaneously testing the covariance matrix against its hypothetical values is of considerable value. This is the $\chi_D{}^2$ test, whose sequential form is given in [14] along with the generalized statistic $\chi_0{}^2 = \chi_M{}^2 + \chi_D{}^2$. However, this latter statistic is of little use in sequential analysis, as an out-of-control situation will generally be indicated by $\chi_M{}^2$ or $\chi_D{}^2$ before $\chi_0{}^2$, which is somewhat less sensitive. Generalizations of the sequential T^2 statistic have not been developed nor do they appear to be of much use in quality-control operations.

5. PROBLEMS ASSOCIATED WITH SPECIFYING HYPOTHESES

Examples of the application of both the sequential χ^2 and T^2 procedures to ballistic-missile testing were given in [13]. The problem is trivariate in nature, requiring simultaneous information for action time, thrust, and pressure of the missiles being tested. The value of λ^2 under the null hypothesis was always $\lambda_0{}^2 = 0$, and the value under the alternative hypothesis was always some sort of compromise with regard to the specifications which were in the form of a rectangular parallelepiped about the aim.

In the ballistic-missile example, the specifications in coded units about the standard were

$$x_1\colon \pm 120, \qquad x_2\colon \pm 300, \qquad x_3\colon \pm 200,$$

and the initial assumptions were that the specifications were the equivalent of $\pm 3\sigma$ limits for individual measurements, so that the assumed standard deviations were $\sigma_1 = 40$, $\sigma_2 = 100$, and $\sigma_3 = 66.7$ and that the variables were independently and normally distributed. These assumptions were made only for the purposes of determining λ_1^2 and setting up the sampling plan. Little or nothing was known about Σ at that point; a sequential T^2 test would be employed so that Σ would be estimated from the sample. A sampling plan was required which would guarantee with risk $\beta = .05$ that no lot would be accepted which contained more than 2.5% defective rounds and with risk $\alpha = .05$ that no lot would be rejected if all three variables were on standard. This means that the true mean could not be farther than $.76\sigma$ from standard. Several possibilities existed. One consisted of inscribing an ellipsoid in a parallelepiped $\mu_{i0} \pm .76\sigma_i$ $(i = 1, 2, 3)$, where μ_{i0} is the standard for the ith variable. The noncentrality parameter for any characteristic would be $(.76)^2$, and since the occurrence of an out-of-control condition for any one of these variables would be enough to reject the lot, λ_1^2 could be set at .5776. Actually, it was set at $\lambda_1^2 = .5$, to conform with existing tables which seemed innocuous enough in view of the crudeness of the approximation in the first place. This means that the alternative hypothesis was actually

$$\lambda_1^2 = .5 = [\mu_1 - \mu_{10} \quad \mu_2 - \mu_{20} \quad \mu_3 - \mu_{30}] \times \begin{bmatrix} 1600 & 0 & 0 \\ 0 & 10{,}000 & 0 \\ 0 & 0 & 4489 \end{bmatrix}^{-1} \begin{bmatrix} \mu_1 - \mu_{10} \\ \mu_2 - \mu_{20} \\ \mu_3 - \mu_{30} \end{bmatrix}.$$

This method might seem to be too restrictive, since the ellipsoid is obtained by *inscribing*. (It might also be said however that specifications in terms of rectangular parallelepipeds are not very realistic and they themselves should be in terms of ellipsoids.) A conservative approach would be, instead to *circumscribe* the ellipsoid *about* $\pm .76\sigma_i$. This produced a value of $\lambda_1^2 = 1.73 = 3(.76)^2$ and would require only about 40% as much sampling as the other plan, because all three variables must be displaced significantly to cause rejection. Other methods were discussed. The general conclusion was that there are indeed many ways of specifying λ_1^2 and that, for this numerical example, at least, they would lead to conflicting conclusions, since a plan with $\lambda_1^2 = .5$ *rejected* the lot after 23 rounds were fired but the plan with $\lambda_1^2 = 2.0$ (nearest tabular plan to $\lambda_1^2 = 1.73$) *accepted* the lot after 9 rounds were fired. Intuitively, the inscribed ellipsoid philosophy has a lot to be said for it, but each situation has to be resolved according to its own characteristics. Often univariate sampling plans would have set λ_0^2 at something other than zero and presumably many multivariate plans require this also which adds to the difficulty of setting up these procedures [21].

Although the above procedures for setting up hypotheses for T^2 tests assuming independence may be difficult, the ones for setting up hypotheses for χ^2 tests are more so, since now the covariance matrix is either known or assumed known with enough assurance that it will be used in the test statistic. If the variables are correlated, this means that the axes of the ellipsoid representing product variability are rotated and do not coincide with the coordinate axes of the variables being measured. A method for inscribing such an ellipsoid in a parallelepiped is also given in [13], but any such scheme could be quite restrictive if the correlations were high, since this ellipsoid might, then, not occupy much of the volume of the parallelepiped. Although it would seem reasonable to state specifications in terms of ellipsoids, this would be difficult to manage when variables are correlated in this way. There is the additional problem that the specifications might not be equally proportional to the variability of each of the variables.

One other possibility should be considered when the covariance matrix is known: A principal-component analysis of the original variables will, of course, transform the original variables into a new set of independent variables whose axes are the principle axes of the ellipsoid. In industrial examples, the transformed variables often have good physical interpretation and, being independent, make better control variables than the original set [11]. Furthermore, the use of principal components may result in fewer transformed than original variables, which also makes for easier control [15]. If principal components can be used in this way, it may then be possible to state specifications in terms of the transformed variables, and this would be an excellent time to employ ellipsoidal specifications. The test statistic χ^2 would involve only a sum of squares, or at worst, a diagonal dispersion matrix if the specifications were not proportional to the standard deviations of the transformed variables.

6. EXAMPLE

The missile problem previously referred to does not readily lend itself to principal components, as the components of that system are not easily interpretable and would not simplify the specification statements. The following example involves the acceptance sampling of a photographic product.

Photographic products and processes are usually monitored by means of a special piece of film which contains a series of graduated exposures designed to represent the entire range of exposures used in actual practice. In this case there are fourteen steps in even increments of log exposure. After the strip is exposed and processed, optical densities are obtained for each of these steps and the resultant curve as a function of exposure displays the photographic characterizations of the product [16]. The high density or "shoulder" portion of the curve represents shadow areas in the picture, the low densities or "toe" represent light areas, and the middle densities represent the average densities in a picture. The aim for this product is shown in Fig. 1. Since there

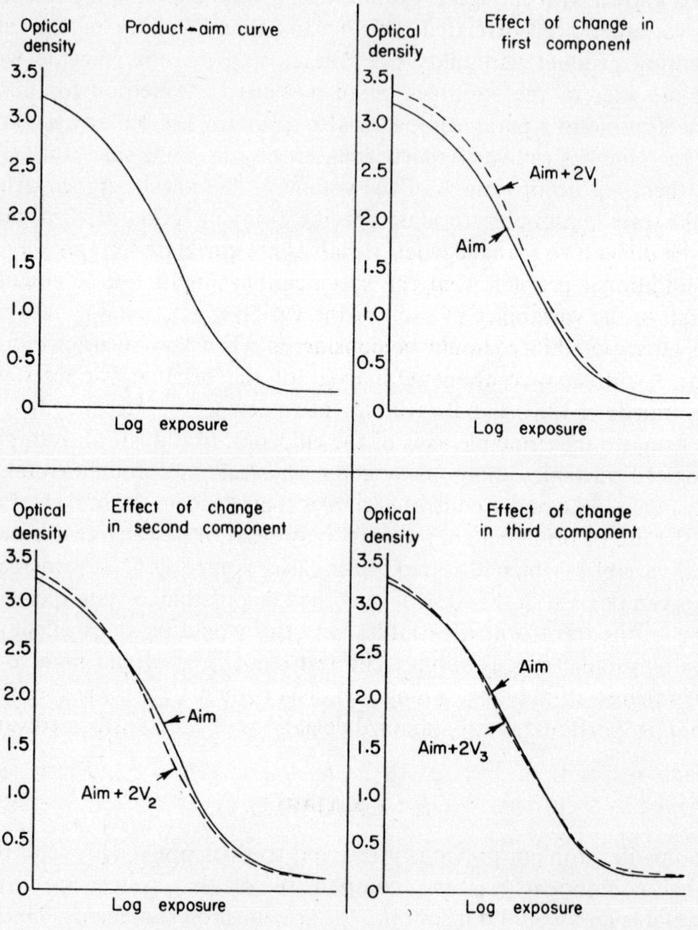

Fig. 1. Product-aim curve for a typical photographic product and the effect on this product of changes in the principal components.

are 14 measurements on this film, this is, then, a 14-variable problem, but the fundamental question is: "Do we accept this lot of material or not?" Only one answer is required, and hence a T^2 or χ^2 statistic is appropriate. In this case it will be the χ^2 statistic, since the covariance matrix has been adequately estimated over a base period (see Table I). Using the trace as a measure of total variability, 99% of the variability is explained by the first three principal components, so the rank of the problem is reduced from 14 to about 3. The variability unexplained by the three vectors in each of the 14 steps is given in

TABLE I
Covariance Matrix for Film Example[a]

1	2	3	4	5	6	7	8	9	10	11	12	13	14
6720	6669	6504	6329	5769	4866	3526	2276	1117	498	167	−15	−61	−152
	6856	6862	6876	6490	5648	4239	2807	1442	662	215	−22	−91	−200
		7260	7586	7477	6767	5299	3634	1998	967	323	3	−111	−256
			8387	8591	8046	6534	4635	2678	1350	486	73	−94	−278
				9238	8919	7451	5431	3249	1695	652	155	−62	−277
					8929	7649	5738	3546	1892	781	254	7	−204
						6875	5348	3409	1876	825	330	91	−95
							4464	2956	1682	822	408	224	83
								2108	1239	654	369	251	158
									811	450	281	216	157
										321	223	198	175
											208	179	176
												211	192
													219

[a] Sample size 232. All entries are multiplied by 1000. Trace = 62,607.

Table II and in all cases is equal to the inherent measurement variability of the system. (Most studies of this type employ the covariance matrix rather than the correlation matrix, since all the variables are in the same units and have the same measurement variability and since the ultimate goal is to produce a set of vectors which will adequately reproduce the original measurements.) The vectors associated with these components are given in Table II, where each vector is normalized to its root (i.e., $\mathbf{v}_i\mathbf{v}_i' = c_i$). These vectors when divided by their own roots yield another set of vectors which will transform the original variables (as difference from standard) into new variables with zero mean, unit variance, and, of course, zero covariances; i.e.,

$$y_i = \frac{\mathbf{v}_i}{c_i}(\mathbf{x} - \boldsymbol{\mu}_0)' \qquad (i = 1, 2, 3),$$

where $\mathbf{v}_i$ is a 1×14 vector and $(\mathbf{x} - \boldsymbol{\mu}_0)$ a 14×1 vector. These, then, become the control variables and in this space,

$$\chi^2 = n \sum_{i=1}^{3} \bar{y}_i^2$$

with 3 degrees of freedom, the other 11 degrees of freedom being associated with the residual sum of squares, a measure of the inability of the principal components to reconstruct the original data [15].

TABLE II

Characteristic Vectors for Film Example

	Normalized to variance c^2			Normalized to unit variance			Residual
Step	v_1	v_2	v_3	v_1/c_1	v_2/c_2	v_3/c_3	variance ×1000
1	.067	.045	.013	1.28	5.38	9.37	52
2	.073	.038	.007	1.40	4.54	4.99	36
3	.081	.025	−.001	1.56	2.98	−.36	46
4	.091	.009	−.006	1.74	1.09	−4.57	65
5	.095	−.009	−.011	1.82	−1.01	−7.62	51
6	.091	−.023	−.009	1.74	−2.77	−6.51	54
7	.076	−.033	−.002	1.45	−3.92	−1.57	55
8	.056	−.035	.010	1.07	−4.11	6.86	77
9	.033	−.028	.013	.64	−3.33	9.09	43
10	.017	−.018	.012	.34	−2.13	8.31	44
11	.007	−.010	.012	.14	−1.18	8.25	34
12	.002	−.006	.011	.04	−.75	7.69	44
13	.000	−.004	.012	.00	−.50	8.22	56
14	−.002	−.003	.012	−.04	−.39	8.47	58
c	.0520	.0084	.0014				

The vector associated with the first component has all positive coefficients except for some "toe" measurements whose differences from zero are negligible photographically, so y_1 can be interpreted as an over-all *density* shift. This component explained 83% of the total variability. y_2 is a measure of *contrast*, and explains 14%. y_3 is a second measure of contrast which is orthogonal to the first, and explains 2%. Figure 1 shows, in relation to the product aim, the effect of an increase of two standard deviations of each of these components. This example is similar to the one discussed in [15], except that it is a black-and-white process and has only one aim curve instead of three and also has measurements at 14 exposure levels instead of only 3. However, that example was used to illustrate process control; the present example, while also useful in process control, is presented to show how the statement of composite hypotheses may be simplified in acceptance sampling problems.

Once the original 14-variable problem was reduced to 3 transformed variables, most of the subsequent operations with this product were in terms of the transformed variables, since they could be interpreted physically. It was, then, a relatively simple matter to set up specifications using these transformed variables. If the specifications were proportional to the lengths of the vectors (i.e., the standard deviations of the transformed variables), then λ^2 could be stated as

$$\lambda^2 = \sum_{i=1}^{3} \mu_i^2,$$

which in matrix form is actually

$$\lambda^2 = [\mu_1 \quad \mu_2 \quad \mu_3]\begin{bmatrix}1 & 0 & 0\\0 & 1 & 0\\0 & 0 & 1\end{bmatrix}\begin{bmatrix}\mu_1\\\mu_2\\\mu_3\end{bmatrix}, \tag{6.1}$$

since these variables are independent with unit variances. The reason for restating it in this manner is that visually some of these components may be more important than others. Let us suppose for the moment that a unit change in y_3 is only half as serious as a unit change in either y_1 or y_2. This can be handled by letting

$$\lambda^2 = [\mu_1 \quad \mu_2 \quad \mu_3]\begin{bmatrix}1 & 0 & 0\\0 & 1 & 0\\0 & 0 & \frac{1}{4}\end{bmatrix}\begin{bmatrix}\mu_1\\\mu_2\\\mu_3\end{bmatrix}, \tag{6.2}$$

so that the test statistic will be

$$\chi^2 = n[\bar{y}_1{}^2 + \bar{y}_2{}^2 + (\bar{y}_3/2)^2], \tag{6.3}$$

in essence, a weighted χ^2.

For this particular example, let $\alpha = \beta = .05$, $\lambda_0{}^2 = 0$, $\lambda_1{}^2 = 1$. This means that, if the product is exactly on standard, 5% of the time the lot will be rejected. Further, if the product mean shifts as far as ± 1 standard unit for y_1 and y_2 or ± 2 units for y_3 or any combination of deviations that will put the mean on the perimeter of the ellipsoid defined by (6.2), only 5% of the time will that lot be accepted. According to Bhate's conjecture, the ASN under H_0 is 14 and under H_1 is 9, while the corresponding fixed sample procedure with

TABLE III

Sequential χ^2 Test for the Hypothesis $H_0: \lambda^2 = 0$ against $H_1: \lambda^2 = 1$ for $\alpha = \beta = .05$, $p = 3$ Variables Using (6.3) as the Test Statistic

Number of observations	Transformed observations y_1	y_2	y_3	Cumulative averages $\bar{y}_1$	$\bar{y}_2$	$\bar{y}_3$	χ^2	Lower limit	Upper limit
1	.03	−.85	.16	.03	−.85	.16	.73		34.98
2	.28	−.90	.85	.15	−.88	.50	1.72		21.19
3	−.89	−1.01	2.03	−.19	−.92	1.01	3.40		16.79
4	−.07	−.13	1.26	−.16	−.72	1.08	3.34		14.72
5	−.58	−.43	1.09	−.25	−.66	1.08	3.95		13.60
6	.40	−1.41	1.03	−.14	−.79	1.07	5.61	.05	12.94
7	.43	−.46	.70	−.06	−.74	1.02	5.68	.52	12.55
8	.83	.31	1.42	.05	−.61	1.07	5.33	.96	12.33
9	−.04	−.58	1.32	.04	−.61	1.10	6.09	1.36	12.22
10	−.21	−1.35	1.28	.02	−.68	1.11	7.76	1.74	12.18
11	.07	−1.34	1.35	.02	−.74	1.14	9.60	2.11	12.20
12	.09	−1.64	1.80	.03	−.82	1.19	12.40	2.46	12.26

the same power requires 18 observations. Table III shows some sample observations from an off-standard lot and shows that this sequential plan would have terminated after the twelfth test with the rejection of the lot. Although not shown in Table III, a $\chi_D{}^2$ test (unweighted) for $H_0: \lambda_{D_0}^2 = 3$ against $H_1: \lambda_{D_1}^2 = 6$ terminated with the acceptance of the null hypotheses after the fourth test. The final conclusion was, then, that the production lot should be rejected because of a level shift but not because of an increase in variability.

ACKNOWLEDGMENT

The covariance matrix used in Section 6 and the characteristic vectors derived from it were obtained from a study carried out by Mr. R. S. Mickelson of the Eastman Kodak Company.

REFERENCES

1. Appleby, R. H. and Freund, R. J. (1962). An empirical evaluation of multivariate sequential procedures for testing means. *Ann. Math. Statist.* **33** 1413–1420.
2. Armitage, P. (1947). Some sequential tests of student's hypotheses. *J. Roy. Statist. Soc. Ser. B* **9** 250–263.
3. Arnold, K. J. (1951) *Tables to Facilitate Sequential t-tests.* Applied Mathematics Series **7**. National Bureau of Standards, Washington, D.C.
4. Barnard, G. A. (1952). The frequency justification of certain sequential tests. *Biometrika* **39** 144–150. [Addendum (1953)] *Biometrika* **40** 468–469.
5. Cox, D. R. (1952). Sequential tests for composite hypotheses. *Proc. Cambridge Philos. Soc.* **48** 290–299.
6. Freund, R. J. and Jackson, J. E. (1960). Tables to facilitate multivariate sequential tests for means. Technical Rept. No. 12 to Office of Naval Research. Dept. Statistics, Virginia Polytechnic Institute, Blacksburg, Va.
7. Hall, W. J., Wijsman, R. A. and Ghosh, J. K. (1965). The relationship between sufficiency and invariance with applications to sequential analysis. *Ann. Math. Statist.* **36** 575–614.
8. Hoel, P. G. (1958). Private correspondence.
9. Hotelling, H. (1943). Some new methods in matrix calculation. *Ann. Math. Statist.* **14** 1–34.
10. Hotelling, H. (1947). Multivariate quality control. *Techniques of Statistical Analysis* (C. Eisenhart, M. W. Hastay, and W. A. Wallis, eds.) 111–184. McGraw-Hill, New York.
11. Jackson, J. E. (1959). Quality control methods for several related variables. *Technometrics* **1** 359–377.
12. Jackson, J. E. (1960). A short table of the hypergeometric function ${}_0F_1(c;x)$. *Sankhyā* **22** 351–356.
13. Jackson, J. E. and Bradley, R. A. (1961). Sequential χ^2- and T^2-tests and their application to an acceptance sampling problem. *Technometrics* **3** 519–534.
14. Jackson, J. E. and Bradley, R. A. (1961). Sequential χ^2- and T^2-tests. *Ann. Math. Statist.* **32** 1063–1077.
15. Jackson, J. E. and Morris, R. H. (1957). An application of multivariate quality control to photographic processing. *J. Amer. Statist. Assoc.* **52** 186–199.
16. James, T. H. and Higgens, G. C. (1960). *Fundamentals of Photographic Theory*, 2nd ed. Chap. 1. Morgan & Morgan, Hastings-on-Hudson, New York.

17. NANDI, H. K. (1948). Use of well-known statistics in sequential analysis. *Sankhyā* **8** 339–344.
18. RAY, W. D. (1956). Sequential analysis applied to certain experimental designs in the analysis of variance. *Biometrika* **43** 388–403.
19. SLATER, L. J. (1960). *Confluent Hypergeometric Functions*. Cambridge Univ. Press, New York and London.
20. WALD, A. (1947). *Sequential Analysis*. Wiley, New York.
21. WALLIS, W. A. (1947). Use of variables in acceptance inspection for percent defective. *Techniques of Statistical Analysis* (C. Eisenhart, M. W. Hastay, and W. A. Wallis, eds.). 3–93. McGraw-Hill, New York.

Multivariate Responses in Comparative Experiments[1]

OSCAR KEMPTHORNE

STATISTICAL LABORATORY
IOWA STATE UNIVERSITY
AMES, IOWA

1. INTRODUCTION

A word of introduction would appear to be necessary to account for my being a participant in this symposium, because I have not worked in the area of theoretical multivariate analysis at all. I have, however, been a consulting statistician to experimental scientists for many years. It is rare for the experimenter to obtain just a single response, and I cannot recall being consulted on an experiment in this class. But I have never used or suggested the procedures of statistical analysis based on the theory presented so excellently by Dr. Anderson [1]. Also I have yet to see any convincing examples of experimental data in which the standard techniques of multivariate analysis have led to scientific insight.

I must emphasize, in making these statements, that the multivariate experiments I am talking about are ones in which the experimenter chooses attributes of the experimental units which are of interest to him individually and collectively. The number of attributes is usually small, and there is not the problem of attempting to comprehend a situation of high dimensionality by reducing the dimensionality through some sort of principal component analysis. I have no doubt that the psychologists find that the techniques of factor analysis give them insight.

I am also aware of discussion papers like Finney's [7] in biometrics, in which he is highly critical of the application by Steel [19] of multivariate techniques to an agronomic experiment. I recall (I hope correctly) a remark by Barnard that he had yet to see an example in which multivariate techniques gave additional insight over that given by separate univariate analyses.

Does this state of affairs exist because experimental statisticians are not knowledgeable with regard to how multivariate techniques can help them

[1] This work was prepared in connection with work on Contract AF-33(615)1737, Aerospace Research Laboratories, United States Air Force, Wright-Patterson Air Force Base, Ohio.

(a possibility to which my mind is quite open), or is it the case that the presently available techniques are not informative?

My talk will give some views on these matters.

2. CLASSES OF EXPERIMENT

It seems to me essential to distinguish between two broad classes of experiment: those that are aimed at the making of decisions, say decision experiments, for short, and those that are aimed at the accumulation of information and knowledge, say information experiments. To illustrate the distinction I have in mind, in the former class I include experiments to find the best feeding ration for cattle, to select the best variety or best five varieties of oats, insecticide, or what you will. In all these cases there is a well-defined criterion of value for the entities, "treatments," "varieties," or whatever, which are being compared, and it is entirely reasonable to ask the experimenter to specify, at least loosely, the losses from incorrect decisions. Obviously without such a specification the decision problem is not completely stated, and an answer cannot be given. In the class of experiments at the other end, in a sense, of the spectrum, the information experiment, the objectives are not as clear. It is not even easy to characterize the information experiment, and perhaps the best prescription I can give is to say that it is the type of experiment for which Nobel prizes are awarded. [Actually I have made no study of Nobel awards, but I am inclined to think that a study of the inferential procedures which were considered by the judges to merit awards would be an *informative* study (actually a decision study for young scientists).] A less spectacular situation would be that of a scientist who is trying to get a picture of the processes by which a plant species uses nutrients (or, if one works for NIH[1a] or wants NIH support, of the processes by which the human species uses nutrients). Obviously such informational studies will provide evidence for decisions on how to feed plants, such decisions being based on a multitude of cost and value considerations. It is, I imagine, a very rare experiment which does not lead to some technological applications, but it is frequently the case that the technological applications were undreamt of by the experimenter and the experimenter's scientific peers at the time of the experiment or for several years later.

It is also essential in the present context to distinguish between design of experiment and analysis of data. The design of experiment must be based on well-formulated aims which enable some sort of ordering of the possible experiments with regard to the "amount of information" they will yield. The analysis of the experiment deals with the handling of the resulting data, and I can do no better than quote R. A. Fisher [8]:

[1a] National Institutes of Health.

In order to arrive at a distinct formulation of statistical problems, it is necessary to define the task which the statistician sets himself: briefly, and in its most concrete form, the object of statistical methods is the reduction of data. A quantity of data, which usually by its mere bulk is incapable of entering the mind, is to be replaced by relatively few quantities which shall adequately represent the whole, or which, in other words, shall contain as much as possibly, ideally the whole, of the relevant information contained in the original data.

I do not, in quoting this passage, claim to understand every word: The passage contains words which must be regarded as heavily "loaded," such as "information" and "relevant." The concept of "reduction of data" must surely be meaningful in general, even if no precise mathematical definition can be made. Consider, for example an experiment I recently met on 25 varieties of oats, with 5 environmental treatments in 20 replications, with 4 traits per experimental plot, that is, a total of 10,000 numbers. This experiment was done purely to accumulate knowledge of the behavior of entities called "varieties of oats" under different controlled environmental conditions. It had no decision aims, such as to pick out the best variety.

What disturbs one about the extremist decision-theory workers is that every investigation and every data analysis has to be associated with it a defined space of decisions and a dollars-and-cents value associated with every decision. If pushed to the wall, these individuals will broaden the idea of decision to the point that one should consider the stating of experimental conclusions to be an act of decision which carries with it some losses for incorrect decisions. There is, I suppose, some possibility of incorporating the loss to the experimental scientist resulting from the drawing of conclusions that do not stand the test of confirmation by other workers, but features of an investigation which carry weight with the scientific community are more frequently the nature of the investigation, (Did the investigator have good ideas to work on?), and the quality of the investigational work (Was his technique "good"? Was his experiment of reasonable size? Were his "controls" adequate? and so on). Also one can bring this type of argument to a conclusion by noting that if one wished to apply decision theory to the whole business of scientific research one would need to know the value function of an investigation as judged by the scientific profession (or the ones who "call the shots") and this we do not have. And even if we had it we should not trust it, because it is continually changing.

So much, then, for the two extreme classes of experiment. I shall talk about the information experiment because there really is no controversy about the decision experiment. Or is there? I have to admit that I find the argument of the Bayesians (e.g., Schlaifer [18]) that the only complete solution to decision problems is by ways of introducing personal probabilities to be quite convincing (but, perhaps, I misunderstand the situation from casual study). This aside prompts me also to express a view that perhaps puts me totally out of court, namely, that Bayesian analysis is really appropriate only in decision situations and has no place in information situations, except as a guide to the scientist on his choice of future lines of work, which is surely a decision matter.

The topics I propose to cover in the realm of informational experiments are:

(1) A brief review of the status of the univariate situation, to try to form some general ideas of what constitutes reasonable statistical treatment of data situations in general.

(2) A statement of opinions on what scientists want from the multivariate informational experiment with some discussion of what one might hope for from a multivariate analysis over and above what separate univariate analyses will give.

I shall also state some problems I would like to be solved.

3. THE UNIVARIATE EXPERIMENT

Let us take one of the simplest univariate experiments which illustrates the main aspects of statisticating, the completely randomized experiment, in which we have t "treatments" to be compared in a trial on rt experimental units, the treatments being associated at random with the experimental units. Also, as stated above, we suppose that the experiment is informational and not of the decision type. What does the experimenter want from the statistician? Or more relevantly, what does the experimenter want to do and in what ways can the statistician help him? Obviously the experimenter would report what he considers to be all relevant respects of the experimental program, and he wishes to report and interpret the results. From a well-defined point of view, the reporting of results is accomplished by reporting every observation that was made, and the only "complete sufficient statistic" is the totality of observations. In the case of some experiments, this is precisely what the experimenter would report, but, in general, this would be almost useless, because the primary purpose is communication of results, and compactness is crucial. One rarely wishes to see the whole of the data, and the primary question is "What do the data tell us?" So one of the main jobs is the apparently simple one of condensation of data. It is not, however, the case that this job is simple. Let us take an experiment on 5 treatments with 8 observations per treatment. It is obvious that the smallest possible condensation of the 40 observations would be to have one measure of central tendency for each treatment and a measure of dispersion of the observations for each treatment. Suppose that the observations are measurements, in contrast to counts. It seems obvious that if one observes a variable y, one also observes any specified one-to-one function of y. So the task of condensation requires consideration of what function of y should be presented. Obviously the commonly used procedure of searching for a transformation which gives apparent homogeneity of variance, and then presenting the treatment means with the common estimated standard deviation is reasonable. A more complete condensation of the data would be a statement such as: "The data appear to follow normal distributions with a common standard deviation estimated at (say) 2.7, with means, say, 5.6, 6.2, 6.3, 6.7, and 8.1." It seems obvious that the basic underlying statistical procedure here is some sort of goodness-of-fit evaluation. My reason for introducing the term "goodness of fit" is to point out what is after all quite obvious, than an evaluation of homogeneity of variance in the situation under discussion is a testing of goodness of fit with regard to one aspect of the whole condensation, conditional on another aspect, normality, holding. One should also make some evaluation of the goodness of fit of the normality, presumably by skewness and kurtosis tests. My reason for talking about this is that I think the above views have some implications with regard to tests of significance or tests of hypotheses. I think it entirely reasonable for the experimenter to say: I make this condensation of the data because a specified skewness test gave me a significance level of 25%, a specified test of kurtosis gave me a significance level of 40%, and a test of homogeneity of variance based on normality gave me a significance level of 8%. To be sure, in the framework of accepting and rejecting hypotheses, these several tests are not independent, and I do not have a definite rule by which I will decide on a condensation of data like the above stated one, for which I can state that the probabilities of my making another type of condensation or of not making another type of condensation for the vast array of situations I will meet. This is not, however, vital from the viewpoint of science and accumulation of knowledge, because a statement of the tests and the resulting P levels tells me on what the given condensation of data is based. It would, notwithstanding, be moderately interesting to me to know the joint distribution of the P levels of the several tests.

A crucial point connected with condensation of data is that the condensation arrived at by the experimenter is almost always completely "wrong" in some respect. Take, for example, the assumption of normality. I think that data never follow a normal distribution—obviously something like total growth of mice to 6 weeks can never follow a normal distribution, because negative growths are impossible. The criteria of goodness of condensation of data do not allow a dichotomy into "right" or "wrong," but into degrees of reasonableness of the condensation, and the only way I know of characterizing this is by P levels (which one may discretize by using devices such as no stars, one star, two stars, etc.). It is obvious that if one is going to use P values of tests as a guide to condensation procedures, one should optimally have some idea of the distribution of P-values sampling from data origins which disagree with the basis (e.g., normality) used in calculating the P level.

What I have been talking about so far is really the mode of condensation of the data, or a class of condensations, this being based on whatever goodness-of-fit tests seem desirable. It is next necessary to consider what particular condensations within the class are reasonable, i.e., what choice of value for the parameters in a parametric specification. " Reasonable " here as elsewhere means "consonant with the data" and the latter implies the use of some test of significance, which as always is some "goodness-of-fit" test. As pointed out clearly by Kurtz *et al.* [15], any test of significance requires an ordering of true discrepancy of the situations from hypothesized representations of it. As pointed out first by Fisher (although the status is uncertain with regard to some cases, such as the Behrens-Fisher test, and it is not the case with some global tests of goodness of fit), the elementary univariate significance tests are invertible in the sense that one can delimit sets of parameter values which are consonant with the data at any particular level of significance. It seems to me that one can make some sense of so-called " multiple comparison " techniques in this way. Scheffé's method uses the over-all F test for differences of means and delimits an ellipsoid of parameter values, all of which are consonant by the F test (at any chosen level) with the data on the usual normal law assumptions. The set of parameter values within the ellipsoid may be described by the range of values for every possible linear function of the parameters. If one wishes to ask what set of values for a subset of the parameters are consonant with the data by the F test at any chosen level, one repeats the process with this subset. Similarly the Tukey procedure based on the range test defines a polytope in the parameter space such that the values of the parameters in the polytope are consonant with the data at the chosen level. To specify the values of a subset of the parameters which are consonant with the data, by the range test, one repeats the process with this subset. The raw use of Tukey's procedure with the whole of the parameters (class differences) leads one into the intuitively quite unreasonable view that one's opinion about, say, $\mu_1 - \mu_2$, $\mu_1 - \mu_3$, and $\mu_2 - \mu_3$ should alter if one happens to have observed μ_4, and hence also $\mu_1 - \mu_4$, $\mu_2 - \mu_4$, $\mu_3 - \mu_4$. (Here I do not of course refer to the dependence on degrees of freedom for error, which will be increased, of course, by the additional replication.) It does not seem reasonable to me to take as my opinion about $\mu_1 - \mu_2$ that portion which concerns $\mu_1 - \mu_2$ of my opinion about $\mu_1 - \mu_2$, $\mu_1 - \mu_3$, $\mu_2 - \mu_3$, etc. It is also quite reasonable that any opinion about $\mu_1 - \mu_2$ and $\mu_1 - \mu_3$, say, is not a "direct" sum of my opinion about $\mu_1 - \mu_2$ and $\mu_1 - \mu_3$.

From my point of view then I can form opinions about what parameter values are consonant with the data with not just one test of significance but with as many preselected ones as I like. It seems to me to be entirely reasonable to say that the certain parameter values are consonant at a particular level by one test, and are consonant at some other level by some other tests.

The upshot of the above viewpoint with regard to univariate experiments is that one has to search for a mode of condensation using goodness-of-fit tests, and one needs tests of significance with regard to whatever subsets of parameters may be of interest, which can be inverted to give value sets of the parameters that are consonant with the data at chosen significance levels. I suppose these may be called confidence regions and indeed are, but the whole confidence argument of saying the probability of the random region covering the unknown parameters with such and such a probability, and the decision type of statement that if one asserts that the parameter (set) is in the region one will be correct 95% (say) of the time, do not appeal to me as a scientist, even though it is manifestly an easy argument to teach.

Perhaps I am belaboring the whole matter of what the scientist wants from the data, but there seems to be a general feeling amongst theoreticians that "inference," whatever it may be, can be accomplished by a single procedure, e.g., likelihood (Fisher, Barnard, and others), Bayesian procedures (Savage and others), or decision procedures (Neyman and others). At least this is what a casual reading of the literature suggests. A naïve extrapolation suggests that in a very few years we will have likelihood journals, Bayesian journals, and so on, and if the past is any guide to the future, these will consist of exhortations to scientists to use the particular panacea, without any discussion at all of real data situations.

It is interesting that one can find in the writings from any one source what seem to be excellent reasons for believing that the procedures of the other groups are misleading. For example, Barnard *et al.* [4] give on pages 326–327 what seems to me to be an excellent example of how "best" confidence regions *à la* Neyman are silly. They also seem to give in Section 4 a proof of the likelihood principle—that two results with the same likelihood must give the same inference (a curious result in that "inference" is not defined)—but state in reply to discussion that some discussants were "quite right in detecting a gap in our argument of Section 4." Also, Barnard and his associates are, apparently, unable to accommodate the standard practices of sample surveys of finite populations within their likelihood framework. The argument about the utility of the likelihood function (the whole of it, not just the portion depending on the unknown parameters) seems utterly pointless in that any evaluation of data must depend on the probability of the data arising, and this *is* the likelihood. Parenthetically, it seems very odd that starting from Fisher, the likelihood for the case of continuous distributions was written down as the probability density of the observations, when it is surely entirely obvious that observations are grouped, and the distribution on which inference must be based is a multinomial.[2] Yet Fisher was aware of the problem as evidenced by the Koshal [14] paper on fitting of a Pearson Type I distribution. In simple cases one can ignore the grouping but in general one cannot. Thus Hill [11] was led to conclude that the likelihood for the log normal with threshold was unbounded—as though the probability of obtaining the observations one actually obtained was infinity. I am not clear as to just what effect this view about the likelihood function has on some of the asymptotic work done, which would appear to use the ideas that not only does the sample size go to infinity, but the grouping interval of measurements also goes to zero.

The best illustration I know of the practical inefficacy of Bayesian analysis is that given by Hill [11], who after a very extensive thought was led to give a fitting to data which has a χ^2 goodness-of-fit P value of less than .001 (which I am sure is not unduly misleading in spite of the χ^2 procedure being " valid " only asymptotically). From a more general viewpoint, it appears that the Bayesians and some others think that unless one can write down probabilities of hypotheses, one has achieved very little. This notion seems to be contradicted pragmatically by the vast accumulation of knowledge of the last 100 years, which was based largely on the idea that subjective opinion enters in the formulation of a study but is quite out of place in the reporting of experimental results.

The fatuousness of the dichotomy: significant if $P < .05$ and otherwise, nonsignificant: was displayed excellently by Dr. Rao at the present symposium with an example. The data situation was that there were bivariate samples (x_1, x_2) from two populations. The usual tests for x_1 and x_2 separately gave significance, while the usual joint test did not give significance. To make matters worse, the data were collected by a student working for his Ph.D., and, apparently, the awarding of a degree depended on the judgment reached being "significant." This example is a comment both on tests with fixed cutoff points, and on procedures for awarding Ph.D.'s at some (unnamed) university. It was not clear, however, just what Dr. Rao's own attitude to the situation was. My own is that a reporting of the significance levels by all the tests used is scientifically informative, and the awarding of the degree would depend on other attributes of the type I mentioned earlier (even if no test gave significance at the 5% level!).

4. WHAT DO SCIENTISTS WANT FROM MULTIVARIATE EXPERIMENTS?

It is obvious that the first need of the scientist is for condensation of the data. The example I mentioned of a multivariate experiment with about

[2] It seems from this point of view that the Borel paradox is a figment of mathematical imagination.

10,000 observations illustrates the point. I shall discuss the completely randomized design and the randomized block design. The case of factorials and fractional factorials has been examined by Wilk and Gnanadesikan [25], and comprise a somewhat special case in that one of the basic problems of such designs is to obtain an estimate of error by internal comparisons, because the replication is very slight, or nonexistent.

In the case of the univariate completely randomized design, the naïve condensations of the data are a measure of central tendency, usually the mean, and a measure of spread, usually the variance or perhaps the range for each treatment. Such a condensation is not usually highly regarded, because one is also interested in obtaining estimates of treatment effects which are additive, in the sense that they are expressed on a scale with regard to which treatments and experimental units do not interact. The next step is, therefore, to examine the data for homogeneity of variance, as, for instance, by plotting the range against the mean. If one wished to have an objective way of examining whether there is an association of treatment means and ranges, one could consider the particular correlation of these that is observed in relation to the $t!$ correlations one would get with random permuting of the ranges (say) over the t treatment groups. But such a "test" would not, one imagines, be worth the effort unless computing time is very cheap. Such a plotting may suggest a transformation which will make the variances homogeneous, and if a replotting on the transformed scale gives no apparent relation of ranges to means, a single measure of variability, such as the mean square within treatments, is given along with the means on the transformed scale.

What should one do for the corresponding multivariate experiment? It would seem that the first step is to follow this procedure for the components of the observation vector separately. But then one has to decide whether the multivariate nature of the observation should also be used. One would wish the relationships between the variates to be the same for all the treatment groups, so that homogeneity of variance for each group is not enough. What appears to be needed are informative procedures of plotting the data, and I am not aware of any in the literature. I suppose the naïve procedure of obtaining the mean-square linear regression or correlation of each variate on every other variate ("slope") and plotting these against the mean values of the variates could suggest whether that the relationships among the variates are the same for all the treatment groups. Again, it would seem that one could assess the observed dependence on means by embedding it in the population that would arise by random permutation among the treatment groups. Perhaps the reader will be aware of other and better procedures. Clearly any such processes would have to be done by a high-speed computer with an attached plotter, a point which serves, perhaps, to explain the paucity of exploratory multivariate techniques. It is relatively easy to examine cursorily univariate data with the aid of a desk calculating machine, but even in this case any detailed examination of possible transformations is possible only with a modern computer. With multivariate data, the situation is much worse, and one can suspect that the fastest machines currently available are hopelessly slow for any detailed inspection and evaluation of multivariate data. Ideally the choice of scales for condensation of the multivariate experiment would lead to scales which have homogeneous variability with regard to the multivariate observation, but this may not be possible.

It is, of course, the case with the completely randomized design that one can calculate any function of the observations and treatment numbers, and evaluate the resulting number in the reference set of numbers that one would have obtained by evaluating the function for each of the possible random assignments of the treatments to the experimental units. Usually this would be a fantastically large computing job, and one could make a reasonable "stab" at this procedure by examining a number, such as 200, of the possible randomizations. If one examined the totality, one would have the validity-of-significance test imparted by the physical act of randomization due to and described with great eloquence by Fisher [9].

The above may be characterized, perhaps not too inappropriately, as a distribution-free condensation of the data, in that the condensation is not based on any hypothetical mathematically defined distribution.

Just as in the univariate case, where a more explicit condensation would often be to say that the data appear to follow normal distributions with a certain variance and certain means, it is inevitable that the experimenter would wish to make a condensation by reference to the multivariate normal distribution. That is, he might well wish to state that the data appear to follow multivariate normal distributions with a common particular variance-covariance matrix and with certain mean vectors. (Parenthetically, it seems appropriate to question the overwhelming desire to obtain the normal distribution as a suitable condensation frame. This is presumably based on the idea that the normal distribution occurs in the central limit theorem and the fact that we have easy tests of significance for normal distributions, but these advantages are less clear with the multivariate normal distribution.)

When I turn to the use of the multivariate normal distribution, questions occur immediately to me which may display culpable ignorance of the literature. What is the status of goodness-of-fit tests for the multivariate normal distribution?[3] Is it reasonable to divide the fitted distribution into k shells which are bounded by the equiprobability contours and which have equal probability content, and use the old standard χ^2 test? And if so, how big may k be? Are there concepts analogous to skewness and kurtosis of

[3] I was very glad to hear Dr. Anderson's talk at the present symposium on this topic.

univariate distributions for multivariate distributions, with associated tests of significance? Are there graphical procedures analogous to probability plots for univariate distributions? Has anyone since Galton actually looked at a bivariate distribution? How does one look at a five-variate distribution, for example? Although it is true that univariate procedures are dominated by the normal distribution, it was considered relevant, and probably still is, to have classes of nonnormal univariate distributions, as exemplified by Pearson's types, but have any classes of nonnormal multivariate distributions been developed?

If we have ways of convincing ourselves that the multivariate normal distribution is an appropriate condensation frame, the question would then arise of whether the variance-covariance matrices for the several treatments can be regarded as estimates of a common matrix. The literature does, indeed, give us such a test, which is described, for example, in Dr. Anderson's book, and is closely analogous to the test in the univariate case in the sense that one works with determinants of the several estimates. Just as in the univariate case, one naturally wonders how robust the test is to nonnormality of the distribution. The univariate test is not robust, and one would suspect that this is even more so for the multivariate case. However, even in the univariate case, the emphasis is on the homogeneity of variance rather than the normality, and this is presumably the case also with multivariate observations. And, as I have said above, lack of dependence of variance on mean is the crucial matter.

In addition, the real question is not whether the variance matrices are different: It is a "million to one" that they are, and the probability of Type II error can be cut to zero by declaring that they are different. The question is whether a reasonable representation of the data is accomplished with a single matrix, where, of course, some specification of "reasonable" has to be devised. So I do not think I would be highly interested in the likelihood ratio test of equality of the variance matrices.

It seems to me that the use of even a large number of nonindependent tests on simple aspects of the separate variance matrices, such as the equality of each of the possible correlations, would be more informative than a global test. The global test seems to suffer on the one hand by being insensitive, and on the other hand from not leading to any ideas of how the matrices differ if the level of significance is low. A possibly informative procedure would be to obtain the roots and principal components of the several matrices, and see if they are somewhat similar, but I found no standard errors of even an approximate nature by which to make a judgment.

Supposing now that the distributions of the observations are reasonably approximatable by normal distributions with common variability, what comes next? An examination of the pooled variance matrix would be desirable. The extraction of principal components could be informative, but the dependence of these on the units of measurement seems to me to make this uninformative. Anderson [1] says: "It might also be pointed out that in some uses of the method the algebra is applied to the matrix of correlation coefficients rather than the covariance matrix. In general this leads to different roots and vectors." Also Anderson says (p. 279) "Analysis into principal components is most suitable when the components are measured in the same units." This is perhaps the appropriate place to record the view that if the components are measured in the same units, attention should first be directed intensively at the possibility of a univariate analysis, because of the inherently greater compressibility of the univariate situation. It seems that some of the precision of roots and vectors of a correlation matrix is highly desirable. I think the early workers like Galton and Pearson were well advised to think heavily in terms of correlation coefficients for the real multivariate situation. I suspect that what brought the correlation coefficient into disrepute was its use in nonmultivariate situations, when only one member of the k-plet observation was a random variable and the others were experimental or logically controlled variables. Fisher gave us a means of forming an opinion about a single correlation coefficient by the z transformation. But we do not appear to have any good means of forming opinions about two or more correlation coefficients. It is tempting to guess that since the z transformation of any single correlation is closely approximated by a normal distribution with known variance, the joint distribution of two correlation coefficients will be reasonably approximable by a bivariate normal distribution, and so on. It is, incidentally, curious that the status of the choice of predictor, which, of course, is the question of comparison of, say, p_{12}^2 and p_{13}^2, is still obscure. Actually it seems to me that one can ask interesting questions about reduction of dimensionality of a random vector in other ways. For instance, if, speaking loosely, most of the variation in attributes x_3, x_4, x_5, and x_6 is explainable by x_1 and x_2, this fact would be scientifically interesting. This suggests that one might well look at all the possible $R_{i,S}^2$, where S is a subset of the variables other than x_i, and all the partial correlations.

A specification of the vector of mean differences between any pair of the treatments that are consonant with the data at any specified level is given by Hotelling's T^2 test. Tests of significance of the difference of the t mean vectors are available, in Dr. Anderson's book, for example, but apparently our knowledge of the power or sensitivity of the tests is almost nil. It is, I suppose, the case that one can have little faith in a test of significance if one has no knowledge of its power. There does not seem to be a usable inversion of the tests to give a series of confidence regions on the differences of the mean vectors, analogous to the Scheffé or Tukey procedures in the univariate case. But, to express a possibly heretical view, suppose we have 6 treatments and 4 components in the observation vector, of what scientific use would a system of confidence regions in 24 dimensions be? From my point of view on the prime role of statistics as a way to the objective formation of opinion, any opinion about the totality would, I think, be essentially useless to me. What does interest me, however, is the relationship of the true means (or whatever measure of central tendency is used). With our 6 treatments we can make a plot of the observed means for any pair of components of the observation vector. Even if the true means were to be almost or exactly on a straight line, the observed means will not. How much of the variability in true means of x_1 can be accounted for by a linear (functional) dependence on the true means for x_2? We can correct for attenuation, but do we have reasonable standard errors for such corrected values? We can certainly compute the components of variation for "samples" or "treatments" by subtracting the error mean square and product matrix from the "treatment" mean square and product matrix and then perform the computation, but we encounter the problem of negative estimates of components of variation in a nasty form. As an illustration we shall use the example of yields of barley varieties in 2 years given by Anderson (p. 218). Actually the situation here appears to be primarily a technological or decision one, but the numbers could have arisen from an information experiment. Also the situation is clearly one for which univariate analysis has potentially at least greater compressibility power, because the units are the same for the components of the vector. The matrix for error is

$$\begin{matrix} 163.95 & 40.10 \\ 40.10 & 200.85 \end{matrix}$$

and for treatments (actually, varieties) is

$$\begin{matrix} 697.00 & 637.50 \\ 637.50 & 715.75 \end{matrix}$$

so that the simple estimate of the treatment variation matrix is

$$\begin{matrix} 533.05 & 597.40 \\ 597.40 & 514.90 \end{matrix}$$

an obviously impossible estimate. What should one do here? What experimenters commonly do is to calculate product-moment correlations and quote them even if they are outside the range -1 to 1. Even if this procedure has no mathematical justification, such results are informative. But we may well ask for a procedure which leads to admissible values. This problem occurs in a specially important form when the treatments are random and a random additive classification model is used, because one would like to obtain variance matrices for treatments and for error which are consonant with the data.[4]

[4] Dr. Anderson informed me at the meeting that he had worked out some aspects of this problem several years ago. I hope that he will publish his results.

One would like to have reasonable standard errors for the correlations in the treatment matrix. The only work I know of on this is by statisticians working on quantitative genetic situations in which some answer, even if very rough and approximate, must be given. The delta argument was used by Harris [10] for such a problem. The problem of evaluating regressions in the "treatment" component is examined by Tukey [22].

A major problem associated with the analysis of comparative experiments is the dependence of our commonly used testing techniques on the assumption of normality or multivariate normality of error. In the simple comparative experiment, errors arise from two sources, error of measurement and variability between experimental units. So the magnitude of error is often a matter of the experimenter's failure to obtain units between which there is little variability. The distribution of error is partly a matter of definition. From the randomization reference there is a finite number of deviations which are distributed among the treatments at random according to the design, and this error is obviously nothing like normally distributed. The error in the simple comparative experiment is strictly a nuisance, and usually has no relation to variability in any population of interest. The use of normality to assess the data is therefore questionable, and that is why Fisher [9] put forward the randomization (or permutation) test of significance of mean differences. This test of significance, like any other test of significance of means, is invertible in principle. One merely modified the observations by a hypothesized set of differences and makes a test of significance on the modified data. One would presumably take the "confidence region" to be the smallest connected set which contained points that do not give significance at the chosen level. Of course the inversion of the randomization test is impossible by theory and computationally very difficult except perhaps in the case of a single parameter. But the validity of applications of normal theory must in the last resort be based, in my opinion, on the extent to which the normal-theory procedure reflects this distribution-free procedure. In the case of the univariate comparative experiment, we have the study of the distribution over the randomization reference set of the normal-theory criterion made by Welch and Pitman, and this gives us some comfort. In the case of multivariate experiments the situation is relatively obscure. I know of only three pieces of work in this area.

Chung and Fraser [6] described how randomization tests can be used for a two-sample problem, even for the case when the dimensionality of the observation vector exceeds the joint sample size minus two, when Hotelling's T^2 test would not exist. There is a considerable degree of arbitrariness in the choice of criterion, but no less, one imagines, than among all possible admissible tests if these could be specified. To reiterate an opinion expressed earlier, this does not bother me, and, indeed, pleases me, and I would give an evaluation with as many criteria as occurred to me before inspection of the actual data. As Chung and Fraser [6] state, their procedure may be extended simply to the r-sample problem, and apparently to any design situation, although the computations would become hopelessly extensive, without some sort of Monte Carlo sampling or reduction of the number of cases in the reference set by other means. In the experimental context there seem to me to be real advantages in using the complete randomization reference set (Kempthorne, [12]). Barton and David [5] considered the case of N points on the plane, each of which has in it one of n groups, and considered the question of whether the arrangement is random. If r_1 of the groups contain a points, r_2 contain b points, and so on, the number of possible ways of allocating the N points to groups of the same size as in the observations is

$$\frac{N!}{r_1!r_2!\cdots a!b!\cdots}.$$

A criterion is chosen and evaluated for each of the possible allocations, and the observed allocation is evaluated as a random one of the total number of possible allocations. This with t groups of r points with a bivariate response is exactly the situation with the completely randomized design for t treatments, each represented on r experimental units. The criterion chosen by Barton and David, which seems entirely appropriate to the type of application they had in mind, was

$$T = \sum_j \frac{1}{r_j} \sum_{uv} \delta(ju, jv) \Big/ \frac{1}{N} \sum_{j,k} \sum_{uv} \delta(ju, kv),$$

where $\delta(ju, kv)$ is the squared distance between the uth point of the jth group and the vth point of the kth group. With the coordinates denoted by (x_{ju}, y_{ju}), j the group number, u the point within the group, over-all average $(\bar{x}, \bar{y})$, and

$$m_{ab} = \frac{1}{N} \sum_{ju} (x_{ju} - \bar{x})^a (y_{ju} - \bar{y})^b,$$

$$k_{1j} = \frac{1}{r_j} \sum_u (x_{ju} - \bar{x}), \qquad k_{2j} = \frac{1}{r_j} \sum_u (y_{ju} -)\bar{y},$$

the criterion is given by

$$T = 1 - \frac{1}{N(m_{20} + m_{02})} \sum_{j=1}^{n} (k_{1j}^2 + k_{2j}^2),$$

which is analogous to the univariate quantity

$$1 - \frac{\text{sum of squares between classes}}{\text{total sum of squares}}.$$

Barton and David give the first three moments of T and suggest using the beta distribution with the same first two moments as an approximation.

In the case where the units of x and y are arbitrary, as would normally be the case with observations in a comparative experiment, they suggest first choosing new coordinates (X, Y), so that X and Y have unit variance and are uncorrelated in the totality. The asymptotic behavior of this criterion for the case of two groups, when it is a monotone function of Hotelling's T^2, was investigated by Wald and Wolfowitz [23]. One concludes that in fact the distribution of Hotelling's T^2 is not particularly sensitive to nonnormality. One can surmize that the likelihood ratio test based on normality for r samples is also not very sensitive to nonnormality. If one had classes of nonnormal multivariate distributions and a very high speed computer, one could examine this matter. It is relevant, also, to note that the evaluation of significance uses the tail of the distribution, and the fact that a particular distribution is a good approximation with regard to mean and variance is indicative but not conclusive that the tail probabilities are reasonably approximated.

I now turn to the case of the randomized block design. It is usually the case, in my opinion, that the blocks of a randomized block experiment are not random. This has the consequence that the randomized block experiment does not have an unambiguous error term. Error is measured by interaction of blocks and treatments, and in order that this provide an unbiased estimate of the precision of treatment comparisons, there must be no true interaction of blocks and treatments. In the univariate case, there are several *ad hoc* ways of looking at the observed interactions of blocks and treatments to obtain an idea of whether they may reasonably be regarded as measuring error. The paper by Anscombe [2] on residual analysis is an excellent account of several possibilities. The one-degree-of-freedom-of-nonadditivity test of Tukey [20] seems to be quite sensitive to the sorts of nonadditivity that can be removed by monotonic transformation of the scale of measurement, and, in spite of the apparently crucial role of normality in the derivation of the distribution of the test statistic, does not appear, from Monte Carlo examination of its distribution for a few cases (by F. Giesbrecht, unpublished) over the randomization reference set, to be dependent on normality. Also there is general evidence of an imprecise type that the usual test of significance of treatment differences does not depend on normality, and reflects fairly accurately the randomization test (Welch [24] and Pitman [16]).

It is obvious that one can apply all the univariate procedures to the components of the multivariate observation separately, and, I imagine, there is no doubt in anyone's mind that this should be done. It is scientifically informative to report the results of such evaluations, even though the observations are correlated. But are there procedures which utilize the multivariate nature of the observations? I know of none, and believe one of the important tasks of data analyzers is to develop procedures. The problem is to obtain a reasonable condensation of the data, and the frequency of error of decision-type conclusions is almost irrelevant.

Some theory of the multivariate analysis of variance with normality is given by Tukey [21], who discusses many of the difficulties mentioned throughout the present paper, and by Anderson [1] and Roy [17].

The behavior of the normal multivariate analysis-of-variance test of treatment differences for the paired design, which is, of course, the randomized block design with two treatments, was examined by Arnold [3]. He examined the average frequency with which the normal theory 5%, $2\frac{1}{2}$%, 1%, and $\frac{1}{2}$% percentage points are exceeded under randomization for 4, 6, and 8 pairs, with data from rectangular, normal, and double exponential distributions. This is not, it seems, what one really wants in these cases, because randomization tests of only a few sizes, not including any of the above, are possible, unless one uses an extraneous random device. The latter is surely irrelevant and misleading except in a decision context, because the real question is "What do the actual data say or indicate?"

From a logical point of view, the Latin-square design introduces no additional theoretical difficulties. The same is true of incomplete block designs if one is concerned only with intrablock information.

The cases of incomplete block designs with utilization of interblock information and split-plot designs introduce the further complexity that there are two sources of error and hence two error-variance matrices. In the split-plot case, the situation is simpler, in that information is either purely intrablock or purely interblock. But even in this case one gets involved in the Behrens-Fisher problem if one wishes to make some sort of comparisons among treatment combinations. The general incomplete block case is much more complex. The cases in which block size is constant are simpler than when block size varies, because one can find a reparametrization such that the new treatment parameters split into groups (Kempthorne, [13]), with the following properties under treatment-unit additivity. For the parameters of group 1 there is no information intra- or interblockwise; for those of group 2 there is only intrablock information; for those of group 3 there is only interblock information; and for those of group 4 there is both intra- and interblock information, all "information" being uncorrelated and with normality of errors independent. It appears that we have no techniques additional to separate univariate analyses, although there are presumably no difficulties in combining the types of information. The difficulties lie in evaluating the results.

5. CONCLUSIONS

At the beginning of my talk, I raised the question of why multivariate techniques have not been used. The answers lie, I think, in the following:

(1) The purpose of statistical analysis of experimental informational data is to form opinions about the underlying situation. One can certainly form opinions on the basis of univariate techniques, which are communicable and fairly easily understood. The question of what multivariate analysis can provide over and above separate univariate analyses has an obvious answer at an elementary level, as in the study of the error matrix, but is unanswered beyond this. It is relevant, for instance, to ask why one would get significance at a particular level by correlated univariate tests and not by the corresponding multivariate test. An observation that this happens is, in itself, informative of the situation under analysis and requires examination of the data to see "why" it happened. There are, however, situations in which the multivariate analysis tells one something about individual components of the observation vector. Suppose one observed the following in a completely randomized design:

	Mean squares and products		
	x_1^2	x_1x_2	x_2^2
Treatments	500	250	190
Residual	100	75	200

The data indicate differences among treatments with regard to x_1, but not with regard to x_2, if one looks at the univariate analyses. But the product analysis indicates that there are differences between treatments with regard to both x_1 and x_2. Exactly how one can quantify these indications is unknown to me, but the data illustrate how the multivariate analysis "tells" one more about one component of the observation than a single univariate analysis.

(2) The state of theoretical knowledge about multivariate observations, in spite of very good books on the subject, seems still very primitive. Naturally enough, the theory is dominated by the multivariate normal distribution, but one wonders how robust the procedures for assessing differences of means are. This will probably have to be assessed by Monte Carlo computations. We have some obviously desirable tests of significance for global questions, but have very few informative multivariate-data dissection procedures.

(3) The future of data analysis obviously lies in the easy use of high-speed computers. The only way "to look at" multivariate data is by means of computers and plotters. Even in the present, after 20 years of modern computation, the problems of communicating with a computer are excessive. Hopefully these problems will be solved soon, and we will have manuals of data analysis just as we have manuals of chemical analysis. The presently low amount of truly multivariate analysis is certainly partly due to the inadequacy of computing processes.

(4) Many of our univariate procedures arose from looking at real data and trying to make sense of them. The same will hold for multivariate data. The job of thinking of ways of looking at data is different from the job of determining the probability behavior of these ways.

(5) Even though the usual multivariate techniques seem from some points of view to assess the totality of the data, they do so only with regard to linear functions of the observations. Ratios and other indices constructed from the components may well behave in a simple way. I recall in this connection an example that I was teaching on the analysis of covariance, and I wished to give the students a numerical example to work through. I found an agronomic experiment, perhaps on sugar beet, with yield and plant number. All the students except one did what I asked, but one examined yield per plant. Curiously, this attribute showed no signs of being affected by treatment—an informative conclusion. The moral is obvious.

REFERENCES

1. ANDERSON, T. W. (1958). *An Introduction to Multivariate Statistical Analysis*. Wiley, New York.
2. ANSCOMBE, F. J. (1961). Examination of residuals. *Proc. Fourth Berkeley Symp. Math. Statist. Prob.* **1** 1–36.
3. ARNOLD, H. J. (1964). Permutation support for multivariate techniques. *Biometrika* **51** 65–70.
4. BARNARD, G. S., JENKINS, G. M. and WINSTEN, C. B. (1962). Likelihood inference and time series. *J. Roy. Statist. Soc. Ser. A* **125** 321–372.
5. BARTON, D. E. and DAVID, F. N. (1961). Randomization basis for multivariate tests. I. The bivariate case. Randomness of points in a plane. *Bull. Inst. Internat. Statist.* **39** 544–567.
6. CHUNG, J. H. and FRASER, D. A. S. (1958). Randomization tests for a multivariate two sample problem *J. Amer. Statist. Assoc.* **53** 729–735.
7. FINNEY, D. J. (1956). Multivariate analysis and agricultural experiments. *Biometrics* **12** 67–71.
8. FISHER, R. A. (1922). On the mathematical foundations of theoretical statistics. *Philos. Trans. Roy. Soc. London Ser. A* **222** 309–368.
9. FISHER, R. A. (1935). *The Design of Experiments*. Oliver and Boyd, Edinburgh.
10. HARRIS, D. L. (1964). Expected and predicted progress from index selection involving estimates of population parameters. *Biometrics* **20** 46–72.
11. HILL, B. M. (1963). The three parameter log-normal distribution and Bayesian analysis of a point-source epidemic. *J. Amer. Statist. Assoc.* **58** 72–84.
12. KEMPTHORNE, O. (1955). The randomization theory of experimental inference. *J. Amer. Statist. Assoc.* **50** 946–967.
13. KEMPTHORNE, O. (1956). The efficiency factor of an incomplete block design. *Ann. Math. Statist.* **27** 846–849.
14. KOSHAL, R. S. (1933). Application of the method of maximum likelihood to the improvement of curves fitted by the method of moments. *J. Roy. Statist. Soc. Ser. A* **96** 303–313.

15. Kurtz, T. E., Link, B. F., Tukey, J. W., and Wallace, D. L. (1965). Short-cut multiple comparisons for balanced single and double classifications. Part I. Results. *Technometrics* **6** 95–162.
16. Pitman, E. J. G. (1937). Significance tests which can be applied to samples from any population. III. The analysis of variance test. *Biometrika* **29** 322–335.
17. Roy, S. N. (1957). *Some Aspects of Multivariate Analysis*. Wiley, New York.
18. Schlaifer, R. O. (1961). *Introduction to Statistics for Business Decisions*. McGraw-Hill, New York.
19. Steel, R. G. D. (1955). An analysis of perennial crop data. *Biometrics* **11** 201–212.
20. Tukey, J. W. (1949). One degree of freedom for non-additivity. *Biometrics* **5** 232–242.
21. Tukey. J. W. (1949). Dyadic anova, an analysis of variance for vectors. *Human Biology* **21** 65–110.
22. Tukey, J. W. (1951). Components in regression. *Biometrics* **7** 33–69.
23. Wald, A. and Wolfowitz, T. (1944). Statistical tests based on permutations of the observations. *Ann. Math. Statist.* **15** 358–372.
24. Welch, B. L. (1937). On the z-test in randomized blocks and Latin squares. *Biometrika* **29** 21–52.
25. Wilk, M. B. and Gnanadesikan, R. (1964). Graphical methods for internal comparisons in multiresponse experiments. *Ann. Math. Statist.* **35** 613–631.

Equating of Grades or Scores on the Basis of a Common Battery of Measurements[1]

RICHARD F. POTTHOFF

DEPARTMENT OF STATISTICS
UNIVERSITY OF NORTH CAROLINA
CHAPEL HILL, NORTH CAROLINA

1. SUMMARY AND INTRODUCTION

This paper deals with some specific estimation problems that arise in certain educational and psychological applications which are concerned with the equating of grades from different schools, the equating of ratings assigned by different raters, or the equating of different tests. The purpose of this paper is to provide the maximum-likelihood estimates of the specified equating parameters under several basic models, different models being appropriate for different practical situations. The equating is always effected via a battery of measurements which is common to all students or subjects.

2. STATEMENT OF THE PROBLEM; NOTATION

We suppose that we have N students or subjects who are distributed into m groups. Let the number of individuals in the ith group ($i = 1, 2, \ldots, m$) be N_i (thus $\sum_{i=1}^{m} N_i = N$). The m groups might arise in various ways. We might, for example, have m schools, each of which has its own grading standards. We might have m forms of the same psychological test which are to be equated, with each form having been administered to one group. We might have m supervisors, each of whom rates employees under his own supervision.

Each of these situations can be viewed as follows. The jth individual ($j = 1, 2, \ldots, N_i$) in the ith group receives a score, grade (or grade average), or rating, which we shall denote by H_{ij}. These H_{ij}'s can legitimately be compared within a group but not between groups. We postulate the existence of

[1] This research was supported by the College Entrance Examination Board through Educational Testing Service, and was also supported in part by National Institutes of Health Research Grant GM 12868-01.

"equating parameters" a_i and b_i ($i = 1, 2, \ldots, m$) which can be determined so that the variable

$$h_{ij} = a_i + b_i H_{ij} \tag{2.1}$$

represents an "equated" value of the grade, score, or rating; i.e., two h_{ij}'s (2.1) from two different groups are always comparable, whereas the corresponding H_{ij}'s are of course not comparable. Thus the role of the a_i's and b_i's is to compensate for differences in standards among the different schools, raters, or tests. As an alternative to (2.1), we might postulate a simpler relation which omits b_i and takes the form

$$h_{ij} = a_i + H_{ij}. \tag{2.2}$$

Actually, the functional relation between h_{ij} (the equated value) and H_{ij} (the unequated value) could obviously be more complicated than either (2.1) or (2.2), and could be written in the form $h_{ij} = f_i(H_{ij})$ if one wanted to be completely general; however, the above formulations, (2.1) or (2.2), would seem to be tenable in many practical situations, and at the same time they are mathematically tractable. In any event, the topic of this paper is the estimation of the a_i's and b_i's which are postulated for (2.1) and (2.2).

In addition to the observed variable H_{ij}, we assume that there is also available for each individual an observed vector $\mathbf{T}_{ij}(p \times 1)$ which consists of a battery of measurements obtained under common standards, i.e., standards which are uniform with respect to all m groups. Thus $\mathbf{T}_{ij}$ might represent scores on a common battery of tests administered to all N individuals, or it might represent a set of grades or ratings assigned under uniform conditions. Since they generally will be correlated with the h_{ij}'s, the $\mathbf{T}_{ij}$'s provide information which can be used in estimating the a_i's and b_i's.

If $p = 1$, the "battery" will consist of a single element. In most of our presentations we shall find it convenient to treat separately the two situations $p = 1$ and $p > 1$. For the situation $p > 1$, we shall give all our formulas and derivations explicitly just for the case $p = 2$, but at the same time the presentations will be made in such a way that the form of the results for $p > 2$ will be immediately discernible. Thus no generality will really be lost by concentrating on the case $p = 2$, but space will be saved and readability will be improved. We shall never actually need such notation as $\mathbf{T}_{ij}(p \times 1) = (T_{ij}^{(1)}, T_{ij}^{(2)}, \ldots, T_{ij}^{(p)})'$, since in all cases we shall be dealing only implicitly with the case of general p; rather, the notation which we are going to use will be just $\mathbf{T}_{ij}(2 \times 1) = (T_{ij}, T_{ij}^{0})'$ for $p = 2$ and $\mathbf{T}_{ij}(1 \times 1) = T_{ij}$ when $p = 1$.

Note that, although we are allowing the T variable $\mathbf{T}_{ij}$ to be vector-valued, we provide only for a single element, H_{ij}, in the H variable. Although the situation of a vector-valued H variable would be of practical interest, this matter is beyond the scope of the present paper.

With the H_{ij}'s, the h_{ij}'s, and the elements of the $\mathbf{T}_{ij}$'s, we shall adopt the convention that these variables are all scored in such a way that a better performance (provided that this concept is well-defined) is reflected in a higher (rather than a lower) value of the variable. This implies, incidentally, that the parameter b_i in (2.1) is >0.

Before we can consider the estimation of the equating parameters (a_i's and b_i's), we shall need to undertake a final and major step in the formulation of the problem: some assumptions have to be made with respect to the distribution of the h_{ij}'s and $\mathbf{T}_{ij}$'s. In Sections 3 and 4 we explore and specify alternative possibilities for these assumptions and for the corresponding models and distributions.

3. THE DIFFERENT MODELS

This section presents the mathematical details of several possible models which might be postulated for the distribution of the h_{ij}'s and $\mathbf{T}_{ij}$'s. Then Section 4 will discuss the appropriateness of these different models for different practical situations.

A. The $H|T$ Model

Our first possible model specifies the conditional distribution of h_{ij} given $\mathbf{T}_{ij}$, but makes no further assumptions. For $p = 2$, this distribution is of the form

$$(2\pi\sigma^2)^{-1/2}\exp(-\tfrac{1}{2}[h_{ij} - \alpha - \nu T_{ij} - \nu^0 T_{ij}^0]^2/\sigma^2). \tag{3.1}$$

Since it is the H_{ij}'s rather than the h_{ij}'s which are the observed quantities, we need to have our distribution in terms of the former. If we apply the transformation of variable $h_{ij} = a_i' + b_i H_{ij}$ to (3.1) (we are using a_i' rather than a_i in order to save the a_i notation for below), we obtain

$$(2\pi)^{-1/2}|b_i|\exp(-\tfrac{1}{2}[a_i + b_i H_{ij} - \nu T_{ij} - \nu^0 T_{ij}^0]^2) \tag{3.2}$$

as the conditional density of H_{ij} given $\mathbf{T}_{ij}$, where $a_i = a_i' - \alpha$ may now legitimately be considered as the additive equating parameter (in place of a_i'). In going from (3.1) to (3.2), we arbitrarily (but with no loss of generality) set $\sigma^2 = 1$, in order to remove all ambiguity concerning the definitions of the a_i's and b_i's for this situation.

If h_{ij} is of the form (2.2) rather than (2.1), we apply the transformation of variable $h_{ij} = a_i' + H_{ij}$ to (3.1) and obtain

$$(2\pi\sigma^2)^{-1/2}\exp(-\tfrac{1}{2}[a_i + H_{ij} - \nu T_{ij} - \nu^0 T_{ij}^0]^2/\sigma^2) \tag{3.3}$$

as the conditional distribution of H_{ij} given $\mathbf{T}_{ij}$, where $a_i = a_i' - \alpha$ as before. This time we cannot set $\sigma^2 = 1$, because σ cannot be absorbed in the other parameters as it was in the case of (3.2).

If $p = 1$ rather than 2, we simply omit the term $(-v^0 T_{ij}^0)$ from (3.1 to 3.3).

We denote the submodel (3.2), which has a b_i term, by $H \mid T(b, p)$. There is no b_i term in (3.3), and we call this submodel $H \mid T(a, p)$. If $p = 1$, we denote the corresponding submodels by $H \mid T(b, 1)$ and $H \mid T(a, 1)$, respectively. Similar notation will be used for the models B, C, and D below.

B. The $T|H$ Model

Our second possible model specifies the conditional distribution of $\mathbf{T}_{ij}$ given h_{ij}, but makes no further assumptions. For $p = 2$, we take this distribution to be of the form

$$(2\pi)^{-1}|\Sigma|^{-1/2} \exp\left(-\frac{1}{2}\begin{bmatrix} T_{ij} - \mu - bh_{ij} \\ T_{ij}^0 - \mu^0 - b^0 h_{ij} \end{bmatrix}' \Sigma^{-1} \begin{bmatrix} T_{ij} - \mu - bh_{ij} \\ T_{ij}^0 - \mu^0 - b^0 h_{ij} \end{bmatrix}\right), \quad (3.4)$$

where Σ is of course 2×2. If we substitute (2.1) in (3.4), we find that the conditional density of $\mathbf{T}_{ij}$ given H_{ij} is

$$(2\pi)^{-1}|\Sigma|^{-1/2} \exp\left(-\frac{1}{2}\begin{bmatrix} T_{ij} - \mu - b(a_i + b_i H_{ij}) \\ T_{ij}^0 - \mu^0 - b^0(a_i + b_i H_{ij}) \end{bmatrix}' \right.$$

$$\left. \times \Sigma^{-1} \begin{bmatrix} T_{ij} - \mu - b(a_i + b_i H_{ij}) \\ T_{ij}^0 - \mu^0 - b^0(a_i + b_i H_{ij}) \end{bmatrix}\right), \quad (3.5)$$

which is the submodel $T \mid H(b, p)$. The submodel $T \mid H(a, p)$ is the same as (3.5) except that the b_i's are omitted. Note that, in (3.5), the (a_i, b_i)'s are not unique, in the sense that, if all a_i's and b_i's are multiplied by the same constant, this constant can be absorbed in b and b^0, and if all a_i's are increased or decreased by the same constant, this adjustment can be absorbed in μ and μ^0.

If $p = 1$, then the conditional distribution of T_{ij} given h_{ij} simply has the form

$$(2\pi\sigma^2)^{-1/2} \exp(-\tfrac{1}{2}[T_{ij} - \mu - bh_{ij}]^2/\sigma^2) \quad (3.6)$$

in place of (3.4). Substituting $h_{ij} = a_i' + b_i' H_{ij}$ in (3.6), we find that the $T \mid H(b, 1)$ submodel is

$$(2\pi\sigma^2)^{-1/2} \exp(-\tfrac{1}{2}[T_{ij} - a_i - b_i H_{ij}]^2/\sigma^2), \quad (3.7)$$

where $a_i = \mu + ba_i'$ and $b_i = bb_i'$. The $T \mid H(a, 1)$ submodel we may formulate by substituting $h_{ij} = a_i + H_{ij}$ in (3.6) to obtain

$$(2\pi\sigma^2)^{-1/2} \exp(-\tfrac{1}{2}[T_{ij} - a_i^* - bH_{ij}]^2/\sigma^2), \quad (3.8)$$

where $a_i^* = \mu + ba_i$. [Incidentally, the different σ^2's which we use in (3.1), (3.3), and (3.6) to (3.8) are of course not all the same.]

C. The *T*, *H* Model

Our third suggested model specifies the joint distribution of $\mathbf{T}_{ij}$ and h_{ij}. For $p = 2$, we take this distribution to be trivariate-normal, of the form

$$(2\pi)^{-3/2}|\Sigma|^{-1/2}\exp\left(-\frac{1}{2}\begin{bmatrix} T_{ij}-\mu \\ T_{ij}^{0}-\mu^{0} \\ h_{ij}-\gamma \end{bmatrix}' \Sigma^{-1}\begin{bmatrix} T_{ij}-\mu \\ T_{ij}^{0}-\mu^{0} \\ h_{ij}-\gamma \end{bmatrix}\right). \tag{3.9}$$

For most of our purposes, however, it will be beneficial to write this distribution (3.9) in a different way—as the product of the marginal density of $\mathbf{T}_{ij}$ by the conditional density of h_{ij} given $\mathbf{T}_{ij}$. Now, the second term of this product is just the expression (3.1), and the first term is free of h_{ij}. Hence the density for the $T, H(b, p)$ or $T, H(a, p)$ submodel is nothing more than the marginal density of $\mathbf{T}_{ij}$ multiplied by (3.2) or (3.3), respectively. The corresponding formulas for the $T, H(b, 1)$ and $T, H(a, 1)$ submodels are analogous.

It will turn out that the estimates for the four T, H submodels will be the same as those for the four respective $H|T$ submodels (see Sections 7 and 8).

For purposes of a comparison to be made later (see Section 5), we mention that our $T, H(b, 1)$ submodel can be written in the form

$$(2\pi)^{-1}\begin{vmatrix} 1 & \rho \\ \rho & 1 \end{vmatrix}^{-1/2}\theta|b_i|\exp\left(-\frac{1}{2}\begin{bmatrix} \theta(T_{ij}-\mu) \\ a_i+b_iH_{ij} \end{bmatrix}'\begin{bmatrix} 1 & \rho \\ \rho & 1 \end{bmatrix}^{-1}\begin{bmatrix} \theta(T_{ij}-\mu) \\ a_i+b_iH_{ij} \end{bmatrix}\right), \tag{3.10}$$

where μ and θ^{-1} are, respectively, the mean and standard deviation of T_{ij}. To obtain (3.10), we apply the transformation (2.1) to a distribution which is like (3.9) except that the T_{ij}^{0} variable is omitted and h_{ij} is arbitrarily assigned a mean of 0 and variance of 1.

D. The *T*, *H*[*i*] Model

It may be instructive to consider a different type of model which specifies the joint distribution of $\mathbf{T}_{ij}$ and h_{ij}, one in which this distribution takes the form

$$(2\pi)^{-1}\begin{vmatrix} 1 & \rho \\ \rho & 1 \end{vmatrix}^{-1/2}\theta_i^{2}\exp\left(-\frac{1}{2}\begin{bmatrix} \theta_i(T_{ij}-\mu_i) \\ \theta_i(h_{ij}-\mu_i) \end{bmatrix}'\begin{bmatrix} 1 & \rho \\ \rho & 1 \end{bmatrix}^{-1}\begin{bmatrix} \theta_i(T_{ij}-\mu_i) \\ \theta_i(h_{ij}-\mu_i) \end{bmatrix}\right) \tag{3.11}$$

for $p = 1$. This model (3.11) allows for group differences, but at the same time implies a certain strict relationship between a group mean or variance for T_{ij} and that for h_{ij}.

The $T, H[i](b, 1)$ submodel, which is obtained by applying the transformation (2.1) to (3.11), is

$$(2\pi)^{-1}\begin{vmatrix} 1 & \rho \\ \rho & 1 \end{vmatrix}^{-1/2}\theta_i^{2}|b_i|\exp\left(-\frac{1}{2}\begin{bmatrix} \theta_i(T_{ij}-\mu_i) \\ \theta_i(a_i+b_iH_{ij}-\mu_i) \end{bmatrix}' \times\begin{bmatrix} 1 & \rho \\ \rho & 1 \end{bmatrix}^{-1}\begin{bmatrix} \theta_i(T_{ij}-\mu_i) \\ \theta_i(a_i+b_iH_{ij}-\mu_i) \end{bmatrix}\right). \tag{3.12}$$

If each b_i in (3.12) is replaced by 1, we have the T, $H[i](a, 1)$ submodel.

It is of some interest to observe that the T, $H[i](b, 1)$ submodel (3.12) leads to simple maximum-likelihood estimators of a_i and b_i [see (7.17) and (7.18)] which, superficially at least, might appear to be the most obvious *a priori* choice of estimators. We also remark at this point that, if each ρ in (3.12) is replaced by ρ_i, then our maximum-likelihood estimates of the equating parameters will be unaltered; a similar statement holds for the T, $H[i](a, 1)$ submodel.

A possible T, $H[i](b, p)$ submodel, representing a generalization of (3.12), would be of the form

$$(2\pi)^{-3/2}\begin{vmatrix} 1 & \rho^* & \rho \\ \rho^* & 1 & \rho^0 \\ \rho & \rho^0 & 1 \end{vmatrix}^{-1/2} \theta_i^3|b^0|\,|b_i|$$

$$\times \exp\left(-\frac{1}{2}\begin{bmatrix} \theta_i(T_{ij}-\mu_i) \\ \theta_i(a^0+b^0T_{ij}^0-\mu_i) \\ \theta_i(a_i+b_iH_{ij}-\mu_i) \end{bmatrix}' \begin{bmatrix} 1 & \rho^* & \rho \\ \rho^* & 1 & \rho^0 \\ \rho & \rho^0 & 1 \end{bmatrix}^{-1} \begin{bmatrix} \theta_i(T_{ij}-\mu_i) \\ \theta_i(a^0+b^0T_{ij}^0-\mu_i) \\ \theta_i(a_i+b_iH_{ij}-\mu_i) \end{bmatrix}\right) \tag{3.13}$$

when $p = 2$. However, in this paper we shall not attempt to deal any further with T, $H[i](b, p)$ or T, $H[i](a, p)$ submodels.

4. APPROPRIATENESS OF THE DIFFERENT MODELS

Each of the four models of Section 3 (which we shall designate here as 3A, 3B, 3C, and 3D, respectively) will be appropriate in certain types of applications. It is of practical importance to consider the conditions under which the different models may be tenable.

If the N individuals in the sample are selected on the basis of T (and not at all on the basis of H), if the H measurement is taken at a later point in time than the T measurement(s), and/or if H is to be predicted from T, then the $H \mid T$ model (3A) may well be appropriate, since its only assumption concerns the conditional distribution of H given T. By the same token, if H (but not T) is utilized in selecting the sample, if T occurs later in time than H, and/or if T is to be predicted from H, then the $T \mid H$ model (3B) may be suitable.

If there has been no selection on the basis of either T or H, then the T, H model (3C) or the T, $H[i]$ model (3D) may be tenable. The former model assumes no group differences, an assumption which would be proper if (for example) the N individuals have been randomly assigned to the m groups. The latter model allows for group differences in a special framework [see (3.11) and (3.12)].

As we already mentioned, the $H \mid T$ model (3A) and the T, H model (3C) lead to the same estimates of the equating parameters. Thus the practical effect of postulating 3A will be no different from that of postulating 3C, except in certain cases where one wishes to estimate some additional parameters besides the a_i's and b_i's.

If one of the variables H or T constitutes the basis for selecting candidates for employment or for admission to a school or college, and if the other variable is a criterion variable which measures later performance on the job or in school, then we cannot avoid having a sample for which there has been selection with respect to one of the variables. In this connection, note that, if the m groups already exist prior to selection, if there is some type of selection on the basis of H, and if the T, H model (3C) holds for the unselected population, then the $T \mid H$ model (3B) will automatically be valid for the selected (as well as the unselected) population; or, if the groups are formed after some type of selection based on T, and if T and H have a joint normal distribution in the unselected population, then the $H \mid T$ model (3A) will automatically hold after selection, even if different selection standards were applied for the different groups.

If the selection is on the basis of H and if the T, $H[i]$ group-difference model (3D) holds for the unselected population, then the $T \mid H$ model (3B) will no longer hold for the selected (or unselected) population. Under other conditions where there are group differences, however, it would obviously be still possible for the $T \mid H$ model (3B) to be valid when there is selection on H.

5. OTHER WORK RELATED TO THIS PAPER

At this point we mention some previous work which relates to score or grade equating. Gulliksen discusses the equating of $m = 2$ forms of a test [4, pp. 296–304]; part of this material consists of some results due to Tucker. We might also point out that Gulliksen's book [4] devotes considerable attention to the matter of selection, a matter which played a major role in our discussion in Section 4.

For $m = 2$, Lord [6 and 7] obtained maximum-likelihood estimates of the equating parameters under a model which differs only slightly from our T, $H(b, 1)$ submodel (3.10), and which would, in fact, be equivalent to the latter if ρ were replaced by ρ_i in (3.10). Lord's model [6, 7] also was later referred to by Anderson [1]. In a more general context, Trawinski and Bargmann [10] recently considered certain types of multivariate maximum-likelihood estimation problems, but none of our submodels of Section 3 happens to be encompassed thereunder.

Certain problems concerning the prediction of college grades involve not only the equating of college grades from different colleges, but also the equating of high school grades from different high schools. Such equating problems are among the matters which Tucker deals with in his work on college grade prediction [11].

Finally, we mention a report [8] which is concerned with the prediction of college grades from test scores and high school grades. Maximum-likelihood estimation of the equating parameters for the college grades and for the high school grades is considered in detail with respect to a particular model which specifies the conditional distribution of the college grade given the high school grade and the test score(s). The mimeographed report [8] also treats most of the submodels of the present paper, in more detail than we are giving here in some cases.

6. FURTHER NOTATION

In preparation for Sections 7 and 8, we introduce some additional notation. We define

$$T_i = \sum_{j=1}^{N_i} T_{ij}, \qquad \bar{T}_i = T_i/N_i, \qquad T. = \sum_{i=1}^{m} \sum_{j=1}^{N_i} T_{ij}, \qquad \bar{T}. = T./N, \tag{6.1}$$

and then define T_i^0, $\bar{T}_i^0$, $T.^0$, $\bar{T}.^0$, and H_i, $\bar{H}_i$, $H.$, $\bar{H}.$, analogously to (6.1). We use the notation

$$S_{TTi} = \sum_j T_{ij}^2 - N_i \bar{T}_i^2, \qquad S_{THi} = \sum_j T_{ij} H_{ij} - N_i \bar{T}_i \bar{H}_i, \tag{6.2}$$

with analogous meanings for S_{HHi}, $S_{T^0T^0i}$, S_{T^0Hi}, and S_{TT^0i}. We may write

$$S_{TT^0} = \sum_i \sum_j T_{ij} T_{ij}^0 - N\bar{T}.\bar{T}.^0, \qquad S_{TT} = \sum_i \sum_j T_{ij}^2 - N\bar{T}.^2, \tag{6.3}$$

and similarly for $S_{T^0T^0}$. We denote

$$r_i = S_{THi}/(S_{TTi} S_{HHi})^{1/2}. \tag{6.4}$$

We define the following (2×1) vectors:

$$\mathbf{V}_{1i} = [S_{THi}, S_{T^0Hi}]', \tag{6.5}$$

$$\mathbf{V}_1 = \left[\sum_i S_{THi}, \sum_i S_{T^0Hi}\right]', \tag{6.6}$$

$$\mathbf{V}_{2i} = [\bar{T}_i - \bar{T}., \bar{T}_i^0 - \bar{T}.^0]', \tag{6.7}$$

$$\mathbf{b} = [b, b^0]', \qquad \boldsymbol{\mu} = [\mu, \mu^0]'. \tag{6.8}$$

Finally, we define some matrices. All of them will be 2×2. Let

$$\mathbf{W}_5 = \begin{bmatrix} S_{TT} & S_{TT^0} \\ S_{TT^0} & S_{T^0T^0} \end{bmatrix}, \tag{6.9}$$

$$\mathbf{W}_6 = \begin{bmatrix} \sum_i N_i(\bar{T}_i - \bar{T}.)^2 & \sum_i N_i(\bar{T}_i - \bar{T}.)(\bar{T}_i^0 - \bar{T}_.^0) \\ \sum_i N_i(\bar{T}_i - \bar{T}.)(\bar{T}_i^0 - \bar{T}.^0) & \sum_i N_i(\bar{T}_i^0 - \bar{T}_.^0)^2 \end{bmatrix}, \tag{6.10}$$

$$\mathbf{W}_1 = \begin{bmatrix} \sum_i \left(S_{TTi} - \dfrac{S_{THi}^2}{S_{HHi}}\right) & \sum_i \left(S_{TT^0i} - \dfrac{S_{THi}S_{T^0Hi}}{S_{HHi}}\right) \\ \sum_i \left(S_{TT^0i} - \dfrac{S_{THi}S_{T^0Hi}}{S_{HHi}}\right) & \sum_i \left(S_{T^0T^0i} - \dfrac{S_{T^0Hi}^2}{S_{HHi}}\right) \end{bmatrix}, \tag{6.11}$$

$$\mathbf{W}_2 = \begin{bmatrix} \sum_i \dfrac{S_{THi}^2}{S_{HHi}} + \sum_i N_i(\bar{T}_i - \bar{T}.)^2 & \sum_i \dfrac{S_{THi}S_{T^0Hi}}{S_{HHi}} + \sum_i N_i(\bar{T}_i - \bar{T}.)(\bar{T}_i^0 - \bar{T}_.^0) \\ \sum_i \dfrac{S_{THi}S_{T^0Hi}}{S_{HHi}} + \sum_i N_i(\bar{T}_i - \bar{T}.)(\bar{T}_i^0 - \bar{T}_.^0) & \sum_i \dfrac{S_{T^0Hi}^2}{S_{HHi}} + \sum_i N_i(\bar{T}_i^0 - \bar{T}_.^0)^2 \end{bmatrix}, \tag{6.12}$$

$$\mathbf{W}_3 = \frac{1}{N}\begin{bmatrix} \sum_i S_{TTi} & \sum_i S_{TT^0i} \\ \sum_i S_{TT^0i} & \sum_i S_{T^0T^0i} \end{bmatrix} - \frac{1}{N\sum_i S_{HHi}} \mathbf{V}_1\mathbf{V}_1', \tag{6.13}$$

and

$$\mathbf{W}_4 = \mathbf{W}_6 + \frac{1}{\sum_i S_{HHi}} \mathbf{V}_1\mathbf{V}_1'. \tag{6.14}$$

7. THE MAXIMUM-LIKELIHOOD ESTIMATES: LISTING OF RESULTS

For the various submodels which were indicated in Section 3, we now present the necessary formulas and equations for obtaining the maximum-likelihood estimates of the equating parameters. The derivations of the estimates will be considered in Section 8.

A. The $H|T$ Model

The maximum-likelihood estimates of b_i and a_i for the $H|T(b, 1)$ submodel are given respectively by

$$\hat{b}_i = \frac{\hat{v}S_{THi}}{2S_{HHi}}\left[1 + \left(1 + \frac{4N_i}{S_{TTi}r_i^2\hat{v}^2}\right)^{1/2}\right] \tag{7.1}$$

and

$$\hat{a}_i = \hat{v}\bar{T}_i - \hat{b}_i\bar{H}_i, \tag{7.2}$$

where $\hat{v}$ is the positive square root of the solution for v^2 of

$$\sum_i S_{TTi}\left[2 - r_i^2 - r_i^2\left(1 + \frac{4N_i}{S_{TTi}r_i^2v^2}\right)^{1/2}\right] = 0. \tag{7.3}$$

Equation (7.3) clearly has one and only one solution for v^2, which can be found via the Newton-Raphson method.[2]

For the $H\,|\,T(b, p)$ submodel (3.2), our estimates are

$$\hat{b}_i = \frac{\hat{v}S_{THi} + \hat{v}^0 S_{T^0Hi}}{2S_{HHi}}\left[1 + \left(1 + \frac{4N_i S_{HHi}}{(\hat{v}S_{THi} + \hat{v}^0 S_{T^0Hi})^2}\right)^{1/2}\right] \tag{7.4}$$

and

$$\hat{a}_i = \hat{v}\bar{T}_i + \hat{v}^0\bar{T}_i^0 - \hat{b}_i\bar{H}_i, \tag{7.5}$$

where $(\hat{v}, \hat{v}^0)$ are obtained by solving the system

$$v\sum_i S_{TTi} + v^0\sum_i S_{TT^0i} = \sum_i b_i^*(v, v^0)S_{THi} \tag{7.6a}$$

$$v\sum_i S_{TT^0i} + v^0\sum_i S_{T^0T^0i} = \sum_i b_i^*(v, v^0)S_{T^0Hi} \tag{7.6b}$$

for (v, v^0). The notation $b_i^*(v, v^0)$ in (7.6) is used to denote the expression on the right side of (7.4), but with the hats omitted. The problem of solving (7.6) can be attacked through methods of numerical analysis, such as the generalized Newton-Raphson method or possibly the method of steepest descent (see, e.g., [3, 5, 9, 12]). In case p is comparatively large in relation to m, an alternative method of solving for the $\hat{b}_i$'s and $\hat{v}$'s, which is mentioned in [8, pp. 60–61], may be preferable to the method based on (7.4) to (7.6).

In practical situations, the condition

$$S_{THi} > 0, \qquad S_{T^0Hi} > 0 \qquad \text{for each } i \tag{7.7}$$

should normally be satisfied. If (7.7) holds, then it can be shown (see Section 8) that there is no more than one solution $(\hat{v}, \hat{v}^0)$ of (7.6) for which $\hat{v}$ and $\hat{v}^0$ are both >0. In practice, one would expect that it would be rare for v or v^0 to be

[2] A questioner at the symposium enquired, in effect, whether the simple formulas

$$\hat{b}_i = S_{TTi}/S_{THi}, \qquad \hat{a}_i = \bar{T}_i - \hat{b}_i\bar{H}_i$$

would produce essentially the same numerical values as the more complicated estimates based on (7.1) to (7.3). [Formulas (7.1) and (7.2) would first have to be divided by $\hat{v}$ in order to obtain comparability.] In some cases, it would appear that his suggested formulas might produce results rather close to those of the maximum-likelihood estimators.

<0; in fact, if the T variables are being used for prediction and selection, then a negative v or v^0 would be most undesirable, since it would cause cognizant candidates to deliberately perform as poorly as possible on the test with the negative weight. In any event, if (7.7) holds, and if we utilize the (unique) solution $(\hat{v}, \hat{v}^0)$ of (7.6) for which $\hat{v}$ and $\hat{v}^0$ are both >0 (assuming that this solution exists), then all $\hat{b}_i$'s (7.4) will be >0.

For the $H \mid T(a, 1)$ submodel, the estimate of a_i is

$$\hat{a}_i = -\bar{H}_i + \left(\sum_{i'} S_{THi'} \Big/ \sum_{i'} S_{TTi'}\right) \bar{T}_i. \tag{7.8}$$

The estimate for the $H \mid T(a, p)$ submodel (3.3) is

$$\hat{a}_i = -\bar{H}_i + \left[\sum_{i'} S_{THi'}, \sum_{i'} S_{T^0Hi'}\right] \begin{bmatrix} \sum_{i'} S_{TTi'} & \sum_{i'} S_{TT^0i'} \\ \sum_{i'} S_{TT^0i'} & \sum_{i'} S_{T^0T^0i'} \end{bmatrix}^{-1} \begin{bmatrix} \bar{T}_i \\ \bar{T}_i^0 \end{bmatrix}. \tag{7.9}$$

B. The $T \mid H$ Model

The estimates for the $T \mid H(b, p)$ submodel (3.5) are given by

$$\hat{b}_i = \frac{N(\mathbf{B}'\mathbf{V}_{1i})}{S_{HHi}(\mathbf{B}'\mathbf{W}_1\mathbf{B})} \tag{7.10}$$

and

$$\hat{a}_i = \frac{N(\mathbf{B}'\mathbf{V}_{2i})}{(\mathbf{B}'\mathbf{W}_1\mathbf{B})} - \hat{b}_i\bar{H}_i, \tag{7.11}$$

where $\mathbf{B}(2 \times 1) = [B, B^0]'$ is a characteristic vector of the matrix $\mathbf{W}_1^{-1}\mathbf{W}_2$ corresponding to the largest characteristic root of $\mathbf{W}_1^{-1}\mathbf{W}_2$. In other words, $\mathbf{B}$ satisfies the equation

$$(\mathbf{W}_1^{-1}\mathbf{W}_2 - \lambda\mathbf{I})\mathbf{B} = \mathbf{0}, \tag{7.12}$$

where λ is the maximum root of $\mathbf{W}_1^{-1}\mathbf{W}_2$, $\mathbf{I}$ (2×2) denotes the identity matrix, and $\mathbf{0}$ $(2 \times 1) = [0, 0]'$.

For the $T \mid H(a, p)$ submodel, the estimate of a_i is

$$\hat{a}_i = \frac{(\sum_{i'} S_{HHi'})(\mathbf{B}'\mathbf{V}_{2i})}{(\mathbf{B}'\mathbf{V}_1)} - \bar{H}_i, \tag{7.13}$$

where $\mathbf{B}(2 \times 1) = [B, B^0]'$ this time denotes a characteristic vector of the matrix $\mathbf{W}_3^{-1}\mathbf{W}_4$ corresponding to the largest root of $\mathbf{W}_3^{-1}\mathbf{W}_4$.

The estimates for the $T \mid H(b, 1)$ submodel (3.7) are

$$\hat{b}_i = S_{THi}/S_{HHi} \tag{7.14}$$

and

$$\hat{a}_i = \bar{T}_i - \hat{b}_i\bar{H}_i. \tag{7.15}$$

For the $T\,|\,H(a, 1)$ submodel (3.8), one finds $\hat{b} = (\sum_{i'} S_{THi'})/(\sum_{i'} S_{HHi'})$ and $\hat{a}_i^* = \bar{T}_i - \hat{b}\bar{H}_i$, from which it follows at once that

$$\hat{a}_i = \frac{(\sum_{i'} S_{HHi'})}{(\sum_{i'} S_{THi'})}(\bar{T}_i - \bar{T}.) - \bar{H}_i \tag{7.16}$$

may be used as the estimate for a_i.

C. The *T, H* Model

The maximum-likelihood estimates of the equating parameters for the $T, H(b, 1)$, $T, H(b, p)$, $T, H(a, 1)$, and $T, H(a, p)$ submodels are obtained by using (7.1) to (7.3), (7.4) to (7.6), (7.8), and (7.9), respectively; i.e., the estimates are the same as under the $H\,|\,T$ model.

D. The *T, H*[*i*] Model

The estimates for the $T, H[i](b, 1)$ submodel are

$$\hat{b}_i = (S_{TTi}/S_{HHi})^{1/2} \tag{7.17}$$

and

$$\hat{a}_i = \bar{T}_i - \hat{b}_i\bar{H}_i. \tag{7.18}$$

The effect of (7.17) and (7.18) will be to base the equating simply on the mean and standard deviation of H and the mean and standard deviation of T which are estimated for each group.

For the $T, H[i](a, 1)$ submodel, we have

$$\hat{a}_i = \bar{T}_i - \bar{H}_i. \tag{7.19}$$

Remarks. (a) We emphasize that formulas (7.4) to (7.7) and (7.9) to (7.13) can all be validly extended, in obvious fashion, to cases where $p > 2$, even though explicitly they have been written just for the case $p = 2$.

(b) Although it might be interesting to compare our different equating formulas on some live data, one should not expect that the different models will necessarily produce similar values of the $\hat{a}_i$'s and $\hat{b}_i$'s. As we pointed out in Section 4, the different models are appropriate for different practical situations and different types of assumptions. It is apparent that sharply differing estimates can result from the different models; e.g., compare (7.14) and (7.17).

(c) Formulas (7.17) and (7.18) have probably been applied rather frequently in practice, but perhaps without full realization of what type of model (or assumptions) might be most appropriate for their use. These formulas are only for $p = 1$, of course. For the situation $p = 1$, both (7.17)–(7.18) and (7.14)–(7.15) are computationally simple, while (7.1)–(7.3) are less simple. When $p > 1$, the computations become more difficult for all the models.

8. THE MAXIMUM-LIKELIHOOD ESTIMATES: DERIVATIONS OF THE RESULTS

Section 7 presented our results without their derivations. In this section we shall give the highlights of the derivations. To start with, let us note that the estimates for the $H \mid T(a, 1)$, $H \mid T(a, p)$, $T \mid H(b, 1)$, and $T \mid H(a, 1)$ submodels are all standard least-squares estimates whose derivations are so well known that no further comment is necessary here. We now consider the derivations for the remaining submodels.

A. The $H|T$ Model

For all submodels we shall use L to denote the logarithm of the likelihood function. Thus, for the $H \mid T(b, p)$ submodel (3.2), the likelihood function is the product over i and j of the expressions (3.2), and so we can write

$$\frac{\partial L}{\partial a_i} = -N_i a_i - b_i H_i + v T_i + v^0 T_i^0 = 0, \tag{8.1}$$

$$\frac{\partial L}{\partial b_i} = (N_i/b_i) - a_i H_i - b_i \sum_j H_{ij}^2 + v \sum_j T_{ij} H_{ij} + v^0 \sum_j T_{ij}^0 H_{ij} = 0, \tag{8.2}$$

$$\frac{\partial L}{\partial v} = \sum_i a_i T_i + \sum_i b_i \sum_j T_{ij} H_{ij} - v \sum_i \sum_j T_{ij}^2 - v^0 \sum_i \sum_j T_{ij} T_{ij}^0 = 0, \tag{8.3}$$

and

$$\frac{\partial L}{\partial v^0} = \sum_i a_i T_i^0 + \sum_i b_i \sum_j T_{ij}^0 H_{ij} - v \sum_i \sum_j T_{ij}^0 T_{ij} - v^0 \sum_i \sum_j T_{ij}^{02} = 0, \tag{8.4}$$

which are the maximum-likelihood equations. If we solve (8.1) for a_i, we obtain (7.5) (after affixing hats). If we substitute this solution for a_i in (8.2), we shall end up with a quadratic equation in b_i one of whose solutions is (7.4); it can be shown that (7.4) always results in a larger value of L than the other solution of the quadratic, no matter what v and v^0 are. Finally, we substitute (7.5) and then (7.4) in Eqs. (8.3) and (8.4), in order to arrive at the system (7.6).

Now note that in the set

$$b_i > 0 \text{ for all } i, \quad -\infty < a_i < \infty \text{ for all } i, \quad -\infty < v,\, v^0 < \infty, \tag{8.5}$$

L and its derivatives are continuous functions of the $(2m + 2)$ parameters. Also, the $(2m + 2) \times (2m + 2)$ matrix of second derivatives of L [which is easily obtained from (8.1) to (8.4)] can be shown to be negative-definite throughout (8.5) (and elsewhere as well). Given these two premises, one can prove (see [8], pp. 59–60 for details) that there can be no more than one solution of the maximum-likelihood equations (8.1) to (8.4) which lies in the set (8.5). Hence, if (7.7) holds, there can be no more than one solution of (7.6) such that v and v^0 are both >0 [since, if there were two such solutions of (7.6), then all $\hat{b}_i$'s (7.4) would be >0 for both solutions, and one would be led to the impossible conclusion that the system (8.1) to (8.4) had two solutions both lying in (8.5)].

Because the derivation for the $H \mid T(b, 1)$ submodel is similar to that described for the $H \mid T(b, p)$ submodel, we need not discuss how (7.1) to (7.3) were obtained. Note, however, that one can easily prove that (7.3) always has one and only one solution for v^2, whereas no similarly clearcut result was available for the system (7.6).

B. The $T|H$ Model

The $T \mid H(b, p)$ and $T \mid H(a, p)$ submodels have perhaps the most interesting of all the derivations. We look first at the $T \mid H(b, p)$ submodel (3.5). If we differentiate L with respect to the elements of $\mathbf{\Sigma}$ and then set the resulting derivatives equal to 0, we obtain

$$N\mathbf{\Sigma} = \sum_i \sum_j \begin{bmatrix} T_{ij} - \mu - b(a_i + b_i H_{ij}) \\ T_{ij}^0 - \mu^0 - b^0(a_i + b_i H_{ij}) \end{bmatrix} \begin{bmatrix} T_{ij} - \mu - b(a_i + b_i H_{ij}) \\ T_{ij}^0 - \mu^0 - b^0(a_i + b_i H_{ij}) \end{bmatrix}', \tag{8.6}$$

which is the condition for L to be maximized with respect to $\mathbf{\Sigma}$ (see, e.g., [2], pp. 46–47, Lemma 3.2.2 for details). The other maximum-likelihood equations are given by

$$\frac{\partial L}{\partial a_i} = -(\mathbf{b}'\mathbf{\Sigma}^{-1}\mathbf{b})(N_i a_i + b_i H_i) + \mathbf{b}'\mathbf{\Sigma}^{-1}[T_i - N_i\mu,\ T_i^0 - N_i\mu^0]' = 0, \tag{8.7}$$

$$\frac{\partial L}{\partial b_i} = -(\mathbf{b}'\mathbf{\Sigma}^{-1}\mathbf{b})\left(a_i H_i + b_i \sum_j H_{ij}^2\right)$$
$$+ \mathbf{b}'\mathbf{\Sigma}^{-1}\left[\sum_j T_{ij}H_{ij} - \mu H_i,\ \sum_j T_{ij}^0 H_{ij} - \mu^0 H_i\right]' = 0, \tag{8.8}$$

$$\frac{\partial L}{\partial \boldsymbol{\mu}} = \mathbf{\Sigma}^{-1}[T_. - N\mu,\ T_.^0 - N\mu^0]' - \mathbf{\Sigma}^{-1}\mathbf{b}\sum_i (N_i a_i + b_i H_i) = \mathbf{0}, \tag{8.9}$$

and

$$\frac{\partial L}{\partial \mathbf{b}} = -\mathbf{\Sigma}^{-1}\mathbf{b}\sum_i \sum_j (a_i + b_i H_{ij})^2$$
$$+ \mathbf{\Sigma}^{-1}\sum_i \sum_j [T_{ij} - \mu,\ T_{ij}^0 - \mu^0]'(a_i + b_i H_{ij}) = \mathbf{0}. \tag{8.10}$$

Solving (8.7) for a_i, we obtain

$$a_i = \frac{\mathbf{b}'\mathbf{\Sigma}^{-1}[\overline{T}_i - \mu,\ \overline{T}_i^0 - \mu^0]'}{(\mathbf{b}'\mathbf{\Sigma}^{-1}\mathbf{b})} - b_i \overline{H}_i. \tag{8.11}$$

Next we solve (8.8) for b_i after first substituting (8.11). We get

$$b_i = \frac{(\mathbf{b}'\mathbf{\Sigma}^{-1}\mathbf{V}_{1i})}{S_{HHi}(\mathbf{b}'\mathbf{\Sigma}^{-1}\mathbf{b})}. \tag{8.12}$$

If we substitute (8.11) in (8.9), we see that

$$\mu = \overline{T}_{\cdot}, \qquad \mu^0 = \overline{T}^0_{\cdot} \tag{8.13}$$

satisfies the resulting equation system and constitutes a proper solution for $\boldsymbol{\mu}$. (The solution for $\boldsymbol{\mu}$ is not unique, owing to reasons mentioned in Section 3.) Now we premultiply (8.10) by $\mathbf{\Sigma}$, substitute from Eqs. (8.11) through (8.13), and multiply by $(\mathbf{b}'\mathbf{\Sigma}^{-1}\mathbf{b})$ to obtain

$$-\frac{(\mathbf{b}'\mathbf{\Sigma}^{-1}\mathbf{W}_2\mathbf{\Sigma}^{-1}\mathbf{b})}{(\mathbf{b}'\mathbf{\Sigma}^{-1}\mathbf{b})}\mathbf{b} + \mathbf{W}_2\mathbf{\Sigma}^{-1}\mathbf{b} = \mathbf{0}, \tag{8.14}$$

where $\mathbf{W}_2$ is given by (6.12). If we substitute Eqs. (8.11) through (8.13) in Eq. (8.6), then (8.6) reduces to

$$N\mathbf{\Sigma} = \mathbf{W}_5 + \frac{(\mathbf{b}'\mathbf{\Sigma}^{-1}\mathbf{W}_2\mathbf{\Sigma}^{-1}\mathbf{b})}{(\mathbf{b}'\mathbf{\Sigma}^{-1}\mathbf{b})^2}\mathbf{b}\mathbf{b}' - \frac{1}{(\mathbf{b}'\mathbf{\Sigma}^{-1}\mathbf{b})}(\mathbf{W}_2\mathbf{\Sigma}^{-1}\mathbf{b}\mathbf{b}' + \mathbf{b}\mathbf{b}'\mathbf{\Sigma}^{-1}\mathbf{W}_2), \tag{8.15}$$

where $\mathbf{W}_5$ is given by (6.9). Now (8.15) reduces further to

$$N\mathbf{\Sigma} = \mathbf{W}_5 - \frac{1}{(\mathbf{b}'\mathbf{\Sigma}^{-1}\mathbf{b})}\mathbf{W}_2\mathbf{\Sigma}^{-1}\mathbf{b}\mathbf{b}' \tag{8.16}$$

if we utilize the relation (8.14). Next we obtain

$$N\mathbf{b} = \mathbf{W}_1\mathbf{\Sigma}^{-1}\mathbf{b} \tag{8.17}$$

upon postmultiplying (8.16) by $\mathbf{\Sigma}^{-1}\mathbf{b}$, and

$$N\mathbf{b}'\mathbf{\Sigma}^{-1}\mathbf{b} = \mathbf{B}'\mathbf{W}_1\mathbf{B} \tag{8.18}$$

after premultiplying (8.17) by $\mathbf{b}'\mathbf{\Sigma}^{-1}$ and then substituting

$$\mathbf{B} = \mathbf{\Sigma}^{-1}\mathbf{b}, \tag{8.19}$$

where (for present purposes) we consider (8.19) to be the definition of $\mathbf{B}(2 \times 1) = (B, B^0)'$. After application of the relations (8.17) through (8.19), Eq. (8.14) will finally reduce to

$$\left(\mathbf{W}_2 - \frac{(\mathbf{B}'\mathbf{W}_2\mathbf{B})}{(\mathbf{B}'\mathbf{W}_1\mathbf{B})}\mathbf{W}_1\right)\mathbf{B} = \mathbf{0}. \tag{8.20}$$

Now the only way for $\mathbf{B}$ to satisfy (8.20) is for it to be a characteristic vector of the matrix $\mathbf{W}_1^{-1}\mathbf{W}_2$. It can be shown that, to maximize L, we must choose a characteristic vector corresponding to the *largest* characteristic root λ of $\mathbf{W}_1^{-1}\mathbf{W}_2$, as indicated by (7.12). Note finally that, upon substitution of (8.13), (8.18), and (8.19) in Eqs. (8.11) and (8.12), we obtain (7.10) and (7.11).

The derivation of (7.13) for the $T \mid H(a, p)$ submodel bears some similarity to the derivation which was just presented for the $T \mid H(b, p)$ submodel. For the $T \mid H(a, p)$ submodel, formulas (3.5), (8.6) and (8.7), (8.9) to (8.11), and (8.13) go through just as before, except with all b_i's replaced by 1. Thus the solution for a_i [corresponding to (8.11)] becomes

$$a_i = \frac{(\mathbf{b}'\boldsymbol{\Sigma}^{-1}\mathbf{V}_{2i})}{(\mathbf{b}'\boldsymbol{\Sigma}^{-1}\mathbf{b})} - \bar{H}_i \tag{8.21}$$

after substitution of (8.13). After this point, the solution of the maximum-likelihood equations takes a somewhat different course. Instead of (8.14) we obtain

$$-\frac{(\mathbf{b}'\boldsymbol{\Sigma}^{-1}\mathbf{W}_6\boldsymbol{\Sigma}^{-1}\mathbf{b})}{(\mathbf{b}'\boldsymbol{\Sigma}^{-1}\mathbf{b})}\mathbf{b} - (\mathbf{b}'\boldsymbol{\Sigma}^{-1}\mathbf{b})\Big(\sum_i S_{HHi}\Big)\mathbf{b} + (\mathbf{b}'\boldsymbol{\Sigma}^{-1}\mathbf{b})\mathbf{V}_1 + \mathbf{W}_6\boldsymbol{\Sigma}^{-1}\mathbf{b} = \mathbf{0}, \tag{8.22}$$

and instead of (8.15) we have

$$\begin{aligned} N\boldsymbol{\Sigma} = \mathbf{W}_5 &+ \left(\frac{(\mathbf{b}'\boldsymbol{\Sigma}^{-1}\mathbf{W}_6\boldsymbol{\Sigma}^{-1}\mathbf{b})}{(\mathbf{b}'\boldsymbol{\Sigma}^{-1}\mathbf{b})^2} + \sum_i S_{HHi}\right)\mathbf{b}\mathbf{b}' \\ &- \mathbf{b}\left(\frac{1}{(\mathbf{b}'\boldsymbol{\Sigma}^{-1}\mathbf{b})}\mathbf{b}'\boldsymbol{\Sigma}^{-1}\mathbf{W}_6 + \mathbf{V}_1'\right) - \left(\frac{1}{(\mathbf{b}'\boldsymbol{\Sigma}^{-1}\mathbf{b})}\mathbf{W}_6\boldsymbol{\Sigma}^{-1}\mathbf{b} + \mathbf{V}_1\right)\mathbf{b}'. \end{aligned} \tag{8.23}$$

If the relation (8.22) is applied to (8.23), then (8.23) reduces to

$$N\boldsymbol{\Sigma} = \mathbf{W}_5 - \frac{1}{(\mathbf{b}'\boldsymbol{\Sigma}^{-1}\mathbf{b})}\mathbf{W}_6\boldsymbol{\Sigma}^{-1}\mathbf{b}\mathbf{b}' - \mathbf{V}_1\mathbf{b}'. \tag{8.24}$$

If (8.22) is premultiplied by $\mathbf{B}'$, where $\mathbf{B}$ is again defined by (8.19), we arrive at the equation

$$\mathbf{b}'\boldsymbol{\Sigma}^{-1}\mathbf{b} = \frac{1}{\sum_i S_{HHi}}\mathbf{V}_1'\mathbf{B}. \tag{8.25}$$

Now if (8.24) is postmultiplied by $\mathbf{B}$, then we shall end up with the relation

$$\mathbf{b} = \mathbf{W}_3\mathbf{B} \tag{8.26}$$

after substituting (8.25) and dividing by N. Observe that from (6.14), (8.25), and (8.26) it follows that

$$\mathbf{B}'\mathbf{W}_4\mathbf{B} = \mathbf{B}'\mathbf{W}_6\mathbf{B} + \Big(\sum_i S_{HHi}\Big)(\mathbf{B}'\mathbf{W}_3\mathbf{B})^2. \tag{8.27}$$

Finally, if (8.26) and (8.27) are applied to the first two terms on the left side of (8.22), and if (8.25) is applied to the third term, then (8.22) becomes

$$\left(\mathbf{W}_4 - \frac{(\mathbf{B}'\mathbf{W}_4\mathbf{B})}{(\mathbf{B}'\mathbf{W}_3\mathbf{B})}\mathbf{W}_3\right)\mathbf{B} = \mathbf{0}. \tag{8.28}$$

From (8.28) it follows that $\mathbf{B}$ must be a characteristic vector of $\mathbf{W}_3^{-1}\mathbf{W}_4$; it can be shown that, to maximize the likelihood, we choose a characteristic vector corresponding to the largest root of $\mathbf{W}_3^{-1}\mathbf{W}_4$. This determines $\mathbf{B}$ except for a multiplicative constant, but obviously it is not necessary to find this multiplicative constant for purposes of using formula (7.13), which is obtained from (8.21) by substituting (8.25).

C. The *T, H* Model

We saw in Section 3 that the density for any of the four T, H submodels is equal to the density for the corresponding $H \mid T$ submodel times the marginal density of $\mathbf{T}_{ij}$. The various parameters which are involved in these latter two densities are defined in such a way that each parameter appears in one density or the other but no parameter appears in both of the densities; the equating parameters, of course, all appear in the first of the two densities. We now conclude at once that, for any T, H submodel, the maximum-likelihood estimates of the equating parameters are the same as those for the corresponding $H \mid T$ submodel. Incidentally, our mode of argument here resembles the method of attack which Anderson used in [1].

D. The *T, H*[*i*] Model

In deriving the estimates (7.17) and (7.18) for the T, $H[i](b, 1)$ submodel (3.12), our first step is to write down the two equations $\partial L/\partial \mu_i = 0$ and $\partial L/\partial a_i = 0$ and solve them simultaneously for μ_i and a_i. The respective solutions are indicated by $\hat{\mu}_i = \overline{T}_i$ and by (7.18). Next we write down the two equations $\partial L/\partial \theta_i = 0$ and $\partial L/\partial b_i = 0$, substitute $\overline{T}_i$ for μ_i and $(\overline{T}_i - b_i\overline{H}_i)$ for a_i therein, and solve the resulting two equations simultaneously for θ_i and b_i. The solution for θ_i involves ρ, but the solution for b_i is simply $\pm$ the right side of (7.17). The plus sign is chosen, assuming that $S_{THi} > 0$.

Under the T, $H[i](a, 1)$ submodel, we derive (7.19) by solving the two equations $\partial L/\partial \mu_i = 0$ and $\partial L/\partial a_i = 0$ simultaneously for μ_i and a_i.

If ρ is replaced by ρ_i wherever ρ appears in the likelihood function for either the T, $H[i](b, 1)$ or the T, $H[i](a, 1)$ submodel, note that the above derivations will remain almost the same, and the maximum-likelihood estimators (7.17) to (7.19) will be unchanged. Thus we establish slightly more general conditions for which these estimators are appropriate.

Remark. In maximum-likelihood estimation problems where there is more than one solution of the maximum-likelihood equations, one frequently is faced with the question of whether a particular solution actually provides an absolute (over-all) maximum rather than (for example) just a local maximum. We may bear in mind that here in Section 8 this question has been covered (implicitly if not explicitly) for every submodel. For the four submodels which yield standard least-squares estimates, as well as for the $T, H[i](a, 1)$ submodel, only a single solution of the equations exists. Multiple solutions exist for the $H \mid T(b, 1)$, $T \mid H(b, p)$, $T \mid H(a, p)$, and $T, H\ [i](b, 1)$ submodels, but for all four of these it has been verified that the solution we have indicated will always be the one which will produce the largest value of L. Multiple solutions also exist for the $H \mid T(b, p)$ submodel, but the approach we provided for it should lead to maximization of L in most practical situations. (We did not mention the four T, H submodels, because they are covered under the corresponding $H \mid T$ submodels.)

Acknowledgments

The author wishes to thank Dr. Richard S. Levine and Dr. Richard W. Watkins of Educational Testing Service, who were responsible for posing to him the broad problem which was the topic of the report [8]. The author also benefited from helpful discussions with Professor R. Darrell Bock of the Psychometric Laboratory at the University of North Carolina, and from useful suggestions by Dr. Frederic M. Lord of Educational Testing Service.

REFERENCES

1. Anderson, T. W. (1957). Maximum likelihood estimates for a multivariate normal distribution when some observations are missing. *J. Amer. Statist. Assoc.* **52** 200–203.
2. Anderson, T. W. (1958). *An Introduction to Multivariate Statistical Analysis.* Wiley, New York.
3. Curry, H. B. (1944). The method of steepest descent for nonlinear minimization problems. *Quart. Appl. Math.* **2** 258–261.
4. Gulliksen, H. (1950). *Theory of Mental Tests.* Wiley, New York.
5. Householder, A. S. (1953). *Principles of Numerical Analysis.* McGraw-Hill, New York.
6. Lord, F. M. (1955). Equating test scores—a maximum likelihood solution. *Psychometrika* **20** 193–200.
7. Lord, F. M. (1955). Estimation of parameters from incomplete data. *J. Amer. Statist. Assoc.* **50** 870–876.
8. Potthoff, R. F. (1964). The prediction of college grades from College Board scores and high school grades. Institute of Statistics Mimeo Series No. 419. Dept. Statistics, Univ. North Carolina, Chapel Hill, N.C.
9. Scarborough, J. B. (1955). *Numerical Mathematical Analysis.* The Johns Hopkins Press, Baltimore, Maryland.
10. Trawinski, I. M. and Bargmann, R. E. (1964). Maximum likelihood estimation with incomplete multivariate data. *Ann. Math. Statist.* **35** 647–657.

11. TUCKER, L. R. (1960). *Formal Models for a Central Prediction System.* Res. Bull. RB-60-14, Educational Testing Service, Princeton, New Jersey.
12. ZAGUSKIN, V. L. (1961). *Handbook of Numerical Methods for the Solution of Algebraic and Transcendental Equations.* Pergamon Press, New York.

Parametric Representation of Nonlinear Data Structures

ROGER N. SHEPARD[1]

and J. DOUGLAS CARROLL

BELL TELEPHONE LABORATORIES
MURRAY HILL, NEW JERSEY

ABSTRACT

A problem that arises in many different contexts is that of determining a smallest set of *independent* variables necessary to account for a redundant set of observed variables. Principal-components analysis or linear factor analysis are ideally suited to deal with this problem when the redundancy of the observed variables is attributable to their *linear* dependence on a smaller set of underlying variables. In a variety of applications of scientific interest, however, this dependence is severely nonlinear. In such cases, these existing techniques will fail to reduce the observed variables to an optimally parsimonious representation; the number of recovered dimensions will necessarily exceed the true degrees of freedom inherent in the data.

The thesis of this paper is that solutions to this more general, nonlinear problem are feasible provided only that the functional dependence of the observed variables on the underlying *latent* variables is sufficiently smooth or *continuous*. Two different approaches to this problem are presented, together with illustrative applications. Both approaches use iterative processes on a digital computer to find a representation of the vectors of observed variables as points in a Euclidean space of the smallest possible dimensionality.

In the first approach we start by computing, for every pair of these *observation vectors*, some quantitative measure of the similarity (or dissimilarity) between them (e.g., the sum of the absolute or squared differences between corresponding variables). We then seek a spatial representation of these observation vectors as points such that the quantitative similarity between any two vectors is a monotonic function of the distance between the two corresponding points—at least locally (i.e., for the set of points within some initially specified distance from each point).

[1] Present address: Department of Psychology, Harvard University, Cambridge, Massachusetts.

In the second approach the emphasis is shifted from the notion of proximity to the notion of continuity. A quantitative index is proposed for the extent to which the functional dependence of the given observation vectors upon the coordinates of the points representing those vectors in some lower-dimensional space is smooth or continuous. The method of steepest descent is then used to find that configuration to which the given data are most *continuously* related in the sense of this index.

Examples of both real and artificial data are presented to show that the proposed methods can flatten nonlinear structures into a Euclidean space of the same intrinsic dimensionality. Points falling on the surface of a sphere, for example, are automatically mapped out into a planar disk. The coordinates of the final, flattened representation are taken to provide the minimal parametric representation in terms of which the original data could still be reconstructed.

1. INTRODUCTION: THE PROBLEM

1.1. Two Types of Multivariate Complexity

Multivariate data are susceptible to two entirely different kinds of complexity, either or both of which can obscure the underlying structure. Trivially simple examples of these two kinds of complexity are illustrated in Fig. 1. In each example there are two samples of objects (represented by circles and crosses) that, we may suppose, have been drawn at random from two underlying bivariate populations. Suppose, now, that we wish to characterize the manner in which the two populations differ, or suppose that we seek a rule for deciding whether a given object belongs to the population of "circles" or the population of "crosses" solely on the basis of its two measurable variables (i.e., its ordinate and abscissa in Fig. 1).

The difficulty in Fig. 1a, of course, arises from the familiar fact that, with respect to the two measurable variables at least, the two underlying populations may have an extensive region of mutual overlap. Statisticians seem to have focused primarily on this general type of difficulty and, as a result, sophisticated techniques are now available to deal with the problems of estimation, discrimination, classification, etc., that tend to arise in this case—particularly when the overlapping distributions are or can be transformed into some known form (e.g., multivariate normal). However it is easy to become preoccupied with the theoretical problem of discovering optimum procedures in this case and to lose sight of the fact that, from the practical standpoint, there just is not much that can be done when there is extensive overlap—even with optimum procedures.

It is in this light that the comparatively neglected type of situation illustrated in Fig. 1b seems, to us, to present the more exciting challenge. The

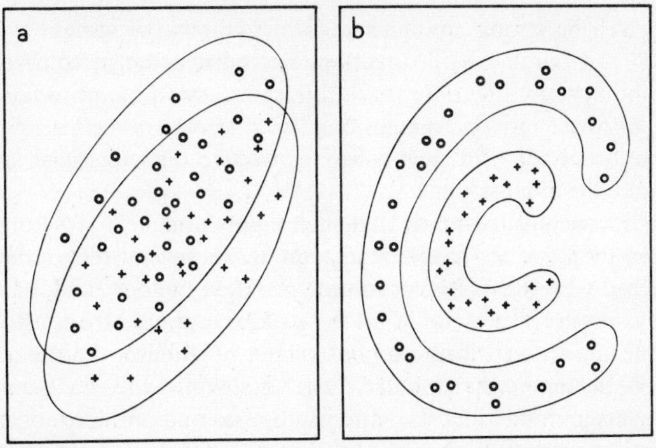

Fig. 1. Two ways in which two multivariate samples can become entangled: (a) by overlapping each other; (b) by bending around each other.

difficulty, there, does not arise from any overlap in the two distributions (for, indeed, there may be none); it arises, rather, from the contorted forms that even connected sets may take on once we move on to spaces of more than a single dimension. Problems of this second general type evidently are, in this sense, more nearly unique to *multi*variate analysis. The tantalizing thing about situations like that shown in Fig. 1b, moreover, is that a proper analysis of this multivariate situation can lead to an essentially perfect discrimination between objects drawn from the two underlying populations.

Again, the example, which was chosen for purposes of illustration only, is of such trivial simplicity that one can discover the underlying structure merely by inspecting the two-dimensional plot. Imagine, however, that the two samples fell on two disjoint manifolds that curved and twisted about each other in a multivariate space of, say, seven or eight dimensions. Would it then be so easy to discover the nonoverlapping character of the two samples? Or might it not rather appear that the samples were inextricably intermixed and, perhaps, even drawn from the same underlying distribution? Here, then, would be a case where the proper sort of multivariate analysis would have surprising and powerful consequences.

1.2. The Neglected Case of Nonlinear Data Structures

We shall not say any more, here, about the problems (specifically of discrimination and classification) that can arise when the multivariate objects are drawn from two or more different populations. In what follows we shall focus exclusively on the simpler problem of discovering the proper characterization of a *single* such population. For, even in the case of a single population, there may well be strong nonlinear relations among the variables. If so, the objects will not scatter in all directions according, say, to some ellipsoidal distribution in the multivariate space. Instead, they will tend to fall on some manifold, of lower intrinsic dimensionality, that may nevertheless curve and twist through the space in such a way as to give the superficial *appearance* of filling an ellipsoidal volume.

Moreover, it begins to appear that such highly nonlinear structures are not at all uncommon, for we have already run across several sets of data of this sort in such diverse fields as astronomy, geology, biology, and, particularly, psychology. Figure 2 presents a rather striking example from astronomy—the Hertzsprung-Russell diagram constructed by Johnson and Sandage [14] for a sample of stars in the globular cluster designated M3. Each point in this plot represents an individual star, and its abscissa and ordinate correspond to the two readily observable variables for that star, its visual absolute magnitude and its color index, respectively. Very luminous stars are represented near the top of the plot, very faint stars near the bottom, blue stars (with high surface temperatures) to the far left, and red stars (with low surface temperatures) to the far right. Such "color-magnitude" diagrams have proved to be a powerful tool for the understanding of stellar evolution [20].

The first thing to be noted about the distribution of points in Fig. 2 is that it is *not* multivariate-normal. Instead, most of the points evidently fall in a curved pattern that, although somewhat convoluted and "noisy," appears to be essentially one-dimensional. (This is consistent with the current hypothesis that these stars condensed out of the same extragalactic cloud of dust and gas

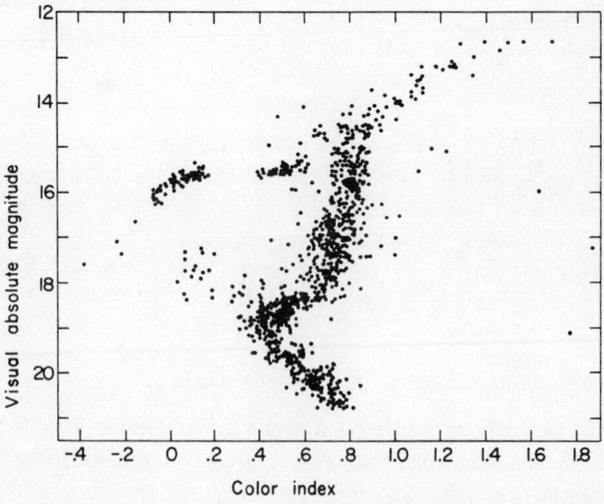

Fig. 2. Hertzsprung-Russell diagram for a sample of stars in the globular cluster M3. (From Johnson and Sandage [14].)

at about the same time and, so, differ with respect to only one underlying parameter, their initial masses.) Clearly, then, a characterization of the plotted distribution in terms of its covariance matrix or its principal components would hardly do justice to the true situation. Fortunately, since only two variables were involved, the true structure could be discovered merely by inspection and, so, the astrophysicists were never tempted to rely on such an inadequate characterization. Isn't it possible, though, that other more complicated cases exist in which the data define, say, a curved three-dimensional manifold in a space of seven or eight dimensions? If so, an examination of the raw data might well fail to penetrate to the true underlying structure.

1.3. An Illustrative Set of Psychological Data

In the behavioral sciences it is quite common to obtain measurements on each of a number (n) of objects (e.g., stimuli or human subjects) with respect to each of a number (m) of psychological variables. Figure 3 presents, in the form of "profiles," an illustrative set of such multivariate data recently obtained by Boynton and Gordon [4]. In this example the objects were 23 spectral colors differing only in wavelength. Four psychological measures were taken on each of these 23 colors. Roughly, these measures were the relative frequencies with which observers applied the color names *blue*, *green*, *yellow*, and *red* to each color (hence the B, G, Y, and R across the top of the square in the upper left corner). Thus, in the next square, we see that the color designated A was never called blue or green but was frequently called yellow and, somewhat less often, red. Likewise, the other profiles present, in graphic form, the four-component observation vector for each of the 22 other colors, designated B through W. (These profiles are based on the mean data for the three observers represented in Boynton and Gordon's Fig. 2 for a luminance of 100 trolands.)

Actually, in this specific example the underlying dimensionality of the stimuli is already known and, so, powerful techniques are not needed to discover this information. In particular, since Boynton and Gordon producd their 23 spectral colors by choosing 23 different settings of a single knob on a grating monochromator, their stimuli were constrained to a single degree of freedom (corresponding to the wavelength of the resulting light). If, then, we make the reasonable assumption that observers' reactions tend to vary continuously with the physical parameters of the stimuli, all four of the measured variables (the frequencies of the four responses, *blue*, *green*, *yellow*, and *red*) should be essentially reconstructable as continuous functions of just one underlying parameter.

The fact that the 23 profiles are unidimensional in this sense has intentionally been obscured in Fig. 3 by arranging and labeling the profiles (from A to

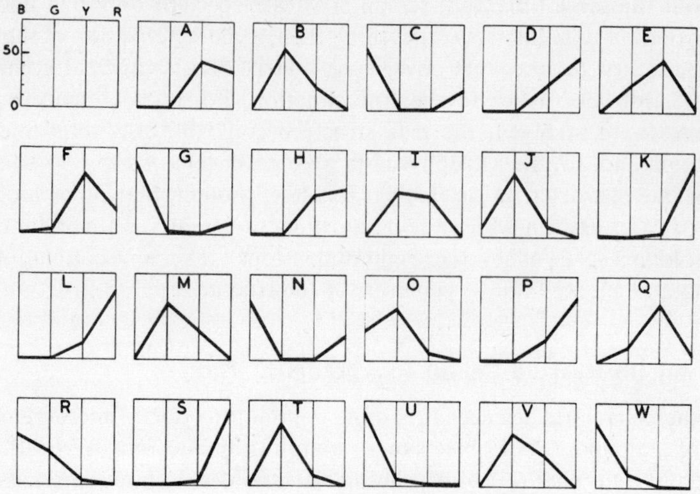

Fig. 3. Profiles indicating the relative frequencies with which the words *blue*, *green*, *yellow*, and *red* were applied to each of 23 spectral colors. (Based on data obtained by Boynton and Gordon [4].)

W) in a haphazard order rather than in the order naturally conferred on them by the physical dimension of wavelength. This was done to emphasize the problem of analysis in cases of real substantive interest in which, generally, the underlying structure—far from being known in advance—is precisely what we want to discover. For purposes of evaluating new techniques, however, it is useful to start with an example for which the structure which these techniques should recover is already known.

1.4. The Problem of Reduction to Parametric Form

To say that the four measures obtained by Boynton and Gordon can all be expressed as continuous functions of a single underlying parameter is to say that, in the four-dimensional space of the given data, the points representing the 23 stimuli fall on some sort of smooth, one-dimensional curve. In general, if the data reflect variations in r underlying parameters, the points will fall on an r-dimensional manifold embedded in the m-dimensional space of the m measured variables. In such cases a method is needed for estimating the intrinsic dimensionality, r, even though the underlying manifold may be quite convoluted and even though the points may be perturbed by the jitter or "noise" inherent in empirical data.

Moreover, to the extent that the intrinsic dimensionality, r, is less than the number of measured variables, m, it should be possible to effect a substantial reduction in the data. In particular, it should be possible to find a representation of the n objects (or, equivalently, the n observation vectors corresponding to these objects) as points in an r-dimensional space such that the measured variables can essentially be reconstructed as continuous functions of the coordinates of this space. The recovery of such a representation, then, would be equivalent to embedding a curvilinear coordinate system within the r-dimensional manifold or nonlinear data structure itself.

Such a reduction could be viewed as accomplishing for nonlinear data structures what principal-components analysis [13] or other varieties of *factor analysis* [12] can accomplish only in the case of linear data structures. Hopefully the underlying parameters discovered in this way will sometimes help to provide scientific insight into the underlying, unobserved processes from which the data originally emerged.

What follows amounts essentially to a progress report describing two related approaches that we have taken to the general problem of discovering such reduced, parametric representations. Although both of these approaches grew out of a mutual interchange between the present two authors, the first approach is due primarily to the first author (RNS) while the second approach is due primarily to the second author (JDC). The first represents a rather direct extension of a technique, called *analysis of proximities*, originally developed by Shepard [21]. We recently discovered that essentially this same extension has also been explored, quite independently, in an unpublished doctoral dissertation in electrical engineering by Bennett [2]. It is also related, more remotely, to some recent unpublished proposals of Guttman (personal communication and [11]). The second approach is based upon a generalization, by Carroll, of a measure that he proposed earlier [5, 6] for the smoothness or "continuity" of the relation between two sets of discrete variables.

2. PROXIMITY ANALYSIS OF DATA PROFILES

2.1. Proximity Relations Among the Profiles

Suppose we wish to discover the true number of dimensions or degrees of freedom of a set of profiles like those shown in Fig. 3 (but of potentially much greater complexity). If we do not know anything initially about the underlying structure, we shall do well to avoid imposing any unnecessary structure from outside; we should let the data speak for themselves. Now one thing that does appear to be inherent in the data themselves is the fact that the profiles in certain pairs (like C and N) are quite similar, whereas the profiles in other pairs (like C and Q) differ widely. If each of these 23 profiles were on a separate card, then a very natural thing to try would be to rearrange these cards (e.g., on the surface of a table) in such a way that similar profiles are brought close together, while dissimilar profiles are moved further apart. Hopefully some over-all pattern might then emerge that was not apparent in the original haphazard arrangement.

Indeed, in the case of the example, it does not take long (even by hand) to rearrange the 23 profiles so that the similarities among these profiles are reflected in their spatial proximities. Moreover—and this is the main point of the illustration—the resulting rearrangement is clearly one-dimensional. This unidimensional ordering can be seen in Fig. 4 by imagining the four rows as strung out, end to end, to form a single row with the profiles appearing, from left to right, in the sequence indicated by the numbers from 1 to 23. Of course we might wish to improve the representation still further by adjusting the spacing even between adjacent profiles. However, for the purpose merely of discovering the number of underlying dimensions (an essentially topological property), we do not necessarily require such metric refinements.

In addition to discovering the true unidimensionality of the 23 profiles we have also recovered the correct ordering of the profiles along this dimension, i.e., the ordering defined by the wavelengths of the 23 spectral colors (which ranged in steps of 10 nanometers from 440 nm, for 1, to 660 nm, for 23). The systematic left-to-right shift of the peak of the profile as we proceed from 1 to 23 in Fig. 4 corresponds to the familiar fact that a monochromatic stimulus of increasing wavelength appears to pass through the successive spectral hues: blue, green, yellow, and red, in that order. The bimodality of the first three profiles reflects the further fact that the shortest wavelengths (violet) are sometimes judged to contain some red (along with the predominant

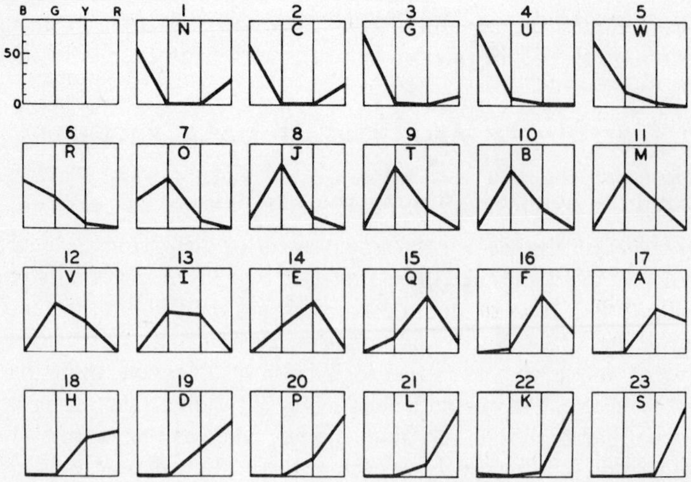

Fig. 4. The 23 profiles of Fig. 3 rearranged to reflect their similarities.

blue). To this extent these first few profiles have some similarity to those at the other end of the series. (It is in order to accommodate this curious tendency of the unidimensional series to fold back on itself that the spectral hues are sometimes represented in the form of a *color circle* rather than as a purely rectilinear series.)

2.2. Proximity and Dimensionality

The possibility, just illustrated, of achieving a reduction from the four measured variables to just one underlying dimension depends upon the existence of strong interdependencies among the measures. Even in the original, unordered set of profiles (Fig. 3), a hint of the existence of such interdependencies could have been gleaned from the absence of whole classes of possible patterns (e.g., the up-down-up-down pattern or its reverse). The standard method of linear factor analysis [12], however, is unable to take full advantage of these strong interdependencies, for they are also strongly nonlinear. An analysis of these same 23 profiles into principal components, for example, yielded three significant dimensions instead of the single one recovered in Fig. 4, here.

The positions of the points representing the 23 profiles in the three-dimensional space of this principal-axis solution are indicated in Fig. 5. (The third principal axis corresponds to height above the picture plane, which has been encoded by the sizes of the spheres around the 23 points.) That there is really only one underlying degree of freedom is given away by the tendency of the 23 points to fall along a one-dimensional curve instead of scattering throughout the three-dimensional volume. Incidentally, this unidimensional curve roughly resembles three connected edges of a tetrahedron, as indicated by the heavy lines drawn between the axes corresponding to the blue, green, yellow, and red factors (in the center of the figure). The bending points in this curve (near 4, 9, 16, and 23) evidently correspond to the subjectively purest hues of blue, green, yellow, and red, respectively.

Again we see that the intrinsic dimensionality, even of empirical data, can be substantially lower than the number of dimensions needed to account for those data in terms of a global, linear model. The true number of degrees of freedom (which, in this example, corresponds to the number of knobs independently varied to produce the stimuli) is not a global, linear property—it is a local, topological property. The advantage of an analysis based upon the *proximity* relations among the profiles is that it is sensitive just to such local properties. The profiles in Fig. 4 have a single degree of freedom in the sense that a single profile (like number 15) evidently can vary only by moving back and forth along the one-dimensional path defined by its two neighbors (14 and 16). For a set of profiles with two degrees of freedom this would no

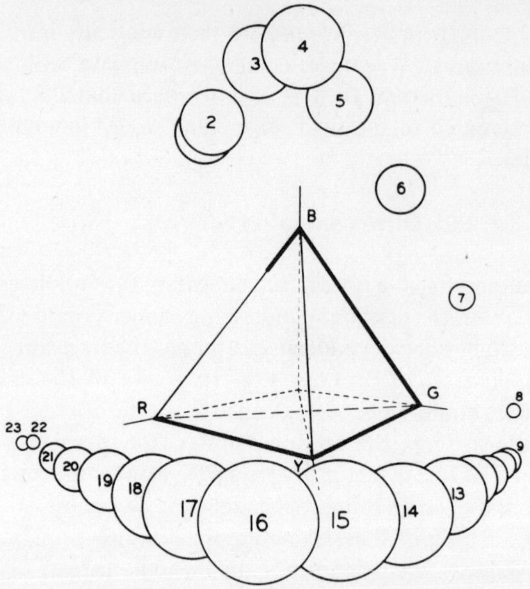

Fig. 5. Three-dimensional results of a principal-axis factor solution for the 23 profiles in Fig. 4.

longer be the case. Any one profile could then vary by moving anywhere in the local two-dimensional region defined by a triangle of *three* neighboring profiles. The similarity relations among such profiles could not be represented by arranging them in a one-dimensional series. A satisfactory spatial representation could then be found only by expanding into the two-dimensional plane.

When the intrinsic dimensionality exceeds two or three (and, particularly, when an objective solution is sought for the *spacing* between neighboring profiles), the method of rearrangement by hand is no longer feasible. We have, then, to consider some possible implementations of this general kind of process on a digital computer.

2.3. Objective Measures of Profile Similarity

In order to have an objective procedure for rearranging the profiles so that their proximity relations mirror their similarity relations, we obviously need an objective measure of similarity or, equivalently, dissimilarity. In what follows we shall use y_{ik} to denote the value of the kth variable in the profile or "observation vector" for the ith object (where $i = 1, 2, \ldots, n$, for the objects, and $k = 1, 2, \ldots, m$, for the variables). We may suppose that these observed "dependent" variables, y_{ik}, have already been normalized in some way if this seems appropriate. We should then want any measure, d_{ij}, of the *dissimilarity* between two profiles, i and j, to increase with any increase in discrepancy between the two corresponding components, y_{ik} and y_{jk}, for any k. A very general class of measures of this kind would include all those of the form

$$d_{ij} = g\left\{\sum_k f_k(y_{ik}, y_{jk})\right\},$$

where the functions f and g are chosen to satisfy the following conditions of symmetry:

$$f(y, y') = f(y', y),$$

and monotonicity:

$$f(y, y'') \geq f(y, y') \quad \text{if} \quad \begin{cases} y'' \geq y' \geq y & \text{or} \\ y'' \leq y' \leq y, \end{cases}$$

$$g(x') \geq g(x) \quad \text{if} \quad x' > x.$$

It also seems reasonable (although not essential) to impose the following additional conventions:

$$f(y, y') = 0 \quad \text{if } y = y',$$
$$g(0) = 0.$$

These conditions do not ensure that the d_{ij} will satisfy the triangle inequality and, for this reason, the d_{ij} should be thought of only as measures of *dissimilarity*—not of distance. For a discrete set of points, however, they can always be made to satisfy the triangle inequality by an appropriate choice of the function g and, so, we can also regard the d_{ij} as (inverse) measures of proximity, i.e., as at least monotonic functions of distance.

Two special cases seem particularly natural in the present context. These are the squared Euclidean distance,

$$d_{ij}^2 = \sum_k (y_{ik} - y_{jk})^2,$$

and the so-called "city-block" distance,

$$d_{ij} = \sum_k |y_{ik} - y_{jk}|.$$

Both of these measures have already been advocated for the purpose of assessing the similarity of profiles: the Euclidean d^2 measure by Osgood and Suci [19] and Cronbach and Gleser [7], and the city-block d measure (sometimes known as the Hamming distance, when the y variables can take on only two different values) by Kruskal and Hart [17].

Of course subclasses of measures of intermediate generality can also be considered, for example,

$$d_{ij} = f^{-1}\left\{\sum_k f(|y_{ik} - y_{jk}|)\right\},$$

where f is again chosen to have appropriate properties—particularly monotonicity. If $f(x)$ is specialized to x^p, here, we obtain the Minkowski p metrics which, for $p \geq 1$, can be shown to satisfy the triangle inequality [1, p. 103]. The Euclidean and *city-block* metrics just mentioned then correspond to the two special cases obtained by setting $p = 2$ and $p = 1$, respectively.

2.4. Iterative Analysis of the Similarity Measures

Shepard [21] has described an iterative process, called *analysis of proximities*, that is able to find a Euclidean configuration of n points of the smallest possible dimensionality consistent with a given rank order for the $n(n-1)/2$ distances among those points. If the number of points is sufficiently large with respect to the number of dimensions required, the metric configuration is determined essentially to within a similarity transformation [3, 21, 24]. For practical purposes, "sufficiently large" has usually been found to mean somewhere between 10 to 15 points (when the true number of dimensions is not greater than two or three, say).

The possibility of such an extraction of metric information from nonmetric data evidently derives from the fact that the number of given nonmetric constraints [roughly $n(n-1)/2$] grows approximately as the square of n, while the number of parameters needed for the complete specification of the metric solution grows only linearly with n. For large n, the solution therefore tends to be highly overdetermined. In any case, since only the rank order of the distances is needed, the method can be applied, as well, to any measures of *proximity* that are related to the distances by some monotone function.

Following the original development of a computer program for recovering such minimum-dimensional structures [21], several variants of the same general type of iterative process have been explored. Probably the most elegant of these is the algorithm due to Kruskal [15, 16], which uses the method of steepest descent to minimize an explicitly defined index of departure from a monotonic relation between given measures of "proximity" and recovered interpoint distances. (The index to be minimized is so defined as to be strictly invariant under monotone transformations of the given proximity data.) Owing, presumably, to the high degree of constraint inherent in the given data, all these various iterative processes have been found to converge to essentially indistinguishable solutions.

Different criteria are available for determining the minimum number of dimensions needed for a satisfactory solution. With errorless data there is no problem; we simply find the smallest number of dimensions in which the departure from the desired condition of monotonicity can be reduced to zero. Empirical data are always somewhat "noisy," however, and so, in practice, we have to be satisfied with a solution in the space of smallest dimensionality for which this departure is just *acceptably small.* In many practical applications, an additional criterion of interpretability has proved quite useful [22, p. 39] and, if two independent sets of data were available, we would also have recourse to a criterion of reliability.

These algorithms for "analysis of proximities" were originally intended for a purpose quite different from what we have in mind here; they were intended for the analysis of purely *subjective* judgments of the similarities between pairs of stimuli, e.g., colors, [21, 22]. Nevertheless, they would seem to be applicable, as well, to *objective* measures of similarity (or dissimilarity) such as the various d-measures considered, for pairs of profiles, above. Indeed, a successful application of this kind using the Euclidean d^2 measure has already been reported by Shepard and Kruskal [25]. And Guttman (personal communication and [11]) has suggested that, by applying these methods to a matrix of correlations, one might recover a representation (such as his one-dimensional *simplex* [10] or two-dimensional *radex* [9]) of lower dimensionality than the solution that would be obtained by linear factor analysis. We regard this as an insightful and potentially fruitful suggestion. However, as we shall now show, a solution of the true, minimum number of dimensions will be attained, in general, only if this approach is modified in an important respect. The desired monotone relation between the given similarity measures and the recovered interpoint distances must be enforced—not at the global level—but only within the local neighborhood surrounding each point.

2.5. Application to the Illustrative Data

Two kinds of measures of dissimilarity were computed for every pair of the 23 profiles shown in Fig. 4. These were the Euclidean d^2 measure (sum of squared differences between corresponding components) and the *city-block* d measure (sum of absolute differences). Two different algorithms for "proximity analysis" were applied to each of the two resulting sets of $n(n-1)/2$ or 253 dissimilarity measures. The results of all four of these analyses were quite similar and, for convenience, only one will be presented here. The dissimilarity measures for that one were the city-block d measures, and the computer program applied to these was a recent version of analysis of proximities that uses a modified gradient method to minimize departures—not from a merely monotonic function—but from a polynomial function of specified degree [23]. (The "smoothness" ensured by the polynomial has sometimes been found to be of practical advantage when n is relatively small.)

The smallest number of dimensions in which monotonicity was essentially maintained at the global level was two. When the polynomial was restricted to second degree, the stationary configuration to which the iterative process converged in two dimensions was that shown in Fig. 6. A smooth curve has been drawn through the 23 recovered points to bring out their inherent unidimensionality. Except for the fact that it has been flattened into two dimensions, this solution resembles the three-dimensional solution of Fig. 5, which was obtained by analysis into principal components. (In particular, the sharpest bends in the essentially one-dimensional series occur at about the same points.) The tendency toward closure of the curve by the *violet* points (1, 2, and 3) is reminiscent of the conventional color circle.

Figure 7 shows the 253 dissimilarity measures plotted against the 253 interpoint distances in the two-dimensional configuration of Fig. 6. In this case it turns out that the relation between the original *d* measures and the recovered distances was not only essentially monotonic but nearly linear as well. Indeed, 95.4% of the variance of the *d* measures is accounted for by the linear (orthogonal) component of the polynomial. (Addition of the quadratic component brings the total variance accounted for to 96.3%.) Clearly, it is not necessary to go to three dimensions (as in the principal-components solution) to provide a good account of these data.

It is now apparent, however, that in order to recover a representation in the true, minimum number of dimensions (one, here) we must relinquish the requirement of global monotonicity. We must not try to accommodate the augmented similarities between relatively remote profiles (like 1 and 23); for the resulting bending of the intrinsically unidimensional series necessarily forces us into a higher-dimensional space (in this case, the plane). Instead, we must focus on the achievement of monotonicity only within local neighborhoods (i.e., for nearby points along the unidimensional series).

Accordingly, the same data were reanalyzed after fixing a cutoff value on the *d* measures so that all but the 100 smallest of the 253 *d* measures were ignored during the iterative process. Since the *d* measures for pairs of profiles from the extremes of the series (like 1 and 23) exceeded this cutoff value, the process was able to converge to a solution in one dimension and still preserve monotonicity (in this revised, local sense). Within this new rectilinear representation (which is indicated by the open circles along the bottom of Fig. 9), the spacing of the 23 points is about what one would expect to get simply by unbending the curved solution shown in Fig. 6. The resulting relation between the original *d* measures and the distances among the points in this new one-dimensional solution is shown in Fig. 8. As before, the open circles are for the *d* measures to which a good fit was sought—in this case just the 100 smallest *d* measures. The dots are for the remaining 153 *d* measures, which were entirely ignored in this analysis. As anticipated, monotonicity has been main-

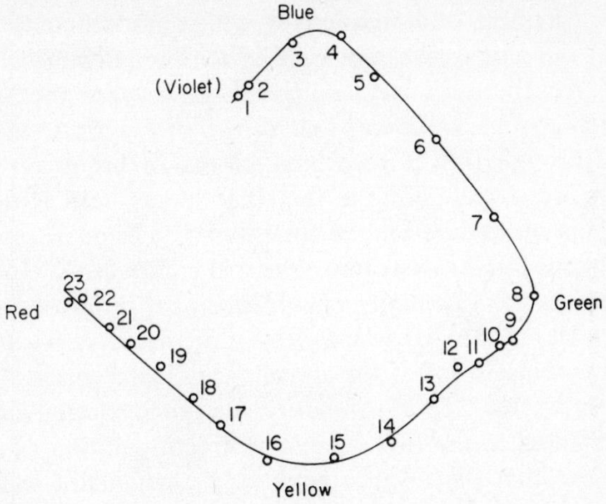

Fig. 6. Two-dimensional representation of the 23 profiles based on a proximity analysis of the *d* measures.

tained only locally (i.e., for the open circles).

The order of the 23 points in the one-dimensional solution is the same as the order of the 23 profiles shown in Fig. 4, but now the separations between

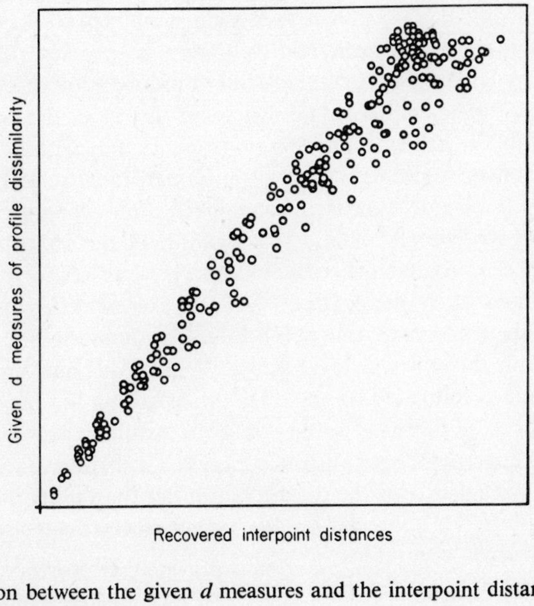

Fig. 7. Relation between the given *d* measures and the interpoint distances in the two-dimensional solution of Fig. 6.

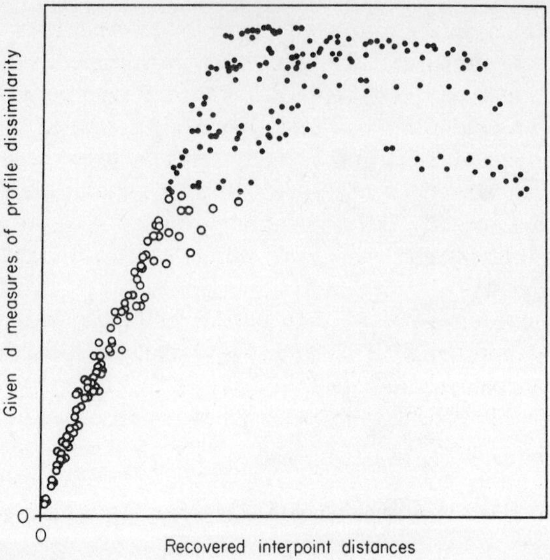

Fig. 8. Relation between the given d measures and the interpoint distances in the one-dimensional solution. (The solution was based only on the 100 smallest d measures, which are indicated by the open circles.)

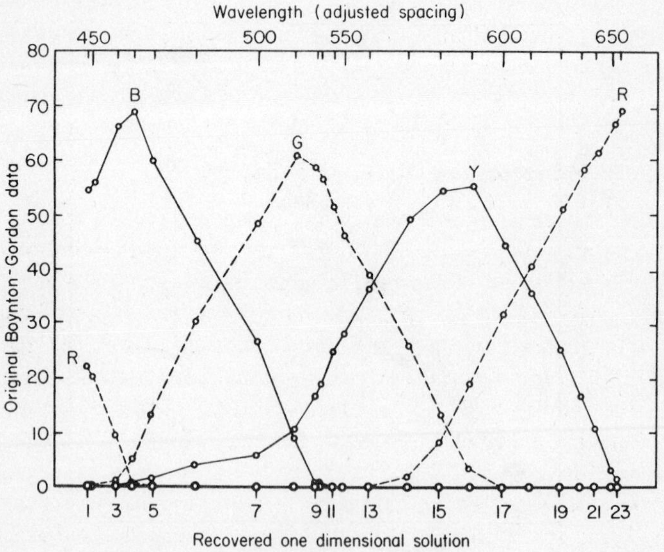

Fig. 9. One-dimensional solution based on a proximity analysis of the 100 smallest d measures (line at bottom), with blue, green, yellow, and red components of original observation vectors plotted above.

neighboring profiles have adjusted themselves to reflect the objective *d* measures of profile similarity. The four curves constructed, in Fig. 9, above this one-dimensional representation show the four components (B, G, Y, and R) of the original profiles plotted against the revised spacing. These blue, green, yellow, and red components can thus be regarded as functions of a single underlying parameter. Moreover, owing to the adjustment in spacing, these functions are now considerably more regular and symmetrical than they are when plotted against the unadjusted, purely physical parameter of wavelength (cf. [4], Fig. 2).

This one-dimensional solution is, of course, more parsimonious than the two-dimensional representation shown in Fig. 6 and, *a fortiori*, than the three-dimensional principal-axis representation shown in Fig. 5. Moreover it still provides a reasonably good account of the data, as can be seen in Figs. 8 and 9. (In Fig. 8, for example, 94% of the variance of the 253 *d* measures is accounted for by the best-fitting quadratic function of the 253 distances among the points in the one-dimensional solution.) However, we do not mean to imply that the solution of minimum dimensionality is necessarily the one to be preferred in every application. For one thing, there is apt to be a trading relation between the simplicity of the spatial representation itself and the simplicity of the relation that this representation bears to the original data. In the case of the example, the principal-axis solution, although it requires three dimensions, does have the advantage of a linear relation to the original data. The much more economical one-dimensional solution obtained here pays for its greater economy by entailing a highly nonlinear relation to the given data (as shown by the functions plotted in Fig. 9).

2.6. Locally Monotone Analysis of Proximities

The simple device of ignoring all pairs of profiles that are more dissimilar than some cutoff value permitted the recovery of an underlying one-dimensional structure (Fig. 9). However this same device appears to be somewhat *too* simple, when we turn to cases in which the true number of underlying dimensions is greater than one. For example, suppose that, in the space of the given data, the points fell on a two-dimensional curved surface resembling, say, the shape of a fish bowl (i.e., a sphere with a hole). In order to recover the desired parametric representation, such a surface would have to be mapped into a flat two-dimensional disk. But, to realize such a mapping, points that were initially close together around the perimeter of the hole would necessarily end up by being spread far apart around the periphery of the flattened disk.

In such a mapping, the rank order of the interpoint distances could still be essentially preserved within each local region, separately. The well-known stereographic projection of a sphere onto a plane is a mapping of this kind.

Since it is conformal, it preserves the ratios of distances within each small neighborhood. It does not, however, preserve the ratios of even small distances in widely separated neighborhoods. Neighborhoods far from the center of the projection are magnified with respect to neighborhoods near that point. A natural generalization of analysis of proximities, then, could be designed to find the configuration of minimum dimensionality such that the approach to the desired condition of monotonicity is enforced—not globally—but, separately, within the region (of some specified cutoff diameter) surrounding each point.

We recently learned that such an extension of analysis of proximities has just been successfully achieved by Bennett and applied, in his doctoral dissertation in electrical engineering, to a problem of recovering "the intrinsic dimensionality of signal collections" [2]. Bennett does not start with a random configuration and then iterate to an optimum solution in each trial number of dimensions. Instead, he starts with the configuration in the higher-dimensional space defined by the "observation vectors" themselves. To flatten a curved data manifold into the smallest possible number of dimensions, he then applies a process, taken from Shepard [21], of iteratively stretching already large distances and shrinking already small distances. These stretching and shrinking adjustments are alternated with the correction of any resulting departures from local monotonicity. The diameters of the local neighborhoods, within which monotonicity is maintained, are fixed by setting a cutoff on the initial (Euclidean) d measures.

Another alternative is to define the diameters of these regions—not in terms of the original data space—but in terms of the (Euclidean) distances within the spatial representation recovered during each iteration. There would then seem to be a greater chance of properly unfolding nearly closed surfaces (like the sphere with a hole). However, we have not tested this alternative, since a rather different approach, described in the remainder of this paper, is, in effect, able to flatten out completely closed data manifolds—such as the surface of a sphere or a torus.

3. PARAMETRIC MAPPING BY OPTIMIZING AN INDEX OF CONTINUITY

3.1. The Relevance of the Concept of Continuity

The application of "analysis of proximities" described above was based upon the central idea that, as two profiles become more similar (or, more precisely, as all their corresponding components simultaneously approach each other), the two points representing those profiles should approach each other as well. When it is formulated in this way, a resemblance emerges between this idea and the idea of continuity; for it is central to the concept of a continuous function f that, as two arguments x and x' approach each other, the resulting values of the functions $f(x)$ and $f(x')$ should do the same. This way of looking at the matter has led to a second approach to our general problem, in which the notion of continuity, rather than that of proximity, plays the central role.

In this approach, the m components of each observation vector are regarded as dependent variables in the sense that they are considered to be continuous functions of r underlying but unobserved variables (where $r < m$). We start, then, with the $n \times m$ given *dependent* variables, y_{ik}, where $i = 1, 2, \ldots, n$ (for the objects) and $k = 1, 2, \ldots, m$ (for the measures taken on these objects). And we seek a smaller set of $n \times r$ "independent" variables, $x_{ik'}$, where again $i = 1, 2, \ldots, n$ (for the objects) but $k' = 1, 2, \ldots, r$ (for the hypothetical *underlying* parameters), such that the given y's can be related to these x's by a function that is as smooth or continuous as possible. The smallest value of r for which the mapping (of x into y) is sufficiently continuous is then taken as the intrinsic dimensionality of the data manifold. The solution associated with that minimum r, moreover, can be regarded as providing a parametric representation of that manifold (or, equivalently, as a curvilinear coordinate system embedded within that manifold).

Of course the mathematical definition of continuity is not really applicable to our problem, since we have only a discrete set of variables, x and y. In particular, we cannot strictly speak of two observation vectors as approaching each other arbitrarily closely since these vectors are always finite in number and since their components are really given as fixed numbers—not as variables. In order to proceed, therefore, we must develop some sort of discrete analogue of the mathematical definition of continuity. And, since we wish to find a mapping that achieves the closest possible approach to continuity in this extended sense, we must be able to say whether one mapping is more or less continuous than another. That is, our measure of "continuity" must be a quantitative one.

3.2. A Quantitative Measure of Continuity in One Dimension

Before presenting a fully general measure of the extent to which two sets of discrete variables are related by a smooth or continuous function, there may be some heuristic advantage in starting with the very simplest case in which values $y_1, y_2, \ldots, y_n$, of a dependent variable correspond to ordered and equally spaced values, $x_1, x_2, \ldots, x_n$, of a *single* independent variable. If we say that the y values seem to change in a continuous manner as we move along the underlying x continuum, we are essentially saying that the change in y as we move from one x value to the next tends to be small compared to the change in y generally associated with larger jumps in x. It seems particularly natural, therefore, to define an explicit index of "continuity" in terms of the ratio of the mean-square difference between successive y values to the over-all sample variance of the y values:

$$\frac{\delta^2}{S^2} = \frac{1}{n-1}\sum_{i=1}^{n-1}(y_{i+1}-y_i)^2 \Big/ \frac{1}{n}\sum_{i=1}^{n}(y_i-\bar{y})^2.$$

This index has previously been considered by von Neumann and others [26 and 27] in the context of the analysis of time series (where, of course, the x's would represent successive times, $t_1, t_2, \ldots$). These authors proposed this index (which they denoted by η) as an (inverse) measure of trend, and it is in fact inversely related to an estimate of the autocorrelation of lag one. Clearly, a trend that is good in the sense that it makes this index small need not be linear or even monotonic. It must, however, be *smooth*, and it is for this reason that Carroll [5] has proposed to use this index as an (inverse) measure of the "continuity" of the functional dependence of y on x.

Since the x values were assumed to be equally spaced, there was no need to incorporate them, explicitly, in the index δ^2/S^2. By rescaling x so that there is a unit separation between successive x values, we see that the expression for the numerator, δ^2, can nevertheless be written in the equivalent form

$$\delta^2 = \frac{1}{n-1}\sum_{i=1}^{n-1}\left(\frac{\Delta y_i}{\Delta x_i}\right)^2,$$

which generalizes immediately to the case of unequal spacing of the x values.

Note, incidentally, that, if a continuous function f does in fact underlie the relation between x and y, then the mean value theorem requires that $\Delta y_i/\Delta x_i$ will be the slope of that function for some value ξ_i between x_i and x_{i+1}. Hence δ^2, as just defined, can be regarded as a sum of the form

$$\delta^2 = \frac{1}{n-1}\sum_{i=1}^{n-1}[f'(\xi_i)]^2,$$

and, thus, might be thought of as a discrete analogue of the integral

$$\int_a^b [f'(x)]^2\,dx,$$

where x is defined on the interval $[a, b]$.

The measure δ^2 cannot be directly extended to the case in which the x's vary in more than one dimension because the notion of adjacency of x points is not defined for irregular spacings in more than one dimension. Then too, even within a single dimension, there are cases in which one might not wish to restrict consideration to adjacent points only. In particular, when the spacing is very irregular, it seems a bit arbitrary to ignore the difference between y values corresponding to two "nonadjacent" x values if these x values are actually much closer together than some "adjacent" x values.

These considerations suggest that we should include a term $(\Delta y/\Delta x)^2$—not just for adjacent x values—but for *every* pair of points. However, if we abandon the notion of adjacency, we must substitute some other means of representing closeness of x points, which, after all, is crucial to any measure of continuity. The obvious way to do this is to weight each term $(\Delta y/\Delta x)^2$ by a factor that decreases monotonically with the separation, Δx. As a more flexible measure of continuity in the one-dimensional case, then, we propose

$$\delta^2 = \sum_{i \neq j}\sum \left[\frac{y_i - y_j}{x_i - x_j}\right]^2 w_{ij},$$

where w_{ij} is some monotone-decreasing function of $|x_i - x_j|$. The double summation, here, ensures the inclusion of all $n(n-1)/2$ pairs of points in the x space and, hence, all the given y data. (In this form, the measure of continuity is essentially equivalent to a generalized measure of nonlinear correlation proposed earlier by Carroll [6] in another context.)

3.3. Generalization of the Measure to the Multidimensional Case

In the case of major interest here, the given *dependent* variables $\{y_{ik}\}$, with $i = 1, \ldots, n$ and $k = 1, \ldots, m$, can be conceived as n points in a space of m dimensions. Likewise, the (to be recovered) *independent* variables $\{x_{ik'}\}$, with $i = 1, \ldots, n$ and $k' = 1, \ldots, r$, can be conceived as n points in another space of r dimensions. The most natural extension of the above formulation for one dimension, then, is that obtained simply by replacing $(\Delta y)^2$ and $(\Delta x)^2$ by the analogous squared Euclidean distances,

$$d_{ij}^2 = \sum_{k=1}^{m} (y_{ik} - y_{jk})^2$$

and

$$D_{ij}^2 = \sum_{k'=1}^{r} (x_{ik'} - x_{jk'})^2.$$

The first of these two expressions is, of course, precisely the d^2 measure already considered, above, as one possible kind of input for the analysis of proximities. (An approach analogous to that developed here could probably be based on other measures, such as city-block distances.)

The multidimensional generalization of δ^2 now becomes

$$\delta^2 = \sum_{i \neq j}\sum \frac{d_{ij}^2}{D_{ij}^2} w_{ij},$$

where the weight, w_{ij}, now decreases monotonically with the *multidimensional* distance, D_{ij}^2, between points in the x space. This can also be factored in the following way:

$$\delta^2 = \sum_k \left[\sum_{i \neq j}\sum \frac{(y_{ik} - y_{jk})^2}{D_{ij}^2} w_{ij} \right] = \sum_k \delta_k{}^2,$$

where $\delta_k{}^2$ (inversely) measures continuity with respect just to the dependent variable y_k.

3.4. Specification of the Weighting Function

If, as we suppose, the x's can be recovered, at best, only to within a general similarity transformation, we should certainly want the weights, w_{ij}, to be invariant under transformations of that type. Actually we need not require, here, that the absolute value of each weight be so invariant (this will shortly be ensured by a normalizing factor). But we must now guarantee at least that the *ratio* of any two weights, w_{ij}/w_{kl}, be invariant under translations, reflections, rotations, and dilations (i.e., changes of scale). The only monotone functions satisfying this condition (cf. [18]) are those of the form

$$w_{ij} = D_{ij}^p \qquad \text{with} \quad p < 0.$$

In practice we have usually set $p = -2$ (so that the weight is simply the reciprocal of the D^2 measure). In the absence of extensive experience with other values for p, this seemed perhaps the most natural case to try first. (Here, as elsewhere in this approach, the real justification for the choices made is the pragmatic one: They have led to a method that seems to do the job.) In any case, for $p = -2$, the multidimensional expression for δ^2 becomes, simply,

$$\delta^2 = \sum_{i \neq j}\sum \frac{d_{ij}^2}{D_{ij}^4}.$$

3.5. Specification of the Normalizing Factor

In the case of the index (η) considered by von Neumann, the inverse of the sample variance of the dependent variables, y, was introduced as a normalizing factor. No normalization was needed for the independent variables, x, since these were assumed already to be fixed in a certain canonical form (ordered and equally spaced). Our present case is just the other way around in the sense that the y's are regarded as fixed (by the given data) while the x's are what we must vary to optimize our index. Clearly, then, it is now more critical to normalize with respect to x. (Otherwise, for example, we could make the measure of departure from continuity, δ^2, as small as we like by simply making the distances, D_{ij}^2, among the x's sufficiently large.)

Now, if we were to minimize our index with respect to the distances, D_{ij}, directly rather than with respect to the coordinates, $x_{ik'}$, in terms of which those distances are defined, we would obtain a minimum that is entirely unconstrained by the restriction of the distances to a Euclidean space of r dimensions. It seems desirable that this *unconstrained* minimum be attained when the D_{ij}^2 are proportional to the given d_{ij}^2; for then the recovered x configuration will match the given y configuration except for a similarity transformation. The simplest and most natural normalizing factor that achieves this condition of *similitude* is

$$\left(\sum_{i \neq j}\sum \frac{1}{D_{ij}^2}\right)^{-2}.$$

The complete index of continuity to which we are finally led, and which we shall call *kappa* is then given by

$$\kappa = \sum_{i \neq j}\sum \frac{d_{ij}^2}{D_{ij}^4} \Bigg/ \left[\sum_{i \neq j}\sum \frac{1}{D_{ij}^2}\right]^2.$$

As in the case of the measures considered above, this final index measures continuity *inversely*; smoother functional relations are indicated by *smaller* values of κ. Now though, since the numerator and denominator are dimensionally homogeneous in the D_{ij}, the index will be invariant under similarity transformations on the x's.

The index κ can also be regarded as a special case of a more general index, κ^*, defined by

$$\kappa^* = \sum_{i \neq j}\sum \frac{(d_{ij}^2)^a}{(D_{ij}^2)^b} \Bigg/ \left[\sum_{i \neq j}\sum (D_{ij}^2)^c\right]^{-b/c}.$$

The similitude condition can be shown to require, in this general case, that $b + c - a = 0$. This condition is of course satisfied in the special case, κ, for which $a = 1$, $b = 2$, and $c = -1$. The computer program to be illustrated in what follows will, however, accept other values for a, b, and c.

3.6. The Minimization Algorithm

In the applications of interest here, the data are given in the form of an $n \times m$ matrix $\|y_{ik}\|$, where y_{ik} is the measured value of object i with respect to variable k. For any arbitrary $n \times r$ matrix $\|x_{ik'}\|$, then, we can compute κ as an index that measures, inversely, the "continuity" of the relation between the given y values and these arbitrary x values. Since κ varies continuously with the x values, the (negative) gradient of κ can be used as the basis for an iterative process in which the x values are repeatedly adjusted by the method of *steepest descent* until an x configuration is reached for which κ is stationary. The "stationary" x configuration thus attained in the smallest number of dimensions, r, for which the associated minimum value of κ is sufficiently small is then taken as the reduced, parametric representation of the original $n \times m$ matrix of y data.

There is, of course, no guarantee that a stationary configuration achieved in this way will correspond to the absolute minimum of κ—as opposed to a merely local minimum. However, if entrapment in such a local minimum is suspected, we can always start over again from a different initial x configuration and see whether or not the process converges to a different x configuration with, perhaps, a smaller stationary value for κ. Moreover, we can always make a direct computation of that absolute minimum of κ that would be attainable if the distances, D_{ij}, among the x points were not constrained to Euclidean r space. To the extent that we approach this *unconstrained* absolute minimum, then, we can be reasonably assured that our solution is about as good as can be attained in any space and, a fortiori, in r dimensions.

In practice it has been found useful to make a slight modification in the index κ by substituting $(D_{ij}^2 + Ce^2)$ for D_{ij}^2 (wherever it occurs, as in the numerator and denominator of the generalized formula for κ^*). In this substitution C plays the role of a fixed normalizing constant of no immediate interest. The index κ, when modified in this way, is then minimized with respect to both the x coordinates and the new variable e. The principal advantage of this modification is the marked facilitative effect it seems to have on the convergence of the iterative process. It does not, however, appear to have any appreciable effect on the final solution. Indeed, when errorless (e.g., artificially generated) data are analyzed, the final value of e is typically found to be very close to zero. Moreover, in the analysis of "noisy" data, there are theoretical reasons for believing that the final value attained by e^2 can be roughly regarded as an estimate of residual error variance.

3.7. Illustrative Application to Artificial Data

One of the limitations of the method based on a locally monotone "analysis of proximities" (described in the earlier part of this paper) is the difficulty that it would seem to encounter whenever the curved data manifold is essentially closed. It could, for example, happen that the observation vectors fall, with a uniform distribution, over the entire surface of a sphere. But, to open such a sphere out into a flat disk, the sphere would have, in effect, to be "punctured" and then radically stretched in the vicinity of this "puncture." It seems doubtful whether the "local" regions within which monotonicity is to be maintained could be so defined as to permit such a radical stretching. On the other hand, for the method based on the optimization of "continuity" (described here), this difficulty seems less severe. In any case, some examples of completely closed data manifolds appeared to offer a particularly challenging test of this second method.

As a first test, the algorithm was applied to the two (Cartesian) coordinates for each of 20 points equally spaced around the perimeter of a circle. Iteration was commenced on a random configuration of points in one dimension, and, in fact, the process converged to the stationary configuration shown along the line at the bottom of Fig. 10. Of course, to open the closed circle into a straight line, it had to be broken somewhere between two adjacent points. As can be seen in the figure, the break happened, in this particular instance, to occur between points 10 and 11. If we proceed around the circle from the arbitrary location of the break, we find that the correct ordering of the 20 points has been reconstructed in the rectilinear solution. Moreover, the spacing between adjacent points is remarkably regular. (There is, in particular, little indication of any *end effect* near the points, 10 and 11, separated by the break.)

The curves plotted above the one-dimensional solution in Fig. 10 present the two original dependent variables, y_1 and y_2, as a function of the one recovered "independent" variable, x. These curves are analogous to those plotted in Fig. 9 for empirical data. In the case of Fig. 10, though, it is the continuity of the two functions that the iterative algorithm was attempting to optimize (by adjusting the 20 x values). Clearly, this optimization has succeeded in recovering the sine and cosine functions originally used to generate the coordinates for the points on the circle (except for a phase shift induced by the arbitrary point at which the circle was broken).

To test the ability of the algorithm to flatten out a manifold of higher intrinsic dimensionality, the initial data were next taken to be the three (Cartesian) coordinates for each of 62 points at the intersections of 5 equally spaced parallels and 12 equally spaced meridians on the surface of a sphere, as illustrated in Fig. 11.

In this case an initially random configuration in two dimensions converged to the stationary pattern shown in Fig. 12. What were the points (1 and 62) at the *north* and *south* poles of the original sphere are now shown at the centers of the concentric rings of points in the upper and lower halves of Fig. 12. It is as if the "northern" and "southern" hemispheres of the globe had been swung apart on an equatorial hinge (arbitrarily situated near points 33 and 34 on the equatorial circle) and, then, the two hemispheres had been flattened out into a common plane. The original circle of 12 equatorial points (26 through 37) is now inflected into an S shape, so that one end of the resulting opened circle curves around the inner rings from one hemisphere while the other end curves around the inner rings from the other hemisphere. (It is as if the cut separating the two hemispheres had been at a very slight angle to the equator of the original sphere.)

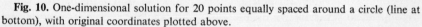

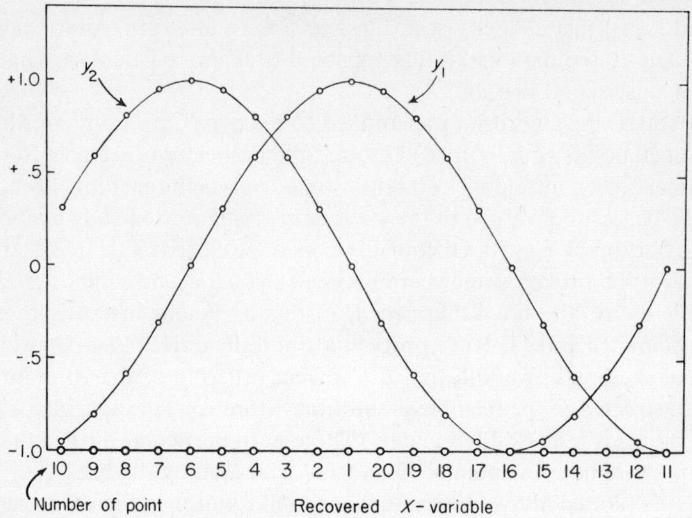

Fig. 10. One-dimensional solution for 20 points equally spaced around a circle (line at bottom), with original coordinates plotted above.

The output of the computer, of course, yields only the positions to which the 62 points converged. The smooth curves corresponding to the original meridians and parallels were subsequently drawn through these points by hand. Except for the fact that the equatorial circle opened out into an S-shaped curve (rather than into a straight line), the final two-dimensional representation is somewhat similar to the "azimuthal equidistant projection" sometimes used to represent the surface of the earth [8, p. 175]. Figure 13 shows such a projection taken around the intersection of the equator and the Greenwich prime meridian, as center.

The configuration shown in Fig. 12 helps to give some feeling for the class of transformations up to which the solutions are determined. We already noted that the solution can be subjected to any similarity transformation without affecting the index of continuity, κ. From considerations of symmetry in the case of the 62 points on the sphere, we can also see that, although the sphere happened to open up between points 27 and 28, on the equator, it could just as well have opened up between any other adjacent pair of equatorial points. The different solutions that could result in this way would clearly not be related to each other by similarity transformations. Rather, they would be related by a "smooth" kind of quasi-topological flow in the two-dimensional plane, in which the rings around the two polar points circulate in contrary, meshing directions, while the equatorial points stream along their S-shaped belt between. (In detail, of course, there is a discontinuous jump as each equatorial point reaches one end of this belt and passes around to the

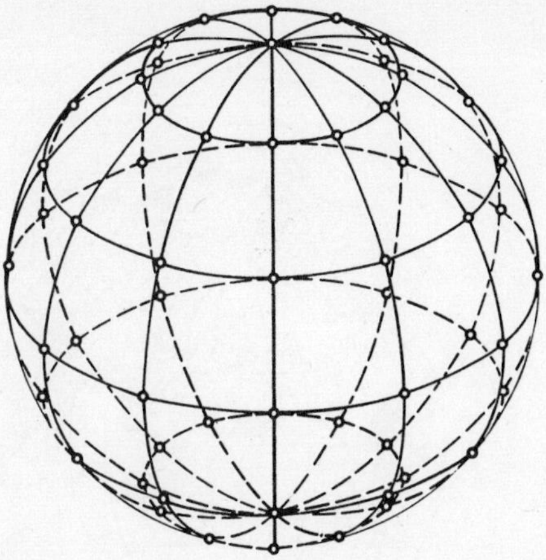

Fig. 11. Arrangement of 62 points on the surface of a sphere.

other end. There is also another discontinuity, in that this S-shaped belt can as well inflect in either of two distinct ways.)

In general, since the greatest distortion in the mapping will necessarily occur in the vicinity of the *puncture* where the sphere is opened up, the minimization of κ requires that this puncture be situated in a region where the points are least densely packed. For the distribution illustrated in Fig. 11, the

Fig. 12. Two-dimensional solution for the 62 points on the surface of a sphere (with analogues of the original meridians and parallels drawn in).

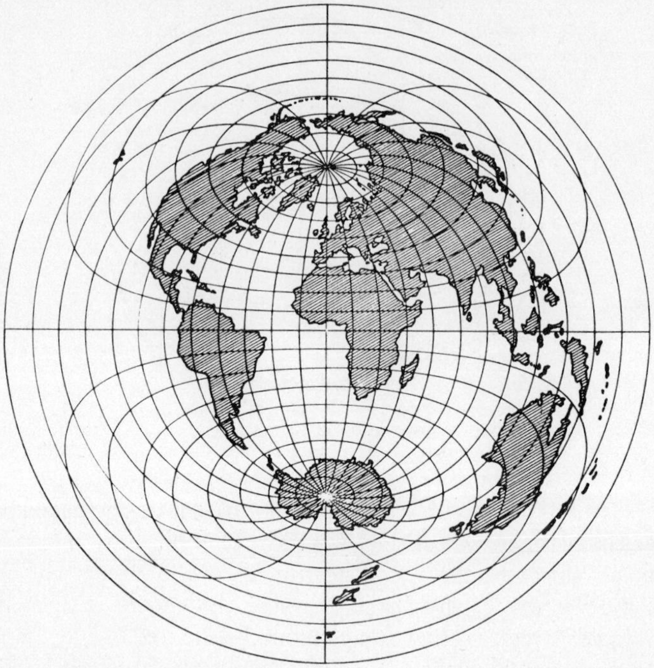

Fig. 13. Azimuthal equidistant projection of the world.

points were closest together near the poles. This is why the sphere opened up at the equator. If the points had been situated in a still more symmetric pattern (e.g., at the vertices of a regular polyhedron) the sphere might have opened up almost anywhere (i.e., in the center of any face of the polyhedron). In the case of real data, of course, such conditions of strict symmetry will seldom if ever arise and, so, the absolute minimum of κ will usually correspond to a configuration that is uniquely determined up to a similarity transformation.

As a final example, we present the results of a test of the algorithm on the four coordinates for each of 49 points falling on the (closed) two-dimensional surface of a torus embedded in four-dimensional Euclidean space. Topologically, this four-dimensional configuration is equivalent to the familiar two-dimensional doughnut-shaped surface in three dimensions, as portrayed in Fig. 14. But, by embedding a surface of this kind in four dimensions, a greater symmetry can be achieved in which, for example, the three diameters, D_1, D_2, and D_3, are all equal. In mathematical terms the surface can be simply defined as the "direct product" of two circles. The coordinates y_1 and y_2 can thus be taken as those of a point that makes seven complete circuits

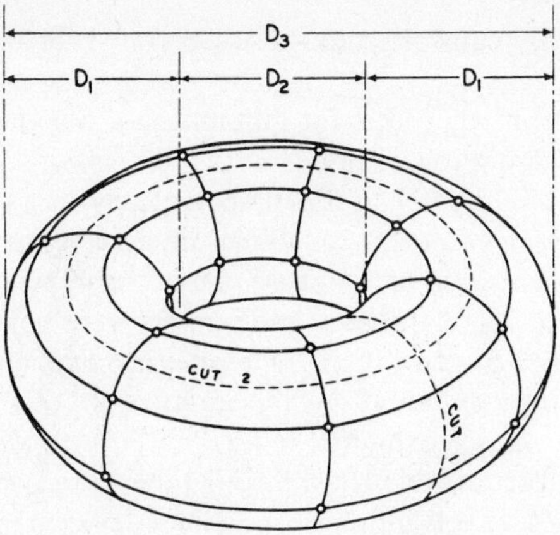

Fig. 14. Three-dimensional representation of the arrangement of 49 points on the surface of a torus embedded in four dimensions.

around a circle of seven equally spaced positions. The remaining coordinates, y_3 and y_4, then, can be taken as those of a second point that, at the same time, completes just one circuit around such a circle but remains at each of the seven positions during the completion of each seven-position revolution of the first point. The 49 resulting four-coordinate points correspond to the intersections of two orthogonal sets of seven equally spaced parallel lines on the

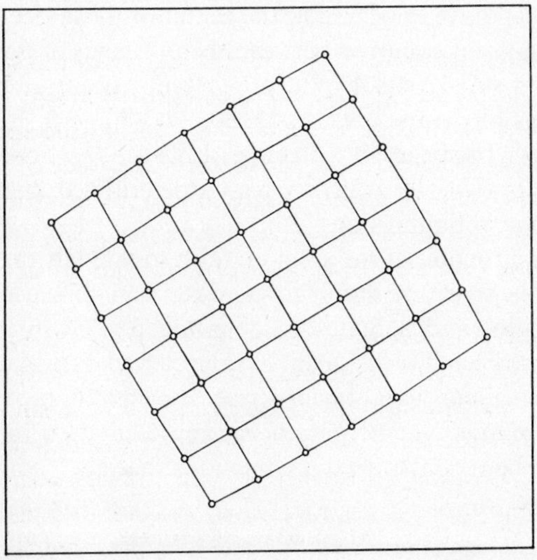

Fig. 15. Two-dimensional solution for the 49 points on the surface of a torus (with analogues of the original intersecting parallels drawn in).

surface (topologically equivalent to those illustrated for three dimensions in Fig. 14).

As before, the iterative process for minimizing κ was started on an essentially arbitrary configuration of points in two dimensions. (For convenience, the initial points are usually assigned, completely at random, to equally spaced positions along two orthogonal lines intersecting to form the shape of an "L" in the plane. In the present case one of the 49 points was situated at the intersection, and 24 of the remaining points were positioned at random along each of the two arms of the L.) Despite the completely arbitrary character of this starting configuration, the iterative process converged to the remarkably regular lattice exhibited in Fig. 15. The two orthogonal sets of lines which were subsequently drawn through the 49 recovered points correspond directly to the two sets of intersecting lines depicted in Fig. 14. In effect, the closed surface was opened up by (a) cutting through the torus between two adjacent rings of seven points; (b) opening the surface, thus severed, into a straight tube; (c) cutting down one side of this tube between two adjacent lines of seven points; and (d) flattening the resulting surface out into a square. (The locations of two such *cuts* are indicated in Fig. 14.) As in the first example, there is little indication of any "end effects" near the boundaries of the solution produced by the "cuts."

Clearly, since there originally were seven rings of points in each direction, there are 7×7 ways in which this mapping into the plane could have been achieved with the same minimum value for κ. That is, any one of the 49 points could as well have appeared at the center of the lattice. As it happened in this instance, one cut occurred between the two rings of points 1, 2, 3, 4, 5, 6, 7 and 43, 44, 45, 46, 47, 48, 49; the other "cut" occurred between the two (orthogonal) rings of points 2, 9, 16, 23, 30, 37, 44 and 3, 10, 17, 24, 31, 38, 45, and, so, point 27 appears in the center. Like the rotational orientation of the solution, this is a wholly arbitrary matter determined, presumably, by the particular starting configuration.

It is the spatial structure of the solution (as a square lattice, here) that is the essential result. The structure itself shows no residual influence of the arbitrary starting configuration and is, therefore, determined solely by the original data. It has the same intrinsic dimensionality as the curved data manifold originally embedded in four-dimensional linear space. It evidently provides, moreover, the most parsimonious type of parametric representation in terms of which those data could be reconstructed as functions that are "continuous" in the sense defined here.

Acknowledgments

During the course of this work, we had the benefit of discussions with several colleagues. We thank, particularly, J. B. Kruskal and C. L. Mallows (of the Bell Telephone Laboratories) and J.-P. Benzécri (of the University of Paris) for a number of helpful suggestions, and W. H. Huggins (of the Johns Hopkins University) for calling our attention to the closely related, unpublished work of R. S. Bennett. We also gratefully acknowledge the assistance of Miss Maureen Sheenan, who conducted many of the computer analyses and who prepared most of the final figures. Greatest of all is our debt to Mrs. Jih-Jie Chang, who implemented the algorithm for optimizing *continuity* as a workable FORTRAN program (for the IBM 7094), and who also wrote subroutines for outputting all the results presented here in graphical form (via the associated Stromberg-Carlson SC-4020 Microfilm Recorder).

REFERENCES

1. Beckenbach, E. and Bellman, R. (1961). *An Introduction to Inequalities*. Random House, New York.
2. Bennett, R. S. (1965). The intrinsic dimensionality of signal collections. Unpublished doctoral dissertation. Johns Hopkins Univ., Baltimore, Maryland.
3. Benzécri, J. P. (1964–1965). Analyse factorielle des proximités. *Publications de l'Institute de Statisque de l'Université de Paris*. Part I, **13**; Part II, **14**.
4. Boynton, R. M. and Gordon, J. (1965). Bezold-Brüke hue shift measured by color-naming technique. *J. Opt. Soc. Amer.* **55** 78–86.
5. Carroll, J. D. (1963). Functional learning: The learning of continuous functional mappings relating stimulus and response continua. *Educational Testing Service Res. Bull. RB*-63-26. Princeton, New Jersey.
6. Carroll, J. D. and Chang, J. J. (1964). A general index of nonlinear correlation and its application to the interpretation of multidimensional scaling solutions (abstract). *Amer. Psychologist* **19** 540.
7. Cronbach, L. J. and Gleser, G. C. (1953). Assessing similarity between profiles. *Psychological Bulletin* **50** 456–473.
8. Deetz, C. H. and Adams, O. S. (1945). *Elements of Map Projection*. U.S. Dept. Commerce Spec. Publ. No. 68. U.S. Government Printing Office, Washington, D.C.
9. Guttman, L. (1954). A new approach to factor analysis: the radex. *Mathematical Thinking in the Social Sciences* (P. F. Lazarsfeld, ed.), 258–348. Free Press, Glencoe, Illinois.
10. Guttman, L. (1955). A generalized simplex for factor analysis. *Psychometrika* **20** 173–192.
11. Guttman, L. (in press). Order analysis of correlation matrices. *Handbook of Multivariate Experimental Psychology* (R. B. Cattell, ed.). Rand McNally, Chicago.
12. Harman, H. H. (1960). *Modern Factor Analysis*. Univ. Chicago Press, Chicago, Illinois.
13. Hotelling, H. (1933). Analysis of a complex of statistical variables into principal components. *J. Educational Psychology* **24** 417–441.
14. Johnson, H. L. and Sandage, A. R. (1956). Three-color photometry in the globular cluster M3. *Astrophys. J.* **124** 379–389.
15. Kruskal, J. B. (1964). Multidimensional scaling by optimizing goodness of fit to a nonmetric hypothesis. *Psychometrika* **29** 1–27.
16. Kruskal, J. B. (1964). Nonmetric multidimensional scaling: A numerical method. *Psychometrika* **29** 115–129.
17. Kruskal, J. B. and Hart, R. E. (in preparation). A geometric interpretation of diagnostic data from a digital machine.
18. Luce, R. D. (1964). A generalization of a theorem of dimensional analysis. *J. Math. Psychology* **1** 278–284.

19. Osgood, C. E. and Suci, G. J. (1952). A measure of relation determined by both mean differences and profile information. *Psychological Bulletin* **49** 251–262.
20. Schwarzschild, M. (1958). *Structure and Evolution of the Stars*. Princeton Univ. Press, Princeton, New Jersey.
21. Shepard, R. N. (1962). The analysis of proximities: Multidimensional scaling with an unknown distance function, Parts I and II. *Psychometrika* **27** 125–140. and 219–246.
22. Shepard, R. N. (1963). Analysis of proximities as a technique for the study of information processing in man. *Human Factors* **5** 33–48.
23. Shepard, R. N. (1964). Polynomial fitting in the analysis of proximities (abstract). *Proc. XVIIth Intern. Congr. of Psychol.* 345–346. North-Holland, Amsterdam.
24. Shepard, R. N. (1966). Metric structures in ordinal data. *J. Math Psychol.* **3** 287–315.
25. Shepard, R. N. and Kruskal, J. B. (1964). Nonmetric methods for scaling and for factor analysis (abstract). *Amer. Psychylogist* **19** 557–558.
26. von Neuman, J. (1941). Distribution of the ratio of the mean square successive difference to the variance. *Ann. Math. Statist.* **12** 367–395.
27. von Neuman, J., Kent, R. H., Bellinson, H. R. and Hart, B. I. (1941). The mean square successive difference. *Ann. Math. Statist.* **12** 153–162.